D0998352

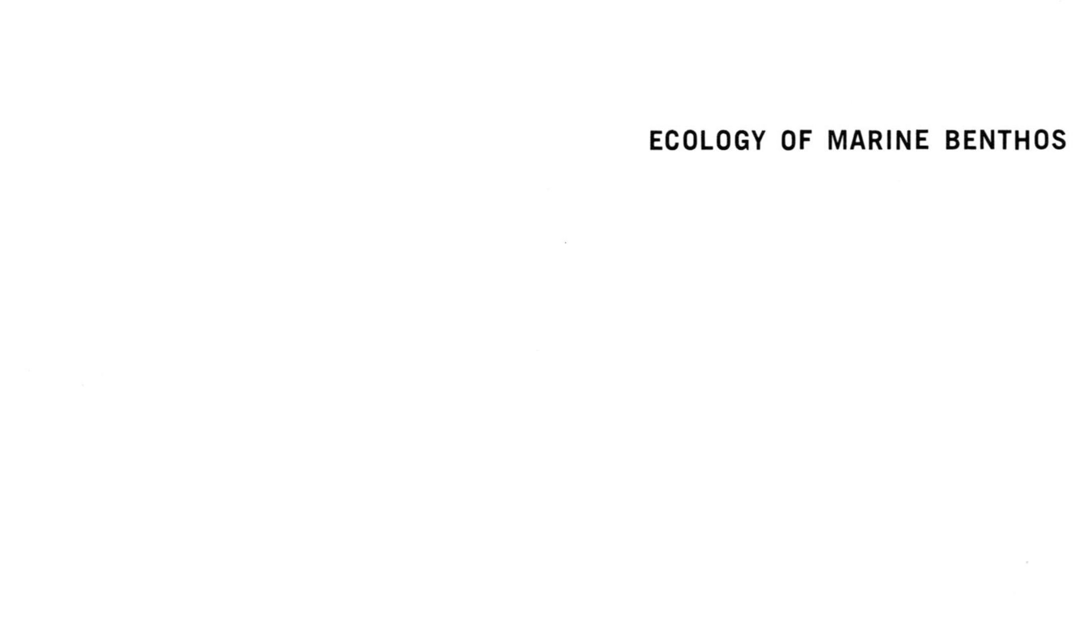

ECOLOGY OF MARINE BENTHOS

THE BELLE W. BARUCH LIBRARY IN MARINE SCIENCE

1 ESTUARINE MICROBIAL ECOLOGY
2 SYMBIOSIS IN THE SEA
3 PHYSIOLOGICAL ECOLOGY OF MARINE ORGANISMS
4 BIOLOGICAL RHYTHMS IN THE MARINE ENVIRONMENT
5 THE MECHANISMS OF MINERALIZATION IN THE INVERTEBRATES AND PLANTS

THE BELLE W. BARUCH LIBRARY IN MARINE SCIENCE NUMBER 6

Ecology of Marine Benthos

Edited by Bruce C. Coull

Published for the Belle W. Baruch Institute for Marine Biology and Coastal Research by the

UNIVERSITY OF SOUTH CAROLINA PRESS

COLUMBIA, SOUTH CAROLINA

First Edition

Published in Columbia, South Carolina by the
University of South Carolina Press, 1977

Manufactured in the United States of America

GUNNAR THORSON
1906 - 1971

In recognition of his role in shaping modern benthic ecology, this volume is posthumously dedicated to Professor Gunnar Thorson. Born on December 31, 1906 in Copenhagen, Denmark, Professor Thorson's decision to be a professional zoologist was made in his thirteenth year. He was awarded the doctorate from Copenhagen University in 1936 with a thesis entitled "The larval development, growth and metabolism of arctic marine bottom invertebrates," a work which obviously set the stage for his continued work on marine benthos. Many of Professor Thorson's scientific contributions have served as the base for our current thoughts on benthic community organization. Although Thorson, himself, realized the non-universality of his parallel-level bottom community concept, his quantitative and larval recruitment approach to the benthos is the one we all have followed, refined and elaborated upon. Thorson's research took him to many parts of the world and there is no doubt that his larval "book" and subsequent works on the benthos have secured for him a place among the outstanding marine biologists of the 20th century. The field of benthic ecology lost a true leader on January 25, 1971.

PARTICIPANTS

ROBERT C. ALLER
Yale University

KARL BANSE
University of Washington

STEPHEN A. BLOOM
University of South Florida

DONALD F. BOESCH
Virginia Inst. Marine Science

DALE R. CALDER
S.C. Wildlife and Marine
Resources Institute

ROBERT R. CHRISTIAN
University of Georgia

WILLIAM G. CONNER
University of South Florida

BRUCE C. COULL
University of South Carolina

ROBERT A. CROKER
University of New Hampshire

RICHARD F. DAME
Coastal Carolina College,USC

DANIEL M. DAUER
Old Dominion University

JOHN MARK DEAN
University of South Carolina

ROBERT J. DIAZ
Virginia Inst. Marine Science

J. F. DÖRJES
Institut für Meeresgeologie und
Meeresbiologie "Senckenberg"
West Germany

BETTYE W. DUDLEY
University of South Carolina

KRISTIAN FAUCHALD
University of Southern California

TOM M. FENCHEL
Aarhus Universitet
Denmark

JOHN W. FLEEGER
University of South Carolina

JOHN D. GAGE
Dunstaffnage Marine Research Lab.
Scotland

MARCIA C. GLENDENING
National Science Foundation

J. F. GRASSLE
Woods Hole Oceanographic Inst.

JOHN R. HALL
University of Georgia

D. HEYWARD HAMILTON
U.S. Energy Research & Development Administration

EDWARD B. HATFIELD
University of Miami

ROBERT P. HIGGINS
Smithsonian Institution

A. FRED HOLLAND
Martin-Marietta Laboratories

M. SUSAN IVESTER
University of Alabama

PETER A. JUMARS
University of Washington

BJÖRN KJERFVE
University of South Carolina

JOHN N. KRAEUTER
Virginia Inst. Marine Science

A. SCOTT LEIPER
Duke Power Company

JEFFERY S. LEVINTON
State University of New York,
Stony Brook

DARCY J. LONSDALE
University of South Carolina

NANCY J. MACIOLEK
University of Texas

JOHN K. MCNULTY
National Marine Fisheries
Service

A. D. MCINTYRE
Department of Agriculture &
Fisheries for Scotland

FREDERIC H. NICHOLS
U.S. Geological Survey

ROBERT J. ORTH
Virginia Inst. Marine Science

MARIO M. PAMATMAT
Auburn University

TIBOR T. POLGAR
Martin-Marietta Laboratories

DONALD C. RHODES
Yale University

GILBERT T. ROWE
Woods Hole Oceanographic Inst.

STUART SANTOS
University of South Florida

JEAN P. SIKORA
University of South Carolina

WALTER SIKORA
University of South Carolina

JOSEPH L. SIMON
University of South Florida

JOHN P. SUTHERLAND
Duke University Marine Laboratory

KENNETH R. TENORE
Skidaway Inst. of Oceanography

DAVID E. THISTLE
Scripps Institution of Oceanography

JOHN H. TIETJEN
City College of New York

F. JOHN VERNBERG
University of South Carolina

ROBERT W. VIRNSTEIN
Virginia Inst. Marine Science

LES WATLING
University of Delaware

RICHARD B. WILLIAMS
National Science Foundation

I. WOLFF
Delta Institut voor Hydrobiologisch Onderzoek
The Netherlands

W. J. WOLFF
Delta Institut voor Hydrobiologisch Onderzoek
The Netherlands

DAVID K. YOUNG
Smithsonian Institution, Fort
Pierce Bureau

MARTHA W. YOUNG
Smithsonian Institution, Fort
Pierce Bureau

symposium participants .....

lunch ......

attentiveness .....

meiofauna advocates .....
B.Coull, R.Higgins, J.Tietjen

night discussion .....

outside discussions .....

lunch again .....

J. Gage lecturing .....

PREFACE

Benthic ecology has come of age. Where the benthos, for many years had been the stepchild of ecology depending on thought generated by our terrestrial or water column colleagues, benthic ecologists today have broken these feters and produced original research and hypotheses now available to the entire ecological world. Ecology has received answers from the benthic world--more are yet to come!

Benthic ecology has in recent years experienced an explosion in increased research and importance. In spite of an increasing amount of information on the benthos, there had been no organized effort to highlight the recent advances with a view toward summarizing our present accomplishments and identifying new research. Thus, a symposium entitled ECOLOGY OF MARINE BENTHOS was held 7-10 May 1975 on Hobcaw Barony, Georgetown, South Carolina toward this end, and this volume represents the papers presented at that symposium.

No symposium and subsequent publication is complete without the assistance of a cast of thousands (or so it seems). To everyone who had a part in producing this volume goes sincere thanks. The symposium was supported, in part, by the National Oceanic and Atmospheric Administration (NOAA) and the Belle W. Baruch Institute for Marine Biology and Coastal Research. The U.S. Energy and Research Development Administration (ERDA) and the Belle W. Baruch Institute for Marine Biology and Coastal Research supported publication costs associated with this volume. Particular thanks are due to Ms. Vicki Macintyre for copy editing, Ms. Dorothy Knight for typing the final manuscript, Ms. Bettye W. Dudley for indexing, Dr. M. Susan Ivester for the reminescent photos, Dr. Donald F. Boesch for the jacket photo, and Mr. Holger Knudsen for the photo of the late Professor Thorson. Each paper published in the volume was reviewed by at least two external reviewers. To each of them our thanks for maintaining integrity.

BRUCE C. COULL
Columbia, SC
January 1977

CONTENTS

Contents (cont.)

Contents (cont.)

ECOLOGY OF MARINE BENTHOS

Feeding and Metabolism

Between-Community Contrasts in Successful Polychaete Feeding Strategies

Peter A. Jumars[1,2] and **Kristian Fauchald**[2]

[1]Department of Oceanography, WB-10
University of Washington
Seattle, WA 98195

[2]Allan Hancock Foundation
University of Southern California
Los Angeles, CA 90007

ABSTRACT

Benthic marine polychaetes are herein classified on the basis of several feeding strategy parameters, notably degree of motility and feeding stratum (suspension, surface deposit, subsurface deposit). Along a depth transect from the Southern California coast (2.4 m) to the central North Pacific (5600 m), the relative abundance of sessile individuals increases ($P < 0.00001$) with depth to at least 400 m and then decreases at greater bathyal and abyssal depths. The increase is postulated to be a response to increasing sediment stability, while the subsequent decrease may be attributable to the relation between optimal foraging area and food availability. Variation in sediment mobility and food input might similarly account for many other biogeographic patterns.

For thou dost fear the soft and tender fork of a poor worm.

-- Shakespeare
Measure for Measure
Act III, Scene 1

The proportional contributions of various taxa to benthic standing stocks change markedly from shallow water to the abyss (e.g., Sanders et al. 1965; Menzies et al. 1973). Although decreasing food supply (implied by decreasing standing stock and decreasing community respiration rate) with increasing depth and increasing distance from shore has been implicated in this change (e.g., Belyaev et al. 1973; Rex 1973), the characteristics which determine successful species at particular depths remain largely unidentified. As Hessler and Jumars

(1974) noted, most of the taxa are largely deposit feeding at all the depths considered, "so the cause of the shift must be at a more subtle level." Several observations suggest what this more subtle level might be. Hessler and Jumars (1974) noted that the vast majority of polychaete individuals in the extremely food-poor abyssal benthos of the central North Pacific are creeping or burrowing deposit feeders. At the other end of the depth spectrum, along exposed coasts, sessile species fare poorly on soft substrates owing to sediment instability (e.g., Purdy 1964; Swedmark 1964). The dearth of sessile polychaetes in the physically stable North Pacific abyss, however, must have a different explanation. To aid in formulating some cogent hypotheses regarding these observations, we attempted to assess changes in feeding strategy (*sensu* Schoener 1971) along a gradient in depth.

The available data are inadequate to parameterize most of the components of foraging strategy, but the Polychaeta provide some hope of a consistent classification dealing with some aspects of feeding patterns. In particular, classes of motility and feeding modes may be distinguished. We confine our present consideration strictly to the marine soft-bottom (sand-silt-clay) habitat, where Polychaeta are typically numerically dominant among macrofaunal taxa at all depths, usually constituting from 50 to 80 percent of the total macrofaunal numbers. Polychaeta are Precambrian in origin (Glaessner and Daily 1959), and their major radiations have taken place some considerable time in the past (Fauchald 1974). We therefore hope that a view of the benthic world through polychaete feeding strategies will reveal a steady state--that the absence of a major feeding type from any extensive area is probably not a function of limited dispersal time.

Our work was supported by NSF grant GA42754. We must also express thanks for the late Dr. Olga Hartman's identifications of the polychaetes in most of the samples. Our hypotheses are guided by one of her favorite sayings, "The only way to avoid mistakes is to do nothing." Some mistakes were avoided, however, through thoughtful reviews by K. Banse, B. C. Coull, J. T. Enright, R. Feller, R. R. Hessler, and M. L. Jones. Contribution No. 925 from the Department of Oceanography, University of Washington, Seattle, Washington 98195.

METHODS AND MATERIALS

We first attempted to classify all benthic, soft-substrate polychaetes on the basis of as many feeding-related parameters as consistently possible. The predominantly morphological data at hand were inadequate to deal with two groups, carnivores and the family Sphaerodoridae. The former category displays a range of behavioral complexity (e.g., Ockelmann and Vahl 1970) which cannot be readily deduced from morphological features, and the latter group's source(s) of nutrition remains unknown. Sphaerodorids typically have a strongly papillated body surface and no apparent gut contents, a condition which is suggestive of carnivory (Hunt 1925) or assimilation of dissolved organics (Stephens 1972) but which gives little firm grounds for dealing with the family under our approach. In the remaining polychaetes, we deal only with adults. This disclaimer is necessary because larvae of detritivores may be carnivorous (e.g., Kühl 1974).

Among the remaining polychaetes, three mobility categories can be recognized: sessile, discretely motile, and motile. We use these terms to refer specifically to feeding strategies. "Sessile" implies that members show no evidence of post-settlement movement away from one feeding location. "Discretely motile" indicates that individuals must be stationary or very slowly moving for efficient operation of their primary feeding mode. The term is used here to imply that the motion is likely to be a discrete or recognizable event, separated from other such events by periods of apparent sessility. This concept corresponds in some respects to Remane's (1940) "semi-sessile" grouping. Finally, by "motile" we mean that the major feeding mode does not require any "setting up" period, and that movement from place to place is relatively frequent, if not continuous.

Similarly, three feeding strata can be recognized. Species which feed on suspended matter may be called "filter feeders." Groups feeding specifically on deposits at the sediment-water interface may be called "surface deposit feeders," and polychaetes feedon buried sediments may be named "burrowers." The latter category might more accurately be termed subsurface deposit feeders, but doing so would interfere with our scheme of abbreviations in tables and figures. In addition to motility classes and feeding strata, the structures which are used in feeding can be recognized. For example, it is relatively easy to note whether an animal feeds with tentacles or jaws.

Space restrictions make it impossible to document fully our reasons for each classification. However, Table 1 gives a complete listing of the results of our literature search and our functional morphological inferences (Jumars and Fauchald, in preparation). We stress the provisional nature of this scheme and our willingness to relocate taxa on the basis of further evidence. Figures 1-3 illustrate the intended differences between categories, but some subjectivity is inevitable. For example, Dragoli's (1960, 1961) observation that *Melinna palmata* (Ampharetidae) may leave its tube under the stress of hydrogen sulfide poisoning does not, in our opinion, compromise our consideration of *Melinna* as a sessile group, but we recognize that alternative interpretations are possible.

Three groups of polychaetes complicate our classification somewhat. *Phyllochaetopterus* (Chaetopteridae) retains the morphological capability to both "surface deposit feed" (with palps) and to "filter feed" (by pumping), accounting for the complex abbreviation F-SST-P. We were unable to assign the Onuphidae (excluding *Hyalinoecia* and

Table 1. Feeding strategy classification of benthic marine polychaetes, excluding predominantly carnivorous species and the family Sphaerodoridae

FST - Filtering, Sessile, Tentaculate	
Sabellariidae	Serpulidae
Sabellinae	Spirorbidae
FSP - Filtering, Sessile, Pumping	
Chaetopteridae (except *Phyllochaetopterus*)	
FDT - Filtering, Discretely motile, Tentaculate	
Fabriciinae	*Owenia*
FDP - Filtering, Discretely motile, Pumping	
Arenicolidae	
FDJ-P - Filtering, Discretely motile, Jawed and Pumping	
Neanthes diversicolor	*Platynereis*
Nereis zonata	*Rhamphobrachium*
F-SST-P - Filtering and Surface deposit feeding, Sessile, Tentaculate and Pumping	
Phyllochaetopterus	
SST - Surface deposit feeding, Sessile, Tentaculate	
Ampharetidae	*Pygospio*
Boccardia	Terebellidae (with exceptions below)
Dodecaceria	*Tharyx* (some species only)
Polydora	Trichobranchidae
SS-DJ - Surface deposit feeding, Sessile or Discretely motile, Jawed	
Onuphidae (except *Hyalinoecia* and *Onuphis conchylega*)	
SDT - Surface deposit feeding, Discretely motile, Tentaculate	
Acrocirridae (with exceptions below)	*Myriowenia*
Apistobranchidae	*Nicolea*
Artacaminae	Polycirrinae
Cirratulidae (except some *Tharyx*)	Sabellongidae
Flabelligeridae	Spionidae (with exceptions above)
Longosomidae	Trochochaetidae
Magelonidae	
SMJ - Surface deposit feeding, Motile, Jawed	
Dorvilleidae (except *Meiodorvillea*)	*Hyalinoecia*
Eunicidae	Nereidae (with exceptions above)
Hesionidae (some without jaws)	*Onuphis conchylega*
BSE - Burrowing, Sessile, Eversible proboscis	
Fauveliopsis glabra	*Myriochele*
Maldanidae	
BMJ - Burrowing, Motile, Jawed	
Lumbrineridae	*Nephtys incisa*
Meiodorvillea	*Nephtys picta*
BMX - Burrowing, Motile, various other modes (X)	
Aphroditidae	Opheliidae
Bogueidae	Orbiniidae
Capitellidae	Paraonidae
Cossuridae	Pectinariidae
Fauveliopsis (except *F. glabra*)	Scalibregmidae
Flabelligella (except palpate species)	Sternaspidae
Lacydoniidae	

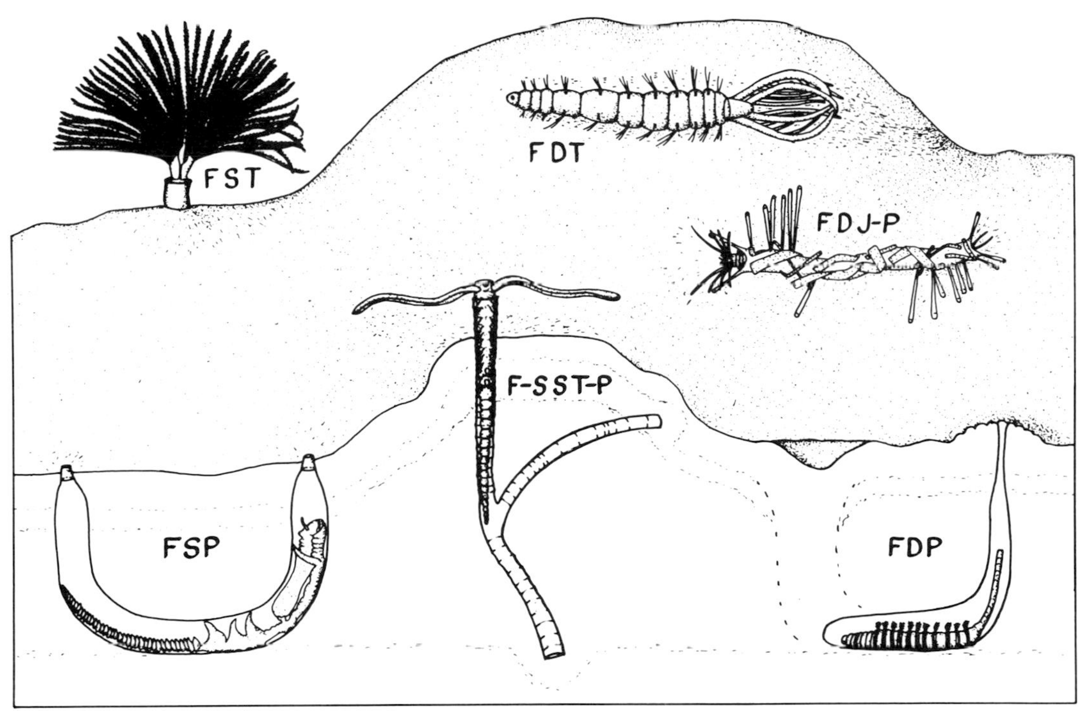

Fig. 1. Examples of filtering strategies (see Table 1). FST: Sabellinae; FDT: Fabriciinae; FDJ-P: *Platynereis* (Nereidae); FSP: *Chaetopterus* (Chaetopteridae); F-SST-P: *Phyllochaetopterus* (Chaetopteridae); FDP: *Arenicola* (Arenicolidae).

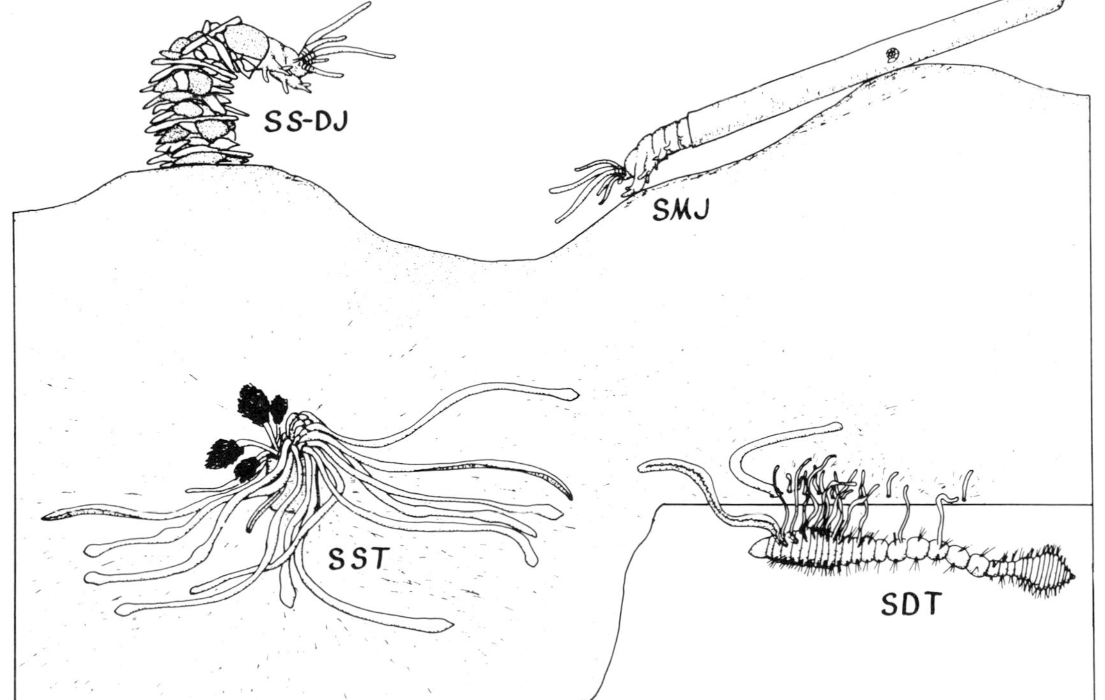

Fig. 2. Examples of surface deposit feeding strategies (see Table 1). SS-DJ: *Diopatra* (Onuphidae); SMJ: *Hyalinoecia* (Onuphidae); SST: *Pista* (Terebellidae); SDT: *Tharyx* (Cirratulidae).

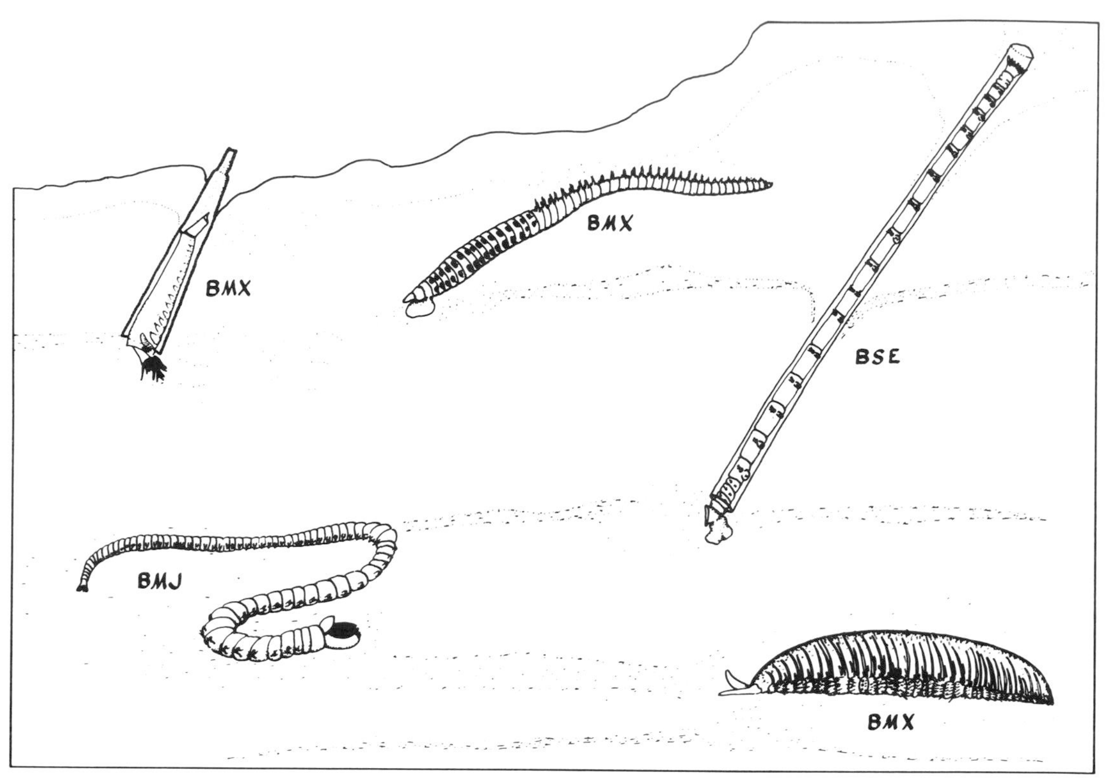

Fig. 3. Examples of burrowing strategies (see Table 1). BMX, upper left: *Pectinaria* (Pectinariidae); BMX, upper middle: Orbiniidae; BSE: Maldanidae; BMJ: Lumbrineridae, jaws everted; BMX, lower right: Aphroditidae.

Onuphis conchylega) with any degree of confidence to either the sessile or discretely motile category, producing the abbreviation SS-DJ. The compound abbreviation FD-JP refers to those nereids which have been observed to filter feed by pumping water through a mucus net. In subsequent analyses, we divided individuals falling into these categories equally between the classes they straddle. For example, in considering feeding strata, if four *Phyllochaetopterus* were sampled, two would be assigned as filter feeders and two, as surface deposit feeders. Without added information, this procedure was the least biased we could devise for dealing with these borderline or compromise cases. In all other instances where the literature gave no information or conflicting information, we were able to make a firm (not necessarily correct) decision to assign taxa to a single category.

We used the multinomial distribution for an analysis of the relative degree of success of the resulting categories. The symbol p_i represents the observed proportion of individuals belonging to the category i, and π_i is used for the corresponding theoretical population parameter (just as $\bar{x}_i$ and μ_i might, respectively, be used for a set of observed or sample, and theoretical or population, means). Proportions sometimes find disfavor because a change in any one p_i produces a complementary change in all other p_j (where $i \neq j$). Snee (1974), however, circumvented some of these objections in an attractive graphical approach. He detailed a principal components procedure to be used when more than three proportions are considered simultaneously, but we limited ourselves to three proportions and a triangular plot, to which our tripartite classifications are suited. Note in Figure 4 that the categories responsible for some changes may be easily identified. Geologists will recognize this format in their familiar sand-silt-clay diagram, and geneticists may recognize it as a convenient means of displaying relative homozygote-heterozygote frequencies (e.g., Schaffer and Mettler 1970). Methods of establishing confidence regions for π_i about the observed proportion p_i were also reviewed by Snee (1974).

We wished to restrict classification errors due to unfamiliarity with the local fauna to a minimum and to have a large body of data from which to draw. The California State Water Quality Control Board (Allan Hancock Foundation, University of Southern California, 1965) has published such data from benthic samples taken along the entire Southern California coast. Hereafter we refer to these samples as belonging to the "state survey." We eliminated those stations not completely sorted and identified (by Dr. Olga Hartman) from consideration, leaving 316 samples ranging in water depth from 2.4 to 397 m. To reduce this number to a manageable size for desk calculator manipulation, with relatively little loss of generality, we stratified the depth range of the 316 samples into ten equal logarithmic intervals and selected three stations at random from each of these intervals. We used a logarithmic stratification because most features we could conceive to exert effects on feeding

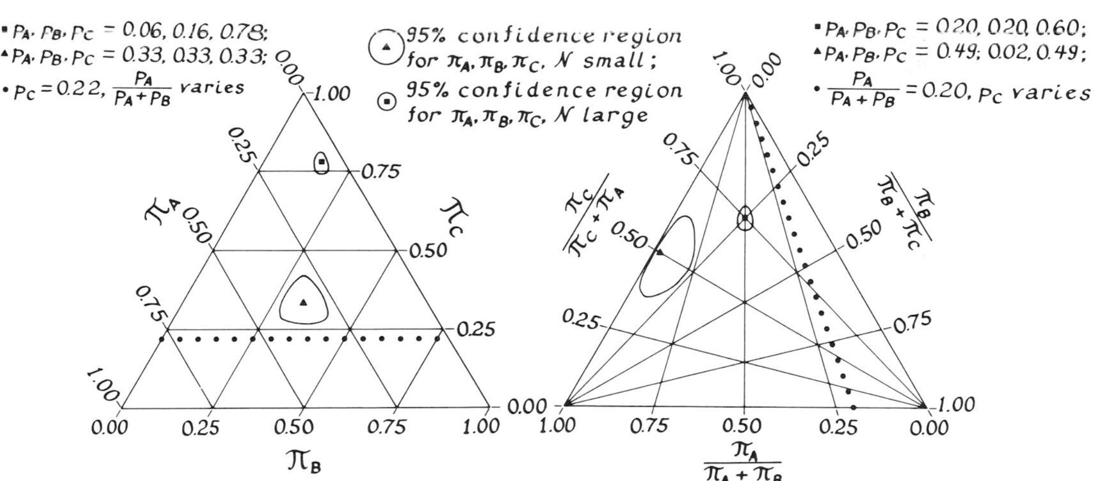

Fig. 4. Two interpretations of triangular charts. Left chart: isolines show constant proportions of each of A, B, and C; right chart: isolines show constant ratios of A, B, and C to each other, in pairs as indicated. Relative utilities of the two interpretations are determined by the patterns of variation observed. Compare with Figures 5 and 6.

strategies vary exponentially with depth (viz. Rowe et al. 1974). A closer spacing (on a linear scale) is thus warranted in shallower water, where a greater rate of change is expected. In subsequent analyses of the state survey material, we are thus dealing with a total of 30 samples unless otherwise stated.

Excluding carnivores and Sphaerodoridae, we then classified the polychaete faunas of each sample according to the scheme of Table 1. Also classified in this manner were polychaetes from the Santa Catalina Basin (five 0.25-m^2 box cores at approximately 1130-m depth), from the San Diego Trough (five 0.25-m^2 box cores at approximately 1230-m depth), and from the central North Pacific (twelve 0.25-m^2 box cores at approximately 5600 m). The bathyal samples came from studies of species' dispersion patterns in the Southern California Continental Borderland (Jumars 1974, 1975a, b), and the abyssal cores were part of a program of quantitative community analysis (Hessler and Jumars 1974). For our preliminary discussion of depth-correlated variation, only the three feeding strata and the three motility classes are considered in detail.

RESULTS

Results of calculating p_i for the strata and the motility classes are presented separately for the state survey (Fig. 5) and for the deep-sea samples (Fig. 6). Confidence regions were drawn in the latter case because sufficient data exist to establish that the animal dispersion patterns do not grossly violate the assumption of random sampling from a multinomial distribution (see Johnson and Kotz 1969). Species' dispersion patterns over small areas in these

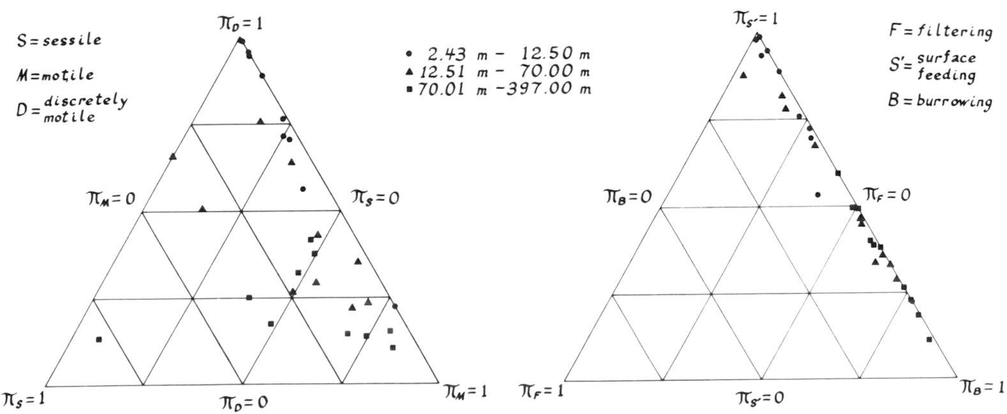

Fig. 5. Triangular chart presentation of feeding strategy variation with depth for state survey samples. Only the values $\pi = 0$ (sides of triangle) and $\pi = 1$ (vertices of triangle) are labeled, but isolines correspond to those of Figure 4 (left).

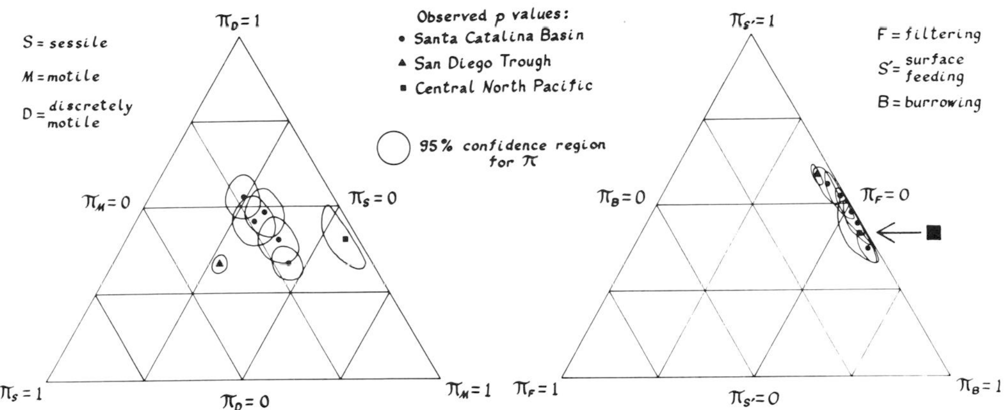

Fig. 6. Triangular chart presentation of feeding strategy variation by location for the deep-sea samples. Only the values $\pi = 0$ (sides of triangle) and $\pi = 1$ (vertices of triangle) are labeled, but isolines correspond to those of Figure 4 (left).

deep-sea regions are not markedly patchy (Hessler and Jumars 1974; Jumars 1974, 1975b). For the San Diego Trough and the central North Pacific, the between-sample results of the classifications are homogeneous enough to permit grouping of all cores, as shown in Figure 6. In the Santa Catalina Basin cores, however, heterogeneity (non-overlap of some pairs of 95 percent confidence regions for π_i) was observed, so that confidence regions for the contents of each of the cores are figured. As Snee (1974) pointed out, this plot is a graphical analogue of the heterogeneity chi-square procedure.

The trends seen in Figure 5 are then analyzed with the nonparametric rank-difference correlation statistic, selected because it is insensitive to the obvious nonlinearities of the figure (Tate and Clelland 1957). If some particular trend were of *a priori* interest, it would be unwise to engage in multiple testing but, in order to facilitate hypothesis formulation, all the possible correlations with depth suggested by Figure 4 are assessed. The data upon which Figure 5 is based show a trend of increasing proportion of motile species with depth, followed, at greater depths, by a decreasing proportion. Because this relationship is not monotonic, the rank-difference correlation coefficient of depth with the proportion of motile individuals underestimates its strength (Tate and Clelland 1957). The probabilities assigned in Table 2 do not reflect this problem or the degree of multiple testing involved and should be interpreted accordingly.

Even after giving appropriate weight to these problems, however, interpretation is not safe. The state survey samples were taken with an orange peel grab (those samples from 10-m depth or greater) or a van Veen grab (the shallower stations). Such grab samplers cannot be expected to penetrate to equal depths in the entire range of sediment types encountered. Specifically, they tend to take a deeper "bite" in softer sediments. One might expect, therefore, a larger

Table 2. Rank-difference correlation coefficients (r) of sample depth with the indicated covariables. Covariable subscripts correspond to the legend of Figure 5, and r^2 gives the approximate portion of variability in one variable "explained" by covariation in the other. P is the probability of obtaining the observed coefficient by chance when the variables are in fact independent (N = 30). See also Figure 4

Motility Analysis				Feeding Stratum Analysis			
Covariable	r	r^2	P	Covariable	r	r^2	P
P_S	0.77	0.59	<0.0001	P_F	-0.22	0.05	>0.20
P_D	-0.78	0.61	<0.0001	P_S'	-0.61	0.37	<0.001
P_M	0.48	0.23	<0.01	P_B	0.59	0.35	≃0.001
$\frac{P_S}{P_S + P_M}$	0.50	0.25	<0.01	$\frac{P_F}{P_F + P_B}$	-0.37	0.14	<0.05
$\frac{P_D}{P_D + P_S}$	-0.86	0.75	<0.00001	$\frac{P_S'}{P_S' + P_F}$	0.06	0.00	>0.70
$\frac{P_M}{P_M + P_D}$	0.61	0.38	<0.001	$\frac{P_B}{P_B + P_S'}$	0.59	0.35	≃0.001

proportion of burrowers in volumetrically larger samples. For the 20 orange peel grab samples in which a sample volume was recorded, our suspicions were, unfortunately, confirmed. The correlation of water depth with sample volume (r=0.42, one-tailed $P < 0.05$) was of the same sign and magnitude as the correlation of depth with the proportion of burrowers (r=0.39, $P < 0.05$). Any possible real trend of increasing porportion of burrowers with increasing water depth was therefore confounded with this apparent sampling bias, and further, the same bias would be expected to affect the proportion of motile individuals because most burrowers were motile in all the samples. Furthermore, grab samplers generally do not enclose the same area for their full depth of bite. This area generally decreases with depth in the sediment (Holme and McIntyre 1971). The proportion of burrowers is thus likely to be an underestimate at all water depths but, a more serious underestimate at shallower stations. For these reasons, we concentrate on one aspect of the analysis which is not severely affected by these biases, namely the numerical ratio of sessile to discretely motile individuals. Some confounding is still possible because the maldanids are not thereby excluded. We believe their exclusion would be unrealistically conservative, although the ratio of sessile to discretely motile individuals would still correlate very strongly with depth (r=0.69, $P \simeq 0.0002$), even with <u>all</u> burrowers excluded.

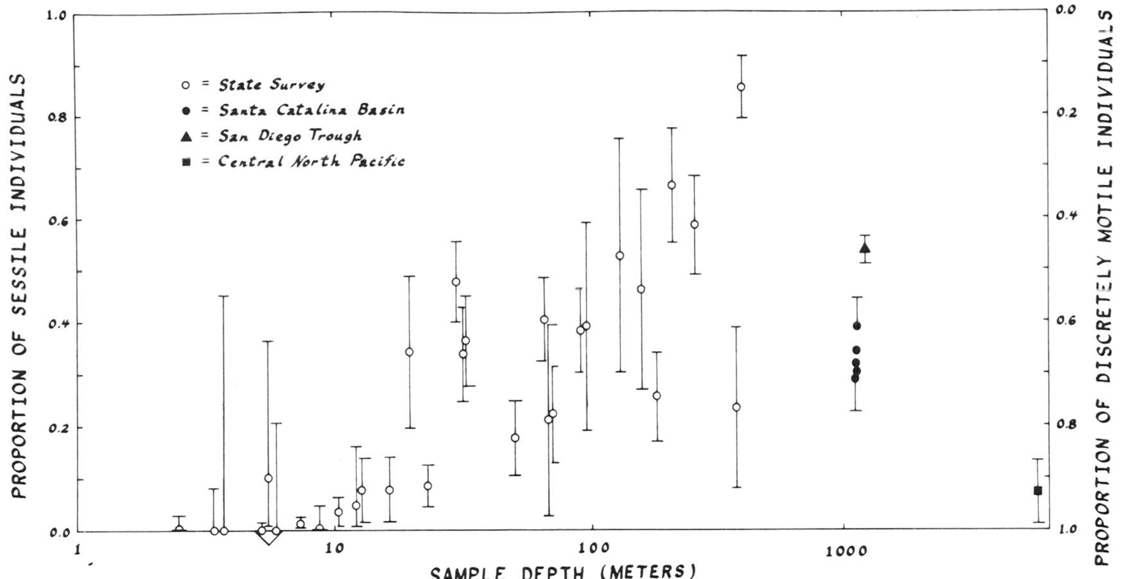

Fig. 7. The ratio of sessile individuals to discretely motile individuals versus sample depths (logarithmic scale). Bars show 95% confidence intervals for the ratio (binomial distribution model). The triangle under the abscissa indicates that the three bracketed samples all fell at the same depth.

Figure 7 combines the data on the ratio of sessile to discretely motile individuals from Figures 5 and 6. The data need not be recalculated, but can be generated graphically by projecting a vector from the vertex, $P_M=1$, through the point of interest onto the axis joining $P_S=1$ and $P_D=1$ to obtain the desired ratio. From the values so obtained, it is obvious that the strong positive correlation between water depth and the proportion of sessile individuals (Table 2) does not extend into the abyss. Figure 7 suggests instead that a maximum in the proportion of sessile individuals might occur between 400 and 1000 m. The 95% confidence limits for the proportions are shown, and, by the above arguments, these limits are probably fairly accurate for the deep-sea samples. For the state survey stations, on the other hand, these error-bars probably represent minimum estimates because dispersion patterns in shallow water tend to show aggregation. They are useful, however, in giving a rough indication of the relative sample sizes involved, smaller error-bars representing larger samples. Most of the following discussion is based on Figure 7.

DISCUSSION

When cross-classified according to our analyses, the classification itself is of some ecological interest. As noted in Table 3, several combinations have not been observed among the world's

Table 3. A cross-classification of the feeding strategies from Table 1. Φ: combination not yet documented; i: apparently incompatible combination; ε: energetically unlikely; ?: problem in the classification. (See text.)

		Sessile	Discretely Motile	Motile
	Tentaculate	FST	FDT	Φ_i
Filter Feeding	Pumping, Jawed	Φ_ε	FDJ-P	Φ_i
	Pumping, no jaws	FSP	FDP	Φ_i
		F-SST-P		
Surface Deposit Feeding	Tentaculate	SST	SDT	Φ_i
	Jawed	SS-DJ		SMJ
	Jawed	Φ_ε	Φ_ε	BMJ
Burrowing	Eversible proboscis or other means (X)	BSE	?	BMX

non-carnivorous, non-sphaerodorid, marine benthic polychaetes. These "null sets" (Φ) seem to fall into one of two categories: functionally incompatible combinations, and energetically unlikely strategies. In the former category, movement on or in the sediment appears incompatible with simultaneous (though not subsequent) filter feeding or with feeding by means of ciliated tentacles. In the latter category, there probably have not been enough large food particles suspended in the oceans to have made the evolution of a jawed, sessile filter feeder a likely event.

One apparent problem with our classification is indicated by the question mark in the table. No species are classified as discretely motile burrowers. Some of the central North Pacific and bathyal maldanids have fragile tubes which are long and geometrically complex. Some maldanids might conceivably add to a tube as they work laterally through the sediments, but, lacking firmer evidence, we currently leave all maldanids in the sessile category.

The magnitudes of the correlation coefficients nevertheless leave no doubt ($P \simeq 0.9998$, even with all burrowers excluded) that we have found a strong pattern which demands explanation. However, there is no limit to the number of possible causes which might be invoked to explain the pattern in Figure 7. Rather than compiling long lists of alternative hypotheses which would be useful in some ways (Platt 1964), we deal with a few that appear to make the most intuitive sense. Our major effort in this discussion will be to devise suitable tests of these few.

First and foremost, the observed correlations of the numerical ratio of sessile to discretely motile individuals probably have little to do with depth per se. We propose that the two depth covariables of primary importance in producing the correlations are (1) sediment stability, and (2) flux of organic matter. On an open, or exposed, coastline, sediment stability generally increases with water depth. Along the Southern California coast in particular, sediment motion is usually appreciable to depths of 30 m or more (Drake et al. 1972). Some such motion is indicated to depths of 100 m (Gorsline and Grant 1972), but infrequent storm surges might be expected occasionally to effect sediment instability in even greater depths (e.g., Draper 1967). Sediment mobility would seem to place a premium on animal motility. Most obvious is the problem of burial, particularly in shallow water (Fager 1968). Less obviously, sediment motion alters local sediment characteristics, probably giving an advantage to those individuals which can move to locally optimum conditions. The characteristics of bivalves found in high-energy (physical energy) environments (e.g., Stanley 1970) support these arguments. We hypothesize (Hypothesis 1) that decreasing intensity and frequency of disturbance with increasing depth accounts for the depth-sessility correlations in the state survey samples.

Although it may (Rowe et al. 1974) or may not (Carey 1972) be reflected in standing stock of macrofauna, community metabolism appears, in general, to decrease in rate with increasing depth and distance from shore, presumably due to a concommitant decrease in the flux of organic matter to the sea bed (Pamatmat 1973). Foraging area, in turn, has been demonstrated to be inversely proportional to food supply in a number of vertebrate species (e.g., Birdsell 1958; Schoener 1968; Smith 1968). For our next hypothesis, however, Bernstein's (1975) study is most pertinent. In examining foraging radii of ants under conditions of varying food supply, she also found an inverse relationship. Foraging radius was relatively constant within species, though, so that species replacement occurred along a gradient in food abundance. We propose that a similar phenomenon may account for the observed decrease in relative abundance of sessile individuals with increasing depth greater than 400 m (Fig. 7). Sessile individuals have a feeding radius limited by the length of feeding appendages or, in the case of maldanids, by the area from which fresh sediment will cave in as the animal feeds. (For the moment, we are not considering filter feeders.) The foraging areas of discretely motile or motile individuals do not have such obvious limits. We hypothesize, then, that (Hypothesis 2) the foraging radius required for adequate nutrition exceeds the reach of most sessile individuals at greater bathyal and abyssal depths.

The apparent maximum in relative abundance of sessile individuals at intermediate depths in Figure 7 would thus result from the interaction of our two hypothesized causes, as will become more apparent when we formulate some predictions (below). It is probably useful at this point to emphasize that we are not redescribing the relatively well-documented reduction in relative importance of filter feeding with increasing depth (Sanders et al. 1965; Jørgensen 1966;

Riedl 1971). Although the arguments for such a reduction parallel ours for the replacement of sessile individuals (albeit filter feeders are usually replaced at considerably shallower depths), suspension feeders are not numerically important in any of the samples we treat (Figs. 5 and 6).

One pattern which cannot be clearly extracted from our present data but which should be mentioned in passing is that of the variation of the relative abundances of the various feeding strata (suspension, surface, subsurface) with water depth. In our deep-sea samples, individuals are divided roughly equally between surface deposit feeders and burrowers (Fig. 6). In grab samples (Fig. 5) from the state survey, burrowers often comprise well over half the individuals. Unless the bow wave of the grabs were quite severe, it is difficult to imagine that grab samplers, which often retain a proportionately smaller area with increasing depth in the sediment (Holme and McIntyre 1971), could unrealistically inflate the proportion of burrowers. Therefore, the proportion of burrowers probably is lower in the deep-sea areas sampled than at some shelf depths. The pattern could be elucidated with further box core samples at shelf depths.

Our two basic hypotheses can more readily be used to generate disprovable predictions (see Platt 1964) if they are stated in more general terms. The first hypothesis may be generalized to state that increasing magnitude and frequency of sediment motion decreases the relative fitness of sessile life styles (Purdy 1964). The second hypothesis may be generalized to state that decreasing food supply increases the relative fitness of foraging strategies utilizing larger foraging areas (Schoener 1968, 1971). Clearly, these general hypotheses are not original, but some of the following predictions based on them appear not to have been made before.

According to these hypotheses, species replacements should occur over short distances where gradients in sediment mobility or food abundance are steep. In Table 4, we propose several "natural experiments" (Diamond 1973) to perform the desired tests. As presented, the hypotheses are easier to discuss separately.

Uniformity in temperature with depth is often cited as a reason for broad species' depth ranges in the Antarctic (e.g., Menzies et al. 1973; Arnaud 1974). We propose in addition, as some of Arnaud's (1974) data substantiate, that the existence of convective mechanisms for food transport to the bottom, coupled with high surface productivity, provides a generally similar amount of food over a broad depth range, thus permitting broad depth distribution of single feeding strategies. We predict much narrower ranges in the Arctic Ocean due to the general nearshore limitation of high productivity (Matheke and Horner 1974). Benthic studies of the Alaskan North Slope fauna (Carey, personal communication) could be used to test this prediction.

Where food input is relatively low over wide depth ranges, we also would expect single feeding strategies to be eurybathic. Eurybathy of species would thus be expected in the poorly productive

Table 4. Predicted rates of change in species composition with depth and distance from shore for various regions, except that the equatorial predictions concern directed distances along similar depth contours. (See text.)

Cause	Rate of Species Replacement With Distance	
	Rapid	Slow
Variations in flux of energy-rich fixed carbon	Arctic Nile Delta S. California Across Equator	Antarctic E. Mediterranean Red Sea Along Equator
Variations in input of turbulent energy	Open Coasts	Sheltered Coasts

regions of the eastern Mediterranean and Red Seas. Contrastingly rapid species (feeding strategy) replacements would be expected near the Nile Delta.

In the deep sea, rapid species replacement would be expected across the equatorial region due to rapid changes in surface productivity with latitude. Conversely lower rates of change would be expected in transects along the equator. Among the polychaetes, we predict a relatively high proportion of sessile species will be found along the equator because of high surface productivity. This hypothesis will soon be tested with samples collected at approximately 3°N, 125°W by Hessler (personal communication) and with samples to be processed during the preparation of an environmental impact statement concerning the effects of manganese nodule mining in the central Pacific (Environmental Research Laboratories, National Oceanic and Atmospheric Administration, in preparation). Similarly, shifting regions of high and low productivity over geologic time might provide a mechanism for geographic isolation and speciation of benthic populations, just as we propose the faunas of the North and South Pacific gyres are separated by a region containing species adapted to the relatively higher food input under the equator.

Although the relationships of various species to sediment mobility have often been noted (e.g., Purdy 1964), we propose the relationship is stronger and of wider application than heretofore realized. Recent interest in the bearing of sediment stability on community composition has been kindled by the hypothesis of trophic group amensalism (Rhoads and Young 1970), which has been largely verified in subsequent investigations (e.g., Aller and Dodge 1974). According to this hypothesis, suspension feeders are not abundant on reworked (by deposit feeders) and unstable sediments. Our results (Fig. 7) suggest that degree of sediment stability also determines the kind of deposit feeder which will predominate (sessile or not).

If our results are indicative, this relationship might be expected at least to the deepest shelf depths of exposed coasts, where storm surges are a normal winter occurrence (Draper 1967).

Another test of the stability-sessility relationship is possible by examination of faunas in sheltered bodies of water. In these cases, if food supply is sufficient, sessile species would be expected to show high relative abundance in shallow water. Day (1974) observed a strong correlation of shelter with species composition in estuaries, but the species were not categorized by sessility. For both the sessility-sediment stability and the sessility-food supply relations it would be useful to examine taxa other than Polychaeta as well. Again, if direct measures of foraging area or sessility could not be obtained, a classificatory scheme might prove useful.

So far our discussion has been limited to community composition, but the characteristics of individuals may also vary. The robustness of animals living in unstable sedimentary regimes is well known (e.g., Stanley 1970). The fragile nature of deep-sea animals from stable regions is also commonly recognized (e.g., Hartman and Fauchald 1971). Morphologies may also be expected to vary with changing food supply. In particular, our hypothesized relation between food supply and foraging area would suggest that individuals existing under low food fluxes may have relatively long or extensible feeding appendages. Polychaeta constitute a poor test of this prediction because feeding appendages are often greatly extensible and are often lost upon preservation. To some extent, the prediction has been confirmed by Allen and Sanders (1966), who observed that the relative weight of feeding palps increases with depth of collection for some closely related protobranch bivalve species. The prediction might be more easily tested, however, by measuring the relative lengths of ampeliscid or corophiid (amphipod) feeding antennae with increasing water depth.

If these predictions are not disproven, the present hypotheses also have implications for species diversity arguments. Structural heterogeneity and species diversity often correspond (e.g., MacArthur and MacArthur 1961). Rhoads (1974) convincingly demonstrated with some recent photographs that soft-bottom communities do exhibit structural heterogeneity, and there are several reasons to believe such heterogeneity should be maximal where sessile species dominate. First, according to our previous arguments, an area dominated by sessile individuals is not physically disturbed or homogenized. Second, with relatively few motile individuals, such an area is probably not quickly biologically homogenized, either. Third, unless the sediment modifications (e.g., tubes) common to sessile animals are so abundant as to abut; these modifications, interspersed with less or differently modified sediment, would be expected to add to the heterogeneity. Not only is environmental heterogeneity effected by sessile species, but such species are most likely to be affected by it as well. As argued in greater detail by Jumars (1975*a*, *b*), animals with small areas of activity or ambits (Lloyd 1967) are most likely to experience a coarse-grained, heterogeneous environment.

If all else were equal, one might then expect species diversity to reach a maximum at the depth with a maximum percentage of sessile individuals. An intermediate-depth diversity maximum has been documented for the gastropods (Rex 1973). However, all else is not equal. In particular, hypsographic curves (e.g., Menard and Smith 1966) reveal that little of the ocean bottom falls at such intermediate depths. Hence, the effective "island size" (MacArthur and Wilson 1967) for species limited to such depths is small relative to the effective island size for species of abyssal regions. Despite this disclaimer and the fact that manganese nodules and abyssal hills (D. A. Johnson 1972) also contribute to deep-sea benthic environmental heterogeneity, the effects of sessile species sometimes appear to dominate (Jumars 1975b).

Perhaps the most salutary prediction arising from the present hypotheses is more painfully obvious: easily measured parameters and biologically important parameters may bear little relation. R. G. Johnson (1974) clearly illustrated this maxim in searching for biologically meaningful sediment descriptions and in contrasting these new appraisals with the standard sedimentary parameters employed by geologists. Our hypotheses point to the desirability of assessing directly such intractable features as individual foraging areas, local fluxes of foods, and frequencies and intensities of sediment motion. Until such observations are made, the importance of easily measured community covariables, such as temperature and mineral grain size, will continue to be overrated, and causes will be difficult to extract.

REFERENCES

Allan Hancock Foundation, University of Southern California. 1965. An oceanographic and biological survey of the Southern California mainland shelf. California State Water Quality Control Board Publ. 27: 1-232; Appendix-Data: 1-445.

Allen, J. A. and H. L. Sanders. 1966. Adaptations to abyssal life as shown by the bivalve *Abra profundorum* (Smith). Deep-Sea Res. 13: 1175-1184.

Aller, R. C. and R. E. Dodge. 1974. Animal-sediment relations in a tropical lagoon Discovery Bay, Jamaica. J. Mar. Res. 32: 209-232.

Arnaud, P. M. 1974. Contribution à la bionomie benthique des régions Antarctiques et Subantarctiques. Téthys 6: 465-656.

Belyaev, G. M., N. G. Vinogradova, R. Ya. Levenstein, F. A. Pasternak, M. N. Sokolova, and Z. A. Filatova. 1973. Distribution laws of the deep-sea bottom fauna in the light of the idea of the biological structure of the ocean. Okeanologia 13: 149-157 [in Russian].

Bernstein, R. A. 1975. Foraging strategies of ants in response to variable food density. Ecology 56: 213-219.

Birdsell, J. B. 1958. On population structure in generalized hunting and collecting populations. Evolution 12: 189-205.

Carey, A. G. 1972. Ecological observations on the benthic invertebrates from the central Oregon shelf, pp. 422-443. In A. T. Pruter and D. L. Alverson [eds.], The Columbia River Estuary and adjacent ocean waters. University of Washington Press.

Day, J. H. 1974. The ecology of Morrumbene Estuary, Mozambique. Trans. Royal Soc. S. Afr. 41: 43-97.

Diamond, J. M. 1973. Distributional ecology of New Guinea birds. Science 179: 759-769.

Dragoli, A. L. 1960. Biology of the Black Sea polychaete *Melinna palmata* Grube. Nauk. Zap. Odessa Biol. Sta. 2: 43-48.

Dragoli, A. L. 1961. Biology of the Black Sea polychaete *Melinna palmata* Grube. Nauk. Zap. Odessa Biol. Sta. 3: 71-83 [in Russian].

Drake, D. E., R. L. Kolpack, and P. J. Fischer. 1972. Sediment transport on the Santa Barbara-Oxnard shelf, Santa Barbara Channel, California, pp. 307-331. In D. J. P. Swift, D. B. Duane, and O. H. Pilkey [eds.], Shelf sediment transport: process and pattern. Dowden, Hutchinson and Ross, Inc.

Draper, L. 1967. Wave activity at the sea bed around northwestern Europe. Mar. Geol. 5: 133-140.

Fager, E. W. 1968. A sand-bottom epifaunal community of invertebrates in shallow water. Limnol. Oceanogr. 13: 448-464.

Fauchald, K. 1974. Polychaete phylogeny: a problem in protostome evolution. Syst. Zool. 23: 493-506.

Glaessner, M. F. and B. Daily. 1959. The geology and late pre-Cambrian fauna of the Ediacara fossil reserve. Records So. Austral. Mus. 13: 369-401.

Gorsline, D. S. and D. J. Grant. 1972. Sediment textural patterns on San Pedro Shelf, California (1951-1971): reworking and transport by waves and currents, pp. 575-600. In D. J. P. Swift, D. B. Duane, and O. H. Pilkey [eds.], Shelf sediment transport: process and pattern. Dowden, Hutchinson and Ross, Inc.

Hartman, O. and K. Fauchald. 1971. Deep-water benthic polychaetous annelids off New England to Bermuda and other North Atlantic areas. Pt. II. Allan Hancock Monogr. Mar. Biol. 6: 1-327.

Hessler, R. R. and P. A. Jumars. 1974. Abyssal community analysis from replicate box cores in the central North Pacific. Deep-Sea Res. 21: 185-209.

Holme, N. A. and A. D. McIntyre. 1971. Methods for the study of marine benthos. IBP Handbook No. 16. Blackwell.

Hunt, O. D. 1925. The food of the bottom fauna of the Plymouth fishing grounds. J. Mar. Biol. Ass. U. K. 13: 560-599.

Johnson, D. A. 1972. Ocean floor erosion in the equatorial Pacific. Bull. Am. Geol. Soc. 83: 3121-3144.

Johnson, N. L. and S. Kotz. 1969. Discrete distributions. Houghton-Mifflin.

Johnson, R. G. 1974. Particulate matter at the sediment-water interface in coastal environments. J. Mar. Res. 32: 313-330.

Jørgensen, C. B. 1966. Biology of suspension feeding. Pergamon Press.

Jumars, P. A. 1974. Dispersion patterns and species diversity of macrobenthos in two bathyal communities. Ph. D. thesis, Univ. of California at San Diego. 204 pp.

_____. 1975a. Methods for measurement of community structure in deep-sea macrobenthos. Mar. Biol. 30: 245-252.

_____. 1975b. Environmental grain and polychaete species diversity in a bathyal benthic community. Mar. Biol. 30: 253-266.

Kühl, Von Heinrich. 1974. Über Vorkommen und Nahrung der Larven von *Magelona papillicornis* O. F. Müller (Polychaeta Sedentaria) im Mündungsgegiet von Elbe, Weser und Ems. Ber. dt. wiss. Kommn. Meeresforsch. 23: 296-301.

Lloyd, M. 1967. Mean crowding. J. Anim. Ecol. 36: 1-30.

MacArthur, R. H. and J. MacArthur. 1961. On bird species diversity. Ecology 42: 594-598.

_____ and E. O. Wilson. 1967. The theory of island biogeography. Princeton University Press.

Matheke, G. E. M. and R. Horner. 1974. Primary production of the benthic microalgae in the Chukchi Sea near Barrow, Alaska. J. Fish. Res. Bd. Can. 31: 1779-1786.

Menard, H. W. and S. M. Smith. 1966. Hypsometry of ocean basin provinces. J. Geophys. Res. 71: 4305-4325.

Menzies, R. J., R. Y. George, and G. T. Rowe. 1973. Abyssal environment and ecology of the world oceans. Wiley.

Ockelmann, K. W. and O. Vahl. 1970. On the biology of the polychaete *Glycera alba*, especially its burrowing and feeding. Ophelia 8: 275-294.

Pamatmat, M. M. 1973. Benthic community metabolism on the continental terrace and in the deep sea in the North Pacific. Int. Rev. ges. Hydrobiol. 58: 345-368.

Platt, J. R. 1964. Strong inference. Science 146: 347-353.

Purdy, E. G. 1964. Sediments as substrates, pp. 238-271. In J. Imbrie and N. D. Newell [eds.], Approaches to paleoecology. Wiley.

Remane, A. 1940. Einführung in die zoologische Ökologie der Nord- und Ostsee. Tierw. Nord- u. Ostsee 1A: 1-238.

Rex, M. A. 1973. Deep-sea species diversity: decreased gastropod diversity at abyssal depths. Science 181: 1051-1053.

Rhoads, D. C. 1974. Organism-sediment relations on the muddy sea floor. Oceanogr. Mar. Biol. Ann. Rev. 12: 263-300.

_____ and D. K. Young. 1970. The influence of deposit-feeding organisms on sediment stability and community structure. J. Mar. Res. 28: 150-178.

Riedl, R. 1971. Water movement--animals, pp. 1123-1149. In O. Kinne [ed.], Marine ecology, v. 1. Environmental factors. Part 2. Wiley-Interscience.

Rowe, G. T., P.T. Polloni, and G. S. Horner. 1974. Benthic biomass estimates from the northwestern Atlantic Ocean and the northern Gulf of Mexico. Deep-Sea Res. 21: 641-650.

Sanders, H. L., R. R. Hessler, and G. R. Hampson. 1965. An introduction to the study of the deep-sea benthic faunal assemblages along the Gay Head-Bermuda transect. Deep-Sea Res. 12: 845-867.
Schaffer, H. E. and L. E. Mettler. 1970. Teaching models in population genetics. BioScience 20: 1304-1310.
Schoener, T. W. 1968. Sizes of feeding territories among birds. Ecology 49: 123-141.
_____. 1971. Theory of feeding strategies. Ann. Rev. Ecol. Syst. 2: 369-404.
Smith, C. C. 1968. The adaptive nature of social organization in the genus of tree squirrels *Tamiasciurus*. Ecol. Monogr. 38: 31-63.
Snee, R. D. 1974. Graphical display of two-way contingency tables. Amer. Statistician 28: 9-12.
Stanley, S. M. 1970. Relation of shell form to life habits of Bivalvia (Mollusca). Geol. Soc. Amer. Mem. 125: 1-296.
Stephens, G. C. 1972. Amino acid accumulation and assimilation in marine organisms, pp. 155-184. In J. W. Campbell and L. Goldstein [eds.], Nitrogen metabolism and the environment. Academic Press.
Swedmark, B. 1964. The interstitial fauna of marine sand. Biol. Rev. 39: 1-42.
Tate, M. W. and R. C. Clelland. 1957. Nonparametric and short-cut statistics. Interstate Printers and Publishers.

NOTE:

The reader wishing to apply a trophic classification to either Arenicolidae of Flabelligeridae would do well to consult references published since this manuscript was submitted, i.e.,

Hylleberg, J. 1975. Selective feeding by *Abarenicola pacifica* with notes on *Abarenicola vagabunda* and a concept of gardening in lugworms. Ophelia 14: 113-137.
Spies, R. B. 1975. Structure and function of the head in flabelligerid polychaetes. J. Morphol. 147(2): 187-207.

Feeding Behavior of Marine Nematodes

John H. Tietjen and **John J. Lee**
Department of Biology and
Institute of Marine and Atmospheric Sciences
City College of New York
New York, NY 10031

ABSTRACT

Qualitative and quantitative data are presented on the feeding activities of four free-living marine nematodes isolated from the aufwuchs assemblages of marine macrophytes. Tracer-feeding experiments with ^{32}P-labelled diatoms, chlorophytes and bacteria indicate that for *Chromadora macrolaimoides* and *Chromadorina germanica*, nematodes equipped with small teeth in the buccal cavity, algae form a significantly greater fraction of their diet than do bacteria. For *Monhystera denticulata* and *Rhabditis marina*, nematodes devoid of buccal armature, the weights of algae and bacteria ingested daily per worm are nearly equal; this similarity is the result of lesser grazing of algae and heavier grazing of bacteria by these worms.

The relationships among feeding preferences of the nematodes, food cell size and calorific content are discussed. Also discussed is the role of selective ingestion and digestion of food in the regulation of species diversity.

INTRODUCTION

Despite the recent active interest in free-living nematodes and other marine meiofauna, detailed information on the quantitative and qualitative aspects of their feeding activities is scant. Such information is necessary if the importance of these omnipresent organisms in the ecosystem is to become known.

Von Thun (1968) summarized the early studies of Allgen, Bütschli, Cobb and others on the feeding habits of marine nematodes, studies which were based largely on gut content analyses. Perkins (1958), Hopper and Meyers (1967), and Tietjen (1969) also studied nematode feeding habits through gut contents, but gut content analyses of small organisms are notoriously inadequate (Edmondson 1957; Perkins 1958; McIntyre 1969; Tietjen 1969). Usually only the hard, more indigestible items are recognizable.

For an accurate assessment of both the qualitative and quantitative aspects of feeding, nematodes must be maintained in laboratory culture on known food organisms. Marine nematodes have been maintained in the laboratory on a variety of known food organisms, mainly bacteria and yeasts (Chitwood and Murphy 1964; Hopper and Meyers 1966a, b; Tietjen 1967; Tietjen and Lee 1972; Tietjen et al. 1970; Gerlach and Schrage 1971, 1972; Hopper et al. 1973), and algae (Chitwood and Timm 1954; Webb 1956; Tietjen 1967; von Thun 1968; Tietjen and Lee 1973; Gerlach and Schrage 1971, 1972). Ciliates have also been cited as a potential food source (Webb 1956; von Thun 1968; Gerlach and Schrage 1971, 1972). To our knowledge, the only quantitative data extant on the feeding activities of marine nematodes are those of Tietjen et al. (1970) for *Rhabditis marina* Bastian, 1865 and Tietjen and Lee (1973) for *Chromadora macrolaimoides* Steiner 1915.

This paper reports the qualitative and quantitative uptake of bacteria and algae by two additional species, *Chromadorina germanica* Butschli 1874 and *Monhystera denticulata* Timm 1952, and compares the feeding habits of these two species with *Rhabditis marina* and *Chromadora macrolaimoides*.

This work was supported by the National Science Foundation Grants GB 19245 and GA 33388. Contribution No. 60 from the Institute of Marine and Atmospheric Sciences, City College of New York.

METHODS

All four species were isolated from the aufwuchs occurring on marine macrophytes collected from North Sea Harbor, Southampton, New York. *Rhabditis marina* was isolated from the aufwuchs occurring on *Zostera marina*, the other species from the aufwuchs occurring on *Enteromorpha intestinalis*. According to the feeding classification scheme developed by Wieser (1953), *Chromadora macrolaimoides* and *Chromadorina germanica* are both epistrate feeders. Both organisms possess three small teeth in the buccal cavity with which it is thought they (1) either scrape food materials off larger particles or (2) pierce a food object and ingest the cell liquid by means of the sucking power of the esophagus. In *C. macrolaimoides* the buccal cavity is about 17 μ deep and 5 μ wide; in *C. germanica* it is about 15 μ deep and 4-6 μ wide.

Rhabditis marina and *Monhystera denticulata*, on the other hand, are deposit feeders according to the Wieser scheme. Both of these species lack the moderately strong buccal armature found in *C. macrolaimoides* and *C. germanica*; thus they feed only by means of the sucking power of the esophagus. In *R. marina*, the buccal cavity is about 25 μ deep and 5-8 μ wide; in *M. denticulata* it is about 7-8 μ deep and 3-4 μ wide.

Data on the life histories of *R. marina, M. denticulata* and *C. macrolaimoides* are available (Tietjen et al. 1970; Tietjen and Lee 1972, 1973); the generation time of *C. germanica* is about 12-15 days (unpublished data).

Isolation

Small samples (0.2 g DW) of the host macrophyte and its epiphytes were collected and brought to the laboratory. Aliquots were streaked out on agar plates composed of solid differential growth media (Lee et al. 1970, 1975; Tietjen et al. 1970), and incubated in front of a fluorescent light bank at 20-25 C. The samples were examined 2-3 times weekly, and aliquots showing good growth were separated and the nematodes subcultured in tissue culture flasks, petri dishes or thin agar slants incubated on their sides.

The nematodes inoculated into fresh media were washed in 9-hole Pyrex spot plates containing sterile (autoclaved) sea water, and transferred to fresh media with potential food organisms carried over from the initial inoculum. Once in continuous culture, it was possible to study the animal's nutrition.

Nutrition

The basic tracer feeding technique developed by Lee et al. (1966) and modified by Tietjen et al. (1970) was followed. Experimental animals were harvested from stock cultures, washed by serial transfer in sterile sea water and transferred to borsilicate test tubes containing 10 ml of sterile sea water. This water was filtered through a Millipore HA (0.45 μ) filter. Experimental animals were of approximately the same size; they were incubated in the sterile sea water under light and temperature conditions identical to those of the stock cultures for 24 hr in order to starve the animals before feeding.

The organisms to be tested as potential food organisms were grown in appropriate media with ^{32}P added as label. After incubation for 24 hr, the potential food organisms were harvested by centrifugation, aseptically washed and diluted to concentrations of 1×10^6-1×10^8 cells/ml. The food organisms were labelled with about 0.1-5.0 dpm/organism and placed in culture with the experimental nematodes. After 24 hr when bacteria were used, or 72 hr when algae were used, the nematodes were collected, washed and transferred to scintillation vials, where they were counted. Dead nematodes served as controls, to ensure that the radioactivity measured was indeed ingested food material and not material adsorbed on to the nematode cuticle. After measuring the uptake of labelled foods, the number and weight (μg) or food organisms ingested per nematode per day were calculated.

RESULTS

Consumption of Algae

The consumption of algae (μg food ingested nematode^{-1}day^{-1}) by all four species is shown in Figures 1 and 2. The algae are presented by code numbers which are given in Table 1 along with specific names of the algae.

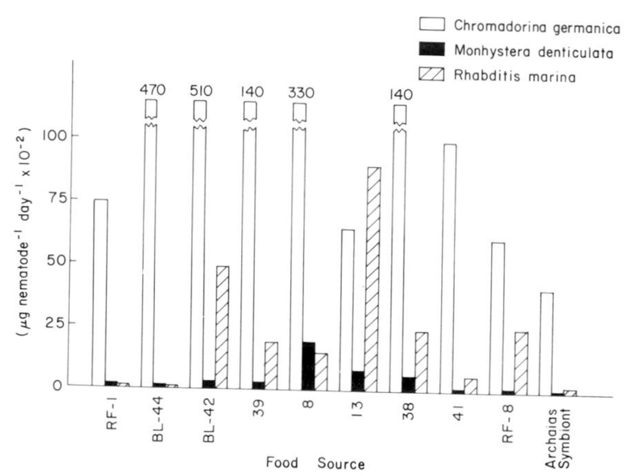

Fig. 1. Consumption of ten species of algae by *Chromadorina germanica*, *Monhystera denticulata* and *Rhabditis marina*.

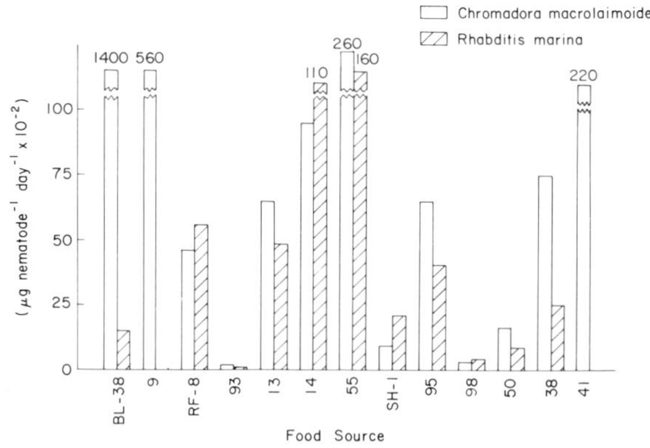

Fig. 2. Consumption of 13 species of algae by *Chromadora macrolaimoides* and *Rhabditis marina*.

Table 1. Algae used in the feeding experiments involving the nematodes *Chromadora macrolaimoides*, *Chromadorina germanica*, *Monhystera denticulata* and *Rhabditis marina*.

Code Number	Alga
	DIATOMS
8, BL-38	*Nitzschia acicularis*
RF-1	*Nitzschia brevirostris*
BL-42	*Achnanthes hauckiana*
BL-44	*Fragillaria construens*
9	*Cylindrotheca closterium*
39	*Phaeodactylum tricornutum*
RF-8	*Amphora acutioscula*
	CHLOROPHYTES
13	*Dunaliella salina*
14	*Dunaliella parva*
50	*Dunaliella quartolecta*
95	*Dunaliella* sp 1
98	*Dunaliella* sp 2
38	*Chlorococcum* sp
41	*Nanochloris* sp 1
55	*Nanochloris* sp 2
93	*Chlamydomonas subehrenberghii*
SH-1	Unidentified chlorophyte

The consumption of algae by *C. macrolaimoides* and *C. germanica* was significantly higher than it was by *R. marina* and *M. denticulata*. The average consumption of algae by *C. macrolaimoides* was 222×10^{-2} μg nematode^{-1}day^{-1} and by *C. germanica*, 216×10^{-2} μg nematode^{-1}day^{-1}. For *Rhabditis marina* there are data from two sets of feeding experiments, in both of which the average rate of consumption of algae was one order of magnitude lower than by the former two species (23×10^{-2} and 40×10^{-2} μg nematode^{-1}day^{-1}). The consumption rate of algae was lowest in *Monhystera denticulata*, which had an average consumption rate of 4.4×10^{-2} μg nematode^{-1}day^{-1}.

Consumption of Bacteria

The consumption of bacteria by *C. germanica*, *M. denticulata* and *R. marina* is shown in Figure 3. Additional data on bacterial consumption by *R. marina* and *C. macrolaimoides* were given by Tietjen et al. (1970) and Tietjen and Lee (1973). The average rates of consumption of bacteria by *C. germanica* and *C. macrolaimoides*, respectively, were 0.2×10^{-2} μg nematode^{-1}day^{-1} (Fig. 3) and 0.0008×10^{-2} μg nematode^{-1}day^{-1} (Tietjen and Lee 1973). Thus the ingestion of bacteria by these two species, on a weight basis, was

3 to 6 orders of magnitude lower than the ingestion of algae. The average consumption rate of bacteria by *M. denticulata* was 5.7 x 10^{-2} µg nematode^{-1}day^{-1}, and by *R. marina* it was 1.8 x 10^{-2} µg nematode^{-1}day^{-1} (Fig. 3) and 81 x 10^{-2} µg nematode^{-1}day^{-1} (Tietjen et al. 1970). Unlike *C. germanica* and *C. macrolaimoides*, therefore, the difference between the mean weight of algae ingested and the mean weight of bacteria ingested by both *M. denticulata* and *R. marina* was at most one order of magnitude.

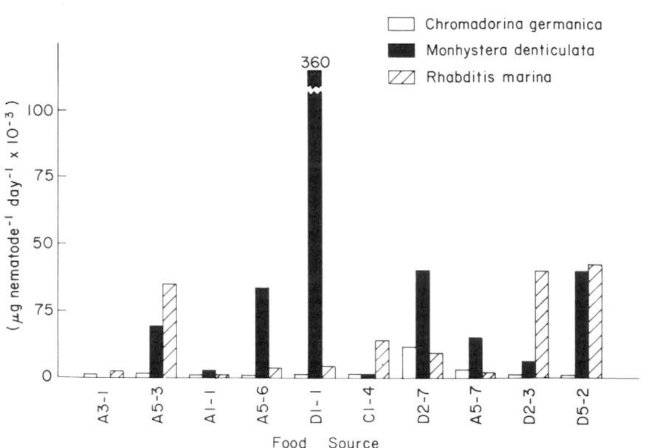

Fig. 3. Consumption of bacteria by *Chromadorina germanica*, *Monhystera denticulata* and *Rhabditis marina*.

DISCUSSION

Our data indicate a significant difference in the feeding habits of *C. macrolaimoides* and *C. germanica* compared with those of *M. denticulata* and *R. marina*. The former two species clearly ingest a significantly greater weight of algae than they do bacteria. They appear to be adept at ingesting both diatoms and chlorophytes (the two types of algae used in these experiments), since there are no significant differences in the ingestion rates of these algae, either in terms of cell numbers or total weight of algae ingested. A first approximation of the feeding habits of *C. macrolaimoides* and *C. germanica*, therefore, would tend to confirm the method of feeding proposed by Wieser (1953) for these species; i.e., that they use the small teeth in the buccal cavity to either scrape food materials (in this case, algae) off a substratum or to pierce an algal cell and suck in the cell contents. Von Thun (1968) has observed this method of feeding in *Hypodontolaimus balticus*, a relatively closely related species.

For *C. germanica*, *M. denticulata* and *R. marina*, data are available on the percentage of algae and bacteria grazed by each species relative to the total number of algae and bacteria available for consumption (Figs. 4, 5). Only one bacterium (strain D2-7) was grazed by *C. germanica* to any extent, whereas most of the algae was more or less equally grazed. The percentage of algae grazed was generally less than 2% of the total available, but this is sufficient to account for an average daily ingestion rate of algae at or nearly equal to the animals body weight.

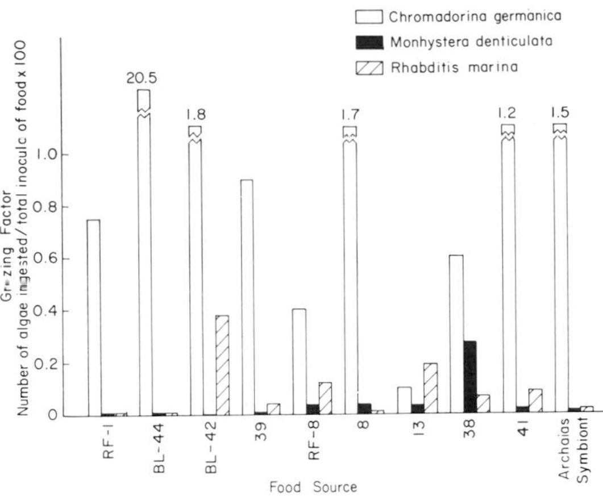

Fig. 4. Grazing of algae by *Chromadorina germanica*, *Monhystera denticulata* and *Rhabditis marina*.

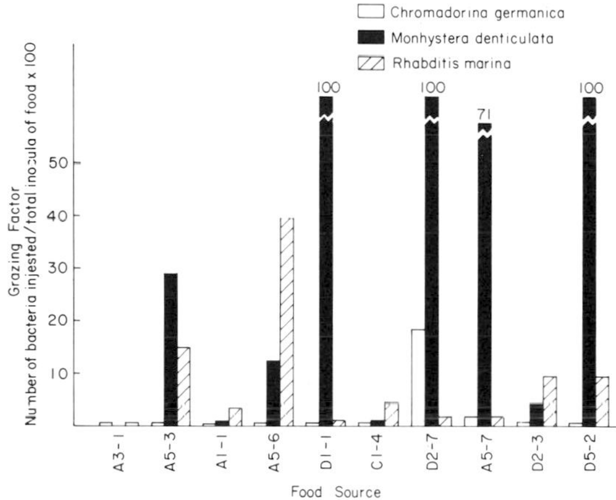

Fig. 5. Grazing of bacteria by *Chromadorina germanica*, *Monhystera denticulata* and *Rhabditis marina*.

For *M. denticulata* and *R. marina*, the lack of a significant difference between the weights of algae and bacteria ingested by each species can easily be accounted for by the fact that each species ingests more bacterial cells than it does algal cells. *R. marina* ingested, on the average, only 0.10 % of the algal cells available to it but nearly 10 % of the bacterial cells available. The disparity between algal and bacterial cell consumption was even greater in *M. denticulata*, which ingested only 0.04 % of the algae available but 37 % of the bacteria.

Particle Size

The differences in the ingestion rates of algae and bacteria by *M. denticulata* and *R. marina* suggested that in a nematode lacking significant teeth, the size of a food particle may be important in determining its ingestion potential. A correlation of the ingestion rate of the algal cells as a function of their individual average sizes yielded the following: for *C. macrolaimoides* and *C. germanica*, no correlation; for *M. denticulata*, a correlation of -0.317 ($p > 0.05$); and for *R. marina*, a correlation of -0.334 ($p > 0.05$). Thus, while some inverse correlation exists between individual algal cell size and ingestion of algae by the two species of non-selective deposit feeding nematodes, the relationship is a weak one. However, it must be remembered that both *M. denticulata* and *R. marina* ingested considerable numbers of bacteria, cells which are significantly smaller than the smallest algal cells used. Furthermore, under axenic conditions *R. marina* will ingest labelled latex microspheres only when such spheres approximate the size of bacterial cells (1-3 μ in diameter) (Tietjen and Lee 1975). The role of particle size, therefore, is unclear at this time. For *C. macrolaimoides* and *C. germanica* particle size is probably not too important. Both species possess teeth with which larger algal cells may be pierced. For *M. denticulata* and *R. marina*, however, cell size probably is important, since ingestion in these species must be at least partially limited by the degree to which they can open the stoma. It should be pointed out here that *R. marina* ingested significantly more algae than *M. denticulata*; it will be remembered that the former species has a larger buccal cavity than the latter. The weak correlation between particle size and ingestion, at least for the algae, suggests that additional factors may be important in regulating food intake by marine nematodes. Size of food has been shown to influence the growth of several crustaceans, notably the copepods, *Calanus finmarchicus* (Marshall and Orr 1956) and *Euterpina acutifrons* (Nassogne 1970).

Calorific Content of the Algae and Feeding Preferences

Most consumers select their food from among a broad spectrum of possible food sources. Such selection has been observed among both primary consumers and predators (Kohn 1959; Connell 1961a, b, 1970; Mullin 1963; Carefoot 1967, 1970, 1973; Paine 1969; Dayton 1971). The efficiency with which an organism utilizes its food resources is a function of many factors, among which may be the species of food and its abundance (Carefoot 1967; Hargrave 1971; Hughes 1971) as well as the organism's ability to digest what it ingests. The latter is dependent upon the concentration and types of digestive enzymes secreted and the amount of surface area available for absorption.

Among the properties of the food itself, calorific content may be of some significance, since one particular feeding strategy may be to prey on foods which return the most energy to the consumer per unit of energy expended. Within the meiofauna, the relationship between energy content of particular foods and feeding preferences (if any) has not been explored.

The calorific contents of six of the algae used in the feeding experiments of the four nematodes cited in this study have been measured (Lee et al. 1972). The data are reproduced below.

Species of alga	Calories per gram ash-free material
Nitzschia acicularis (B1-38, 8)	2415
Nitzschia brevirostris (RF-1)	2421
Cylindrotheca closterium (9)	765
Amphora sp (RF-8)	1147
Nanochloris sp 2 (55)	3968
Unidentified chlorophyte (SH-1)	2430

If a relationship exists between the calorific content of these six foods and the rates at which they are ingested, it is not clear from our feeding data. All of the algae, with the exception of the chlorophyte SH-1 were readily consumed by the two epistrate feeders (*C. macrolaimoides* and *C. germanica*). Furthermore, the nutritional value of the six algae in question appears to be a function of factor(s) other than calorific content, since both *Nitzschia acicularis* (2415 cal/g) and *Cylindrotheca closterium* (765 cal/g) are readily consumed by *C. macrolaimoides* and *C. germanica* and each will support the continuous growth of these worms for many generations. The generation times, individual body sizes, fecundity, sex ratios of the offspring, etc. are the same for each species of nematode when each is maintained on either *N. acicularis* or *C. closterium.* These two algal species also appear to be good food sources for the foraminifer, *Archaias angulatus* (Lee and Zucker 1969), and other herbivores in culture in our laboratory. Therefore some quality of these foods other than calorific content may render their nutritional value high. A further indication that calorific content is not the only factor governing the nutritional value of food for the nematodes is that *Nanochloris* sp 2 (55), the algal species with the highest caloric value, although readily ingested by *R. marina*, passed through the gut undigested. This same alga, however, has served as an excellent food source for *C. macrolaimoides* (Tietjen and Lee 1973). The lack of a relationship between calorific content of algae and feeding preferences of herbivores has been noted by several workers (Paine and Vadas 1969; Carefoot 1973).

Although most of the algae were ingested in significant quantities by *C. macrolaimoides* and *C. germanica*, some exceptions did occur. For example, in the set of feeding experiments involving *C. macrolaimoides*, *Chlamydomonas subehrenberghii* (93), *Dunaliella quartolecta* (50) and *Dunaliella* sp (98) were consumed at very low levels. It may be pointed out that these three algae were also sparingly consumed by *R. marina.* However, it must also be pointed out that there is not necessarily a direct relationship between the rate at which an alga is ingested by a nematode and its "nutritional value." Tietjen et al. (1970) observed that the chlorophyte *Nanochloris* sp 2, although ingested in high numbers by *R. marina*, passed through the gut almost totally undigested. They were unable to grow the nematode on this alga alone.

Five of the algae tested were fed to both *C. macrolaimoides* and *C. germanica*. The algal species involved and the rates of consumption by both nematodes are given in Table 2. The consumption of these five algal species by both nematodes employing the same method of feeding is remarkably similar. There appears to be some relationship between the rates of consumption of the algae listed in Table 2 and their ability to sustain the continuous growth of *C. germanica* and *C. macrolaimoides*. We have observed that *N. acicularis* and *Nanochloris* sp. 1 will support the growth of these nematodes for many generations in the laboratory; *C. germanica*, furthermore, has also been maintained in continuous culture on *Chlorococcum* sp. The other species listed in Table 2 will not support the continuous growth of the nematodes.

Table 2. Consumption of five algae by *Chromadora macrolaimoides* and *Chromadorina germanica*.

Alga	Consumption (μg nematode^{-1}day^{-1})	
	C. macrolaimoides	*C. germanica*
Nitzschia acicularis	1400	300
Amphora sp	46	61
Dunaliella salina	65	65
Chlorococcum sp	75	140
Nanochloris sp 1	220	100

Similarly, these five algae were fed to *Rhabditis marina* in a series of two experiments conducted a few years apart, and the results of which are given in Table 3. The consumption rates of these five algae by *R. marina* on two separate occasions were quite similar. Aside from the fact that the average consumption rate of these algae by *R. marina* was much lower than by the two species of epistrate feeders, it is interesting to note that *Nanochloris* sp 1 (41) was consumed in very low quantities by *R. marina*. Another

Table 3. Consumption of five algae by *Rhabditis marina* in two feeding experiments.

Alga	Consumption (μg nematode^{-1}day^{-1})	
	Experiment I	Experiment II
Nitzschia acicularis	15	15
Amphora sp	55	25
Dunaliella salina	48	90
Chlorococcum sp	25	24
Nanochloris sp 1	0	6

species of *Nanochloris* of the same size, however, was ingested at a rate two orders of magnitude greater. The reasons for this selection are unknown at this time, since both species appear to be equally ingestible.

Subtle differences in the chemical and/or physical composition of the food may also explain the differences observed in the ingestion of bacteria by the nematodes. All bacteria were approximately the same size and shape (gram negative rods, approximately 2 μ by 0.5 μ), yet two strains (A1-1 and A3-1) were virtually unconsumed by *Monhystera denticulata* and *Rhabditis marina*, while others (A5-3, A5-6, D1-1, D5-2) were ingested in significant numbers. Again, the reason(s) for this apparent selection are unknown.

SUMMARY

Our feeding data indicate that *Chromadora macrolaimoides* and *Chromadorina germanica*, two nematodes classed as epistrate feeders on the basis of buccal morphology (Wieser's Group 2 A), ingest significantly more algae per unit body weight of nematode than they do bacteria. However, *Monhystera denticulata* and *Rhabditis marina*, nematodes classed as non-selective deposit feeders (Wieser's Group 1 B), ingest approximately the same weight of algae and bacteria per unit body weight of nematode. The presence of teeth in the buccal cavity of the former two species undoubtedly adapts them rather well for algal feeding; these species can probably process most of the algae with which they come in contact, since both species ingested most of the algae used in the feeding experiments. On the other hand, *M. denticulata* and *R. marina*, species not as well adapted for algal feeding, may ingest more bacteria (largely left alone by the epistrate feeders) and whatever algae they can physically handle. With regard to the latter, cell size and shape are probably quite important. In these nematodes essentially devoid of buccal armature, a cell which is too large for the stoma undoubtedly cannot be processed (ingested). The potential importance of cell size and/or shape in food selection was suggested by the fact that *R. marina*, with a larger buccal cavity, ingested significantly more algae than the smaller-mouthed *M. denticulata*.

Selective ingestion of food particles is but a part of the feeding process. Of equal or greater significance is the question of selective digestion. Digestive secretions in nematodes are produced by a few esophageal gland cells and a single layer of gut cells. This low number of secretory cells may limit the spectrum of digestive enzymes secreted by these cells. The secretion of a large number of digestive enzymes may also be limited by the fact that the secretory gut cells also function in the absorption process (Lee 1965).

The secretion of a limited number of digestive enzymes presents an important problem to the nematode: How to utilize a wide variety of food sources, when each food species presents a different arrangement of molecules to be hydrolyzed? Of first concern is the penetration and breakdown of the cell envelope surrounding each food cell so that the cell contents may be removed. Algal cell walls vary from species to species (Lewin 1962), and the chemical composition of algal cell walls differs from that of bacterial cell walls (Schliefer and Kandler 1972). From the standpoint of energy expenditure, the feeding strategy of small organisms with limited synthetic abilities might conceivably involve both selective ingestion and selective digestion of food materials. A selective diet, attuned to the particular set of digestive enzymes secreted by the organism, would minimize the chances of the consumer ingesting large quantities of material that it is unable to digest.

There is evidence that the digestive enzymes of the nonmarine nematodes that have been studied are related to the type of food they ingest (Lee 1965). To our knowledge, the only information available on the digestive enzymes of marine nematodes is that for *Monhystera denticulata* and *Chromadorina germanica* (Jennings and Deutsch 1975). In *M. denticulata* the glycosidase beta-glucuronidase was observed to act both extra- and intracellularly during the digestion of bacteria by this species; this enzyme was not detected in *Chromadorina germanica*. Beta-glucuronidase hydrolyzes various components of mucopolysacchraides, and may well be important in digesting the polysaccharide covering of the bacterial cells (Jennings and Deutsch 1975). Beta-glucuronidase is also produced in the guts of the polychaetes, *Histriobdella homari* and *Ctenodrillus serratus*, both of which feed extensively on bacteria (Jennings, unpublished); this enzyme, then, may be characteristic of bacterial feeders (Jennings and Deutsch 1975). More comparative information is needed on the digestive secretions of marine nematodes in order to ascertain the degree to which selective digestion occurs in these animals.

Selective ingestion and digestion may be one method by which interspecific competition is reduced. Fractionation of the resources in this manner would enable a large number of species to occur in a small geographic area, and enable them to utilize the diverse food sources present with maximum efficiency. Such fractionation would also permit a high species diversity in habitats where the number of available food sources is limited, such as in the deep sea.

REFERENCES

Carefoot, R. H. 1967. Growth and nutrition of *Aplysia punctata* on a variety of marine algae. J. Mar. Biol. Assoc. U.K. 47: 656-689.

_____. 1970. A comparison of absorption and utilization of food energy in two species of tropical *Aplysia*. J. Exp. Mar. Biol. Ecol. 5: 47-62.

_____. 1973. Feeding, food preference, and the uptake of food energy by the supralittoral isopod *Ligia pallasii*. Mar. Biol. 18: 228-236.

Chitwood, B. G. and D. G. Murphy. 1964. Observations on two marine monhysterids--their classification, culture and behavior. Trans. Am. Micr. Sco. 83: 311-329.

_____ and R. W. Timm. 1954. Free-living nematodes of the Gulf of Mexico. In Gulf of Mexico, its origin, waters and marine life. Fishery Bull. Fish Wildl. Ser. U. S. 55: 313-323.

Connell, J. H. 1961a. The influence of interspecific competition and other factors on the distribution of the barnacle *Cthamalus stellatus*. Ecology 42: 710-723.

_____. 1961b. Effect of competition, predation by *Thais lapillus*, and other factors on natural populations of the barnacle *Balanus balanoides*. Ecol. Mongr. 31: 61-104.

_____. 1970. A predator-prey system in the marine intertidal region. I. *Balanus gladula* and several predatory species of *Thais*. Ecol. Monogr. 40: 49-78.

Dayton, P. K. 1971. Competition, disturbance, and community organization: the provision and subsequent utilization of space in a rocky intertidal community. Ecol. Monogr. 41: 351-389.

Edmondson, W. T. 1957. Trophic relations of the zooplankton. Trans. Am. Micros. Soc. 76: 205-245.

Gerlach, S. A. and M. Schrage. 1971. Life cycles in marine meiobenthos. Experiments at various temperatures with *Monhystera disjuncta* and *Theristus pertenuis* (Nematoda). Mar. Biol. 9: 274-280.

_____ and _____. 1972. Life cycles at low temperatures in some free-living marine Nematodes. Veröff. Inst. Meeresforsch. Bremerh. 14: 5-11.

Hargrave, B. T. 1971. An energy budget for a deposit-feeding amphipod. Limnol. Oceanogr. 16: 99-103.

Hopper, B. E. and S. P. Meyers. 1966a. Aspects of the life cycles of marine nematodes. Helgoländer wiss. Meeresunters. 13: 444-449.

_____ and _____. 1966b. Observations on the bionomics of the marine nematode, *Metoncholaimus* sp. Nature 209: 899-900.

_____ and _____. 1967. Population studies on benthic nematodes within a sub-tropical sea grass community. Mar. Biol. 1: 85-96.

_____, J. W. Fell, and R. C. Cefalu. 1973. Effect of temperature on life cycles of nematodes associated with the mangrove (*Rhizophora mangle*) detrital system. Mar. Biol. 23: 293-296.

Hughes, R. N. 1971. Ecological energetics of the keyhole limpet *Fissurella barbadensis* Gmelin. J. Exp. Mar. Biol. Ecol. 6: 167-178.

Jennings, J. B. and A. Deutsch. 1975. Occurrence and possible adaptive significance of β-glucuronidase and arylamidase (Leucine aminopeptidase) activity in two species of marine nematodes. Comp. Biochem. Physiol. 52A: 611-614.

Kohn, A. J. 1959. Ecology of *Conus* in Hawaii. Ecol. Monogr. 29: 47-90.

Lee, D. L. 1965. The physiology of nematodes. W. H. Freeman and Co.

Lee, J. J. and W. Zucker. 1969. Algal flagellate symbiosis in the foraminifer *Archaias*. J. Protozool. 16: 71-81.

_____, M. McEnery, E. Kennedy, and H. Rubin. 1975. A nutritional analysis of a sublittoral epiphytic diatom assemblage from a Long Island salt marsh. J. Phycol. 11: 14-49.

_____, _____, S. Pierce, H. H. Freudenthal, and W. Muller. 1966. Tracer experiments in feeding littoral foraminifera. J. Protozool. 13: 659-670.

_____, J. H. Tietjen, R. J. Stone, W. A. Muller, J. Rullman, and M. McEnery. 1970. The cultivation and physiological ecology of members of salt marsh epiphytic communities. Helgoländer. wiss. Meeresunters. 20: 136-156.

_____, _____, _____, _____, M. McEnery, N. M. Saks, C. Mastrpaolo, and E. Kennedy. 1972. The effects of environmental stress on the community structure, productivity, energy flow and mineral cycling in salt marsh epiphytic communities, pp. 816-828. In D. J. Nelson [ed.], Proc. 3rd nat. sympos. radioecol. Vol 2. U.S.A.E.C.

Lewin, J. C. 1962. Silicification, pp. 445-455. In R. A. Lewin [ed.], Physiology and biochemistry of algae. Academic Press.

Marshall, S. M. and A. P. Orr. 1956. On the biology of *Calanus finmarchicus*. 8. Food uptake and digestion in the young stages. J. Mar. Biol. Assoc. U. K. 35: 587-603.

Mullin, M. 1963. Some factors affecting the feeding of marine copepods of the genus *Calanus*. Limnol. Oceanogr. 8: 239-250.

McIntyre, A. D. 1969. Ecology of marine meiobenthos. Biol. Rev. 44: 245-290.

Nassogne, A. 1970. Influence of food organisms on the development and culture of pelagic copepods. Helgoländer. wiss. Meeresunters. 20: 333-345.

Paine, R. T. 1969. The *Pisaster-Tegula* interaction: Prey patches, predator preference, and intertidal community structure. Ecology 50: 950-961.

_____ and R. L. Vadas. 1969. Calorific values of benthic marine algae and their postulated relation to invertebrate food preference. Mar. Biol. 4: 79-86.

Perkins, E. J. 1958. The food relationships of the microbenthos, with particular reference to that found at Whitstable, Kent. Ann. Mag. Nat. Hist. Ser. 13(1): 64-77.

Schliefer, K. H. and O. Kandler. 1972. Peptidoglycan types of bacterial cell walls and their taxonomic implications. Bact. Rev. 36: 407-477.

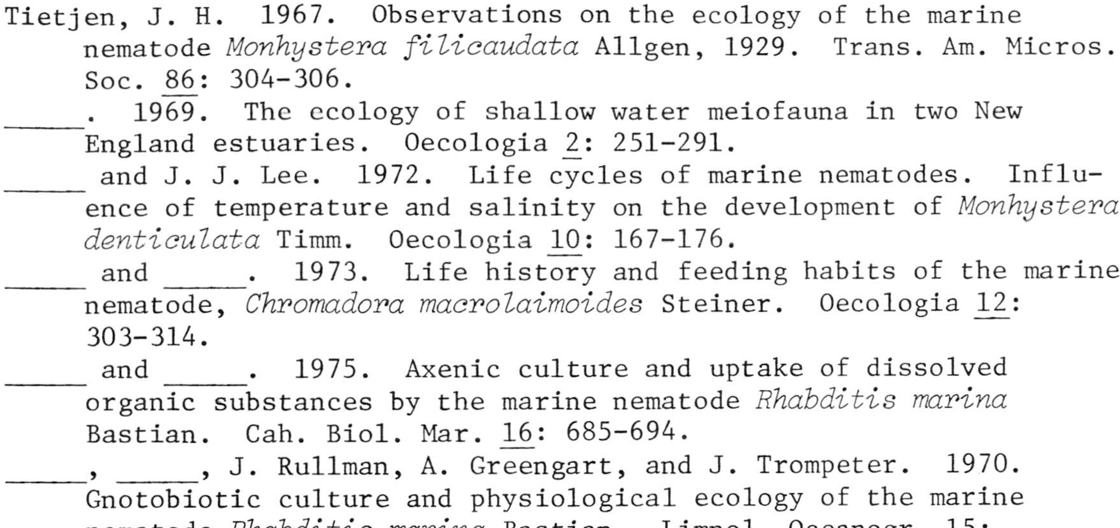

Tietjen, J. H. 1967. Observations on the ecology of the marine nematode *Monhystera filicaudata* Allgen, 1929. Trans. Am. Micros. Soc. 86: 304-306.

_____. 1969. The ecology of shallow water meiofauna in two New England estuaries. Oecologia 2: 251-291.

_____ and J. J. Lee. 1972. Life cycles of marine nematodes. Influence of temperature and salinity on the development of *Monhystera denticulata* Timm. Oecologia 10: 167-176.

_____ and _____. 1973. Life history and feeding habits of the marine nematode, *Chromadora macrolaimoides* Steiner. Oecologia 12: 303-314.

_____ and _____. 1975. Axenic culture and uptake of dissolved organic substances by the marine nematode *Rhabditis marina* Bastian. Cah. Biol. Mar. 16: 685-694.

_____, _____, J. Rullman, A. Greengart, and J. Trompeter. 1970. Gnotobiotic culture and physiological ecology of the marine nematode *Rhabditis marina* Bastian. Limnol. Oceanogr. 15: 535-543.

von Thun, W. 1968. Autokologische Untersuchungen an freilebenden Nematoden des Brackwassers. Thesis, Universität Kiel, 72 p.

Webb, M. G. 1956. An ecological study of brackish water ciliates. J. An. Ecol. 25: 149-175.

Wieser, W. 1953. Die Beziehung zwischen Mundhöhlengestalt, Ernährungsweise und Vorkommen bei freilebenden marinen Nematoden. Ark. Zool. 4: 439-484.

Food Chain Pathways in Detrital Feeding Benthic Communities: A Review, With New Observations on Sediment Resuspension and Detrital Recycling

Kenneth R. Tenore
Skidaway Institute of Oceanography
Savannah, GA 31406

ABSTRACT

Many workers have emphasized the importance of detrital-based food chains in marine ecosystems and the need for information on the role of detritus in benthic energetics. However, in reviewing the available information on detritus in estuarine systems Darnell (1967) pointed out that most studies only infer the importance of detritus and little information is available on the actual nutritive value of detritus. Thus, beside the readily available data on the levels and sources of detritus, information is needed on the availability and nutritive value of this detritus to benthos and on the food chain interrelations that regulate energy flow in the detrital food chain.

SOURCES OF DETRITUS IN MARINE ECOSYSTEMS

In coastal waters, detritus is derived primarily from the biodeposits (feces and pseudofeces) of animals and the decay of macrovegetation. Data in the literature show that suspension feeders, both zooplankton and benthos, make available large amounts of potential energy in the tremendous amount of fecal pellets and pseudofeces. For example, Cushing (1966) stated that up to 30% of the organic carbon ingested by the zooplankton ends up in fecal pellets.

Keeping in mind that Jorgensen's (1966) review on the feeding and biodeposition rates of suspension feeders pointed out the tremendous filtration capability of such species, a considerable amount of organic matter ends up as detritus derived from fecal pellets and pseudofeces. For example, in controlled laboratory experiments Tenore and Dunstan (1973) and Tenore et al. (1973) found that suspension-feeding bivalves filtered approximately 8 gm carbon/g dry weight of animal per day at food concentrations typical of coastal environments. Of this filtered food, 20 to 30% was deposited as feces and pseudofeces. Ito and Imai (1955) calculated that a 60-m^2 raft of oysters would annually produce 0.6 to 1.0 metric tons dry weight of biodeposits. Verwey (1952) estimated in the Dutch Waddenzee that the cockle, *Cardium edule*, deposits 100,000 metric tons in dry weight of biodeposits per year and the edible mussel, *Mytilus edulis* up to 175,000 tons per year. Haven and Morales-Alamo (1966) studied the deposition rate of oysters under natural conditions and estimated that in Chesapeake Bay the oysters in 0.4 hectares may produce up to 981 kg of biodeposits per week with an organic carbon concentration of 4 to 12%. Frankenberg et al. (1967) calculated the production rate of fecal material of the burrowing shrimp, *Callianassa major*, a dominant species of the sand beach community at Sapelo Island, Georgia, to be 0.06 g carbon/m^2/day. Thus the production of biodeposits due to these suspension feeders is a major source of detritus in sediments and many workers have emphasized their possible nutritive value to deposit feeders.

However, owing to their high rate of productivity, decaying macrophytes, both marsh and sea grasses, are perhaps the major primary source of detrital material in most coastal environments. Especially along the middle and southeastern coast of the United States the adjacent salt marshes are a major component of the primary production and an important source of detritus; the high productivity of these marshes is well documented. For example, Teal (1962) estimated the net production of a Georgia salt marsh to be 2570 to 8970 cal/m^2/year and Williams and Murdoch (1972) estimated an annual above-ground production of 754 g dry weight/m^2/year ($\simeq$230 g carbon) of black needle rush, *Juncus roemerianus*, in North Carolina. This marsh plant provided about 23% of the total net primary productivity.

Seaweeds and submerged sea grasses such as eel grass, *Zostera marina*, and turtle grass, *Thalassia testudinum*, are also highly productive. Mann's (1972) literature review on seaweeds noted an average production rate of from 500 to 1000 g carbon/m^2/day. *Zostera* and *Thallasia* are dominant seaweeds in sedimented coastal areas of boreal regions and are important in primary production. Petersen (1918) calculated the average production of *Zostera* in coastal waters of the North Sea to be 340 g carbon/m^2/year. Phillips (1969) measured a production of 58 to 330 g carbon/m^2/year in Puget Sound, and McRoy (1970) estimated the production in Alaska waters from 19 to 552 g carbon/m^2/year. Burkholder and Doheny (1968) cited the maximum standing crop of eel grass (approximately 340 g carbon/m^2) as a measure of the high production rate in Great South Bay, L.I.

Odum (1957) estimated that 520 to 640 g carbon/m^2/year of *Thalassia* was produced in Florida waters, and Moore (1963) emphasized the importance of this to the total primary production in shallow water areas off the Florida coasts.

The main reason that a great portion of this production of macrophytes ends up as detritus is the low rate of exploitation by herbivorous grazers typical of most marsh and submerged vegetation ecosystems (Odum and de la Cruz 1967). For example, Teal (1962) showed that only 5% of cord grass, *Juncus*, was grazed on by herbivores; about 45% of the total annual production was exported as detritus to the adjacent estuary. Estimates in the literature (Williams and Murdoch 1972) of the rate of decay of marsh grasses based on loss of weight of bagged materials are: 0.27/year (Latter and Craig 1967), 0.36/year (Heald 1971), and 0.49/year (Waits 1967). Williams and Murdoch (1972) estimated the annual proportion of grass disappearing as dead material from the marsh surface at 0.462. They further estimated that 60% of the standing biomass of *Juncus* was dead material, which eventually contributed to the detrital pool. Schelske and Odum (1962) stated that the high productivity of the Georgia salt marshes depends on the decay of *Spartina alterniflora* as the basis of a detrital food chain. Tenore (1972) stressed the importance of the fall influx of detritus into a North Carolina estuarine system due to the decay of the dominant rooted submerged macrophytes, *Ruppia* and *Potomogeton*. Day et al. (1973) also found an increase in the standing crops of holo- and meroplanktonic animals associated with peaks of detrital material from the marsh entering the estuary in late spring and early fall.

Seaweeds are also little utilized by grazers and end up as detrital matter in the sediments. Mann (1972) calculated the food requirements of the largest herbivorous browser in the seaweed zone (the sea urchin, *Strongylocentrotus*) to be only 5% of the seaweed production. Khailov and Burlakova (1969) estimated that 11% of the gross production of seaweeds in the Barents Sea was consumed by herbivores and indicated that about 30% of the gross production may enter the detrital pool. Using data from Conover (1964), Marshall (1970) estimated the yearly organic carbon contribution of macroflora, mostly eel grass and its associated aufwuchs, to estuarine areas in southern New England at 125 g carbon/m^2/year.

CORRELATIONS OF BENTHOS WITH DETRITUS

The large amounts of detritus entering estuarine and coastal ecosystems led many early researchers to speculate on its nutritive value to the benthos. Petersen (1918) hypothesized that the basic source of food of the benthos in the shallow Danish wadden area was the organic detritus derived chiefly from the decay of shallow-water rooted vegetation. This idea was further enunciated by other Danish workers (Blegvad 1914; Jensen 1919; Ekman 1947) who pointed out the large production of detritus from the decay of macrophytes that entered the sediments and the predominance of deposit feeders in these detritus-enriched areas. Hedgpeth (1957) suggested that the majority of benthic organisms in the tidal zone derive their nourishment from detritus carried to the beach and worked into the sand by wave action; and Dexter (1944, 1950) stated that detritus derived from *Zostera* was the basis for the food chain associated with eel grass beds and correlated the decline in secondary productivity associated with eel grass beds with the disappearance of eel grass by the "wasting" disease. Williams and Thomas (1967) compared the standing crop of the benthic biomass in four types of substrates near Beaufort, North Carolina: sand, muddy sand, soft mud and the area of a *Zostera* bed. The *Zostera* substrate contained the greatest number of animals (672/m^2 compared to an average of 107/m^2 in the muddy sand) and the greatest amount of wet weight biomass (294 g/m^2 compared to 38/m^2 in the muddy sand).

Investigators have demonstrated that the observed correlation between particle size of the sediment and the density of deposit feeders is due to associated levels of organic matter. Davis (1925) hypothesized that not the particle size per se but its associated nutritive conditions were the cause of differences in the density of benthos. Sanders (1960) demonstrated that the density of soft-bottom macrobenthos was correlated with the percent clay in the sediment and suggested that the associated increase in organic matter with increasing clay composition was responsible for increased numbers of benthos. Bader (1954) demonstrated that not only the amount of organic matter in the sediment, but also its state of decomposition, were the primary factors affecting the distribution and density of bivalve infauna. He stated that as the organic matter increases in the sediment, the density of bivalves increases until bacterial decomposition of the organics results in deoxygenation, and the predominance of lignin and the density of bivalves decreases. Thus detrital quality can affect related food chain dynamics. Tenore and Gopalan (1974) found significant differences in feeding rates and growth efficiencies of the polychaete, *Nereis virens*, fed on detritus derived from different sources.

Other workers have demonstrated that decaying turtle grass contributes a significant amount of detritus to the sediments of the continental shelf and that it is responsible for the parallel zonation of density of the benthos (Menzies and Rowe 1969; Rowe and Menzies (1969). Tietjen (1971) found significant increases in the density of deposit-feeding meiobenthos, especially nematodes, in areas of high sedimentary organic matter on the continental shelf off North Carolina. Nematodes comprised up to 80% of the detrital meiofauna. Tietjen (1969) also found increased densities of deposit-feeding meiofauna in areas of relatively high detritus in estuarine benthic communities in New England, and Wigley and McIntyre (1964) and Wieser (1960) found similar conditions in and around Buzzards Bay, Massachusetts.

Higher trophic levels also benefit from this enrichment of

detritus. Monitoring the development and functioning of experimental benthic communities off La Jolla, Fager (1971) found that detritus derived from kelp supported populations of invertebrates that were preyed upon by the fish. He estimated that a standing crop of 1 mg dry weight of the invertebrates was associated with every 2 g wet weight of detrital kelp material. Several investigators have used gut observation data to illustrate the importance of detritus to fish. Darnell (1961) studied the feeding habits of fish in an estuarine community and found that the guts of mullet, shad and menhaden all contained large amounts of detrital material, and Odum (1970) emphasized the importance of the detrital pool to fish food chains, particularly for the striped mullet, *Mugil cephalus*. Prinslow et al. (1974) studied the nutritive value of detritus to *Fundulus heteroclitus*. In a more sensitive method based on fatty acid concentration in various food sources and in the gut, Jeffries (1972 and unpublished) determined the dietary ratio of juvenile menhaden, *Brevoortia tyrannus*, in different parts of an estuary. In general, the greater the availability of detritus, the greater its importance to the diet. In the open bay, the diet ratio was 15% detritus and 85% living plankton. In contrast, in a marsh area the ratio was 96% detritus and 4% living plankton.

MICROBIAL ACTIVITY ON DETRITUS

Using Darnell's (1967) definition of detritus (all types of biogenic material in various stages of microbial decomposition that represent a potential energy source for consumer species) many researchers have studied the role of microbial activity in detrital food chains in marine benthic communities. Investigators have reported the heterogenous nature of the microbial life occurring on the surfaces of detrital particles and agree that the activity of these microbes is an important initial step in detrital food chains. As early as 1938 Zobell and Feltham pointed out that marine bacteria efficiently converted and utilized detrital waste and might be a food source to larger organisms. The surfaces both of particles derived from decaying macrovegetation and fecal pellets of macrobenthos support large numbers of microbes. Odum and de la Cruz (1967), Fenchel (1969; 1970), and Heald (1971) showed an increase in protein of the particles derived from macrophytes with increasing age due to microorganisms growing on the surfaces. Burkholder (1959) pointed out the significant numbers of ciliates associated with detrital particles and stressed their possible role in nutrient cycling and regeneration and as a food source for macroconsumers. Fenchel (1970) studied the quantitative composition of these microbial communities living on detritus derived from turtle grass. Counts of samples taken from the field showed an average of 3×10^9 bacteria, 5×10^7 small zooflagellates, 5×10^4 ciliates and 2×10^4 diatoms per gram dry weight of detritus. The numbers were highest in detrital samples with smaller average diameter particles and lowest with new and large-sized particles. Similarly, Gosselink and Kirby (1974) found an inverse relationship of particle size of detritus derived from marsh grass to decomposition rate. They found that the conversion efficiency of substrate to microbial biomass decreased as particle size increased. These microbes can serve as a food source for the benthos. For example, Fenchel (1969) reported on the partitioning of this food resource for ciliates. Larger benthos such as the polychaete, *Arenicola marina*, can also utilize these microfauna associated with detrital particles (Longbottom 1970). Adams and Angelovic (1970) found the shrimp, *Palaemonetes*, and the snail, *Bittium*, assimilated carbon-14 from labeled bacteria associated with eel grass detritus and Tenore (in press) investigated the incorporation of detritus derived from eel grass by the polychaete, *Capitella capitata*. The detritus showed an initial rapid decrease then a slower rate of increase in nitrogen content. Using isotope tracer techniques, he also found a corresponding increase in the rate of net incorporation with increasing aging of the detritus. The observed changes might be related to increase microbial populations with increased aging of the detritus.

Bacterial populations on the surface of fecal pellets are also a utilizable food source for macrobenthic species. Johannes and Satomi (1966) studied the composition and nutritive value of fecal pellets of the grass shrimp, *Palaemonetes pugio*, and found that the fecal pellets were rich in assimilable protein. An average of 20% of the fecal material was organic carbon, and protein predominated among the organic compounds. This organic matter was largely in the form of bacteria. The bacteria developed on the food residues in the posterior portion of the alimentary tract of the shrimp. *Palaemonetes* reingested these bacteria-enriched fecal pellets. Johannes and Satomi calculated an average assimilation efficiency (organic carbon eaten-organic carbon of feces excreted/organic carbon eaten x 100) of 78%, a value comparable to assimilation efficiencies of fresh food. Not only did *Palaemonetes* reingest its own fecal pellets but also those of several other deposit feeders: the teleost, *Fundulus heteroclitus*, the gastropod, *Nassa obsoleta*, and the crustaceans, *Uca pugnax* and *Pagurus longicarpus*. Johannes and Satomi found that the initially high levels of nitrogen and total organics of the fecal pellets declined with time. Investigating coprophagy by the burrowing shrimp, *Callianassa major*, Frankenberg et al. (1967) found that bacteria adhering in dense clusters to clay-sized particles comprised the bulk of the organic matter of the fecal pellets. For fecal pellets of this species, they found much lower levels of organic carbon (2.9%) and nitrogen (0.29%) and also found that these levels decreased with the age of the pellet. In contrast, Newell (1964) showed that the fecal pellets of the deposit-feeding snail, *Hydrobia ulvae*, and the tellinid clam, *Macoma balthica*, were initially void of nitrogenous materials but still rich in cellulose. Microbes quickly grew on the surfaces of these pellets and they were subsequently reingested by the animals. Newell also found that the percent nitrogen increased as the particle size of the detritus increased. Similarly, Hargrave (1970) found that the fecal pellets produced by the deposit-feeding amphipod, *Hyalella*, were also initially devoid of microorganisms but were rapidly colonized. The bacteria on the reingested fecal pellets were subsequently ingested by the amphipod. Fenchel (1970) found a similar situation for the fecal pellets of the amphipod, *Parhyalella whelpleyi*. When the fecal pellets were cultured in filtered water in the laboratory, the microbial populations were re-established within four days. Fenchel also found that the fecal pellets per se passed undigested through the gut of the amphipod; only the microorganisms on the surface of the pellets were utilized by the amphipod. Newell's (1964) results were similar for coprophagous activity by *Hydrobia ulvae* and *Macoma balthica*. Frankenberg and Smith (1967) pointed out these discrepancies of coprophagy in the literature on the organic carbon and nitrogen levels and effect of "aging" of fecal pellets: in the literature, C and N values of fecal pellets of marine invertebrates range from 2 to 20% and 0.02 to 4.48%, respectively. As shown above, although the nutritive changes undergone with aging do not follow a single pattern, the microbenthos are important as an initial heterotrophic trophic level in detrital food chains.

MEIOFAUNAL-DETRITAL RELATIONSHIPS

In comparison with the microbenthos, the distribution and density of the meiofauna is better documented, but less is known of the quantitative effect on energy flow in detrital food chains. Mare (1942) suggested that observed differences in the density and distribution of the meiofauna were correlated with levels of organic matter in the sediments. Remane (1933) examined gut contents of different groups of meiofauna and divided them into deposit and episubstrate feeders--both feeding types deriving their nourishment from either detritus per se or associated microbes. Wieser's (1960) study of the meiobenthos in Buzzards Bay, Massachusetts indicated that mud sediments rich in fine detrital deposits were characterized by several species of deposit-feeding forms.

Although data on the utilization rates of detritus by the meiofauna are scarce, investigators have attributed the importance of these forms to the energetics of detrital food chains. Tietjen (1966) estimated the organic matter demands of the meiofauna by applying nematode respiration rate data from Wieser and Kanwisher (1961). The average respiration of the meiobenthic component of the benthos was 53 g carbon/m^2/year. This was 10 to 20% of the total utilization of the interstitial community. Tietjen (1967) also suggested that biodeposits and associated microbes of larger invertebrates are a possible food source for nematodes.

Although the exact pathways of detrital food chains is not well documented, the production of the meiobenthos might be important to the productivity of higher trophic levels. Marshall (1970) reviewed this question in his discussion of energy transfer in benthic food chains and suggested that the meiofauna, utilizing both organic detritus and the associate microbes, might constitute a highly significant food source for demersal fish. But, Tietjen (1966) noted the paucity of meiofauna, especially nematodes, in stomach analysis of bottom fish. However, in the Ria de Arosa, Spain--an area of intence mussel aquaculture--a concomitant detrital-based food chain is associated with the rich food supply of mussel biodeposits (Tenore and Conzalez in press). Chesney (personal communication) has found significant numbers of foraminifera in the guts of small-sized demersal fish. Besides such possible direct feeding relations, McIntyre (1961) noted that non-selective deposit feeders of the macrobenthos, for example bivalves and polychaetes, must ingest the meiofauna and that these in turn serve as a major food source for bottom-feeding fish. Thus, the typical detrital food chain in coastal marine ecosystems might be: detritus → microbenthos → meiobenthos → macrobenthos → demersal fish. However, Lee et al. (in preparation) found no significant difference in the net incorporation of carbon-14 labelled eel grass detritus by *Capitella capitata*, with or without the presence of a meiofaunal assemblage. Concurrent studies with Phosphorous-32 tracer techniques showed noningestion of the meiofauna by other macrobenthos could not constitute a significant contribution to a realistic energy budget.

Even if the meiofauna are not a direct food source, their mechanical activity on detrital material might be a controlling factor in the food chain dynamics of larger deposit-feeding benthos. For example, Fenchel (1970) found that the amphipod, *Parhyalella whelpleyi*, decreased the particle size of detritus derived from turtle grass. Similarly, Heald (1971) reported that the amphipods, *Melita nitida* and *Corophium lacustre*, were instrumental in the breakdown of larger detrital fragments. Besides such physical alterations in detritus, the meiofauna might have an important role in carbon and nutrient recycling in detrital-based systems. For example, although no energetic relations were found between meiofauna and *Capitella capitata* by Lee et al. (in press) the presence of the meiofauna doubled the rate of detrital mineralization, an increase comparable to that of the effect of the presence of the polychaetes.

SEDIMENT RESUSPENSION AND DETRITAL RECYCLING

Rhoads and Young (1971) reported that reworking of mud sediments by benthic deposit feeders resulted in an unstable substrate because the sediments were frequently resuspended in shallow coastal areas by tidal flow; this resuspension reached a turbidity maximum during the ebb phase of the tidal cycle in Buzzards Bay. In measuring sedimentation rates in a deeper Scottish loch Steele and Baird (1972) stated that such resuspension, consisting mostly of zooplankton fecal pellets, accounted for a significant portion of their high values of sedimentation. Zeitzschel (1965), working on sedimentation rates in the Baltic, attributed occasional higher values to sediment stirred up by wind mixing. Rhoads et al. (in press) followed the occurrence of maximum resuspension for a year at a level mud bottom station, about 13 m deep, off Weepecket Island in Buzzards Bay, Massachusetts, and showed that the nutritive value, in terms of chlorophyll-a and particulate carbon and nitrogen concentrations, at the time of maximum resuspension were significantly higher than these materials in the upper photic zone. Tidal scouring of the sediment was thought to cause this periodic resuspension in Buzzards Bay.

These resuspended materials, especially microalgae, might significantly influence the bioenergetics of shallow water benthos because resuspended chlorophyll-a has been identified by several authors as a food resource in the deposit feeding community. Tenore et al. (1974) found that biodeposits of oysters fed on the diatom, *Phaeodactylum* sp., contained large amounts of nondigested cells that supported a large population of the polychaete, *Capitella capitata*. In isotope tracer experiments, Lee et al. (unpublished) found that this polychaete ingested several species of benthic microalgae. Although the importance of benthic microalgae production in tidal and very shallow waters is well documented, the augmentation to primary production (due to resuspension of viable microalgae from a non-photic zone bottom into the photic zone of the water column) is neither well understood nor appreciated.

An example of the possible magnitude of this resuspension is given in Figures 1 and 2. These data were collected with field and analytical procedures described in Rhoads et al. (in press). Water samples were collected from different depths at regular intervals during several tidal cycles spanning a year. Particulate carbon concentrations were measured with a Perkin Elmer Model 240 Elemental Analyzer and chlorophyll-a concentrations were measured by fluorometric analysis (Yentsch and Menzel 1963). In addition, in situ carbon-14 primary productivity was measured throughout the year. During the tidal cycle carbon-14 incubations were also measured in situ in water samples collected at 2-hr intervals from 4 and 10 m. In addition, current data was continually recorded with a Hydro Product Model 505A current meter.

Results typical of tidal resuspension in the spring-summer period are presented in Figures 1 and 2. Current data (Fig. 1A) indicated an increase in current speed approximately one hour after mean high water. Particulate carbon concentrations in the deeper portions of the water column showed a concurrent increase (Fig. 1B). An integration of the particulate carbon of the total water column indicates the degree of increase of organic carbon due to sediment resuspension (Fig. 1C).

There was also a similar change in the concentration of chlorophyll-a in the deeper portions of the water column (Fig. 2A). During the past year we regularly conducted in situ measurement of primary productivity at this station and occasionally noticed not

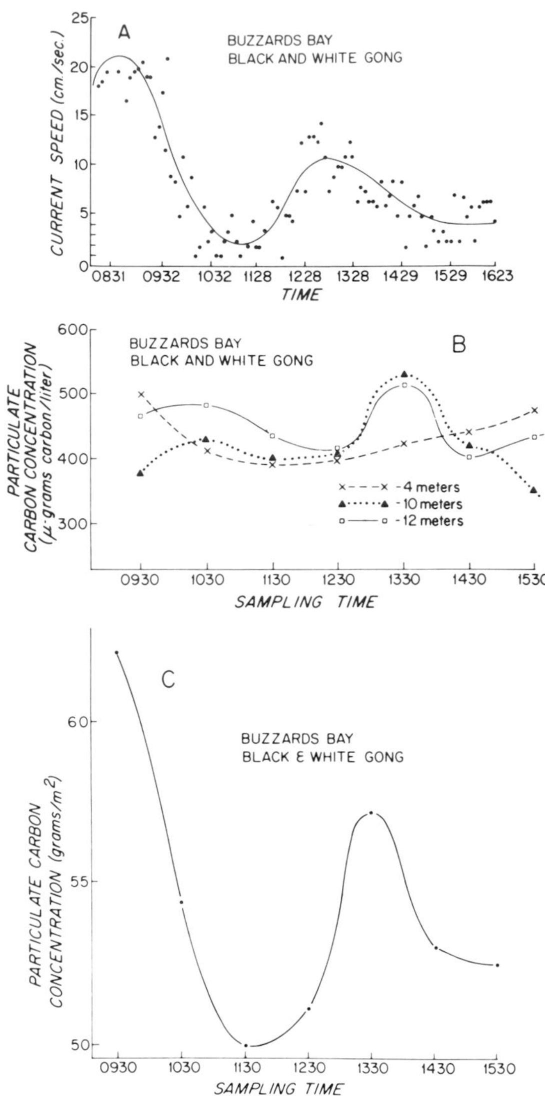

Fig. 1. Bottom current speed and related resuspension of particulate carbon during a tidal cycle at a level mud bottom station in Buzzards Bay, Massachusetts.

the usual single-curve characteristic of the vertical profile of carbon fixation, but a "double hump" profile of which Figure 2B is a representative example. In order to test whether the resuspended chlorophyll-a we had measured was viable phytoplankton biomass we conducted a time series through the tidal cycle of in situ carbon-14 measurements of primary productivity of water collected from 4 and 10 m. In order to remove changes in light penetration as a possible factor, controls consisted of "reverse incubation," i.e. 0.4-m water also incubated at 10 m and vice versa. Samples were taken and incubation carried out every two hours. We found a tremendous increase in carbon fixed in the 10-m water which coincided with the resuspension phenomenon (Fig. 2C). No corresponding increase was found in the 4-m water unaffected by resuspended sediment. Thus at least a portion of the resuspended chlorophyll belongs to viable phytoplankton

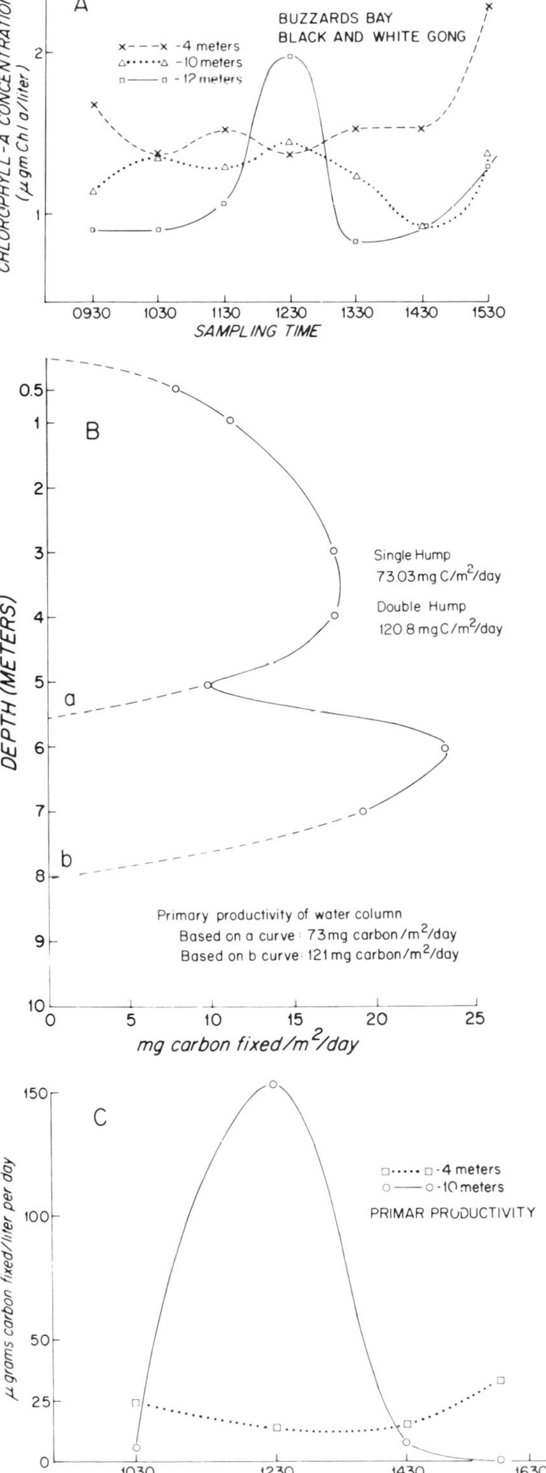

Fig. 2. Resuspension of chlorophyll-a during a tidal cycle at a level mud bottom station in Buzzards Bay, Massachusetts and related increase in primary productivity.

that are exposed to light and nutrients in the water column, and it contributes an additional autotrophic source of food to benthic deposit feeders. The primary production due to this resuspension phenomenon is about 75% of the traditional curve with the single shallower photosynthetic maximum (Fig. 2B). Even if augmentation due to resuspension is calculated only for a three day-light hours per day, the increase is significant, especially in the light of the resedimentation of this food supply to the benthos.

Besides this autotrophic production, microbial heterotrophy associated with detrital particles might be enhanced owing to the resuspension into oxygenated water. Thus resuspension could result in a dual recycling of sedimented carbon and augmentaton of the benthic food resource (Fig. 3). This possibility is important to bear in mind in attempts to model sedimentation rates and benthic production. Although we may be tempted to model food chain energetics solely on the basis of standing crops and production and particulate excretion estimates, and thus attempt to estimate food supply to the benthos, such gross simplifications regarding a system that is not a simple flow-through system but probably a complex multi-cycling system, could lead to serious errors in our understanding of benthic food chains.

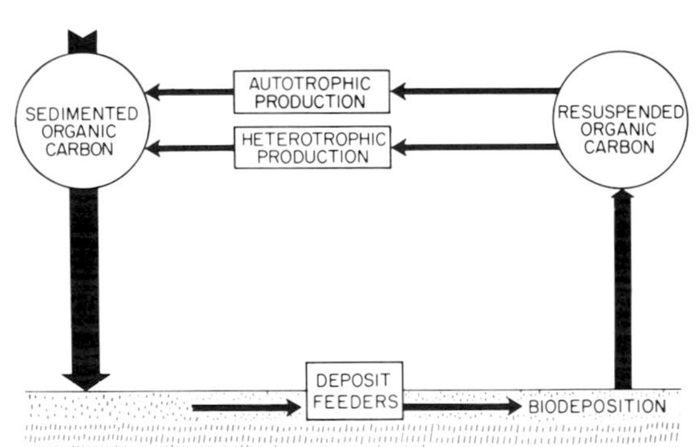

Fig. 3. Illustration of possible role of resuspended organic carbon and augmentation of food resource to the benthos by related autotrophic and heterotrophic production.

REFERENCES

Adams, S. M. and J. W. Angelovic. 1970. Assimilation of detritus and its associated bacteria by three species of estuarine animals. Chesapeake Sci. 11: 249-254.

Bader, R. G. 1954. The role of organic matter in determining the distribution of bivalves in sediments. J. Mar. Res. 13: 32-47.

Blegvad, H. 1914. Food and conditions of nourishment among the communities of invertebrate animals found in the sea bottom in Danish waters. Rep. Danish Biol. Stat., Univ. Copenhagen, Denmark 22: 41-78.

Burkholder, P. R. 1959. Some microbiological aspects of marine productivity in shallow waters. Proc. Salt Marsh Conf., Univ. Georgia, p. 70-75.

_____ and T. E. Doheny. 1968. The biology of eel grass. Contrib. No. 3, Dept. Conservation and Waterways, Town of Hempstead, Long Island, New York. 120 p.

Conover, J. T. 1964. Environmental relationship of benthos in salt ponds. Tech. Rep. Publ. Health Serv., Grant No. WP-0023(3).

Cushing, D. H. 1966. Models of the productive cycle in the sea, pp. 103-116. In Morning review lectures. Sec. Int. Oceanogr. Conf., Moscow, UNESCO. 250 p.

Darnell, R. M. 1961. Trophic spectrum of an estuarine community based on studies of Lake Pontchartrain, Louisiana. Ecology 43: 553-568.

_____. 1967. Organic detritus in relation to the estuarine ecosystem, pp. 376-382. In G. H. Lauff [ed.], Estuaries. Am. Assoc. Adv. Sci. Publ. No. 83. 757 p.

Davis, F. M. 1925. Quantitative studies on the fauna of the sea bottom. No. 2. Southern North Sea. Gt. Brit. Fish. Invest., Ser. II 8: 1-50.

Day, J. W., W. G. Smith, P. R. Wagner, and W. C. Stowe. 1973. Community structure and carbon budget of a salt marsh and shallow bay estuarine system in Louisiana. Cent. Wet. Res. Publ. LSU-SG-72-04. 79 p.

Dexter, R. W. 1944. Ecological significance of the disappearance of eelgrass at Cape Ann, Massachusetts. J. Wildl. Mgmt. 8: 173-176.

_____. 1950. Restoration of *Zostera* faciation at Cape Ann, Massachusetts. Ecology 31: 286-288.

Ekman, S. 1947. Uber die Festigkeit der Marinen Sediments als Faktor der Tierverbreitung, ein Beitrag zur Associations - Analyse. Zool. Biol., Univ. Uppsala, Sweden 25: 1-20.

Fager, E. W. 1971. Pattern in the development of a marine community. Limnol. Oceanogr. 16: 241-253.

Fenchel, T. 1969. The ecology of marine microbenthos. IV. Structure and function of the benthic ecosystem, its chemical and physical factors and the microfauna communities with special reference to the aliated protozoa. Ophelia 6: 1-182.

_____. 1970. Studies on the decomposition of organic detritus derived from the turtle grass, *Thalassia testudinum*. Limnol. Oceanogr. 15: 14-20.

Frankenberg, D. and K. L. Smith, Jr. 1967. Coprophagy in marine animals. Limnol. Oceanogr. 12: 443-450.

_____, D., S. L. Coles, and R. E. Johannes. 1967. The potential trophic significance of *Callianassa* major fecal pellets. Limnol. Oceanogr. 12: 113-120.

Gosselink, J. G. and C. J. Kirby. 1974. Decomposition of salt marsh grass, *Spartina alterniflora* Loisel. Limnol. Oceanogr. 19: 825-832.

Hargrave, B. T. 1970. The effect of deposit-feeding amphipods on the metabolism of benthic microflora. Limnol. Oceanogr. 15: 21-30.

Haven, D. and R. Morales-Alamo. 1966. Aspects of biodeposition by oysters and other invertebrate filter feeders. Limnol. Oceanogr. 11: 487-498.

Heald, E. J. 1971. The production of organic detritus in a south Florida estuary. Univ. Miami Sea Grant Tech. Bull. No. 6. 110 p.

Hedgpeth, J. W. 1957. Sandy beaches, pp. 587-608. In J. W. Hedgpeth [ed.], Treatise on marine ecology and paleoecology, v. 1. Geol. Soc. Am. Mem. 67.

Ito, S. and T. Imai. 1955. Ecology of an oyster bed. I. On the decline of productivity due to repeated culture. Tohoko J. Agr. Res. 5: 251-268.

Jeffries, H. P. 1972. Fatty-acid ecology of a tidal marsh. Limnol. Oceanogr. 17: 433-440.

_____. The use of fatty-acid patterns to determine feeding relationships in the sea. Unpublished manuscript.

Jensen, P. B. 1919. Valuation of the Limfjord. I. Studies on the fish food in the Limfjord 1909-1917, its quantity, variation and animal production. Rep. Danish Biol. Stat., Univ. Copenhagen, Denmark 26: 1-44.

Johannes, R. E. and M. Satomi. 1966. Composition and nutritive value of fecal pellets of a marine crustacean. Limnol. Oceanogr. 11: 191-197.

Jorgensen, C. M. 1966. Biology of suspension feeding. Pergamon Press.

Khailov, K. M. and Z. P. Burlakova. 1969. Release of dissolved organic matter by marine seaweeds and distribution of their total organic production to inshore communities. Limnol. Oceanogr. 14: 521-527.

Latter, P. M. and J. B. Craig. 1967. The decomposition of *Juncus squarrosus* leaves and microbial changes in the profile of *Juncus moor*. J. Ecol. 55: 465-482.

Lee, J. J., K. R. Tenore, J. H. Tietjen, and C. Mastropaolo. In press. An experimental approach toward understanding the role of meiofauna in a detritus based marine food web. Proc 3rd Radioecology Symposium.

Longbottom, M. R. 1970. The distribution of *Arenicola marina* with special reference to the effects of particle size and organic matter of sediments. J. Exp. Mar. Biol. Ecol. 5: 138-157.

Mann, K. H. 1972. Macroscopic production and detritus food chains in coastal areas. In IBP-UNESCO symposium detritus and its ecological role in aquatic ecosystems. Me. Inst. Ital. Hydrobiol.

Mare, M. F. 1942. A study of a marine benthic community with special reference to the microorganisms. J. Mar. Biol. Assoc. U.K. 25: 517-554.

Marshall, N. 1970. Food transfer through the lower trophic levels of the benthic environment, pp. 52-66. In J. H. Steele [ed.], Marine food chains. Univ. Calif. Press.

McIntyre, A. D. 1961. Meiobenthos of sub-littoral muds. J. Mar. Biol. Assoc. U.K. 44: 665-674.

McRoy, C. P. 1970. Standing stocks and other features of eel grass (*Zostera marina*) populations on the coast of Alaska. J. Fish. Res. Bd. Can. 27: 275-292.

Menzies, R. J. and G. T. Rowe. 1969. The distribution and significance of detrital turtle grass, *Thalassia testudinata* on the deep-sea floor off North Carolina. Int. Rev. Ges. Hydrobiol. 54: 217-222.

Moore, D. R. 1963. Distribution of the sea grass, *Thalassia* in the U.S. Bull. Mar. Sci. Gulf Carib. 13: 329-342.

Newell, R. 1964. The role of detritus in the nutrition of two marine deposit feeders, the prosobranch, *Hydrobia ulvae* and the bivalve, *Macoma balthica*. Proc. Zool. Soc. London 144: 25-45.

Newell, R. 1964. The role of detritus in the nutrition of two marine deposit feeders, the prosobranch, *Hydrobia ulvae* and the bivalve, *Macoma balthica*. Proc. Zool. Soc. London 144: 25-45.

Odum, E. P. and A. A. de la Cruz. 1967. Particulate organic detritus in a Georgia salt marsh-estuarine ecosystem, pp. 383-388. In G. H. Lauff [ed.], Estuaries. Am. Assoc. Adv. Science Publ. No. 83. 757 p.

Odum, H. T. 1957. Primary productivity in 11 Florida springs and a marine turtle grass community. Limnol. Oceanogr. 2: 85-97.

Odum, W. E. 1970. Utilization of direct grazing and plant detritus food chains by the striped mullet, *Mugil cephalus*, pp. 22-240. In J. H. Steele [ed.], Marine food chains. Univ. Calif. Press.

Petersen, C. G. 1918. The sea bottom and its production of fish food. A survey of the work done in connection with the valuation of the Danish waters from 1883-1917. Rep. Danish Biol. Stat., Univ. Copenhagen, Denmark 25: 1-62.

Phillips, R. C. 1969. Temperate grass flats, pp. 737-773. In H. T. Odum, B. J. Copeland, and E. A. McMahan [eds.], Coastal ecological systems of the United States. Government Printing Office, Washington.

Prinslow, T. E., I. Valiella, and J. M. Teal. 1974. The effect of detritus and ration size on the growth of *Fundulus heteroclitus*. J. Exp. Mar. Biol. Ecol. 16: 1-10.

Remane, A. 1933. Verteilung und Organisation der benthonischens Mikrofauna der Kieler Bucht. Wiss. Meeresuntersuch, Abt. Kiel. N.F. 21: 161-222.

Rhoads, D. C. and D. K. Young. 1971. Animal-sediment relations in Cape Cod Bay, Massachusetts. II. Reworking by *Molpadia oolitica* (Holothuroidea). Mar. Biol. 11: 255-261.

______, K. R. Tenore, and M. G. Browne. In press. The role of resuspended bottom muds in the food chain of shallow embayments. 2nd Inter. Estuarine Res. Conf.

Rowe, G. T. and R. J. Menzies. 1969. Zonation of large benthic invertebrates in the deep sea off the Carolinas. Deep-Sea Res. 16: 531-537.

Ryther, J. H. 1963. Geographic variations in productivity, pp. 347-380. In W. N. Hill [ed.], The sea, vol. 2. J. Wiley and Sons.

Sanders, H. L. 1960. Benthic studies in Buzzards Bay. III. The structure of the soft-bottom community. Limnol. Oceanogr. 5: 138-153.

Schelske, C. L. and E. P. Odum. 1962. Mechanisms maintaining high productivity in Georgia estuaries. Proc. Gulf Carib. Fish. Inst., 14th Ann. Ses. 75-80.

Steele, J. H. and I. A. Baird. 1972. Sedimentation of organic matter in a Scottish sea loch. Mem. 1st Ital. Idrobiol., 29 Suppl.: 73-88.

Teal, J. M. 1962. Energy flow in the salt marsh ecosystem of Georgia. Ecology 43: 614-624.

Tenore, K. R. 1972. The macrobenthos of the Pamlico River estuary, North Carolina. Ecol. Monogr. 42: 51-69.

_____. In press. Detrital utilization by the polychaete, *Capitella capitata*. J. Mar. Res.

_____ and W. M. Dunstan. 1973. Comparison of feeding and biodeposition of three bivalves at different food levels. Mar. Biol. 21: 190-195.

_____ and N. Gonzalez. In press. Food chain patterns in the Ria de Arosa, Spain: an area of intense mussel aquaculture. 10th European Sympo. Mar. Biol., Ostende, Belgium.

_____ and U. K. Gopalan. 1974. Food chain dynamics of the polychaete, *Nereis virens* cultured on animal tissue and detritus. J. Fish. Res. Bd. Can. 31: 1675-1678.

_____, M. G. Browne, and E. J. Chesney, Jr. 1974. Polyspecies aquaculture systems: the detrital trophic level. J. Mar. Res. 32: 425-432.

_____, J. C. Goldman, and J. P. Clarner. 1973. The food chain dynamics of the oyster, clam and mussel. J. Exp. Mar. Biol. Ecol. 12: 157-165.

Tietjen, J. H. 1966. The ecology of estuarine meiofauna with particular reference to the class nematode. Ph.D. Thesis, Univ. Rhode Island.

_____. 1967. Observations on the ecology of the marine nematode *Monhystera filicaudata* Allgen. Trans. Am. Microsc. Soc. 86: 304-306.

_____. 1969. The ecology of shallow water meiofauna in two New England estuaries. Oecologia 2: 251-291.

_____. 1971. Ecology and distribution of deep-sea meiobenthos off North Carolina. Deep-Sea Res. 18: 941-957.

Verwey, J. 1952. On the ecology of distribution of cockle and mussel in the Dutch Waddensee, their role in sedimentation, and the source of their food supply, with a short review of the feeding behavior of bivalve mollusks. Arch. Neerl. Zool. 10: 172-239.

Waits, E. D. 1967. Net primary production of an irregularly-flooded North Carolina salt marsh. Ph.D. Thesis, North Carolina State Univ.

Wieser, W. 1960. Benthic studies in Buzzards Bay. II. The meiofauna. Limnol. Oceanogr. 5: 121-137.

_____ and J. Kanwisher. 1961. Ecological and physiological studies on marine nematodes from a small salt marsh near Woods Hole, Massachusetts. Limnol. Oceanogr. 6: 262-270.

Wigley, R. L. and A. D. McIntyre. 1964. Some quantitative comparison of offshore meiobenthos and macrobenthos. Limnol. Oceanogr. 9: 485-493.

Williams, R. B. and L. K. Thomas. 1967. The standing crop of benthic animals in a North Carolina estuarine area. J. Elisha Mitchell Sci. Soc. 83: 135-139.

_____ and M. B. Murdoch. 1972. Compartment analysis of the production of *Juncus roemerianus* in a North Carolina salt marsh. Chesapeake Sci. 13: 69-79.

Yentsch, C. S. and D. W. Menzel. 1963. A method of the determination of plankton chlorophyll and phaeophyton by fluorescence. Deep-Sea Res. 10: 221-231.

Zeitzschel, B. 1965. Zur Sedimentation von Seston, eine productions-biologische Untersuchung von Sinkstoffen und Sedimenten der westlichen und mittleren Ostsce. Kieler Meeresforsch. 21: 55-80.

Zobell, C. E. and C. B. Feltham. 1938. Bacteria as food for certain marine invertebrates. J. Mar. Res. 1: 312-317.

Benthic-Pelagic Coupling in the Mid-Atlantic Bight

Gilbert T. Rowe and **K. L. Smith, Jr.**
Woods Hole Oceanographic Institution
Woods Hole, MA 02543

ABSTRACT

The hypothesis that the continental shelf is an important site of nutrient regeneration is supported by hydrographic data collected in Mid-Atlantic Bight and a theoretical relationship between bottom oxygen demand and the breakdown of sediment organic matter. Nutrient flux out of the bottom is estimated from near-bottom ammonia gradients in a finite difference equation.

INTRODUCTION

In a simplified marine ecosystem, phytoplankton utilize inorganic nutrients and light to produce organic matter, which can either be eaten by herbivores, usually zooplankton, or sink to the bottom as organic matter. The herbivorous zooplankton, other heterotrophs which eat them, or the detrital consumers on the bottom utilize the organic energy to grow, respire and reproduce, but they also excrete waste materials. The excreted material closes the marine ecosystem by becoming a feedback or nutrient supply to the phytoplankton.

Although many of the variables in this simple system have been the subject of intensive study, the coupling of the bottom to the pelagic system is still poorly known. Traditionally the benthic ecologist has studied the structure of invertebrate assemblages, with the idea that the invertebrates are important sources of food for demersal fishes. Recent benthic studies, as reviewed in this volume, have elucidated both secondary production and energy utilization (respiration), but we want to consider the importance of the regeneration of nutrients from the bottom. The purpose of this paper, then, is to explore the hypothesis that benthic nutrient regeneration couples the bottom with processes in the water column.

Regeneration of nutrients, or the degradation of organic matter, has been presumed to occur near the surface (Menzel 1968; Menzel and Ryther 1968) or on the bottom nearshore (Barnes 1957; Ryther 1963). Bottom nutrient regeneration has been estimated in closed aquatic systems (Mortimer 1942), but it has seldom been quantified on the continental shelf. Harris (1959) attempted to balance the nitrogen cycle in Long Island Sound and Rittenberg et al. (1955) made estimates of ammonia regeneration in the deep basins off California. Goering and Pamatmat (1971) presented evidence that owing to denitrification the anoxic sediments below the upwelling area off Peru act as a nitrate sink. Rowe et al. (in press) measured fluxes of nutrients out of the bottom sediments off Cap Blanc, Spanish Sahara, by _in situ_ incubation of the bottom under bell jars. The ratio of regenerated Si:N:P averaged 11:8:1 and they suggested that the average flux of nitrogen out of the sediments would account for approximately 35% of the nitrogen presumed to be required for photosynthesis. They also found that sediment pore water nutrient concentrations were several orders of magnitude higher than those of bottom water, but this gradient decreased off shore. Rowe et al. (1975) measured the nutrient flux out of sediments in Buzzards Bay, Massachusetts, and suggested that the recycled ammonia could supply a large fraction of the nitrogen required for photosynthesis. A similar conclusion was drawn for Harrington Sound, Bermuda (Thorstensen and Mackenzie 1974) and Narragansett Bay, Rhode Island (Nixon et al. 1975).

The theoretical possibilities for nutrient recycling can be explicitly portrayed by a box model (Fig. 1). As nitrogen is usually the nutrient in critical supply in marine systems, our model is a simple conception of nitrogen as it enters the benthic subsystem, is consumed by the biota or is buried. Consumed organic nitrogen becomes living cellular matter or it is excreted. For simplicity we presume the latter is mostly ammonia. Ammonia, because it is dissolved in the bottom water or pore water, is susceptable to diffusion processes (Berner 1971), or it can be oxidized to nitrite and nitrate by nitrifying bacteria. Nitrate and nitrite are dissolved and either lost from the bottom to the water, or reduced to dissolved nitrogen gas by denitrifying bacteria. The N_2 can be converted to ammonia by still another functional group of microflora, the nitrogen fixers, but we know of no published accounts of this in offshore marine sediments.

The portion of the sediment subsystem most important in our model is the conversion of organic nitrogen by the biota into the dissolved forms: ammonia and nitrate. That is, the model attempts to establish what fraction of sedimented matter lost from the water is returned to it in a form utilizable by plants in photosynthesis. One approach recently used to determine energy consumption by the bottom was to equate oxygen uptake, based on heat liberated with

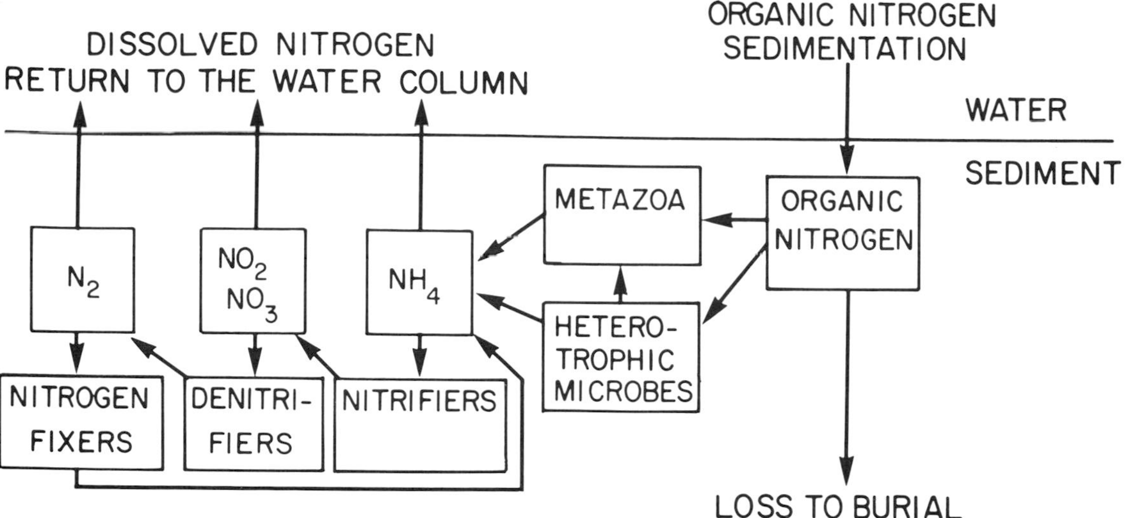

Fig. 1. Conceptual model of the nitrogen cycle in sediments. Dissolved organic nitrogen excretory products have been omitted, but may be important.

oxidation of organic matter, to total energy utilization (Pamatmat 1971, 1973; Smith et al. 1973; Smit et al. 1974). With this approach the amount of organic carbon converted to CO_2 can be estimated by means of a Respiratory Quotient table which takes into consideration the presumed relative proportions of lipid, carbohydrate and protein consumed. The usual assumptions are RQ = 0.85, or 1 ml O_2 = 0.456 mg C (Hargrave 1973), although they may be somewhat lower (Pamatmat 1971, 1977).

Hargrave (1973) in reviewing numerous recent studies convincingly argued that there is a positive relationship between oxygen demand of sediments and rate of primary production, but a negative relationship between sediment oxygen demand and the depth of the mixed layer of the water column. The proportion of total primary production utilized by the sediments decreases, compared to that metabolized by pelagic organisms, as either primary production or mixed layer depth increase. According to Pamatmat and Baghwat (1973), however, such a view may significantly underestimate total catabolism in that it does not account for total anaerobic metabolism. Nonetheless, converting oxygen demand to energy utilization (Smith et al. 1973), or to organic carbon utilization (Smith et al. 1974), is a straightforward method of estimating at least a lower limit of the fraction of pelagic production that is consumed by the benthic biota.

Rowe et al. (1975) estimated nutrient regeneration by assuming that organic nitrogen would be remineralized relative to carbon at a rate proportional to the nitrogen:carbon ratio in sediments (1:10). Direct _in situ_ measurements of nutrient flux and oxygen demand in Buzzards Bay indicated that an average of about 80% of the predicted remineralized nitrogen could be accounted for. Measurements of benthic oxygen demand in nearshore water are no longer rare, and the reviews in this volume indicate that temperature and relative productivity of an area can be used to estimate oxygen demand. But are we justified in predicting benthic nutrient recycling from a general model of oxygen demand? Furthermore, if sediment nitrogen remineralization is as intense as the O/N model would predict, what is the evidence for it in nutrient data from the water column? This paper presents a set of hydrographic data taken in the Mid-Atlantic Bight which can be interpreted to support our hypothesis that the bottom is a major site of nutrient recycling.

Contribution No. 3122 from the Woods Hole Oceanographic Institution, Woods Hole, Mass. This investigation was supported by U.S. Atomic Energy Commission Contract No. AT(30-1)-3862, National Science Foundation Grants GA 31235X, GA 22339, GA 39910 and GX 33502 and Office of Naval Research Contract N00014-66-C-0262.

METHODS

R/V ATLANTIS II Cruise 52 occupied 55 stations (Fig. 2) between Cape Hatteras and Cape Cod in September 1969. Routine hydrographic casts were made at each station, the bottom Niskin bottle of each being 1-3 m off bottom. The raw data and the methods used, all routine, are available in a Technical Report (Corwin 1970). Our attention was directed to the ammonia concentrations, which were measured by the method of Solorzano (1969).

RESULTS

The concentration of ammonia in the bottom water at almost all the stations on the continental shelf was several times higher than that in surface waters or in deep water offshore (Fig. 3). This high ammonia evidently formed a layer that blanketed the bottom from south of Long Island to just north of Cape Hatteras (Fig. 4). Most surface water had concentrations near 0.5 μg-atm NH_4^+-N L^{-1} and the majority of the stations on the shelf had bottom water values of 2 to 5 μg-atm NH_4^+-N L^{-1}. Radical exceptions were uniformly high values ($\bar{X}$ = 35 μg-atm NH_4^+-N L^{-1}) in Hudson River and Raritan Bay, and uniformly intermediate to low values in Chesapeake Bay (not plotted). High bottom or high deep values were not found at several stations between Chesapeake Bay and Cape Hatteras (36°00"N Lat. transect and 36°35'N Lat. transect, Fig. 4), probably because of storm-induced vertical mixing (Meade et al. 1975), or at 1548 and 1549 south of Block Island and Martha's Vineyard (not plotted). At all four locations (1538, 1534, 1948 and 1549) concentrations were more or less uniform with depth, ranging from 0.5 to 2 μg-atm L^{-1} in the south and about 1 to 2 μg-atm L^{-1} in the north. Stations on the outer margin of, and off the continental shelf had uniformly low values at all depths.

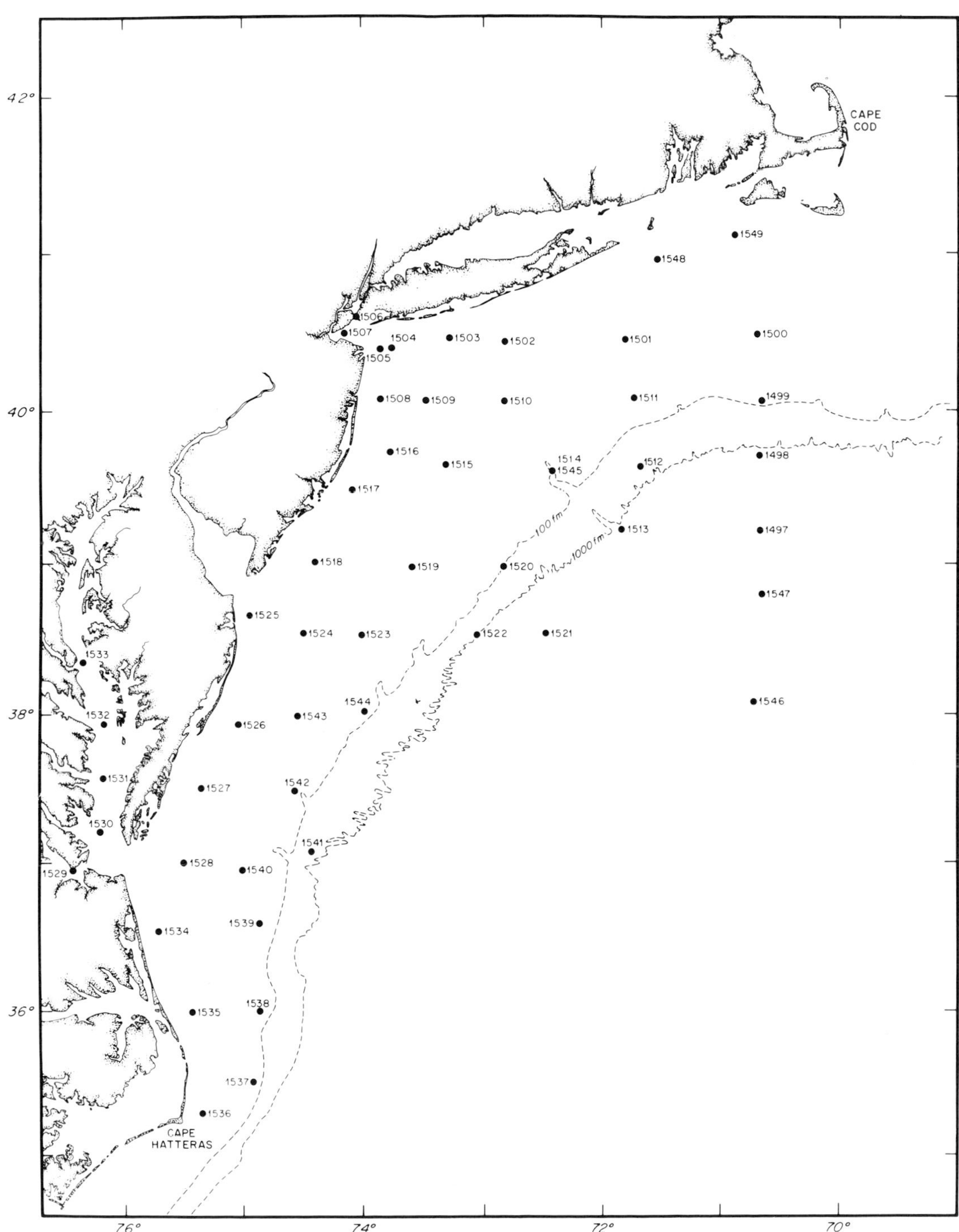

Fig. 2. Station locations on R/V ATLANTIS II Cruise 52.

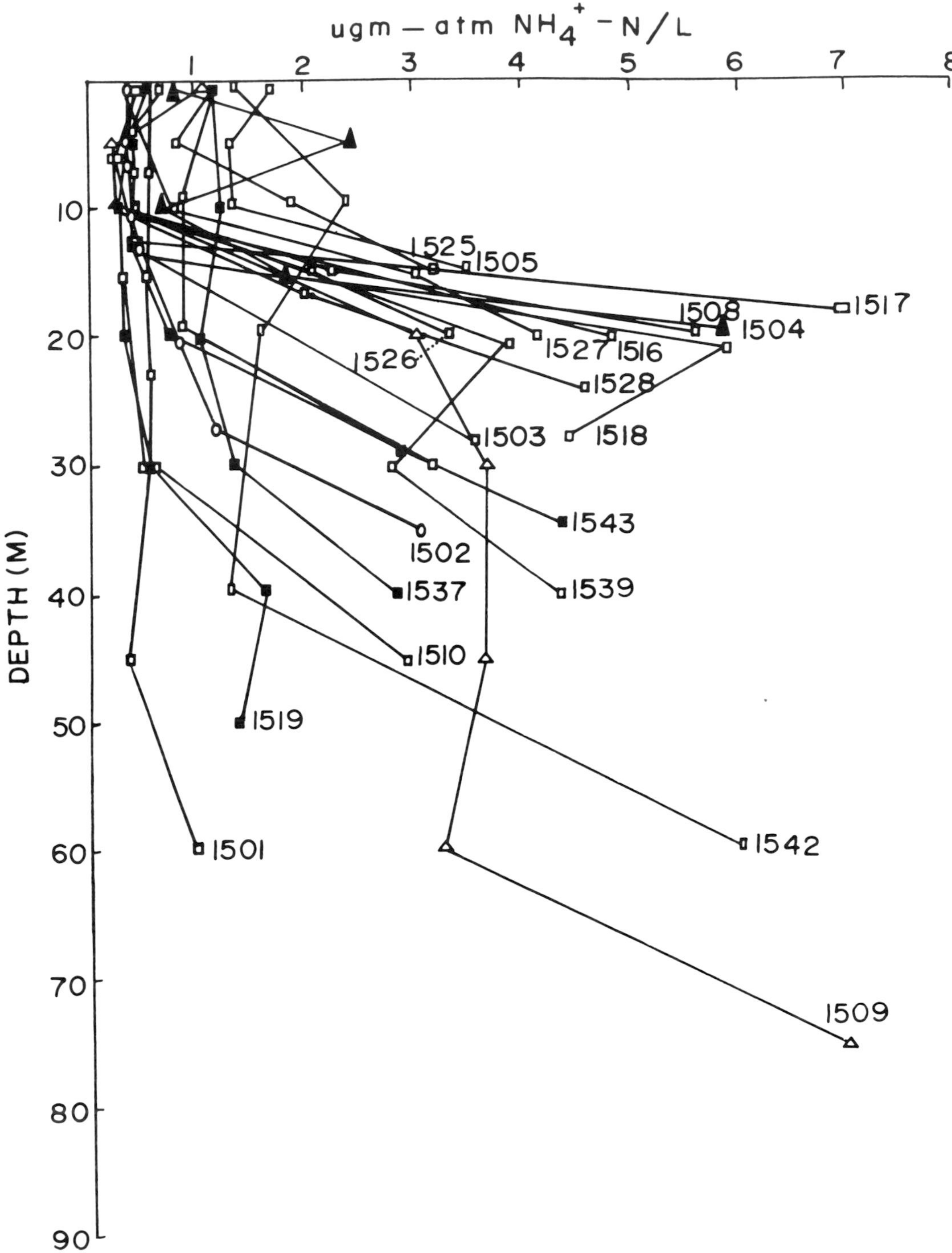

Fig. 3. Concentration on ammonia at selected nearshore hydrographic casts, R/V ATLANTIS II Cruise 52. Terminal datum points of each cast are from bottom Niskin bottles, about 1-3 m off bottom. Station numbers correspond to those in Fig. 2.

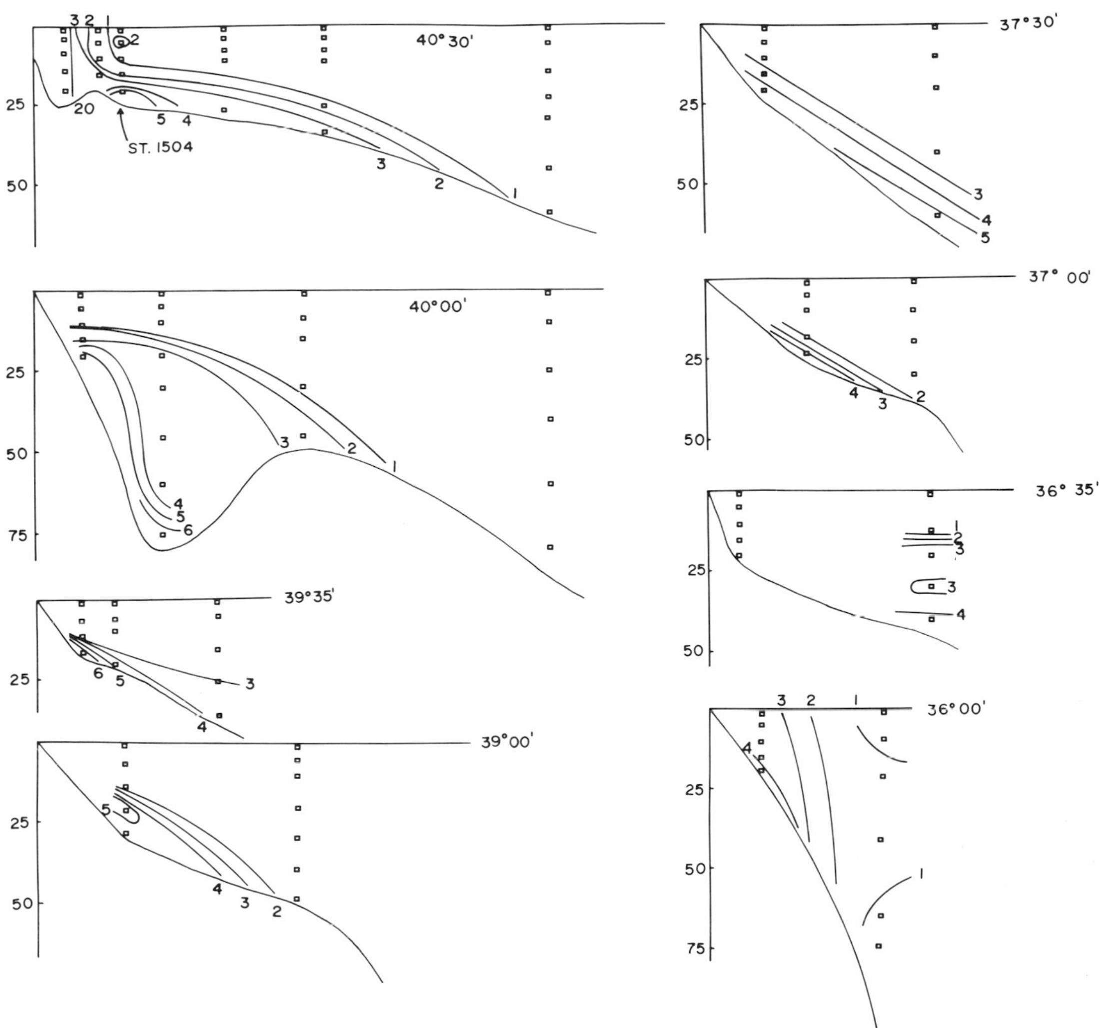

Fig. 4. Profiles of ammonia concentration (μg-atm L^{-1}) versus depth along selected east to west transects. Transects correspond to lines of stations on Fig. 2. Station 1504 is the designated location for the New York City sewage sludge dump.

Unexpected gradients in ammonia concentration with depth were noted at Stations 1504 and 1505 in the New York City sewage sludge and the U.S. Army Corps of Engineers dredge spoil dump sites, and at Station 1509, which was over the continental shelf trough linking the Hudson River with the Hudson Submarine Canyon. Additional exceptions (Stations 1518 and 1519) having no geographic signature of which we are aware had a near-bottom reversal in the ammonia concentration gradient.

The concentration gradient with depth at nearshore stations (depths of 20 m) clustered around 1 μg-atm L^{-1} m^{-1}, but as depth increased, the gradients decreased. At 40-m depth, the gradients were near 0.1 μg-atm L^{-1} m^{-1}, and off the shelf no depth gradients could be recognized.

DISCUSSION

The near-bottom ammonia gradients have several possible origins. Our data confirm that the largest point source of ammonia in the mid-Atlantic Bight is the Hudson River and Raritan Bay estuarine system. The river ammonia no doubt originates from raw and treated sewage effluents. The contours along the east-west transects (Fig. 4) suggest that this water might move out of the estuary either along the bottom or in a wedge along shore, with the vertical gradient resulting from uptake of ammonia by phytoplankton in the surface waters. Such movements are unlikely, however, since the water is warm, relatively fresh and should therefore flow offshore on the surface and not at depth. (Average σ_T value for Stations 1506 and 1507 was 16.10, compared to 20.85 at Station 1505.) Abrupt thermoclines and abrupt density gradients at other near-shore stations along the coast to the east and south make it unlikely that the estuary supplied the bottom ammonia. Alternatively the ammonia may have resulted from regeneration in the water column, but below the thermocline. If that were the case, why would there be low concentrations in deep water off shore?

A third alternative is that the near bottom ammonia was a direct result of the metabolism of benthos. A method of exploring this possibility is to consider, from our model, the ranges of regeneration that might be expected and compare these to inferences from the depth gradient, i.e., to assess how much flux out of the bottom there must be to maintain the gradient, given a range of vertical eddy diffusion. This method can be represented by modifying an equation such as that in Pytkowicz (1975) to represent vertical rather than horizontal processes:

$$\frac{\partial c}{\partial t} = 0 = R + \sum_i K \frac{\partial^2 c}{\partial Z_i{}^2} - \sum_i V_i \frac{\partial c}{\partial Z_i}$$

Maintenance of a steady state, or $\partial c/\partial t = 0$, requires a balance between release from the bottom (R), eddy diffusion ($K * \partial^2 c/\partial Z_i{}^2$) and advection ($V_i * \partial c/\partial Z_i$). If vertical advection is negligible, we can estimate vertical flux from vertical eddy diffusion (K [dc/dz]), where K is the vertical eddy diffusion coefficient and dc/dz is the vertical concentration gradient, with the following finite difference equation:

$$\text{FLUX} = \frac{K\ ([NH_4{}^+]\ \text{depth A} - [NH_4{}^+]\ \text{depth B})}{\text{Depth A} - \text{Depth B}}$$

K is known to vary, even in stratified conditions, by several orders of magnitude (<1 to >1000 cm^2/sec), but in stratified water it would be expected to be small. In abyssal waters a value of 2 cm^2/sec has been estimated and used frequently (Craig 1970;

Wollast 1974). Higher values have been estimated near bottom (Koczy 1956, K = 4 - 30 cm^2/sec) and at shallow depths (Kajihara et al. 1974, K = 10 - 50 cm^2 sec^{-1}).

Since most of the water in our study was stratified, we can make a conservative choice of K values near 1 cm^2 sec^{-1}, which would yield 70 µg-atm NH_4^+ m^{-2} hr^{-1}, using a gradient of 0.2 µg atm NH_4^+ L^{-1} m^{-1}. Using a larger gradient such as 1 µg atm NH_4^+ L^{-1} m^{-1}, which is not unreasonable for many of the 20-m stations (Fig. 2), flux out of the bottom would be 350 µg atm NH_4^+ m^{-2} hr^{-1}, again using K = 1.

During the cruise, bottom water temperatures at the shelf stations averaged 14.8°C, which would correspond approximately to the temperature when bottom oxygen demand was measured in New York Bight (Smith et al. 1974). The bottom in that study was fine sand, temperature was 17°C and total oxygen demand averaged 36.3 ml m^{-2} hr^{-1}. Another measurement in the Bight in April (5°C) was 11.1 ml m^{-2} hr^{-1}. Interpolation would suggest that on fine sand oxygen uptake would be about 25 ml m^{-2} ml^{-1} at 15°C. Nearby, in the area where Smith et al. (1974) assumed sewage sludge was accumulating, they estimated that oxygen demand would be 43 ml m^{-2} hr^{-1} at 13°C, and converted this to 0.43 g carbon m^{-2} d^{-1}, using an RQ of 0.85. We assumed nitrogen is regenerated at a rate proportional to carbon, and we estimated that regeneration, very close to Station 1504 (with a fine sand bottom) would be 24.7 mg N m^{-2} d^{-1} and 42.5 mg N m^{-2} d^{-1} from the organic-rich mud bottom at the head of the trough 2-km northwest of Station 1504. This is equivalent to 73.5 and 126 µg-atm NH_4^+ N m^{-2} hr^{-1}, values close to those estimated from the finite difference equation.

In comparing benthic oxygen demand stations in Smith et al. (1974) and the ATLANTIS II 52 cruise, confusion may arise since ATLANTIS II 52 Station 1504 is the site designated as the New York sludge dump, whereas Smith et al. (1974) discovered that accumulation occurred several km to the west in the shelf trough. They therefore called Station 1504 (their Station B) a "control", and made "sludge influenced" measurements in the trough. If our hypothesis that bottom regeneration is proportional to oxygen demand is correct, we would expect the bottom gradient to be greatest over the trough, but no station was made there during ATLANTIS II 52.

The proposed oxygen-nitrogen model must be accepted with caution because there is reason to believe that the stoichiometric relationship actually overestimates nitrogen fluxes in some situations. For example, in Buzzards Bay and Narragansett Bay somewhat less nitrogen evolved from the sediments than would be predicted directly from the oxidation of organic matter (Rowe et al. 1975, Nixon et al. 1975). The loss was presumed to result from fluxes of organic nitrogen and denitrification and could account for the low nitrogen:phosphorus ratio characteristic of coastal waters.

We can assess the significance of benthic regeneration by comparing our flux estimates with phytoplankton requirements. Primary productivity, measured by the C^{14} method at 16 shelf stations on

AII 52, averaged 0.244 g c m^{-2} d^{-1} (Corwin 1970). If the nitrogen required for this production was 15% of the carbon, the phytoplankton nitrogen assimilation was 36.6 mg N m^{-2} d^{-1} or 109 µg atm N m^{-2} hr^{-1}, or a value similar to the estimates of flux from the bottom based on both the O/N model and the vertical flux equation. This similarity implies that bottom regeneration keeps pace with primary production, and that primary producers depend very little on pelagic regenerative processes,

It is relevant to quantify benthic as opposed to pelagic nutrient regeneration because benthic rates, which are affected mostly by only temperature on a short time scale, should not be affected by variability common in pelagic advective processes and the capricious behavior of schooling nekton. Regeneration from the bottom may therefore provide stability to rates of primary production. This feedback of nutrients from the bottom might be especially important in stabilizing ecosystems largely dominated by nutrient input from river runoff or upwelling, which may be subject more to climatic than to seasonal (temperature) variations.

REFERENCES

Barnes, H. 1957. Nutrient elements, p. 297-344. In J. Hedpeth [ed.], Marine ecology and paleoecology. Geol. Soc. Am. Mem. 67. 1296 p.

Berner, R. A. 1971. Principles of chemical sedimentology. McGraw-Hill.

Corwin, N. 1970. Reduced data reports for GOSNOLD cruise 140 and ATLANTIS II cruise 52. Appendix I. Woods Hole Oceanographic Institution Ref. No. 70-15. A.E.C. Rt. NYO-3862-30.

Craig, H. 1970. Abyssal carbon in the South Pacific. J. Geophys. Res. 75: 691-695.

Goering, J. J. and M. M. Pamatmat. 1971. Denitrification in sediments of the sea off Peru. Invest. Pesq. 35: 233-242.

Hargrave, B. 1973. Coupling carbon flows through some pelagic and benthic communities. J. Fish. Res. Bd. Can. 30: 1317-1326.

Harris, E. 1959. The nitrogen cycle in Long Island Sound. Bull. Bingham Oceanogr. Coll. 17: 31-64.

Kajihara, M., K. Matsunaga, and Y. Maita. 1974. Anomalous distribution of suspended matter and some chemical compositions in seawater near the seabed: transport processes. J. Oceanogr. Soc. Japan 30: 232-240.

Koczy, F. F. 1956. Vertical eddy diffusion in deep water. Nature 178: 585-586.

Meade, R. H., P. L. Sachs, F. Manheim, J. Hathaway, and D. Spencer. 1975. Sources of suspended matter in waters of the middle Atlantic Bight. J. Sediment. Petrol. 45: 171-188.

Menzel, D. W. 1967. Particulate organic carbon in the deep-sea. Deep-Sea Res. 14: 229-238.

_____ and J. H. Ryther. 1968. Organic carbon and the oxygen minimum in the South Atlantic Ocean. Deep-Sea Res. 15: 327-337.

Mortimer, C. H. 1942. The exchange of dissolved substances between mud and water in lakes. Ecology 30: 147-201.

Nixon, S. W., C. A. Oviatt, and S. S. Hale. 1975. Nitrogen regeneration and the metabolism of coastal marine bottom communities. British Ecol. Soc. Symp. Decomposition. Coleraine, Northern Ireland.

Pamatmat, M. M. 1971. Oxygen consumption by the sea bed. IV. Shipboard and laboratory experiments. Limnol. Oceanogr. 16: 536-550.

_____. 1973. Benthic community metabolism on the continental terrace and in the deep-sea in the North Pacific. Int. Rev. ges. Hydrobiologie 58: 345-368.

_____. 1977. Benthic community metabolism: a review and assessment of present status and outlook, p. 55-66. In B. C. Coull [ed.], Ecology of marine benthos, No. 6, Belle W. Baruch Library in Marine Science. Univ. South Carolina Press.

_____ and A. M. Bhagwat. 1973. Anaerobic metabolism in Lake Washington sediments. Limnol. Oceanogr. 18: 611-627.

Pytkowicz, R. M. 1975. Some trends in marine chemistry and geochemistry. Earth-Sci. Rev. 11: 1-46.

Rittenberg, S. C., K. O. Emergy, and W. L. Orr. 1955. Regeneration of nutrients in sediments of marine basins. Deep-Sea Res. 3: 214-228.

Rowe, G. T., C. H. Clifford, K. L. Smith, Jr., and P. L. Hamilton. 1975. Benthic nutrient regeneration and its coupling to primary productivity in coastal waters. Nature 225: 215-217.

_____, C. H. Clifford, K. L. Smith, Jr., and P. L. Hamilton. 1975. Regeneration of nutrients in sediments off Cap Blanc, Spanish Sahara. Deep-Sea Res. (in press)

Ryther, J. H. 1963. Geographic variations in productivity, p. 347-380. In M. N. Hill [ed.], The sea, v. 2. Interscience.

Smith, K. L., Jr., G. T. Rowe, and C. H. Clifford. 1974. Sediment oxygen demand in an upwelling and outwelling area. Tethys 6: 223-230.

_____, G. T. Rowe, and J. A. Nichols. 1973. Benthic community respiration near the Woods Hole sewage outfall. Estuarine and Coastal Marine Sci. 1: 65-70.

Solorzano, L. 1969. Determination of ammonia in natural waters by the phenol-hypochlorite method. Limnol. Oceanogr. 14: 799-801.

Thorstensen, D. C. and F. T. MacKenzie. 1974. Time variability of pore water chemistry in recent carbonate sediments, Devil's Hole, Harrington Sound, Bermuda. Geoch. Cosmochim. Acta 38: 1-19.

Wollast, R. 1974. The silica problem, p. 359-392. In E. D. Goldberg [ed.], The sea, v. 2. Interscience.

Experimental Trends in Sediment Microbial Heterotrophy: Radioisotopic Techniques and Analysis

R. R. Christian[1] and **J. R. Hall**[2*]
Department of Microbiology and
Marine Institute
University of Georgia
Sapelo Island, GA 31327

ABSTRACT

Heterotrophic uptake of various ^{14}C labeled compounds by salt marsh soil microbial communities was investigated. Separate techniques were required for aerobic and anaerobic studies owing to the differences in the nature of substrate availability and production of end products within each habitat. A greater understanding of sediment communities is available through an experimental approach linked to radioisotopic analysis.

INTRODUCTION

Benthic microbial ecologists, like benthic ecologists in general, often think that the organisms they work with are of dominant importance in the energetic functioning of a community or assemblage. Some, for example Smith (1973) and Smith et al. (1972), have even tried indirectly to assay the importance of particular microorganisms, but direct application of standard microbial techniques toward this end is not easy. We believe, however, that recent advances in the use of radioisotopic analyses for studying water column microbial

---

[1]Present address: Drexel University, Dept. of Biological Sciences, Philadelphia, PA 19104

[2]Present address: 422 Whitaker St., Savannah, GA 31401.

*Order of authorship was determined by the method of P. K. Dayton and R. R. Hessler, 1972. Deep-Sea Res. 19: 199-208.

heterotrophy (Parsons and Strickland 1962; Wright and Hobbie 1965) are, with some modifications, applicable to aerobic and anaerobic sedimentary microbial processes. This approach was first used in the work of Munro and Brock (1968), Wood (1970), Hall et al. (1972), and a few others. We would like to review this progress, present our own approaches, and speculate on the future use of this powerful tool.

The importance of microorganisms in sediments is well established. Dale (1974) has shown that the numbers of bacteria in intertidal sediments range from 1.17 x 10^8 to 9.97 x 10^9 g^{-1} of dry sediment, with bacterial biomass (based on 2.2 x 10^{-13} g $cell^{-1}$) varying from 5.5 to 26.8 g m^{-2} (to 10-cm depth). This high microbial biomass has also been shown for the marsh soils with which we work (Christian et al 1975).

The small size of sediment bacteria, coupled with large biomass and Zeuthen (1947) type size: metabolic rate relationships, unquestionably suggests a very high potential activity (Brock 1966). Among the aerobic microorganisms, there are nondiscriminatory heterotrophs that are capable of utilizing a wide variety of natural occurring substrates (Wiebe and Liston 1972). Additionally, specialized microbes such as methane oxidizers can be found in salt marsh soils (King personal communication) and should be expected in other sediment types. Also, Darley (personal communication) has isolated autotrophs possessing heterotrophic potential from salt marshes. The anaerobic heterotrophic microorganisms in sediments represent a wide variety of metabolic approaches to the transformation of matter. Four general classes of microbe found are: (1) fermenters (Molongoski and Klug 1975), (2) dissimilatory sulfate reducers (Cappenberg and Prins 1974), (3) dissimilatory nitrogenous oxide reducers (Payne 1973), and (4) methane producers (Jones and Paynter 1975). Each of these organisms or groups has its own specific role in carbon transformations in the sediment. Organic compounds in nature represent a continuum from the biologically active to the recalcitrant (Alexander 1965), with an inverse relationship between turnover time and ambient concentration (Pomeroy 1971, 1974). Since many analytical techniques are inadequate to measure the concentration, let alone utilization of these highly active compounds having small molecular weight, radioisotope analysis is an obvious choice because of its sensitivity.

Various sources describe isotopic techniques that are applicable to sediment microbial ecology. Biochemists and physiologists were among the first to use radioisotopes in kinetic analyses. Aspects of these short-term approaches were then appropriated by aquatic ecologists to measure bacterial heterotrophic potential (Wright and Hobbie 1965). Soil microbial ecologists have adapted tracer analyses to longer term experimentation (Jenkinson 1971). Even exobiology has adapted some of these approaches, with the added sophistication of remote sensing (Radmer and Kok 1974). Techniques from each of these disciplines may be fruitfully applied to marine sediment biogeochemistry.

Contribution No. 296 from University of Georgia Marine Institute, Sapelo Island, Georgia 31327. This study was supported by National Science Foundation Grant GA 35793X. We thank W. J. Wiebe and S. M. Bunker for their help.

PERSPECTIVE

The utilization of a single labeled substrate by microbial communities is amenable to kinetic analysis. For this reason we will present a brief review of the major kinetic orders that may be applied. These include zero order, first order, and the mixed order kinetics as described by the Michaelis-Menten equation. Each is depicted graphically in Figure 1.

In a zero order reaction the velocity of reaction (v) is independent of substrate concentration (S) (Fig. 1A). This reaction may be expressed as $v = kS^{\circ}$, where k represents the rate constant. S is displayed to the zero power and hence the equation reduces to $v = k$. In a first order reaction the velocity is proportional to the first power of substrate concentration as $v = kS^1$ (i.e., $v = kS$) (Fig. 1B). Catalyzed, single substrate-single enzyme reactions display mixed order kinetics that are defined by the equation $v = V_{max}S/(Km + S)$ (Fig. 1C). V_{max} is the maximum velocity and Km is the Michaelis-Menten constant representing the concentration when $v = \frac{1}{2}V_{max}$. When S<<<K, first order kinetics approximate v; whereas when $v = V_{max}$, zero order kinetics are operative. The former case is called pseudo-first order because when S = K/100 the deviation from first order is <1%. Since the shape of a mixed order curve restricts easy analysis of the data, a number of data transformations may be applied. The modified Lineweaver-Burk transformation is shown in Figure 1D. It is of the form $S/v=K/V_{max}+(1/V_{max})$. In Figure 1D S/V represents the turnover time of the substrate. For a more complete discussion of kinetics see Mahler and Cordes (1966).

The kinetics described above (especially Michaelis-Menten) have been developed for controlled chemical and biochemical systems under restricted conditions (Mahler and Cordes 1966). The results of a large number of single substrate experiments on ecological systems appear, however, to fit these kinetic models. The model most often used is the Michaelis-Menten equation. This kinetic approach was first applied to aquatic systems by Parsons and Strickland (1962). Single concentrations of glucose and acetate were added to coastal waters, the radioactivity assimilated by microorganisms was counted, and the relative rates of heterotrophy determined for 250 mg C/m^3. The results of experiments using varying concentrations of glucose and acetate were analyzed assuming Michaelis-Menten kinetics to derive $[K+S_n]$ factors. S_n represents the natural concentration of substrate, and K is analogous to Km. This latter approach was further developed by Wright and Hobbie (1965, 1966) in order to derive relations for turnover time (T_t), V_{max} and $[K+S_n]$.

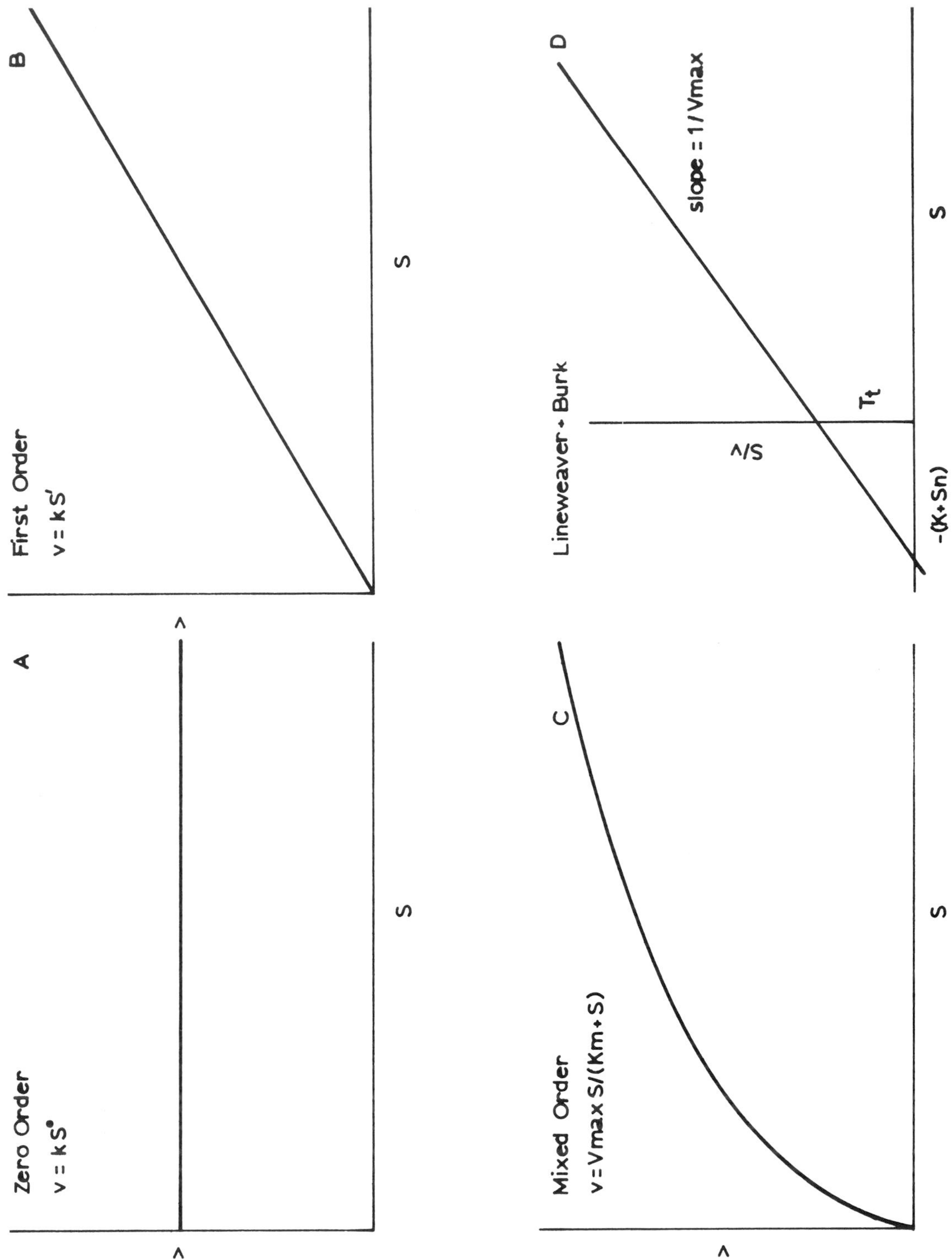

Fig. 1. Activity curves for three kinetic orders. A. zero order, B. first order, C. Michaelis-Menten mixed order, D. transformed mixed order by modified Lineweaver-Burk equation.

As certain modifications in the Michaelis-Menten equation must be made in analyzing ecological experiments, a further derivation will be developed. The first modification involves relating the distribution of label to organic matter uptake. The second is necessitated by the usual lack of knowledge of the natural concentration of substrate in the system (S_n).

The Michaelis-Menten formula becomes the following:

$$\frac{f(S_n+A)}{t} = v = \frac{V_{max}(S_n+A)}{K + (S_n+A)}$$

where f = the fraction of radioactivity utilized, t = incubation time, and A = the concentration of added substrate. This can be transformed to:

$$\frac{t}{f} = \frac{(K+S_n)}{V_{max}} + \frac{A}{V_{max}}$$

Transformed data are then plotted at t/f vs A. The slope of the line equals $1/V_{max}$, the y-intercept equals $K+S_n/V_{max}$ or the turnover time when no substrate is added (T_t), and the x-intercept equals $-(K+S_n)$.

If derived results appear to follow zero or first order kinetics, comparable equations to an "ecological" Michaelis-Menten equation are, respectively:

$$v = k\ (S_n + A)^0 \quad \text{(zero order)}$$

$$v = k\ (S_n + A)^1 \quad \text{(first order)}$$

Hence different ecological kinetic parameters may be derived depending upon which kinetic model is satisfied. If the data fit a zero order condition, the velocity is derived as a constant. The turnover time is directly proportional to the amount of substrate. For a first order reaction, k is again derived from f/t, and turnover time is the inverse. Velocity can only be obtained if S_n is known.

The use of Michaelis-Menten kinetics is enticing since more "ecological parameters" can be obtained from the data. These include T_t of natural concentrations, V_{max}, and $K+S_n$ when the natural substrate concentration is unknown. When the natural substrate concentration is known, v and K can also be obtained. The meanings of these parameters are more difficult to interpret than their biochemical counterparts. Wright (1973) discussed these problems of interpretation, but here we will only point out that V_{max} appears to be related to the biomass of organisms active in utilization and edaphic factors that regulate their metabolism (e.g. temperature) (Wright 1973). K represents an unknown factor which may be related to the transport of substrate into the cells (Wright and Hobbie 1966). When S_n is unknown, $K+S_n$ is taken to be the upper limit of K; however, the true nature of this parameter remains nebulous.

Once Wright and Hobbie (1965, 1966) developed the ecological application of Michaelis-Menten kinetics, several studies were conducted in various aquatic systems with modifications on the original technique. For instance, the natural concentrations of glucose were obtained by bioassays (Hobbie and Wright 1965; Vaccaro and Jannasch 1966) and of amino acids by chemical means (Hobbie et al. 1968). These assays allowed for the calculation of K and v. The importance of respired label was demonstrated by Williams and Askew (1968) and Hobbie and Crawford (1969). These techniques allowed the study of other parameters, i.e., the turnover time with respect to mineralization and percent respiration. The above modifications represent the major base from which various other studies have developed. It is not our intent, however, to review all of the aquatic heterotrophy literature. Many of these studies are cited by Wright (1973) and Burnison and Morita (1974).

Radioisotopic analysis of sediment heterotrophy was first reported by Munro and Brock (1968). Ten grams of sandy sediment was diluted into 25 ml of filtered sea water, and uniformly labeled acetate was added at concentrations from approximately <10 to 2,000 ng acetate carbon x cc^{-1}. Lineweaver-Burk transformations were performed on data in which less than 100 ng C x cc^{-1} were added. Saturation kinetics were observed in only two of four reported experiments at these lower concentrations. In the other two experiments first order kinetics were observed although the authors referred to this situation as "zero order" kinetics. The t/f remained constant over the concentration range. If the velocity had remained constant, zero order kinetics would have been operative.

Wood (1970) measured the utilization of glucose and acetate by an estuarine sediment microbial community. Sediments were diluted 1:100 and 2-ml subsamples were used for heterotrophy experiments. This procedure increased reaction time. Acetate-1,2-^{14}C or glucose-6-^{14}C was added to subsamples representing concentration gradients from 52 to 130 and 34 to 85 ng substrate x cc^{-1}, respectively. $^{14}CO_2$ and label associated with sediments were assayed during the glucose experiments. As approximately 3% of the acetate stock was found to be trapped in phenethylamine during the procedure, $^{14}CO_2$ production was not measured for this substrate. It was later noted that this volatization was $^{14}CO_2$ contamination (Wright 1973). The Michaelis-Menten kinetic model was then used for data analysis. Turnover times for glucose gross uptake and acetate assimilation were generally of the order of minutes. Maximum velocities indicated that hundreds of μg x gm^{-1} dry wt of sediment x hr^{-1} could be utilized, while sediment K values were all less than 1.00 μg x gm^{-1} for both substrates. The sediment microbial community was thus found to utilize these substrates much more actively than the water column. The percent respiration of glucose was extremely low, averaging 1.01%. The reasons for this are not obvious although the use of glucose-6-^{14}C may bias the percentage depending on the metabolic pathways in operation (Mayaudon 1971).

Later, Wood and Chua (1973) applied the same techniques to the study of glucose uptake in Lake Ontario. Both water column and sediment heterotrophic analyses were conducted. Substrate concentrations were measured and used in calculating velocities of uptake. Velocity of glucose uptake was greater in the sediments in every experiment. Percent respiration in these sediments using uniformly labeled glucose ranged from 9 to 38. These data were incorporated into a model of glucose flux in Toronto Harbour (Wood and Chua 1973).

Other studies have used mud slurry systems of varying dilutions to determine the uptake kinetics of single organic substrates. In an attempt to reduce any adverse effects of dilution, Harrison et al. (1971) added 5 cc of slurried lake sediment (ca 350 mg dry wt) to 2 ml of water containing label. Experiments were terminated after 5 min rather than 1 to 3 hr for highly dilute sediments (Wood 1970). Only $^{14}CO_2$ was analyzed in studies of glucose and acetate utilization. Radioactivity trapped within the acetate stock by phenethylamine was acknowledged as a source or error in $^{14}CO_2$ measurements. Glucose was added in the range of approximately 200 to 700 ng x cc^{-1}, and acetate was added in the range of approximately 1250 to 7500 ng x cc^{-1}. Results were analyzed using the Michaelis-Menten model. Again rapid turnover times were found.

Hall et al. (1972) measured net uptake and mineralization of acetate, glucose and glycine in sediments of Marion Lake, British Columbia. Sediments were diluted 20:1 to 50:1, and concentrations of 20 to 100 ng substrate x cc^{-1} were added. Results from such slurry systems were compared to those of intact cores. Although saturation kinetics were obtained in slurry systems, intact cores did not saturate at substrate concentrations as high as 1 μg x cc^{-1}. The appendices of this paper present correction factors for significant substrate loss during incubation and dilution effects on the kinetic parameters, together with statistical analysis of the parameter calculations.

The research described above focused primarily on the aerobic utilization of single substrates. Similar approaches were used by Kadota et al (1966) and Wirsen and Jannasch (1974). Although several different experimental designs have been used, all results indicate that the sediments are highly active toward substrate utilization or at least its potential utilization.

Anaerobic utilization has received only cursory attention (Hall et al 1972). The studies of anaerobic metabolism have often taken a different course. The tracer $^{35}SO_4$ has been used in the study of dissimilatory sulfate reduction (Sorokin 1962; Jørgensen and Fenchel 1974). The latter authors added $^{35}SO_4$ to various depths of a sediment model system, and its transformations were followed for 7 months. The rate of sulfate reduction was based on the following equation:

$$- SO_4^{=} = \frac{[SO_4^{=}] \times a \times 1.06}{A \times V \times t} \text{ nM S:cc}^{-1}\text{day}^{-1}$$

where $[SO_4^{=}]$ is the sulfate content of the segment in nM, a is the total radioactivity of free sulfide and acid soluble sulfide, A is the radioactivity of sulfate, V is the volume of the sediment in cm^3, t is the incubation time in days, and 1.06 is a correction factor for the microbial fractionation of the ^{32}S and ^{35}S isotopes. Sulfate reduction occurred at rates between 55 and 135 nM S x cc^{-1} day^{-1}.

The interaction between sulfate reduction and methanogenesis in lake sediments was examined using ^{14}C-labeled substrates by Cappenberg and Prins (1974). Labeled lactate acted as the substrate for dissimilatory sulfate reducing bacteria, while acetate-1,2-^{14}C acted as the substrate for methanogenesis. Single concentrations of substrate were added and utilization was plotted against time. The $^{10}\log$ of the remaining lactate was plotted and turnover rate was determined by regression analysis. The ratio of $^{14}CO_2/^{14}CH_4$ from acetate was also determined. Fluoro inhibitors were also used to demonstrate the specificity of substrate transformation. The authors concluded that only a portion of the dissimilated lactate enters the acetate pool, and this acetate represents a major potential source for CH_4 production. The potential for use of comparable techniques in anaerobic studies is great, since various functional populations have different nutritional requirements which may be used advantageously in designing experiments to study specific populations.

Although experimental design and analysis have taken various forms, most researchers have developed their experimentation around the Michaelis-Menten model. We wish to stress here that it is a model into which certain sets of data appear to fit. Analysis of these data by Michaelis-Menten kinetics requires simplifying assumptions and satisfied criteria. It is important that these criteria are critically met. A number of theoretical and methodological difficulties have been acknowledged in the adoption of the model to one's results, many of which were discussed by Wright (1973). One major difficulty is inability to derive proper saturation kinetics in all experiments. From 40 to 90% of experiments by various authors were found to have "acceptable kinetics" (see Wright 1973). This percentage may depend on the substrate used. Vaccaro (1969) found saturation kinetics for various substrates in sea water only after a 24-hr enrichment with the respective substrates. Unfortunately, the percentage of "acceptable" experiments of the total is not presented in many instances.

Williams (1973a) discussed the mathematical validity of applying the Michaelis-Menten equation to heterogeneous microbial populations. Uptake for the entire community was represented by:

$$v = \frac{V_{max} S}{K + S}$$

in these radioisotope studies. However, each organism or population within the community has its own V_{max} and K. As such, the sum of the individual organism kinetics is not mathematically equivalent to the above representation. The expanded equation is as follows:

$$v = \frac{V_{max_1} S}{K_1 + S} + \frac{V_{max_2} S}{K_2 + S} + \ldots + \frac{V_{max_n} S}{K_n + S}$$

The estimation of the turnover time and average K by the simplified equation becomes less valid as the community increases in heterogeneity, especially with respect to K. Over a wide range of substrate concentrations, the S/v vs S plot is nonlinear for heterogeneous populations. The Michaelis-Menten model assumes linearity over the entire range. We suggest that systems be examined over a wide range of substrate concentrations in order to determine the extent of linearity (i.e., nature of heterogeneity).

Another problem in interpreting results was recently examined by Griffiths et al. (1974), who pointed out that the method of terminating experiments may affect the results obtained owing to the leakage of radioactivity within cells. They suggested that the material released by acid or formalin treatment may be associated with intracellular pools and binding proteins, and the remaining radioactivity is associated with macromolecule biosynthesis. It is interesting that the percent respiration remained constant over time for acidified samples but not for samples terminated by filtration. This work was conducted on water samples. The authors suggested that duplicate samples be terminated by acid and filtration so that percent leakage could be determined. Such controls should also be done for sediment experiments. In highly dilute systems filtration may be acceptable as a termination method, but in less dilute systems another mode of termination must be adopted.

APPROACH

Aerobic Studies

If one considers how a particular organic compound is made available to sediment microorganisms in nature, it becomes obvious that the process is distinctly different for aerobic and anaerobic organisms. Aerobes most presumably "see" organic compounds from overlying water, although the possibility exists that fermentative end products may diffuse upwards from anaerobic populations. For this reason, we used intact sediment surfaces in cores with substrates added from the free surface.

Substrates were predominantly limited to glucose, glycine and acetate in concentration ranges of 2-300 $\mu g \times l^{-1}$, as representative of the basic types of small molecular weight substrates available in nature. Each was made up in artificial sea water with cold substrate to provide appropriate final substrate concentrations.

A schematic presentation of the aerobic system appears in Figure 2. Eight glass cores of 1/212 m^2 cross-sectional area were used. All cores were placed in water baths, kept in the dark at or close to ambient temperature. CO_2-free air was kept flowing through each core to prevent any from becoming anaerobic. Air coming from the cores was passed through two CO_2 traps containing phenethylamine in scintillation cocktail (Woeller 1962). Two cores were poisoned with full-strength formalin as controls. Incubation time was usually four hr with water samples removed (via the aforementioned cannula)

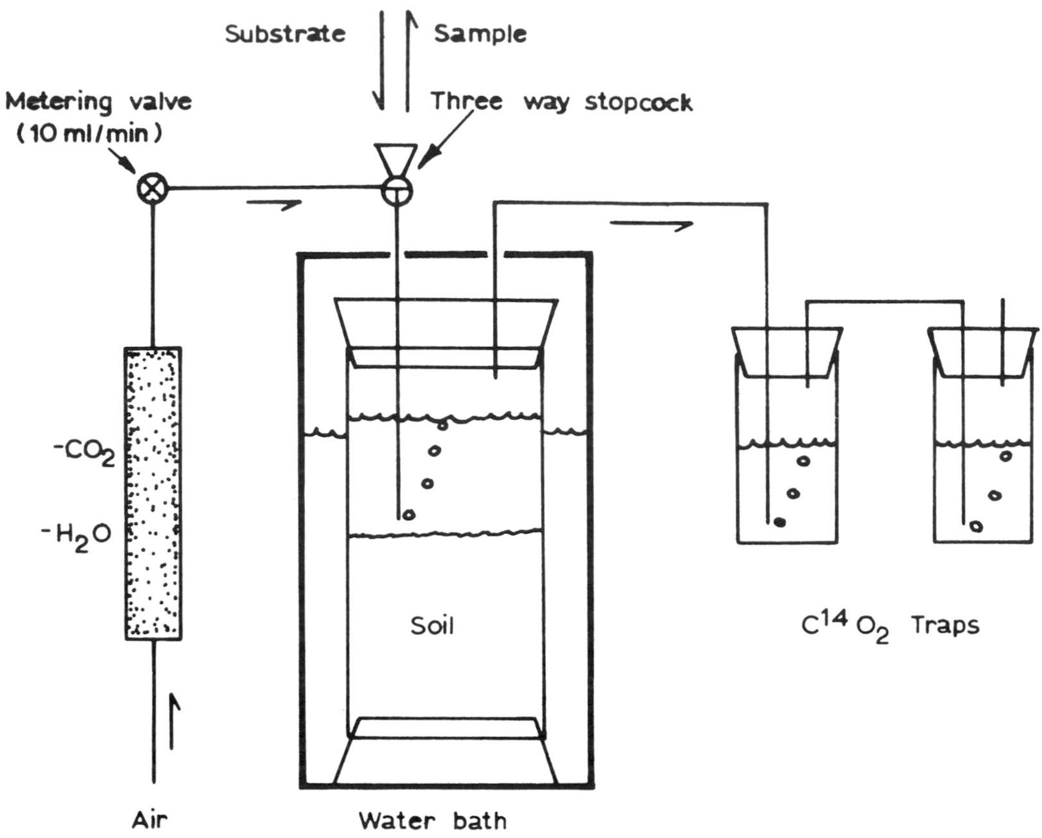

Fig. 2. Diagram of apparatus for aerobic heterotrophy experiments.

and CO_2 traps replaced at half-hour intervals. Removed water samples (1.0 ml) were placed in scintillation vials, stoppered with serum stoppers containing a centerwell and fluted filter paper (Hobbie and Crawford 1969). Concentrated phenethylamine (0.1 ml) was injected into the paper, followed by 0.1 ml of 5N sulfuric acid injected past the centerwell into the sample. All vials were held for 10 to 15 hr with periodic agitation to degas CO_2. Each was then disassembled, with 2.5 ml Triton-X 100 (Packard) scintillation cocktail added to the water sample, and 5.0 ml of the same cocktail combined with the filter paper in another vial.

All samples were counted, internal standard added and recounted. Corrected counts from filters plus CO_2 traps for each time interval represent substrate mineralized. Activity remaining in degassed water samples represents amount of unused substrate. Substrate incorporated in bacterial biomass was calculated by difference. All values were corrected for uptake by control cores (adsorption never greater than 1% of added substrate, with never any detectable mineralization).

Data were analyzed using both first order and Michaelis-Menten kinetics. Typical results for glycine are shown in Figure 3A-C).

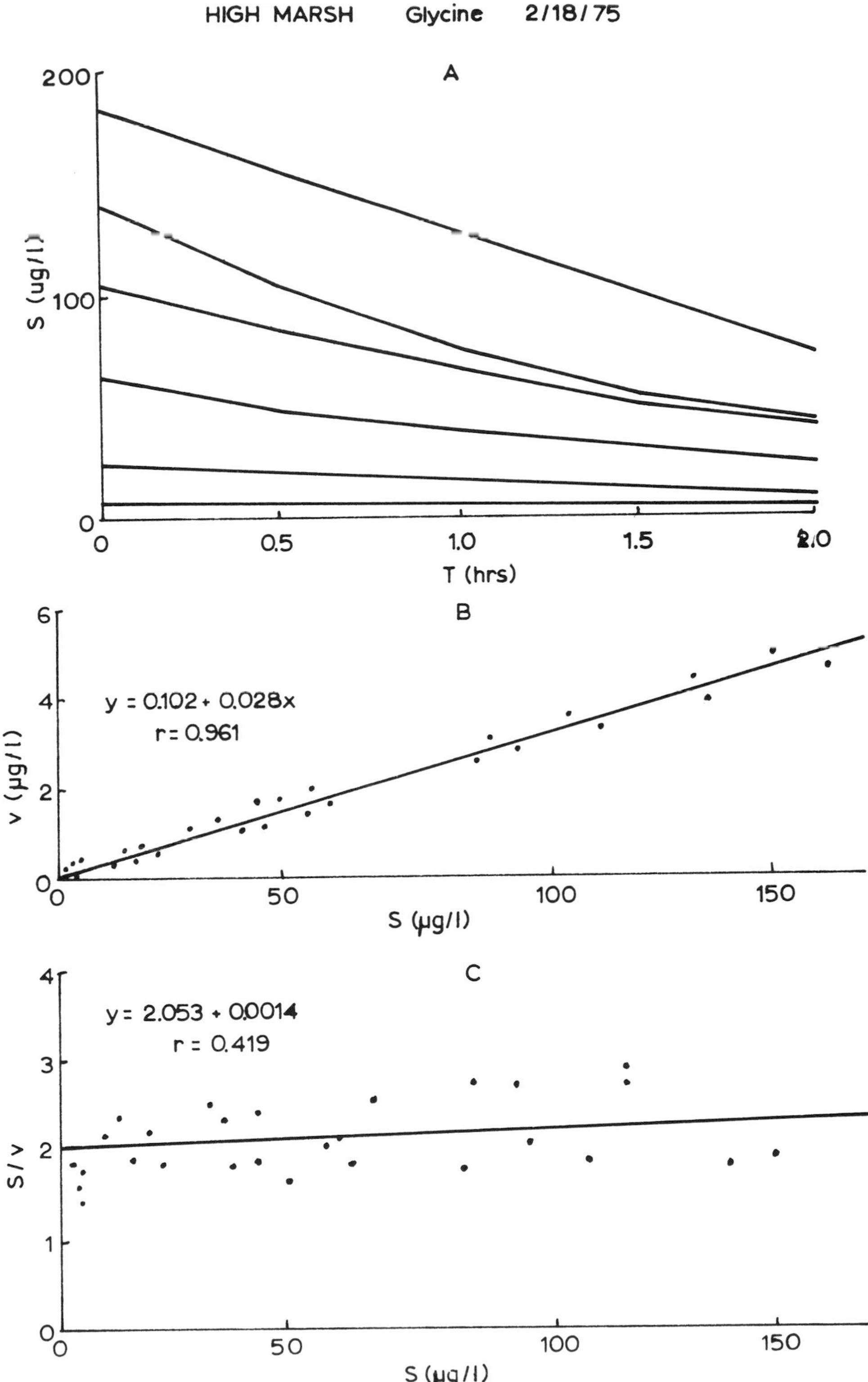

Fig. 3. Activity curves for glycine utilization by high marsh soil (2-18-75). A. time course of utilization, B. velocity of uptake as related to substrate concentration, C. modified Lineweaver-Burk.

Velocities were corrected for changing substrate concentration with time. As can be seen in Figure 3C, the data are not analyzable with Michaelis-Menten kinetics as saturation cannot be achieved at substrate concentrations up to 180 μg x 1^{-1}. Indeed, substrate concentrations up to 500 μg x 1^{-1} fail to provide saturation. A total of forty-three such experiments have been concluded and analyzed to date, with saturation occurring only once. Failure to achieve saturation, also reported by Hall et al. (1972) and Munro and Brock (1968), limits kinetic information to estimates of turnover time and uptake velocity (if natural substrate concentration is known).

Additional valuable information can be derived from these types of experiments, however, such as percent mineralization and gross uptake. From these can be calculated growth yields (Williams 1973b) and turnover times with respect to CO_2. Almost a year's information of this nature is available for glucose utilization by the high-marsh sediment microbial community. No seasonal pattern emerges, but turnover times with respect to substrate range from 1.80 to 9.15 hr. Percent mineralization varies from 9.2 to 36.4, with turnover times with respect to CO_2 of 15.8 to 68.7 hr and growth yields of 52.6 to 91.4%.

We carried out similar radioisotopic analyses *in situ* by containing the substrate over the sediment within a plastic tube used as a dam. Additionally, CO_2 evolution and fate of label incorporated into the sediment microbes can be followed for a longer time without changes or deterioration in the microbial community as seen in cores held in the laboratory.

Our preliminary experiment using glycine as the substrate (30 μg x 1^{-1}) showed uptake velocities and mineralization to be closely similar to those observed in laboratory experiments. $^{14}CO_2$ evolution was followed for a month after labeling using 10-cm diameter bell jars fitted with center wells and fluted filter papers wetted with 0.2 ml phenethylamine. No $^{14}CO_2$ could be detected.

Replicate (n=3) small diameter cores (2.5 cm diameter x 0.5 cm length) were removed from the labeled marsh suface at 1, 2, 7, 10, 17 and 31 days after labeling. Each was dried at 55°C and subsamples were treated as described in the anaerobic studies to determine activity or amount of label associated with the sediment microorganisms. Over 50% of the initially incorporated label was still present after 31 days.

Additional subsamples (~20 mg) of these time series, small-diameter cores were subjected to a preliminary biochemical extraction (Holland and Gabbot 1971, as modified by Wetzel 1975) in which cold methanol/chloroform (equal parts by volume) was used to extract lipids. The water soluble fraction was extracted with distilled water and protein was extracted with boiling 1N sodium hydroxide. Although only about 65% of the total label was extracted by this combined schema, 71% of this was in the lipid fraction, with 18% and 11% in water and hot base fractions, respectively. These results, both $^{14}CO_2$ evolution and extractable label, suggest that substrates (at least glycine) are taken up, rapidly incorporated into cell structural material and are thus removed from any "active" metabolic pool. Obviously, much work has yet to be done.

Anaerobic Studies

Although the aerobic heterotrophy method presented here has been operational for almost a year, the anaerobic heterotrophy method is still largely in its developmental stages. At present we are studying the uptake of glucose during short term experiments. The reason for our choice of glucose as a substrate is twofold. First, glucose represents a major monosaccharide component in the breakdown of plant polysaccharides. Second, the physiology of glucose fermentation is well known and serves as a strong data base. The utilization of this substrate is then followed through three operational pools. The first is the label that is volatilized by acidification and trapped in phenethylamine. Ether soluble labeled compounds represent a second pool. Label remaining associated with particulate matter comprises the third pool. Presumptive interpretations of these pools are CO_2, fermentation and dissimilatory sulfate reduction soluble end products, and "bound" biomass, respectively. In this section we describe the present state of the methods and present representative results.

In order to assay the three pools, existing methods required modification. Three criteria were placed upon each method: (1) it must be rapid in order to handle large numbers of samples; (2) it must require the minimum of equipment in order to be feasible at a field station; and (3) it must be quantitative. Hobbie and Crawford (1969) used fluted filter paper permeated with phenethylamine to trap $^{14}CO_2$. We have adopted their technique using 0.2 ml phenethylamine (Packard) on a 2 x 5 cm strip of Whatman No. 1 paper in a cup suspended from a vaccutainer top. Experiments were terminated by addition of 1 ml 0.225 N H_2SO_4 and 2.5% formalin to a 3cc sample. Phenethylamine was added, and the sample was refrigerated overnight. Refrigeration reduced residual activity and volatization of short chain fatty acids. The filter paper was placed in the toluene-Triton X 100 cocktail and counted.

The particulate fraction radioactivity determination is a modification of the procedure by Cheshire et al. (1972). The sample was centrifuged after the phenethylamine trap was removed, and the supernatant poured off and saved. The pellet was resuspended in 20 ml artificial sea water (ASW) (Lyman and Fleming 1940) and centrifuged. This wash procedure was repeated to remove residual soluble label within the pellet. The pellet was then placed between two 2 x 3 inch glass slides and dried at 55°C. A fine powder was obtained by merely scraping the dried soil off the slides. Five to 15 mg of soil was then placed in a scintillation vial. The weight was noted. Four ml of distilled water was added, and the sample was sonicated for dispersion. Five ml Instagel (Packard) was added and the sample vortexed until the soil was dispersed within a gel. The vial was then counted, internal standard added, vortexed, and recounted. A linear relationship was established between percent efficiency of counting and dry weight added to each vial (Fig. 4). Percent

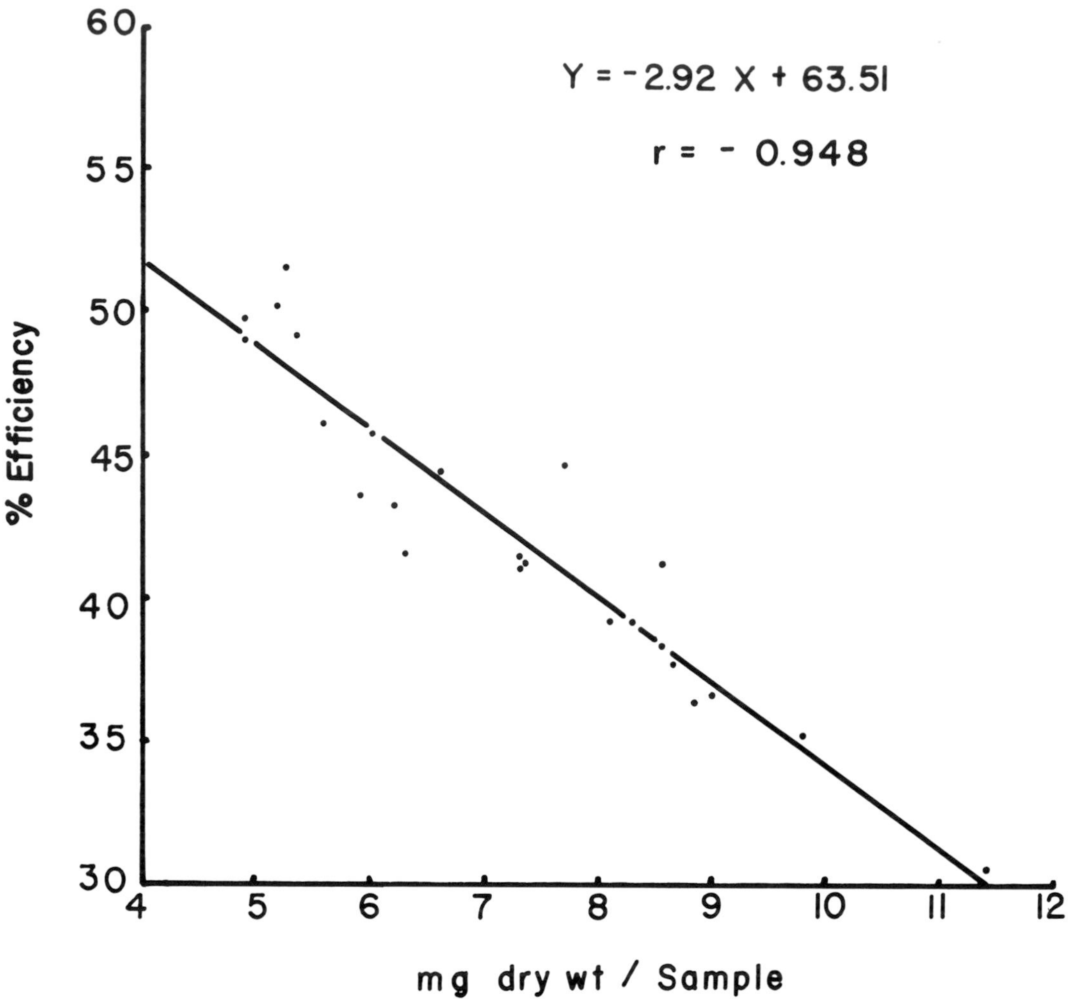

Fig. 4. Counting efficiency of dried soil with respect to the weight added to each scintillation vial.

efficiency for each sample as calculated from the regression line allowed the conversion to dpm ver vial. This was then converted to a dpm per mg soil. By separately determining the dry weight per initial sample, the total radioactivity associated with soil of each sample was known.

Ether has been used to extract fermentation end products for gas chromatographic analysis (Holdeman and Moore 1972). Two ml acidified culture medium was placed in 1 ml ethyl ether and shaken for 10 min. This procedure allowed for qualitative and semiquantitative results. In order to obtain quantitative results for radioisotopic analysis, 1 ml aqueous supernatant was added to 5 ml ether and vortexed for 30 sec. The aqueous phase was transferred to another 5 ml ether, and the process was repeated for a total of three extractions. The radioactivity of aliquots of the aqueous phase before and after extraction was determined. Water is slightly soluble in ether, but glucose is not. Therefore, the activity of an acidified glucose solution was assayed before and after extraction. A correction factor was obtained for the loss of water (increase in glucose activity) during extraction. This factor was used to correct "after extraction" radioactivity and generally ranges between 1.1 and 1.2. The difference between the before and corrected extraction results represented the amount extracted. The percent extraction efficiencies of several fermentation end products are shown in Table 1. All but lactate were extracted at greater than 95% efficiency.

Table 1. Ether extraction efficiency of selected fermentation end products.

Compound (ng x cc^{-1})	Acetate (152)	Formate (122)	Propionate (866)	Butyrate (440)	Lactate (800)
% extraction efficiency-					
mean	96.6	95.0	99.5	99.8	71.7
range	96.3-97.1	94.5-95.5	99.4-99.7	----*	69.0-72.4

*Four replicates produced the same percent efficiency.

Figure 5 shows the schema for a single treatment (incubation time or concentration of added substrate). Great care must be taken to maintain anaerobiosis. One cc sediment was diluted with ASW (adjusted to salinity required). Acid formalin was added to one tube. All were capped, flushed with helium, and vortexed. Samples were preincubated at the prescribed temperature for 30 min. One ml labeled substrate was added. The sample was again vortexed and incubated for a previously determined incubation time (see Harrison et al. 1971). Experimental samples were terminated with acid formalin. Then volatilized, ether soluble, and particulate fractions were assayed as described.

An example of results we have obtained is shown in Table 2. Concentrations of 22 to 457 ng glucose x cc^{-1} were added to high marsh soil, and the samples were incubated for 20 min at 18°C. Most of the label was found in the ether soluble fraction and least in the volatile fraction. The particulate label represents the "bound label" (Griffiths et al. 1974). Little or no label was found to be released by our termination treatment (Christian unpublished data).

The turnover times for each fraction are also presented in Table 2. These were calculated assuming both first order and mixed order kinetics. The reason for using both approaches is the lack of a significant slope from zero for the volatile and particulate fractions. As might be expected, no significant differences at the 0.05 level were found between the turnover times computed by either

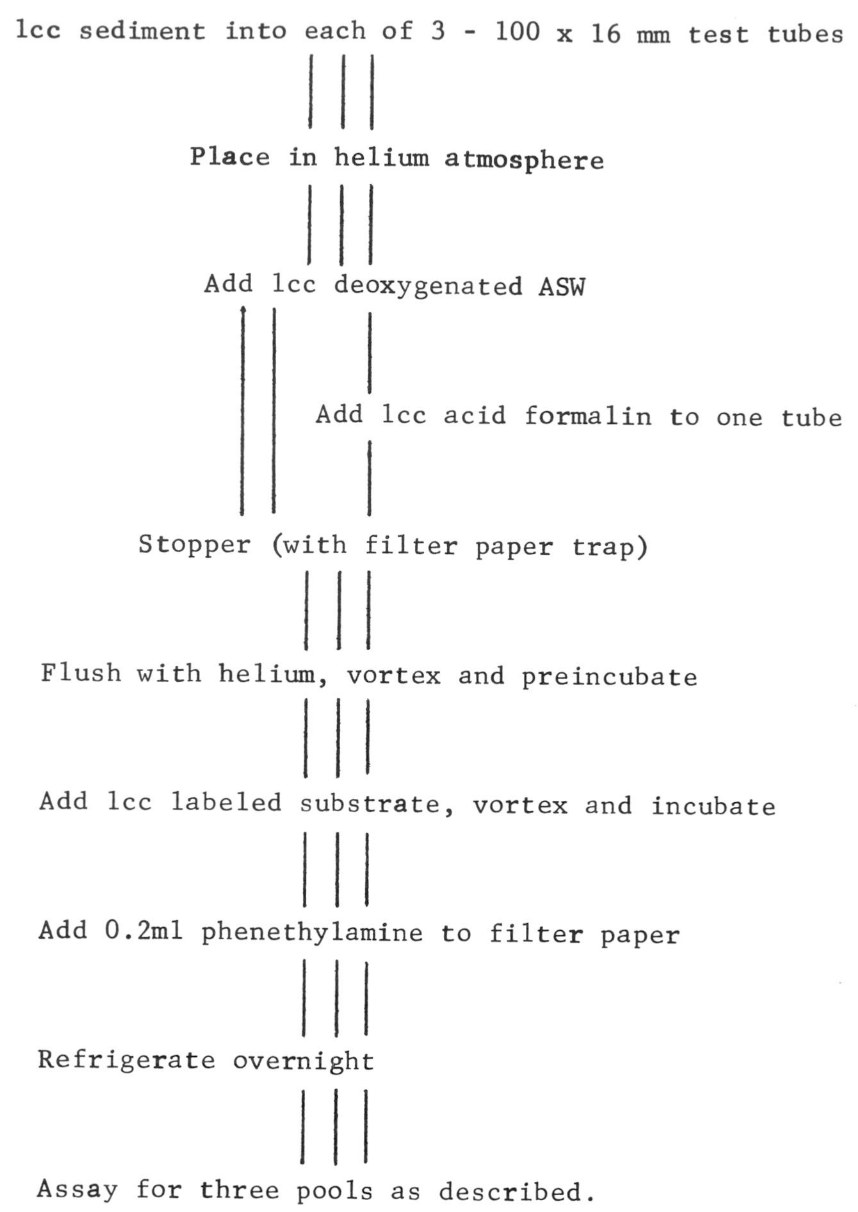

Fig. 5. Schema for single treatment of glucose utilization by and anaerobic mud slurry.

method. The close relationship between the kinetic approaches would indicate a large K. In fact, the volatile and particulate fractions had K+S values greater than 2000 ng x cc^{-1} based on the 22 to 457 ng glucose x cc^{-1} range. However, results at concentrations above 457 ng x cc^{-1} were uninterpretable with respect to Michaelis-Menten kinetics.

Table 2. Anaerobic utilization of glucose in high marsh soil from a depth of 1-5 cm (4-3-75). Samples were incubated at 18°C with 22 to 457 ng glucose x cc^{-1}.

	Volatile	Ether	Particulate	Combined
% distribution				
mean	4.7	72.5	22.6	
range	3.3 - 6.0	64.3 - 79.4	16.6 - 28.7	
First order T_t mean ± S.E.	92.6 ± 5.4	6.5 ± 1.3	19.8 ± 1.9	4.5 ± 0.7
Lineweaver-Burk T_t mean ± S.E.	84.9 ± 8.0	4.9 ± 1.3	18.2 ± 3.5	3.6 ± 0.6
r	0.69	0.83	0.42	0.87
n	6	5	6	5
t	1.91	2.55*	0.92	3.13*

*Indicates significant slope from zero at 0.1 level.

FUTURE DIRECTIONS

We believe that the full potential of radioisotopic analysis in sedimentary microbial ecology has not been realized. We therefore offer some suggestions on future directions. We have preliminary data on some of the following approaches, and others remain in the realm of proposed research.

Using radiorespirometry and compounds with specifically labeled carbon atoms Mayaudon (1971) has begun to unravel major biochemical pathways in soil microorganisms (see also Wang et al. 1958). The relative rates of $^{14}CO_2$ mineralization with respect to glucose labeled in varying positions provide information on whether the Embden-Meyerhof or phosphopentose shunt is operative. For example, instead of using solely uniformly labeled glucose in the apparatus previously described for aerobic heterotrophy, we also used glucose-1-^{14}C and glucose-3,4-^{14}C. Results from a preliminary experiment suggest that the Embden-Meyerhof pathway dominates in the aerobic microorganisms, but the phosphopentose shunt is also operative.

Soluble fermentation end products may act as a source of carbon for the surface aerobic microorganisms and represent a link between the two zones. It has been hypothesized that the surface community is fed as a continuous culture by the organic end products of fermentation and methanogenesis (Wiebe personal communication). Here, there, are two approaches to studying the linkage problem. The ether soluble fraction of the anaerobic experiments previously described may be re-extracted into aqueous solution by a KOH extraction. This can then be neutralized and added to intact cores as previously described. Alternately, such an aqueous solution could be perfused from beneath a thin layer of surface sediment.

Unlike the case for aerobic heterotrophs, inorganic nutrients directly affect the dissimilatory processes for certain anaerobic heterotrophs. Dissimilatory sulfate reducers and dissimilatory nitrogenous oxide reducers require $SO_4^=$ and oxided nitrogen species (e.g. NO_3^- and NO_2^-) respectively as electron acceptors. These nutrients may be limiting within the anaerobic zones of the sediments, and such limitations can be examined via radioisotopic analysis. A preliminary study has been performed to discern the effects of $SO_4^=$ limitation (Christian unpublished data). The addition of $SO_4^=$ to the sediments stimulated the production of $^{14}CO_2$ at the expense of the ether soluble fraction when ^{14}C-glucose utilization was followed. This result may indicate a linkage between the microorganisms capable of utilizing glucose with the dissimilatory sulfate reducers which utilize smaller organic compounds such as lactate. Further research is obviously needed to fully understand this linkage.

Additional aspects of anaerobic metabolism may be studied by radioisotope analysis. We are investigating three pool fractions but others could also be assayed. Some fermentation end products can best be extracted in chloroform as methyl derivatives (Holdeman and Moore 1972). This procedure could be adapted as was the ether extraction. Amino acid separation techniques that are available may also be applicable to this type of work.

Our discussion thus far has been concerned with the utilization of single substrates. These compounds possess a rapid turnover time compared to more complex substances. Tracer techniques, however, are still amenable to the study of these larger compounds and complexes of various species. Added problems arise in the design and interpretation of such studies. Conover and Francis (1973) have described some of the theoretical problems involved in multi-compartment studies. For example, the preparation of labeled detritus has certain methodological problems. Methods for the labeling of plant material have been developed by various workers (Adams and Angelovic 1973; Wetzel 1975). The distribution of label within the plant material may vary with respect to the length of time of incubation and the period within the growing season at which label is added (Wetzel 1975).

Once labeled plant material is available, a variety of experiments can be envisioned. Hanson and Wetzel (personal communication) have followed the evolution of $^{14}CO_2$ from *Spartina alterniflora* detritus by both aerobic and anaerobic sediment slurries. Wetzel (1975) has compared the ingestion and assimilation of labeled detritus, algae, and heterotrophic microorganisms by the gastropod, *Nassarius obsoletus* Say, on the surface of intact cores. The algal and heterotroph labeled cores were prepared in the same manner as described earlier in this paper. It is obvious, then, that the same samples in which one may study the aerobic microbial processes can also be used in subsequent grazing experiments.

As Jannasch and Wirsen (1973) have shown, isotopic techniques can also be adapted for use in the deep sea. Certainly some of the approaches developed for life detection systems by the Viking biology team for the U.S. Martian lander (Klein et al 1972; Horowitz et al. 1972; Levin 1972; Hubbard 1973) could be adapted to the deep sea.

In summary, we believe radioisotopic analysis is an extremely effective tool for the study of sedimentary microbial ecology. In particular, it has established the use of simple enzyme kinetic models. If the assumptions of these models are met, highly useful ecological results may be obtained. The uses of isotopic techniques for studying sediment anaerobic metabolism are just now receiving the attention needed to utilize their potential.

REFERENCES

Adams, S. M. and J. W. Angelovic. 1973. Assimilation of detritus and its associated bacteria by three species of estuarine animals. Chesapeake Sci. 11: 249-254.

Alexander, M. 1965. Biodegradation problems of molecular recalcitrant and microbial fallibility, pp. 35-80. In W. W. Umbreit [ed.], Advances in applied microbiology. Academic Press.

Brock, T. D. 1966. Principles of microbial ecology. Prentice-Hall.

Burnison, B. K. and R. Y. Morita. 1974. Heterotrophic potential for amino acid uptake in a naturally eutrophic lake. Appl. Microbiol. 27: 488-495.

Cappenberg, Th. E. and R. A. Prins. 1974. Interrelations between sulfate-reducing and methane-producing bacteria in bottom deposits of a fresh-water lake. III. Experiments with ^{14}C-labeled substrates. Antonie van Leewenhoek 40: 457-469.

Cheshire, M. V., H. Shepherd, A. H. Knight, and C. M. Mundie. 1972. Determination of ^{14}C in soil by a gel suspension method. J. Soil Sci. 23: 420-423.

Christian, R. R., K. Bancroft, and W. J. Wiebe. 1975. Destribution of microbial adenosine triphosphate in salt marsh sediments at Sapelo Island, Georgia. Soil Sci. 119: 89-97.

Conover, R. J. and V. Francis. 1973. The use of radioactive isotopes to measure the transfer of materials in aquatic food chains. Mar. Biol. 18: 272-283.

Dale, N. G. 1974. Bacteria in intertidal sediments: factors related to their distribution. Limnol. Oceanogr. 19: 509-518.

Griffiths, R. P., F. J. Hanus, and R. Y. Morita. 1974. The effects of various water-sample treatments on the apparent uptake of glutamic acid by natural marine microbial populations. Can. J. Microbiol. 20: 1261-1266.

Hall, K., P. M. Kleiber, and I. Yesaki. 1972. Heterotrophic uptake of organic solutes by microorganisms in the sediment. Mem. 1st. Ital. Idrobiol., Suppl. 29: 441-471.

Harrison, M. J., R. T. Wright, and R. Y. Morita. 1971. Method for measuring mineralization in lake sediments. Appl. Microbiol. 21: 698-702.

Hobbie, J. E. and R. T. Wright. 1965. Bioassay with bacterial uptake kinetics: glucose in freshwater. Limnol. Oceanogr. 10: 471-474.

_____ and C. C. Crawford. 1969. Respiration corrections for bacterial uptake of dissolved organic compounds in natural waters. Limnol. Oceanogr. 14: 528-532.

_____, _____, and K. L. Webb. 1968. Amino acid flux in an estuary. Science 159: 1463-1464.

Holdeman, L. V. and W. E. C. Moore. 1972. Anaerobe laboratory manual. Virginia Polytechnic Institute and State University Anaerobe Laboratory, Blacksburg, Virginia.

Holland, D. L. and P. A. Gabbott. 1971. A micro-analytical scheme for the determination of protein, carbohydrate, lipid and RNA levels in marine invertebrate larvae. J. Mar. Biol. Assoc. U.K. 51: 649-668.

Horowitz, N. H., J. S. Hubbard, and G. L. Hobby. 1972. The carbon-assimilation experiment: the Viking Mars lander. Icarus 16: 147-152.

Hubbard, J. S. 1973. Radiorespirometric methods in measurement of metabolic activities in soil. Bull. Ecol. Res. Comm. (Stockholm) 17: 199-206.

Jannasch, H. W. and C. O. Wirsen. 1973. Deep-sea microorganisms: *in situ* response to nutrient enrichment. Science 180: 641-643.

Jenkinson, D. S. 1971. Studies on the decomposition of C^{14} labeled organic matter in soil. Soil Sci. 11: 64-70.

Jones, W. J. and M. J. B. Paynter. 1975. Populations of methanogenic organisms in salt marsh and creek sediments. (Abstr.) Am. Soc. Microbiol. 75th Annu. Meeting.

Jørgensen, B. B. and T. Fenchel. 1974. The sulfur cycle of a marine sediment model system. Mar. Biol. 24: 189-201.

Kadota, H., Y. Hata, and H. Miyoshi. 1966. A new method for estimating the mineralization activity of lake water and sediment. Mem. Res. Inst. Food Sci., Kyota Univ. 27: 28-30.

Klein, H. P., J. Lederberg, and A. Rich. 1972. Biological experiments: the Viking Mars lander. Icarus 16: 139-145.

Levin, G. V. 1972. Detection of metabolically produced labeled gas: the Viking Mars lander. Icarus 16: 153-166.

Lyman, J. and R. H. Fleming. 1940. Composition of sea water. J. Mar. Res. 3: 134-146.

Mahler, H. R. and E. H. Cordes. 1966. Biological chemistry. Harper and Row.

Mayaudon, J. 1971. Use of radiorespirometry in soil microbiology and biochemistry, pp. 202-256. *In* A. D. McLaren and J. Skujiņš [ed.], Soil biochemistry. Marcel Dekker, Inc.

Molongoski, J. J. and M. J. Klug. 1975. The metabolism of organic compounds in freshwater lake sediments by *Clostridium* species. (Abstr.) Am. Soc. Microbiol. 75th Annu. Meeting.

Munro, A. L. S. and T. D. Brock. 1968. Distinction between bacterial and algal utilization of soluble substances in the sea. J. Gen. Microbiol. 51: 35-42.

Parsons, T. R. and J. D. H. Strickland. 1962. On the production of particulate organic carbon by heterotrophic processes in sea water. Deep-Sea Res. 8: 211-222.

Payne, W. J. 1973. The use of gas chromatography for studies of dentrification in ecosystems. Bull. Ecol. Res. Comm. (Stockholm) 17: 263-268.

Pomeroy, L. R. 1971. The strategy of mineral cycling, pp. 171-190. In R. F. Johnson, P. W. Frank, and C. D. Michener [eds.], Annual review of ecology and systematics, v. 1. Annual Reviews Inc.

______. 1974. The ocean's food web, a changing paradigm. Bioscience 24: 499-504.

Radmer, R. and B. Kok. 1974. A unified procedure for the detection of life on Mars. Science 174: 233-239.

Smith, K. L. 1973. Respiration of a sublittoral community. Ecology 54: 1065-1075.

______, K. A. Burns, and J. M. Teal. 1972. In situ respiration of benthic communities in Castle Harbor, Bermuda. Mar. Biol. 12: 196-199.

Sorokin, Yu. I. 1962. Experimental investigation of bacterial sulfate reduction in the Black Sea using ^{35}S. Mikrobiologiya 31: 402-410. [Transl. Microbiology 31: 329-335.]

Vaccaro, R. F. 1969. The response of natural microbial populations in seawater to organic enrichment. Limnol. Oceanogr. 14: 726-735.

______ and H. W. Jannasch. 1966. Studies on heterotrophic activity in seawater based on glucose assimilation. Limnol. Oceanogr. 11: 596-607.

Wang, C. H., I. Stern, C. M. Gilmour, S. Klungsoyr, D. J. Reed, J. J. Bialy, B. E. Christensen, and V. H. Cheldelin. 1958. Comparative study of glucose catabolism by the radiorespirometric method. J. Bact. 76: 207-216.

Wetzel, R. L. 1975. An experimental-radiotracer study of detrital carbon utilization in a Georgia salt marsh. Ph.D. Thesis, Univ. Georgia, Athens. 103 p.

Wiebe, W. J. and J. Liston. 1972. Studies of the aerobic, nonexacting, heterotrophic bacteria of the benthos, pp. 281-312. In A. T. Pruter and D. L. Alverson [eds.], The Columbia River estuary and adjacent ocean waters: bioenvironmental studies. Univ. Washington Press.

Williams, P. J. leB. 1973a. The validity of the application of simple kinetic analysis to heterogeneous microbial populations. Limnol. Oceanogr. 18: 159-165.

_____. 1973*b*. On the question of growth yields of natural heterotrophic populations. Bull. Ecol. Res. Comm. (Stockholm) 17: 400-401.

_____ and C. Askew. 1968. A method of measuring the mineralization by micro-organisms of organic compounds in sea-water. Deep-Sea Res. 15: 365-375.

Wirsen, C. O. and H. W. Jannasch. 1974. Microbial transformations of some ^{14}C-labeled substrates in coastal water and sediment. Microbial Ecol. 1: 25-37.

Woeller, F. H. 1962. Liquid scintillation counting of $^{14}CO_2$ with phenethylamine. Anal. Biochem. 2: 508-511.

Wood, L. W. 1970. The role of estuarine sediment microorganisms in the uptake of organic solutes under aerobic conditions. Ph.D. Thesis, North Carolina State Univ.

_____ and K. E. Chua. 1973. Glucose flux at the sediment-water interface of Toronto Harbor, Lake Ontario, with reference to pollution stress. Can J. Microbiol. 19: 413-420.

Wright, R. T. 1973. Some difficulties in using ^{14}C-organic solutes to measure heterotrophic bacterial activity, pp. 199-217. *In* L. H. Stevenson and R. R. Colwell [eds.], Estuarine microbial ecology. Univ. South Carolina Press.

_____ and J. E. Hobbie. 1965. The uptake of organic solutes in lake water. Limnol. Oceanogr. 10: 22-28.

_____ and _____. 1966. Use of glucose and acetate by bacteria and algae in aquatic ecosystems. Ecology 47: 447-464.

Zeuthen, E. 1947. Body size and metabolic rate in the animal kingdom with special regard to the marine micro-fauna. C. R. Lab. Carlsberg, Ser. Chim. 26: 17-161.

Benthic Community Metabolism: A Review and Assessment of Present Status and Outlook

Mario M. Pamatmat
Department of Fisheries and Allied Aquacultures
Agricultural Experiment Station
Auburn University
Auburn, AL 36830

ABSTRACT

Benthic community metabolism has been commonly measured in terms of oxygen uptake by the sediment surface with different *in situ*, laboratory, and shipboard techniques. These measurements have given us knowledge of technical problems, the rate of oxygen uptake in nature, and various factors that govern rates of benthic oxygen consumption. Some basic problems, e.g., the accuracy of partitioning total oxygen uptake into aerobic respiration and chemical oxidation by poisoning, especially with formaldehyde, need to be studied further. Whether laboratory measurement of core respiration accurately estimates *in situ* rate is still questioned.

Annual oxygen uptake by the sediment surface may represent the metabolic activity of organisms responsible for the oxidation of current organic matter deposits. It does not represent total benthic community metabolism because it does not include anaerobic activity in deeper layers. A single holistic method for measuring soft-bottom community metabolism has not been developed. Community anaerobic metabolism has been estimated as rate of reduction of 2,3,5-triphenyltetrazolium chloride (TTC) but more research is needed to establish the quantitative relationship between TTC reduction and metabolic rate in various species and metabolic types.

Benthic community metabolism has been related to organic matter sedimentation and energy flow through the entire ecosystem; the relationship will vary according to the erosional or depositional character of the area.

Benthic community metabolism is inferred to be a sensitive and useful parameter for assessing environmental perturbation, but profiles of metabolic activity in the sediment column would be even more useful than single measures of total community metabolism.

REVIEW

The structure of benthic communities is complex and still superficially understood in terms of species composition, species diversity, distribution of biomass and numbers among species, size groups, or feeding types, etc. The static view of community structure has been supplemented though only partially, by energy flow studies which postulate dynamic relationships within the community. Benthic population energetics has been widely studied; however, the number of species involved, plus the technical difficulty of dealing with individual populations of microorganisms and meiofauna, prevent an all-inclusive analysis of community energetics at present.

Bornebusch (1930), a soil ecologist, early saw the need for a holistic approach to the study of animal communities. Confronted by species diversity, large numbers of small, active organisms and smaller numbers of larger, less active organisms, various life habits, and complex interactions between biotic activities and physical and biochemical processes, he nonetheless tried to calculate oxygen uptake of Metazoa per square meter per hour in different forest soils to obtain a comparable measure of "intensity of animal life." He thus noted for the first time that tiny animals are metabolically more important in a community than their small biomass alone might indicate. He also recognized the significance of estimating annual respiration per square meter for the purpose of assessing the soil fauna's degradation of annual litter fall. Thamdrup (1935) applied a similar approach to the study of a benthic community.

Hoppe-Seyler (1896), according to Hutchinson (1957), initiated an important aspect of modern limnology, i.e., the study of community metabolism, by suggesting that the evidence of oxygen uptake in deep water of Lake Constance is a reasonable measure of biological activity in the water and Birge (1906) clearly recognized that the disappearance of dissolved oxygen in lake hypolimnion is due to both the respiration of organisms in the mud and in the water column. Later Alsterberg (1922) suggested that oxygen uptake by mud surface was the major cause of oxygen loss in the hypolimnion, while Lonnerblad (1930) showed that some sediments had purely chemical oxygen uptake and others showed biological consumption which could be abolished by heat, ether, or heavy metals.

In 1941 Fair et al. had the same concepts and perceptions of the problems related to benthic community metabolism as we have now. They, and Allgeier et al. (1932) before them, recognized the importance of anaerobic metabolism and measured it in terms of gas production. They also studied reduced products of anaerobic metabolism, both subsequent diffusion out of the sediment and mass vertical transport as deposits compacted and squeezed out interstitial water. They observed that sub-surface deposit feeders defecate on the sediment surface and that gas bubbling out of the sediment disturbs the surface. These problems still require investigation.

Subsequently, Grote (1934) formulated from theoretical considerations the relationship between rate of oxygen uptake, molecular diffusion coefficient for oxygen in mud, oxygen concentration at the mud surface, and the gradient of oxygen in the mud surface. In accord with Grote's hypothesis, Mortimer (1942) found in English lakes an inverse relationship between summer oxygen absorption rate by the mud and the thickness of the oxidized surface mud layer. More recently, Bouldin (1968), Howeler and Bouldin (1971), and Howeler (1972) have applied mathematical modeling to oxygen diffusion into sediments and oxygen uptake.

Benthic community respiration in Lake Windermere was estimated from hypolimnetic oxygen deficit by Mortimer (1942) on the assumption that the mud and associated organisms were the predominant consumers of oxygen. In Lake Esrom, Hargrave (1972*a*) found that oxygen uptake by sediment cores accounted fully for hypolimnetic oxygen decline during both winter and summer periods of stratification. On the other hand, using metabolic carbon dioxide anomaly in Linsley Pond, Hutchinson (1941) estimated that pelometabolism (= benthic community metabolism) was only one-fourth of total metabolism in the hypolimnion. Uncertainties in partitioning hypolimnetic oxygen deficit between pelometabolism and hydrometabolism arise from insufficient knowledge of vertical turbulence, inaccuracy of laboratory measurements of respiration at the mud surface, and unknown profile of metabolism in the overlying water column (Lund et al. 1963). Hutchinson (1941) also recognized the effects of horizontal currents on the mud surface in stratified lakes.

Significant progress has been made in the last two decades in measuring benthic community metabolism with a conscious effort to estimate metabolic rates under various natural conditions. New techniques have made these measurements possible. On one hand, membrane-covered oxygen electrodes facilitated continuous *in situ* measurements of oxygen uptake regardless of depth. Furthermore, technological developments in SCUBA diving, deep-sea submersibles, electronics, and general oceanographic instrumentation have contributed to advanced research in benthic community metabolism.

Benthic community metabolism has been measured primarily in terms of oxygen consumption, *in situ* or in the laboratory. Carbon dioxide liberation was studied by gasometric methods (Pomeroy 1959; Teal and Kanwisher 1961; Pamatmat 1968). The metabolic interpretation of carbon dioxide changes in water may involve the entire carbonate system (Smith and Key 1975), making it much more complicated than oxygen changes.

Various *in situ* oxygen techniques include the use of (1) bell jar or glass cylinder enclosing unstirred water (Odum 1957; Teal 1957; Pomeroy 1959; Pamatmat 1968; Rybak 1969), (2) bell jar equipped with oxygen electrode and stirrer and monitored aboard ship (Pamatmat and Fenton 1968; Pamatmat and Banse 1969), (3) bell jar, plastic dome, or annular chamber equipped with electrode, stirrer or pump, with or without self-contained recorder, and emplaced by divers (Stein and Denison 1966; Smith et al. 1972, 1973, 1974; Edberg and Hofsten 1973; Wells 1974; Davies 1975, (4) flow-through box or tunnel (Pamatmat 1965; James 1974), (5) bell-jar system placed on the bottom by manipulation from inside a submarine (Smith and Teal 1973), (6) bell-jar system placed by remotely controlled underwater vehicle and manipulator (Smith 1974), (7) bell-jar system allowed to free-fall to the bottom (Smith et al. 1976). Oxygen uptake has also been measured inside Plexiglas boxes _in situ_ in conjunction with measurements of pH, Eh, Es, etc. and experimentally elevated temperature in order to study interrelated dynamics of sediment-water exchange (Schippel et al. 1973). Concerning the accuracy of estimating _in situ_ rates, questions are still raised about _in situ_ versus laboratory measurements (Edberg and Hofsten 1973), stirring versus no stirring (Rybak 1969), flow-through versus stirred enclosures (James 1974). Rybak (1969) pointed out the importance of simulating the natural turbulence of the bottom water as this determines the supply of oxygen to the sediment surface and thus favored the use of "gradient" tubes for stratified lakes. He presumed, however, that diffusivity inside undisturbed tubes is the same as in the hypolimnion, which is rather doubtful.

Laboratory samples were usually sediment cores (Hayes and MacAulay 1959; Teal and Kanwisher 1961; Duff and Teal 1965; Edwards and Rolley 1965; Carey 1967; Rybak 1969; Hargrave 1969_a_, 1972_a_, _b_; Johnson and Brinkhurst 1971; Smith 1973; Gallagher and Daiber 1974). Hayes and MacAulay (1959) and many sanitary engineers experimented with resettled sediments in the laboratory, but Stein and Denison (1966) showed the error of overestimation which results from this procedure. Oxygen uptake of sediment cores has been measured aboard ship (Pamatmat 1971_a_, _b_, 1973; Pamatmat and Bhagwat 1973); if taken carefully, the oxygen uptake of sediment cores at _in situ_ temperature is the same as rates measured _in situ_, at least to 23-m depth, and probably to 180 m (Pamatmat 1971_a_, _b_).

Contrary to the findings of Pamatamat (1971_a_, _b_) and Davies (1975), James (1974) and Edberg and Hofsten (1973) found that sediment cores tend to respire less than sediments enclosed _in situ_. Edberg and Hofsten attributed this discrepancy to disturbance of sediment structure and biological activity. Another explanation might be that the very long water column overlying the sediment surface of their cores, compared to that in the bell jars, was not homogeneously mixed; stratification could have resulted in apparently low oxygen uptake. The data of James (1974) do not seem to warrant the conclusion that core respiration underestimates _in situ_ rates. In the absence of evidence to the contrary, sediment cores will probably still be used for estimating oxygen uptake of soft sediment. Other techniques that provide vigorous mixing similar to natural conditions should be considered in turbulent environments and benthic communities with very high rates of uptake.

Published measurements have given us knowledge of the range of oxygen uptake in nature: 0.02 ml O_2 $m^{-2}hr^{-1}$ at 5,200 mm in the North Atlantic (Smith et al. 1976), 0.50 at 1,850 m (Smith and Teal 1973), respiratory uptake ranging from 0 at 3,145 to 5,830 m to 1.5 at 2,510 m (Pamatmat 1973), progressively higher rates in shallower inshore waters and especially in polluted waters (Stein and Denison 1966; Pamatmat et al. 1973; Smith et al. 1974) with values not uncommonly exceeding 100 ml O_2 $m^{-2}hr^{-1}$; these areas include macrovegetation (see Pamatmat 1968). Salt marsh mud in summer, at 20 to 25°C, has shown the highest rates of uptake (190 ml O_2 $m^{-2}hr^{-1}$) for bare soft sediment (Duff and Teal 1965).

Rates of oxygen consumption have been shown, or thought, to be related to pH (Hayes 1964), temperature (Duff and Teal 1965; Pamatmat 1968; Hargrave 1969a, b; Edberg and Hofsten 1973; Gallagher and Daiber 1974), tidal cycle (Pamatmat 1968), diel cycle (Hargrave 1969a; Hunding 1973), season (Teal 1957; Edwards and Rolley 1965; Pamatmat 1968; Pamatmat and Banse 1969; Rybak 1969; Pamatmat 1971b; Gallagher and Daiber 1974; Davies 1975), primary productivity of phytobenthos (Pamatmat 1968; Hargrave 1969a; Hunding 1973), primary productivity of phytoplankton (Hargrave 1973; Davies 1975), dissolved oxygen (Edwards and Rolley 1965; Hargrave 1969a; Pamatmat 1971a,1973; Edberg and Hofsten 1973), organic pollution (Stein and Denison 1966; Smith et al. 1973, 1974; Pamatmat et al. 1973), organic matter content of sediments (Rybak 1969), bacterial count (Hayes and MacAulay 1959), a "quality index" purporting to describe basic productivity (Hayes and MacAulay 1959), irrigational effects of macrofauna (Edwards and Rolley 1965). On the other hand, rates of oxygen uptake could not be related to oxygen concentration of bottom water, mean sediment grain size, silt-and-clay fraction, organic matter or organic nitrogen content of sediment (Pamatmat and Banse 1969), organic matter content (Edberg and Hofsten 1973), organic carbon content, chemical oxidizability, dehydrogenase activity, or bacterial populations (Edwards and Rolley 1965). Martin and Bella (1971) found benthic oxygen consumption to be independent of oxygen concentration and primarily affected by rate of diffusion from the sediment of oxidizable reduced substances. Below the photic zone, season, primary productivity, and depth are probably related to benthic oxygen consumption through their influence on the flux of fresh, oxidizable organic matter to the bottom; this flux may be considered the primary influence on benthic metabolic activity.

Depth, or pressure, by itself appears to be negligible, at least to 180 m (Pamatmat 1971a) and the low rates of uptake in the deep sea are probably related to the lesser oxidizability of the small amount of organic matter that reaches the seabed (Pamatmat 1973). Jannasch et al. (1971), Jannasch and Wirsen (1973), and Wirsen and Jannasch (1974) found hydrostatic pressure inhibited metabolism, but the existence in the deep sea of barophilic, psychrophilic bacteria that can metabolize *in situ* at the same rate as shallow-water microbes if provided with appropriate substrate has likewise been shown (Seki et al. 1974). Preliminary investigation of the relationship between benthic oxygen consumption and nutrient regeneration has been conducted in the laboratory (Pamatmat et al. 1973) and in the field (Hale 1974; Hartwig 1974; Davies 1975; Rowe et al. 1975). Salinity changes have been shown to affect the rate of oxidation of organic matter (Baity 1938). Turbulence and water currents of sufficient velocity to erode surface sediment enhance the rate of oxygen uptake (Edwards and Rolley 1965; Carey 1967; Pamatmat 1971a, b; Davies 1975); otherwise, rate of uptake appears to be independent of stirring rate unless an oxygen-deficient boundary layer develops at the sediment-water interface.

Effects of antibiotic treatment (Hargrave 1969a; Smith et al. 1972; Smith 1973) and calculations of macrofaunal respiration from standing stock estimates (Teal 1957; Wieser and Kanwisher 1961; Edwards and Rolley 1965; Carey 1967; Pamatmat 1968; Hargrave 1969a; Smith 1973; Smith et al. 1972; Davies 1975) in comparison with community oxygen uptake have indicated how evergy might be partitioned among the members of the benthic community. Commonly used antibiotics, however, will not delineate bacterial respiration from the respiration of the respiration of the rest of the community (Yetka and Wiebe 1974).

These measurements may be useful in determining the effects of organic and waste pollution (Pamatmat et al. 1973). Unfortunately, some measurements have been misinterpreted. For example, a dynamic relationship (Teal and Kanwisher 1961) does not exist between anaerobic metabolism, formation of reduced metabolic products, and their subsequent oxidation as chemical oxygen uptake by the sediment surface. On one hand, Baity (1938) noted that oxygen did not diffuse below 1-cm depth in sludge deposits; the increase in oxygen uptake was not proportional to the thickness of deposit but related to it according to the equation, $Y = 270\ X^{0.485}$ where X is depth in cm and Y is mg $O_2\ m^{-2}hr^{-1}$. Baity saw that aerobic decomposition is primarily a surface phenomenon and any increase in oxygen uptake with increasing sediment thickness was due to gas formation which disturbed the sediment surface. Oxygen uptake has been found to be independent of core length from 2 to 17 cm (Edwards and Rolley 1965; Stein and Denison 1966; Martin and Bella 1971; Fillos and Molof 1972). Therefore, reduced substances below a certain depth, which could vary according to porosity and mixing by infauna, no longer diffuse upward to any significant extent and oxygen becomes used up in the surface layer. In Puget Sound (Pamatmat 1971b) chemical oxygen uptake was correlated with concentration of total reduced substances, but only of the upper 3-cm layer. Total reduced substances increased with depth of sediment layer but their concentration below 3 cm was not reflected by rate of chemical oxidation. In an open sea loch on the other hand, Davies (1975) found that a drop in redox potential in the sediment surface and to the 18-cm layer following sedimentation of phytoplankton indicates that some oxidation is taking place to a depth of 18 cm.

These data, while suggesting an imbalance between formation of reduced substances and chemical uptake at the sediment surface, do not indicate the degree of imbalance at the time of measurement because it is not known how long the pool of reduced substances had been accumulating. Theoretically, anaerobic activity could be estimated on the basis of chemical oxidation if reduced substances were forming only in the surface layer. This hypothesis was tested by direct measurement of anaerobic metabolism: when anaerobic activity was measured through dehydrogenase enzyme assay in Lake Washington (Pamatmat and Bhagwat 1973), active anaerobic metabolism was found to a depth of 31 cm and, when integrated over the sediment column, it was up to 39 times the rate indicated by inorganic chemical oxygen uptake. The enzyme assay involved sediment mixing,which could have produced unnatural results, but the assay was calibrated using results of direct calorimetry on undisturbed sediment; thus the final estimates are believed to be reasonable values. Therefore, wherever anaerobic metabolism occurs in subsurface sediment the oxygen uptake by the sediment surface will underestimate benthic community metabolism.

It should be pointed out that present estimates of benthic oxygen consumption are based on measurements from undisturbed sediments, while in nature sediments are disturbed periodically by tidal currents (Pamatmat 1971b), aperiodically by burrowing organisms (Schäfer 1972; Rhoads 1974), by gas ebullition, or by wind- and wave-generated turbulence, which may be aperiodic as well as seasonal. Increased rates of oxygen uptake resulting from any of these causes are difficult to measure in nature. Davies (1975) tried to take into account the effect of sediment resuspension by integrating two annual curves of oxygen uptake, one based on measurements for undisturbed sediment and another on measurements at higher water flow rates that resuspended sediment inside his annular chamber.

Even if annual oxygen uptake of disturbed sediments could be estimated, it would still underestimate benthic community metabolism for many reasons (see Pamatmat 1975): (a) some by-products of anaerobic metabolism such as N_2 gas and CH_4 are not oxidized by oxygen; (b) lactate and other by-products of fermentation are of the same oxidation state as the original substrate; (c) chemical oxidation of sulfides may result in formation of sulfite, thiosulfate, etc. of lower oxidation state than sulfate (Cline 1968); (d) furthermore, sulfide from sulfate reduction could be tied up in the formation of humus (Nissenbaum and Kaplan 1972), which is extremely refractory. The underestimate caused by all these could be negligibly small, but the expectation of a simple relation between oxygen consumption and benthic community metabolism appears too simplistic in view of the complicated dynamic sequence of oxidation-reduction that takes place in anaerobic sediments (Ponnamperuma 1964). Nevertheless, it will still be useful to obtain empirical relationships between anaerobic metabolism in sediments of different organic and mineral composition and the resulting accumulation of reduced substances (Pamatmat et al. 1973). If a strong correlation could be shown, total reduced substances in the sediment, could be a useful measure of total anaerobic metabolism that has taken place from the time a layer was buried below the level of effective oxygen diffusion (Pamatmat and Bhagwat 1973). In this connection, more work is needed on the rate of upward diffusion of reduced substances from the sediment.

PRESENT STATUS OF RESEARCH

Oxygen Uptake

If total oxygen uptake by the sediment does not represent total metabolism, what does it represent? Consider the profile of metabolic activity in the sediment column (Fig. 1) as determined by

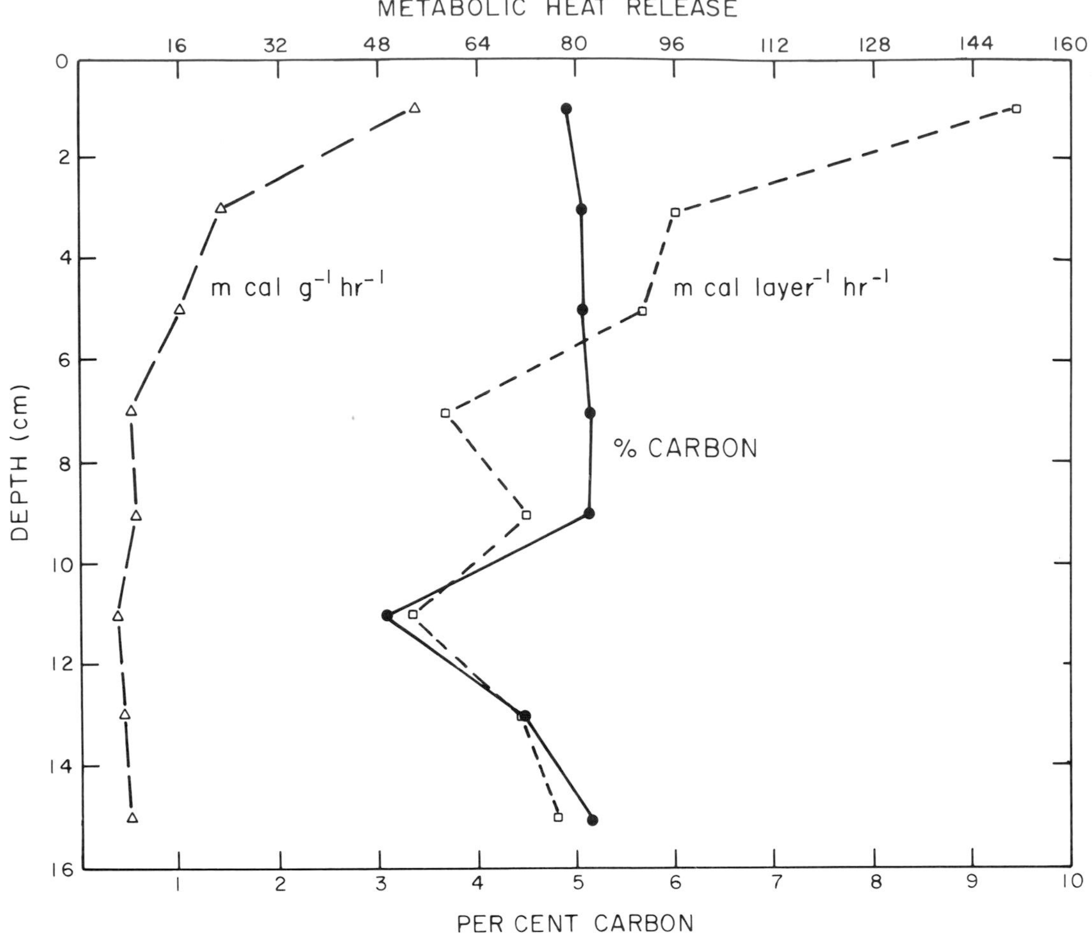

Fig. 1. Profile of metabolic activity in the sediment column at station 19, Lake Washington (see Pamatmat and Bhagwat 1973) determined in the laboratory by dehydrogenase assay and direct calorimetry.

dehydrogenase assay and direct calorimetry. These data are from one station in Lake Washington where five other stations showed differences in metabolic rates between stations and sediment layers (Pamatmat and Bhagwat 1973). There is a general trend of decreasing activity with depth of sediment layer but some deeper layers show higher activity than shallower layers. It is not known how much TTC reduction was by aerobes; true metabolic activity in the surface layer could be much higher than indicated if some aerobes do not respire and reduce TTC in the absence of oxygen. Metabolic rate is clearly not correlated with organic carbon content of the sediment in Lake Washington but high metabolic rates in subsurface layers must be attributed to input of metabolizable organic matter during the year those layers were deposited.

Sedimentation rate in Lake Washington is about 3 mm per year (Stockner and Benson 1967). Vertical mixing of sediment is not appreciable (Kleckner 1967) and undisturbed laminations are still detectable by X-radiography (Edmondson and Allison 1970). Assuming no vertical mixing whatsoever, only the annual metabolic activity in the top 3-mm layer would represent the degradation of organic matter deposited during the year. This metabolic activity seems to be only aerobic. Metabolic activity in deeper layers, therefore, is not related to present-day sedimentation of organic matter and should be related to past sedimentation only.

In relating benthic metabolism to energy flow in the whole ecosystem, it seems most appropriate to use the metabolic activity traceable only to newly sedimented organic matter. In the presence of burrowing macrofauna, however, various degrees of mixing occur in nature. Freshly deposited organic matter is quickly buried and metabolized anaerobically while long-buried organic matter is brought back to the surface and oxidized aerobically. If vertical mixing proceeded at some average steady state, from year to year, the metabolic activity traceable to present annual sedimentation might be estimated from the annual oxygen uptake by the sediment surface. The lack of evidence for such a steady state led Pamatmat and Bhagwat (1973) to suggest the need for information on sedimentation rates and average annual leftover organic matter in the sediment; the difference would equal estimated annual oxygen consumption, possibly excluding chemical oxygen uptake in some cases and including it in others, such as where periodic oxygen depletion in bottom waters occurs.

In an attempt to formulate a general model for sediment oxygen consumption in different bodies of water, Hargrave (1973) found that oxygen uptake correlated positively with phytoplankton production and inversely with mixed-layer depth. His mathematical equation derived from step-wise multiple linear regression analysis describes decreasing fraction of primary production oxidized at the sediment surface (although absolute amount of carbon respired increases) as primary production increases. This result indicates not only that the total plankton respiration becomes increasingly important with increasing primary productivity of the ecosystem but also probably results from increasing rate of burial of unoxidized organic matter; i.e., the total fraction of primary production that settles to the bottom does not decrease as much as the annual fraction which is respired. Thus with increasing primary productivity anaerobic metabolism in the benthic community may increase as much as, or even more than aerobic metabolism does. The equation tends to overestimate measured rates of oxygen uptake beyond the continental shelf (Hargrave 1973; Smith 1974), probably because organic matter falling past the upper water columns is increasingly resistant to biological oxidation. The inhibitory effect of pressure could also be a controlling factor. Before this state of affairs can be clarified, annual sedimentation must be estimated in conjunction with measurements of benthic oxygen consumption, chemical oxidation, and anaerobic metabolism, in addition to plankton respiration and oxidizability of freshly sedimented organic matter.

Chemical Oxygen Uptake

Because chemical oxygen uptake has not received enough attention we do not understand chemical oxygen uptake except that it indicates anaerobic activity in the upper two or three cm of sediments. Chemical uptake is most commonly partitioned from total oxygen uptake by poisoning the water with formaldehyde at final concentrations from 1% (Hargrave 1969a) to 2.5-5% (Pamatmat 1971a), to 10% (Smith 1973), and measuring the residual rate of uptake. While this procedure appears to be routinely practiced, it has by no means been established as a true measure of rate of chemical oxidation. Initial attempts by Teal and Kanwisher (1961) and Pamatmat (1971a) to clarify the relationship between chemical oxidation and respiration need to be pursued further.

Figure 2 (from Pamatmat 1971a) shows that chemical oxidation decreases faster than respiration as oxygen concentration decreases. Since the procedure for partitioning total uptake may involve time effects, it is necessary to show that both total uptake and chemical

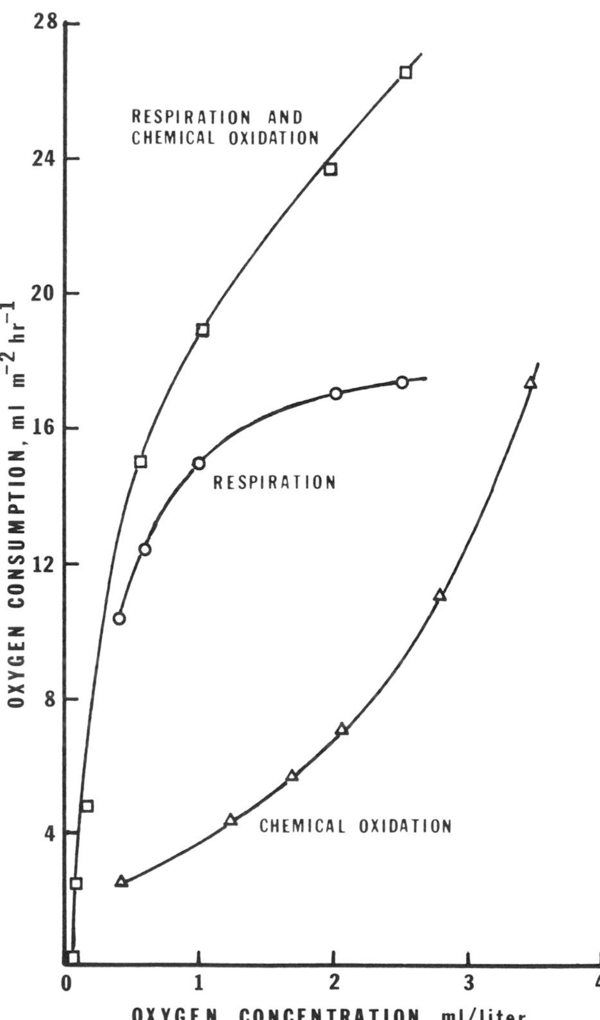

Fig. 2. Rates of total oxygen uptake, inorganic chemical oxidation following formaldehyde treatment, and respiration of a sediment core as functions of oxygen concentration (from Pamatmat 1971a).

uptake are constant during the duration of an experiment. Pamatmat (1971a) showed that total uptake appears to be constant for at least 6 hr but did not show that chemical oxidation was also constant. Thus the decrease in oxygen consumption with decreasing oxygen concentration shown in Figure 2 might have been confounded by the effect of time.

In order to pursue the matter, four replicate cores of coarse, coralline sand, collected by divers from the southern shelf of the Grand Bahama Island at 4.6-m depth, were used in a laboratory experiment at 25°C. During the 36-hr experiment, the water over the cores was flushed several times to replenish dissolved oxygen, and poisoned, as indicated in Figures 3, 4, and 5. All cores showed the same relationship between total uptake and oxygen concentration, but three (Fig. 3, 4), following the first flushing at the end of the first 7-hr run, showed an increased rate of total uptake from ca 60 to 80 ml O_2 $m^{-2}hr^{-1}$ at ca 3.5 ml $liter^{-1}$. This increase may have been due to bacterial growth during incubation, as observed by Edwards and Rolley (1965). Since oxygen concentration dropped close to zero, dissolved organics constituting increased biochemical oxygen demand might have been released into the water (Fillos and Molof 1972). A fourth core (Fig. 5), however, did not show this increase; its initial rate at 3.5 ml O_2 $liter^{-1}$ during the first and second run was about 70 ml O_2 $m^{-2}hr^{-1}$. This core had sand lodged between the bottom stopper and the coring tube; water drained out through the entire core when it was lifted out of the container but did not appear to have flushed out any particulate material. Bacterial growth in the other three cores, if this was indeed the reason for the increase, may have been stimulated by dissolved substances which were lost in the fourth core.

Following the second flushing and addition of formaldehyde, all four cores showed an increased rate of uptake to ca 80-90 ml O_2 $m^{-2}hr^{-1}$, which dropped much more quickly than before. When flushed again, without additional formaldehyde, the rate of uptake increased to about 40-50 ml $m^{-2}hr^{-1}$ as the oxygen concentration was raised to almost 4 ml $liter^{-1}$. At the end of the fourth run, three different treatments were performed: (1) flushing only (Fig. 3), (2) flushing plus additional formaldehyde (Fig. 4), and (3) additional formaldehyde without flushing (Fig. 5). "Flushing only" raised the rate of uptake to the same curve as the previous run. "Flushing plus additional formaldehyde" resulted in increased rate of chemical uptake at the same oxygen concentration as in the previous run. "Additional formaldehyde only" also increased chemical uptake in comparison to the previous run at the same oxygen concentration. The curves for the last run of the latter two treatments, however, appeared to coincide with the extrapolation of the fourth run, to lower oxygen concentrations.

The experiment should have been extended to at least a sixth run after flushing only, without additional formaldehyde, to see if the rate of uptake would again increase and coincide with the curve of the fourth run. It is believed that this result would have been

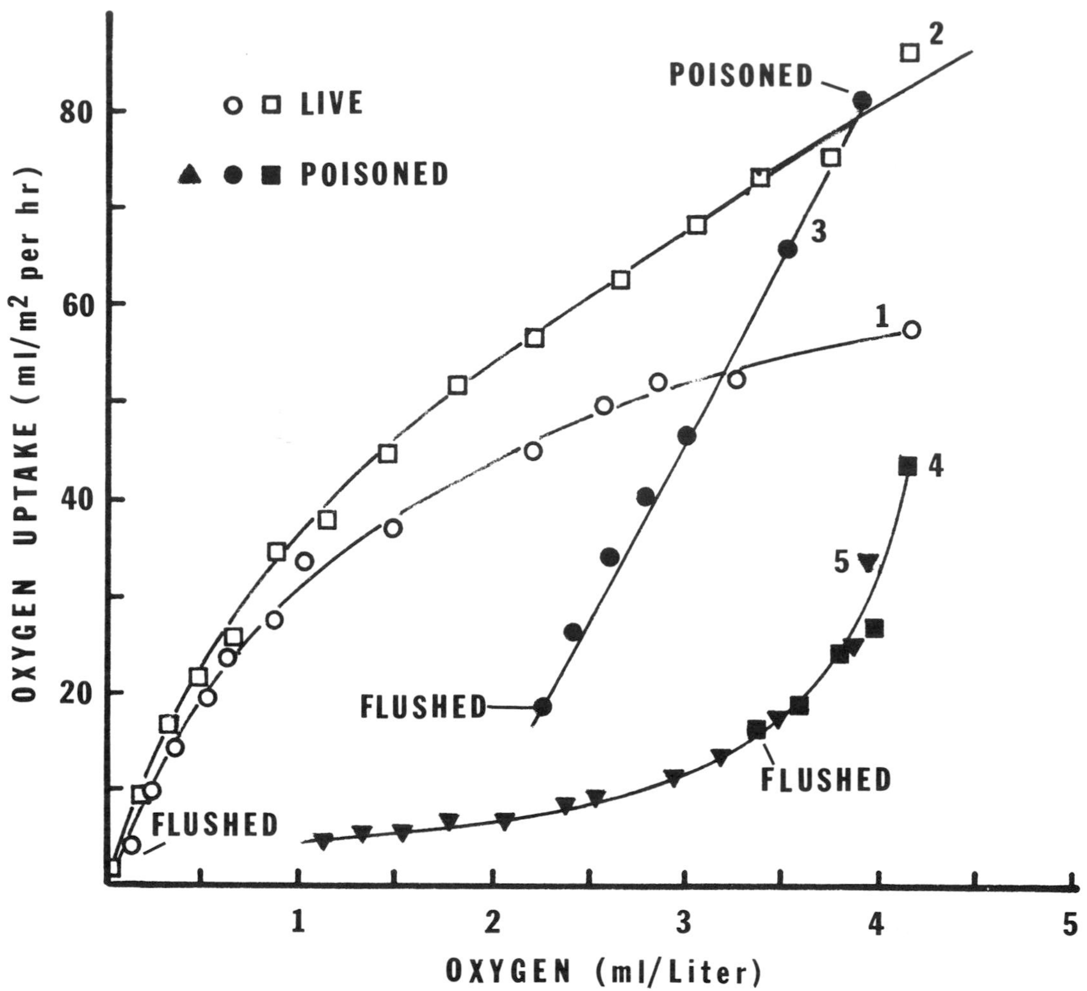

Fig. 3. Oxygen consumption of coralline sediment core from Grand Bahama shelf showing the relationship between rates of oxygen uptake and oxygen concentration. The experiment lasted ca 36 hr and consisted of five runs as labeled. After the first run the water over the core was flushed to replenish dissolved oxygen; after the second run, the water was flushed again and formaldehyde was added. The difference between the first and second runs may have been caused by bacterial growth stimulated by dissolved organic substances released from the sediment. After the third and fourth runs, the water was flushed again. Formaldehyde treatment appears to give spuriously high rates of chemical oxidation.

obtained, and would have indicated that the rate of chemical uptake is fairly stable with time at constant oxygen concentration. A sixth run would have further strengthened the present contention that formaldehyde increases the apparent chemical oxygen uptake by coralline sediment cores.

Egbert Driscoll of Wayne State University (personal communication)

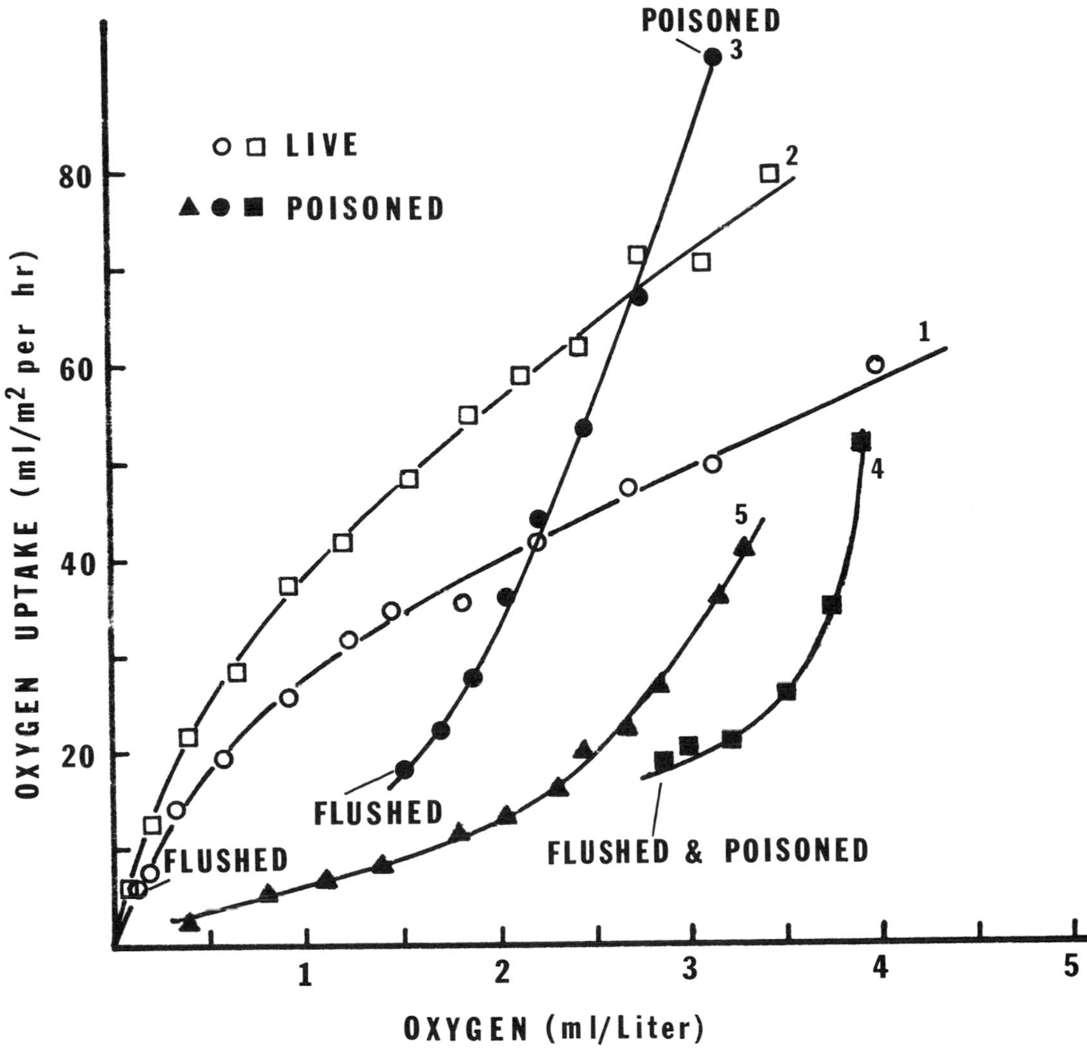

Fig. 4. Oxygen consumption of coralline sediment core from Grand Bahama shelf showing the relationship between rates of oxygen uptake and oxygen concentration. The experiment lasted ca 36 hr and consisted of five runs as labeled. After the first run the water over the core was flushed to replenish dissolved oxygen; after the second run, the water was flushed again and formaldehyde was added. The difference between the first and second runs may have been caused by bacterial growth stimulated by dissolved organic substances released from the sediment. After the third run the water was flushed again; after the fourth the water was flushed and more formaldehyde was added. Formaldehyde treatment at the beginning of the third and fourth runs appears to give spuriously high rates of chemical oxidation.

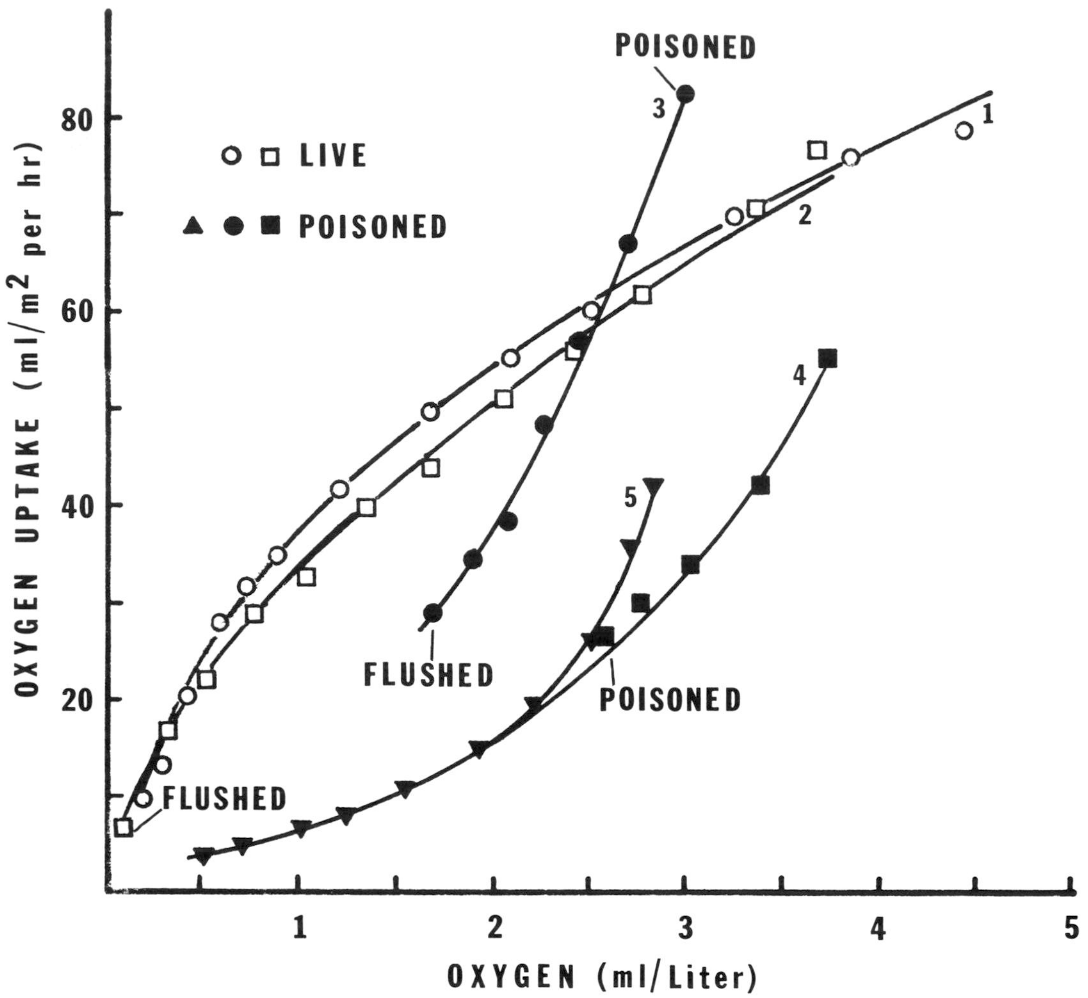

Fig. 5. Oxygen consumption of a coralline sediment core from Grand Bahama shelf showing the relationship between rates of oxygen uptake and oxygen concentration. The experiment lasted ca 36 hr and consisted of five runs as labeled. After the first run the water over the core was flushed to replenish dissolved oxygen. After the second run, the water was flushed again and formaldehyde was added. Little, if any, difference between first and second runs suggests total uptake probably would have been constant at constant oxygen concentration over a period of at least 7 hr. The only difference between this core and three other replicate cores was that water had drained through this core and probably washed out dissolved organic substances. After the fourth run more formaldehyde was added without prior flushing. As in Figures 3 and 4 the effect of formaldehyde treatment on chemical oxygen uptake is evident.

has data indicating that oxidation of formaldehyde might lead to spuriously high rates of chemical oxygen uptake by the sediment. When formaldehyde was added to water only in the Bahamas experiment, however, there was zero oxygen uptake. The increased rate of uptake in the cores following formaldehyde treatment seems to be the result of an interaction between formaldehyde and some other substance associated with the sediment, and not between formaldehyde and dissolved oxygen. This problem might be avoided by using another poison such as mercuric chloride; unfortunately, galvanic oxygen electrodes soon become erratic after immersion in water containing this poison.

The validity of equating residual oxygen uptake with chemical oxidation in nature following the use of any poison might be questioned because wherever chemoautotrophs oxidize reduced compounds like H_2S, their rate of sulfide uptake would appear as chemical oxidation after they are killed. This could be a serious error in areas where the sulfur cycle is important (see Jorgensen and Fenchel 1974). In this case, however, the poison might also kill the sulfate reducers and therefore eventually stop sulfide production. Killing chemoautotrophs, in any case, should not lead to higher rates of chemical oxidation than total uptake, or to increased rates of uptake following further injections of formaldehyde; hence, this could not have been the reason for the Bahamas findings.

A key question might be, how long after the application of a poison should one wait before measuring residual uptake? One hour after formaldehyde injection a uniform decline in oxygen appears for several hours and this rate has been taken as the chemical uptake in my work (Pamatmat 1971a, b, 1973). The initial first hour, showing much higher rates of chemical uptake, has been ignored to allow temperature re-equilibration and complete mixing of formaldehyde. It is possible that some formaldehyde effect is still included in this apparent chemical uptake during the succeeding several hours. More experiments are obviously needed to clarify this issue. To eliminate the problems experienced in the foregoing experiment, a continuous flow set-up (Fillos and Molof 1972) might be better.

Benthic Community Metabolism

Howard (1972) expressed doubt that, in view of the biochemical complexity of soil, a single holistic measurement of biological activity would include the metabolism of all the organisms therein. He was obviously referring to a biochemical method, in which case such doubt may very well be extended to aquatic sediments.

Direct calorimetry has been advocated as a means of measuring metabolic activity of mixed metabolic types in a complex biochemical system in order to circumvent these complexities and yet obtain comparable measures of the metabolic activity of all organisms (Forrest et al. 1961; Doyle 1963; Pamatmat 1971a). In practice working with a calorimeter large enough to contain large samples like sediment cores has been unmanageable, and the basic assumption that enthalpy changes exhibited by sediment and organisms was due mainly to the metabolic heat release by living organisms, appears to be untenable (Pamatmat 1975), at least in some sediment types. This problem would not have been discovered if sediment samples always showed heat evolution or not at all, but high rates of heat absorption (which are not directly attributable to metabolic activity) point to the substantial chemical side effects which could take place and completely mask or affect the accuracy of metabolic measurements. Endothermy in sediments could be an indication of chemical disequilibrium and increase in entropy as the sediment approaches equilibrium.

Continued experimentation with calorimeters is necessary, however, because this appears to be the only instrument which can measure metabolic activity of undisturbed communities of organisms. The problem of determining metabolic heat production from enthalpy change will, of course, have to be solved. If this can be done, calorimetry will offer a means of calibrating chemical methods for estimating anaerobic metabolism in sediments. Until such calibration is performed, it appears that all chemical methods (enzyme assays, radioisotope techniques, or any other method which involves disruption of the sediment, or enrichment with substrate or artificial electron acceptor) will be of doubtful accuracy, although they may be extremely useful for comparative purposes.

The measurement of dehydrogenase activity with 2,3,5-triphenyltetrazolium chloride (TTC), an artificial electron acceptor, is still promising because, unlike other methods which are highly selective or deal only with specific metabolic groups, TTC reduction could theoretically result from the metabolic activity of all organisms. It is doubtful, however, that the same rate of TTC reduction by different metabolic types means the same rate of metabolic activity (Pamatmat 1975)--hence, the critical need for calibration by direct calorimetry,using different metazoans and pure microbial cultures of different metabolic types, in order to find the range of quantitative relationship between TTC reduction and metabolic heat release.

OUTLOOK FOR BENTHIC COMMUNITY METABOLISM MEASUREMENTS

Anticipated engineering developments and increasing industrial activity in coastal waters have made us all acutely aware of the complexity of this ecosystem, our ignorance of it, its inestimable value and many benefits to man, and its vulnerability to man's actions. There is widespread feeling of urgent need to understand the biology, chemistry, geology, hydrography, etc. of coastal waters so that possible subtle and long-term effects arising from man's engineering constructions, their operations and other concomitant activities might be predicted and prevented, or detected and corrected.

Baseline studies should include, besides basic biology and chemistry, for example, characteristic properties of whole communities and entire ecosystems, such as primary productivity and community metabolism. In a long list of parameters which have been, and could be, measured for the purpose of environmental assessment and monitoring, benthic community metabolism has apparent advantages which make it potentially more useful than others.

The sediment ultimately integrates environmental events, and for the same reason that stratigraphy reveals previous environmental conditions, metabolic profile in the sediment column should do likewise. In places where effects of pollutants in the water are undetectable, sedimentological processes would concentrate such pollutants in sediments, perhaps causing deleterious effects in bottom deposits on both community structure and/or metabolism. More baseline measurements are clearly needed before we can assess deleterious effects and environmental degradation.

Annual metabolic profiles of depositional basins where the rates of sedimentation and decomposition are at steady state might be expected to show exponential decline with depth of sediment layer (Fig. 6). Metabolic activity in the topmost layer should represent

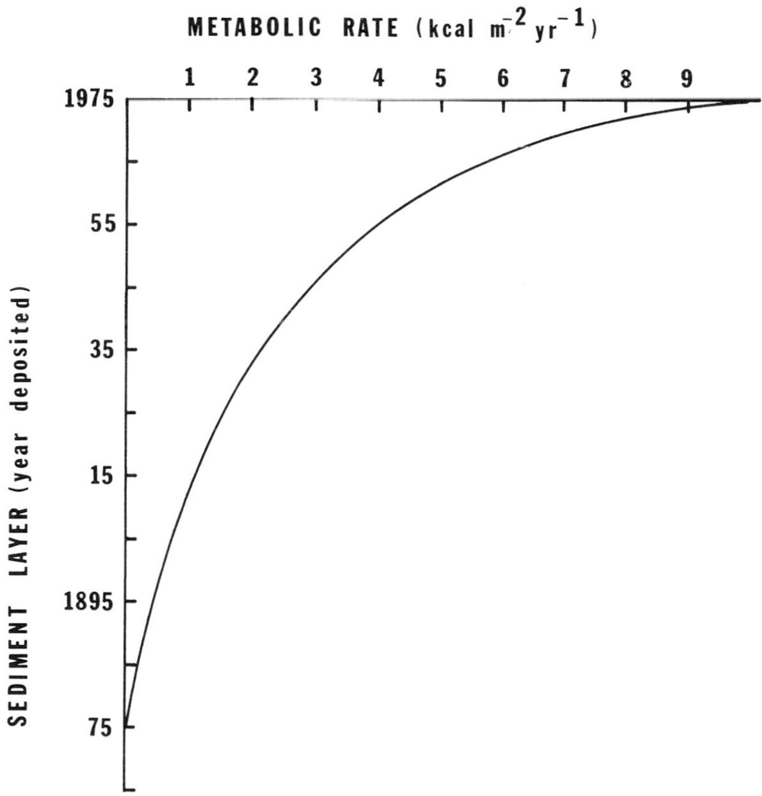

Fig. 6. Hypothetical curve of decreasing metabolic rate with depth of sediment layer in a depositional basin at steady state. Integrated value of the curve equals annual benthic community metabolism. The metabolic activity of the surface layer, as perhaps measured by sediment oxygen uptake, represents the fraction of annual energy supply that is lost as heat during the year it is deposited. Differences in metabolic profile between areas should reflect differences in depositional history.

degradation of organic matter deposited during any given year. Annual community metabolism, the integrated value of the curve, should represent the total fraction of annual deposits that is oxidized in the sediment until the layer is removed from the metabolically active zone, in this hypothetical example, 100 years later. It follows, in this case, that the energy equivalent of annual community metabolism should be less than that of annual sedimentation. The difference sould represent refractory organic matter. Also, annual benthic community metabolism would then be a first order approximation of the fraction of net primary production that settles to the bottom.

On the other hand, if the ecosystem is not at steady state, and the rate of sedimentation is increasing or decreasing, total community metabolism could underestimate or overestimate, respectively, the fraction of annual sedimentation that is oxidized. A range of possible situations can be postulated from erosional to equilibrium in which the amount of sediment is constant, to where the amount of deposit varies temporally owing to massive horizontal shifting, to a steady depositional environment. The relationship between total community metabolism and energy flow in the rest of the ecosystem will vary under these different conditions.

The shape of a metabolic curve could indicate past periods of organic enrichment resulting from eutrophication. If the integrated curve turned out to be greater than the current supply of organic matter to the bottom, one might infer that an area annually received more organic matter in the past than it is receiving at present. On the other hand, if the sediment layer showed very low metabolic activity for its organic matter content, it might indicate the presence of toxic pollutants. We need to know the "normal relationship" between benthic community metabolism and energy supply; then any large departure from this value would alert us to unusual situations.

More detailed knowledge about benthic community metabolism, such as the quantitative relationship between metabolic types under various conditions, can only enhance the practical usefulness of community metabolism in assessing the condition of our environment.

The study conducted in Grand Bahama was supported in part by Manned Undersea Science and Technology, National Oceanic and Atmospheric Administration. The assistance rendered by Dr. J. Morgan Wells is gratefully acknowledged.

REFERENCES

Allgeier, R. J., W. H. Peterson, C. Juday, and E. A. Birge. 1932. The anaerobic fermentation of lake deposits. Int. Revue ges. Hydrobiol. Hydrograph. 26: 444-461.

Alsterberg, G. 1922. Die respiratorischen Mechanismen der Tubificiden. Acta Univ. Lund (Lunds Univ. Arsskr.) NF avd. 2, 18, No. 1. 175 p.

Baity, H. G. 1938. Some factors affecting the aerobic decomposition of sewage sludge deposits. Sewage Works J. 10: 539-568.

Birge, E. A. 1906. Gases dissolved in the waters of Wisconsin lakes. Trans. Am. Fish. Soc. 35: 143-163.

Bornebusch, C. H. 1930. The fauna of forest soil. Forstl. Forsogsv. Danm. 11: 1-158.

Bouldin, D. R. 1968. Models for describing the diffusion of oxygen and other mobile constituents across the mud-water interface. J. Ecol. 56: 77-87.

Carey, A. G., Jr. 1967. Energetics of the benthos of Long Island Sound. I. Oxygen utilization of sediment. Bull. Bingham Oceanogr. Coll. 19: 136-144.

Cline, J. D. 1968. Kinetics of the sulfide-oxygen reaction in seawater. An investigation at constant temperature and salinity. Master's thesis, Univ. Washington, Seattle. 68 p.

Davies, J. M. 1975. Energy flow through the benthos in a Scottish Sea Loch. Mar. Biol. 31: 353-362.

Doyle, R. W. 1963. Calorimetric measurements of the anaerobic metabolism of marine sediments and sedimentary bacteria. Master's thesis, Dalhousie Univ., Halifax. 51 p.

Duff, S. and J. M. Teal. 1965. Temperature change and gas exchange in Nova Scotia and Georgia salt-marsh muds. Limnol. Oceanogr. 10: 67-73.

Edberg, N. and B. v. Hofsten. 1973. Oxygen uptake of bottom sediments studied *in situ* and in the laboratory. Water Res. 7: 1285-1294.

Edmondson, W. T. and D. E. Allison. 1970. Recording densitometry of X-radiographs for the study of cryptic laminations in the sediment of Lake Washington. Limnol. Oceanogr. 14: 317-326.

Edwards, R. W. and H. L. J. Rolley. 1965. Oxygen consumption of river muds. J. Ecol. 53: 1-19.

Fair, G. M., E. W. Moore, and H. A. Thomas. 1941. The natural purification of river muds and pollutional sediments. Sewage Works J. 13: 270-307.

Fillos, J. and A. H. Molof. 1972. Effect of benthal deposits on oxygen and nutrient economy of flowing waters. J. Water Poll. Control Fed. 44: 644-662.

Forrest, W. W., D. J. Walker, and M. F. Hopgood. 1961. Enthalpy changes associated with the lactic fermentation of glucose. J. Bacteriol. 82: 685-690.

Gallagher, J. L. and F. C. Daiber. 1974. Oxygen consumption at the soil-water interface in a Delaware salt marsh. Chesapeake Sci. 15: 248-250.

Hale, S. S. 1974. The role of benthic communities in the nutrient cycles of Narragansett Bay. Master's thesis, Univ. Rhode Island. 123 p.

Hargrave, B. T. 1969a. Epibenthic algal production and community respiration in the sediments of Marion Lake. J. Fish. Res. Board Can. 26: 2003-2026.

______. 1969b. Similarity of oxygen uptake by benthic communities. Limnol. Oceanogr. 14: 801-805.

_____. 1972a. A comparison of sediment oxygen uptake, hypolimnetic oxygen deficit and primary production in Lake Esrom, Denmark. Verh. Internat. Verein. Limnol. 18: 134-139.

_____. 1972b. Oxidation-reduction potentials, oxygen concentration and oxygen uptake of profundal sediments in a eutrophic lake. Oikos 23: 167-177.

_____. 1973. Coupling carbon flow through some pelagic and benthic communities. J. Fish. Res. Board Can. 30: 1317-1326.

Hayes, F. R. 1964. The mud-water interface. Oceanogr. Mar. Biol., Ann. Rev. 2: 121-145.

_____ and M. A. MacAulay. 1959. Lake water and sediment. V. Oxygen consumed in water over sediment cores. Limnol. Oceanogr. 4: 291-298.

Hartwig, E. O. 1974. Physical, chemical and biological aspects of nutrient exchange between the marine benthos and the overlying water. Ph.D. thesis, Univ. Calif, San Diego. 174 p.

Hoppe-Seyler, F. 1896. Ueber die Vertheilung absorbierter Gase im Wasser des Bodensees und ihre Beziehungen zu den in ihm lebenden Thierens und Pflanzen. Schr. Ver. Gesch. Bodensees 24: 29-48.

Howard, P. G. A. 1972. Problems in the estimation of biological activity in soil. Oikos 23: 235-240.

Howeler, R. H. 1972. The oxygen status of lake sediments. J. Environ. Quality 1: 366-371.

_____ and D. R. Bouldin. 1971. The diffusion and consumption of oxygen in submerged soils. Soil. Sci. Soc. Am. Proc. 35: 202-208.

Hunding, C. 1973. Diel variation in oxygen production and uptake in a microbenthic littoral community of a nutrient-poor lake. Oikos 24: 352-360.

Hutchinson, G. E. 1941. Limnological studies in Connecticut: IV. Mechanism of intermediary metabolism in stratified lakes. Ecol. Monogr. 11: 21-60.

_____. 1957. A treatise on limnology. I. Geography, physics and chemistry. Wiley.

James, A. 1974. The measurement of benthal respiration. Water Res. 8: 955-959.

Jannasch, H. W. and C. O. Wirsen. 1973. Deep-sea microorganisms: in situ response to nutrient enrichment. Science 180: 641-643.

_____, K. Eimhjellen, C. O. Wirsen, and A Farmanfarmaian. 1971. Microbial degradation of organic matter in the deep sea. Science 171: 672-675.

Johnson, M. G. and R. O. Brinkhurst. 1971. Benthic community metabolism in Bay of Quinte and Lake Ontario. J. Fish. Res. Board Can. 28: 1715-1725.

Jorgensen, B. B. and T. Fenchel. 1974. The sulfur cycle of a marine sediment model system. Mar. Biol. 24: 189-201.

Kleckner, J. F. 1967. The role of the bottom fauna in mixing lake sediments. Master's thesis, Univ. Washington, Seattle. 61 p.

Lonnerblad, V. G. 1930. Uber die Sauerstoffabsorption des Bodensubstrates in einigen Seentypen. Bot. Notiser. 1930: 53-60.

Lund, J. W. G., F. J. H. Mackereth, and C. H. Mortimer. 1963. Changes in depth and time of certain chemical and physical conditions and of the standing crop of *Asterionella formosa* Hass. in the North Basin of Windermere in 1947. Phil. Trans. Roy. Soc. London B246: 255-290.

Martin, D. C. and D. A. Bella. 1971. Effect of mixing on oxygen uptake rate of estuarine bottom deposits. J. Water Poll. Control. Fed. 43: 1865-1876.

Mortimer, C. H. 1942. The exchange of dissolved substances between mud and water in lakes. J. Ecol. 30: 147-201.

Nissenbaum, A. and I. R. Kaplan. 1972. Chemical and isotopic evidence for the in situ origin of marine humic substances. Limnol. Oceanogr. 17: 570-582.

Odum, H. T. 1957. Trophic structure and productivity of Silver Springs, Florida. Ecol. Monogr. 27: 55-112.

Pamatmat, M. M. 1965. A continuous-flow apparatus for measuring metabolism of benthic communities. Limnol. Oceanogr. 10: 486-489.

______. 1968. Ecology and metabolism of a benthic community on an intertidal sandflat. Int. Revue ges. Hydrobiol. 53: 211-298.

______. 1971a. Oxygen consumption by the seabed. IV. Shipboard and laboratory experiments. Limnol. Oceanogr. 16: 536-550.

______. 1971b. Oxygen consumption by the seabed. VI. Seasonal cycle of chemical oxidation and respiration in Puget Sound. Int. Revue ges. Hydrobiol. 56:769-793.

______. 1973. Benthic community metabolism on the continental terrace and in the deep sea in the North Pacific. Int. Revue ges. Hydrobiol. 58: 345-368.

______. 1975. In situ metabolism of benthic communities. Cah. Biol. Mar. 16: 613-633.

______ and K. Banse. 1969. Oxygen consumption by the seabed. II. In situ measurements to a depth of 180 m. Limnol. Oceanogr. 14: 250-259.

______ and A. M. Bhagwat. 1973. Anaerobic metabolism in Lake Washington sediments. Limnol. Oceanogr. 18: 611-627.

______ and D. Fenton. 1968. An instrument for measuring subtidal benthic metabolism in situ. Limnol. Oceanogr. 13: 537-540.

______, R. S. Jones, H. Sanborn, and A. Bhagwat. 1973. Oxidation of organic matter in sediments. U.S. Environmental Protection Agency, EPA-660/3-73-005. Supt. Documents, Wash., D.C. 104 p.

Pomeroy, L. R. 1959. Algal productivity in salt marshes of Georgia. Limnol. Oceanogr. 4: 386-397.

Ponnamperuma, F. N. 1964. Dynamic aspects of flooded soils and the nutrition of the rice plant, pp. 295-328. In The mineral nutrition of the rice plant, Symp. Int. Rice Res. Inst., 1964. Johns Hopkins Press. 494 p.

Rhoads, D. C. 1974. Organism-sediment relations on the muddy sea floor. Oceanogr. Mar. Biol. Ann. Rev. 12: 263-300.

Rowe, G. T., C. H. Clifford, K. L. Smith, Jr., and P. L. Hamilton. 1975. Benthic nutrient regeneration and its coupling to primary productivity in coastal waters. Nature 225: 215-217.

Rybak, J. I. 1969. Bottom sediments of the lakes of various trophic type. Ekol. Polska Ser. A 17: 611-662.

Schäfer, W. 1972. Ecology and paleoecology of marine environments. Translated by I. Oertel. Oliver & Boyd.

Schippel, F. A., L.-E. Bågander, and R. O. Hallberg. 1973. An apparatus for subaquatic in situ measurements of sediment dynamics. Askö Lab., Univ. Stockholm, Contrib. 2: 7-16.

Seki, H., E. Wada. I. Koike, and A. Hattori. 1974. Evidence of high organotrophic potentiality of bacteria in the deep ocean. Mar. Biol. 26: 1-4.

Smith, K. L., Jr. 1973. Respiration of a sublittoral community. Ecology 54: 1065-1075.

_____. 1974. Oxygen demands of San Diego Trough sediments: an in situ study. Limnol. Oceanogr. 19: 939-944.

_____ and J. M. Teal. 1973. Deep-sea benthic community respiration: an in situ study at 1850 meters. Science 179: 282-283.

_____, K. A. Burns, and J. M. Teal. 1972. In situ respiration of benthic communities in Castle Harbor, Bermuda. Mar. Biol. 12: 196-199.

_____, G. T. Rowe, and C. H. Clifford. 1974. Sediment oxygen demand in an outwelling and upwelling area. Tethys 6: 223-229.

_____, _____, and J. A. Nichols. 1973. Benthic community respiration near the Woods Hole sewage outfall. Estuar. Coast. Mar. Sci. 1: 65-70.

_____, C. H. Clifford, A. H. Eliason, B. Walden, G. T. Rowe, and J. M. Teal. 1976. A free vehicle for measuring benthic community metabolism. Limnol. Oceanogr. 21: 164-170.

Smith, S. V. and G. S. Key. 1975. Carbon dioxide and metabolism in marine environments. Limnol. Oceanogr. 20: 493-495.

Stein, J. E. and J. G. Denison. 1966. In situ benthal oxygen demand of cellulosic fibers, pp. 181-190. In Advances Water Pollution Research, Proc. 3rd Int. Conf. Water Poll. Control Fed., Wash., D. C.

Stockner, J. G. and W. W. Benson. 1967. The succession of diatom assemblages in the recent sediments of Lake Washington. Limnol. Oceanogr. 12: 513-532.

Teal, J. M. 1957. Community metabolism in a temperate cold spring. Ecol. Monogr. 27: 283-302.

_____ and J. Kanwisher. 1961. Gas exchange in a Georgia salt marsh. Limnol. Oceanogr. 6: 388-399.

Thamdrup, H. M. 1935. Beiträge zur Ökologie der Wattenfauna auf Experimenteller Grundlage. Medd. Komm. Danm. Fisk. Havunders. Ser. Fisk. 10: 1-125.

Wells, J. M. 1974. The metabolism of tropical benthic communities: in situ determinations and their implications. Mar. Tech. Soc. J. 8: 9-11.

Wieser, W. and J. Kanwisher. 1961. Ecological and physiological studies on marine nematodes from a small salt marsh near Woods Hole, Massachusetts. Limnol. Oceanogr. 6: 262-270.

Wirsen, C. O. and H. W. Jannasch. 1974. Microbial transformations of some ^{14}C-labeled substrates in coastal water and sediment. Microb. Ecol. 1: 25-37.

Yetka, J. E. and W. J. Wiebe. 1974. Ecological application of antibiotics as respiratory inhibitors of bacterial populations. Appl. Microbiol. 28: 1033-1039.

Recruitment and Competition

The Influence of Colonizing Benthos on Physical Properties and Chemical Diagenesis of the Estuarine Seafloor

Donald C. Rhoads, Robert C. Aller, and **Martin B. Goldhaber***
Department of Geology and Geophysics
Yale University
New Haven, CT 06520

ABSTRACT

Diver-taken box cores from a dredge-spoil dump and control station were used to document changes in: benthos, seafloor stability, sedimentary structures, redox depth, water content, and pore water profiles.

The colonization of the dump surface may be divided into three stages: Stage I (June-July) represented initial recruitment of shallow burrowing surface deposit feeders, suspension feeders, and meiofauna. Stage II (August-November) was a phase of exponential recruitment of stage I populations and new recruitment of deeper-feeding infauna. Stage III (December-April) was a period of leveling off in population densities. The control station showed relatively constant standing crops of deep-feeding deposit feeders over the sampling period. Late stage II and stage III abundances and diversities on the dump exceeded those at the control station.

Habit modification related to the three colonization stages are: Stage I (Summer)--Fecal pellet production starts and the redox potential discontinuity (RPD) is depressed to about one cm by bioturbation and respiration activities. Stage II (Fall)--The surficial layer of pellets experiences some destruction by meiofaunal grazing (?). The RPD is depressed to 2-3 cm and pore water profiles in $SO_4^=$ NH_4^+ approach constant values to a depth of 3-6 cm. The seafloor is bound by microbial exudates (?). Stage III (Winter)--The pelletal surface decays, the RPD rebounds to a depth of 1-2 cm. Pore water profiles become predominately diffusion controlled. Microbial binding decreases. Several hypotheses are stated regarding the potential importance of these habitat modifications to the colonization sequence.

INTRODUCTION

Activities of organisms produce changes in the physical and chemical properties of their habitat. Cumulative changes in the habitat resulting from these activities and associated changes in

*Present address: U.S. Geological Survey, Branch of Uranium and Thorium Resources, Denver Federal Center, Denver, Colorado 80225.

flora and fauna through time characterize ecologic successions. The concept of succession was first used to explain sequential appearances of different plants in new habitats (Cowles 1901; Clements 1904; Warming 1918). Concepts of well-defined successions and habitat modification have been applied only recently to studies of marine benthic invertebrates (e.g., Mills 1967; Johnson 1972; McCall 1975). In this paper we follow the benthic colonization of newly deposited dredge-spoil in central Long Island Sound over an 11-month period. Colonization of this sediment-pile is compared with normal temporal changes in the benthos of the surrounding seafloor. We have concentrated on physical and chemical changes in the substratum as they relate to colonization of the dump by invertebrates. These changes are compared with data from a natural bottom. Finally, we speculate on the importance of the observed habitat modification to the colonization sequence.

The conclusions drawn from our results are considered tentative and are in the form of an interim report. This investigation is part of a continuing study which will ultimately extend over a period of at least one and one-half years. We have not included tabulated faunal data in this paper. Readers interested in details of the colonization sequence may obtain faunal lists and abundance data by writing to D. C. Rhoads.

Much of our data was obtained under difficult diving conditions. We thank our chief diver William Ullman as well as Peter McCall, R. B. Fisher, Page Hiller, and Josephine Yingst for assistance in collecting samples. Allan Michael assisted us in faunal identification. Robert Wells helped us in many ways at sea, in constructing equipment, and preparing the manuscript. R. Aller was supported by a NSF Fellowship during this study. We have benefited from discussions with K. K. Turekian and acknowledge funding from his ERDA grant E(11-1)03573. D. C. Rhoads acknowledges the major source of funding from NSF grant GA 42838, and U.S. Army Crops of Engineers contract DACW 33-74-M-035.

PAST WORK

All previous work on faunal succession in central Long Island Sound is unpublished. However, experimental studies on the colonization of defaunated boxes of mud placed south of the Connecticut coast in 20 m of water (Fisher 1973; McCall 1975) were done in 1972 and repeated in 1973 on three different bottom types. Three groups of species were identified in the colonization sequence on the basis of recruitment rates, development time, reproductive frequency, and death rates. Successional data are also available from grab-sample studies of benthos colonizing a dredge-spoil dump ground in 20 m of water south of New Haven over the period 1972-1974 (Rhoads and Michael 1974). The published work of Sanders (1956) provides comparative data on the benthos of the central Sound taken over twenty years ago. Information on habitat changes related to organism-sediment interaction in subtidal muds has been summarized by Rhoads (1974).

STUDY AREA

Three sampling stations were established 6-10 km south of the New Haven, Connecticut harbor entrance in central Long Island Sound (Fig. 1A-C). The dump-top station (DT) is located on the apex of a dredge-spoil pile. The deposit consists of over $10^6 m^3$ of organic-rich sand and silt dredged from the New Haven Harbor channel edge. This material was dumped near a buoy on the spoil ground between 6 October 1973 and 23 April 1974 and is located in 12 m of water (Fig. 1C).

The dump-edge station (DE) is located approximately 150 m west of the dump-top in an organic-rich silty sand at a depth of about

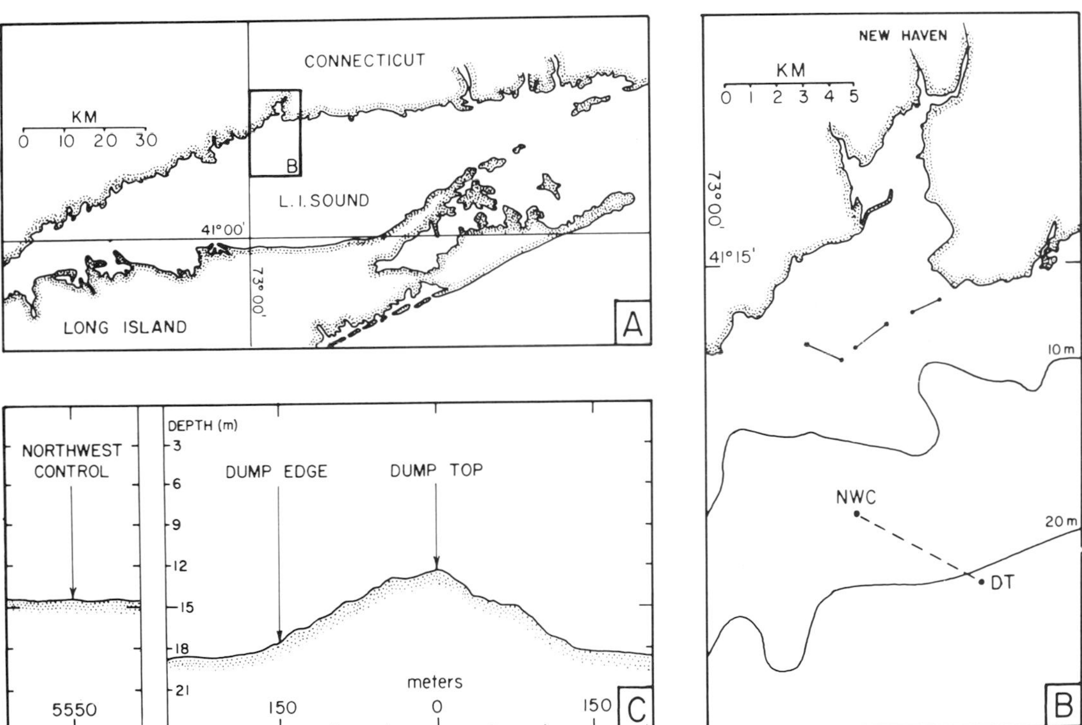

Fig. 1. Index map of sampling stations in central Long Island Sound. A. Regional map showing location of sampling area (B) relative to the Connecticut shoreline. B. Enlarged map of sampling transect extending from the dump-top (DT) to the northwest control (NWC). C. Cross-sectional profile extending from DT to NWC showing topographic and bathymetric positions of the dump-top, dump-edge, and northwest control stations. Note contracted horizontal scale.

18 m. Much of the dump surface is overlain with sand and interbedded with finer grained organic-rich sediments. Both the dump-top and dump-edge stations are covered with this sand cap. Tidally resuspended mud from the surrounding seafloor has settled out on this surface covering the sand layer with a few mm of sediment characteristic of the natural seafloor.

The northwest control station (NWC) is located 5.5 km northwest of the dump on a topographically flat silty-clay seafloor in 14 m of water. The NWC station was chosen as a control because it has not received dredge spoils and because it is well populated by protobranch bivalves. These bivalves are characteristic of a late successional stage on silt-clay bottoms (Rhoads and Young 1970; Rhoads 1974; McCall 1975).

METHODS AND APPARATUS

Bottom samples consisted of three types of plexiglas box cores which were taken by SCUBA divers. The dimensions and shapes of these cores varied according to the types of data being collected. The equipment is discussed below together with methods used to analyze samples (see Table 1).

Table 1. Sampling history of the three stations. 1 = flume core, 2 = x-ray core, 3 = chemical core.

Date / Station	1974 June		July			Aug		Sept	Oct	Nov			Dec	Jan	Mar	Apr		
	5	18	6	18	21	28	29			1	11	25			19	1	10	15
Dump Top (DDT)	1	2, 3		1		1, 2				1, 2, 3						1, 2, 3		
Dump Edge (DE)		1, 2, 3		1		1, 2						1, 2, 3					1, 2, 3	
Northwest Control (NWC)			1		2, 3		1				1, 2, 3				1, 2, 3			1

Flume Cores

These plexiglas boxes can be inserted or removed from a closed-channel salt-water flume. The boxes are a 45-cm long removable segment of a 100-cm^2 flume channel (Fig. 2), and their inside dimensions are: length 45 cm, width 10 cm, and height 17.5 cm. The area sampled by the box is 0.045 m^2. The ends of the box, when not coupled to the flume channel, are sealed by water-tight covers. The bottom is open and the edges sharpened to facilitate coring. A water-tight base plate held in place by rubber straps covers the bottom after a core is taken.

Divers push the box core into the bottom to a depth of about 7-8 cm. Vent holes in the top of the box are then plugged and the

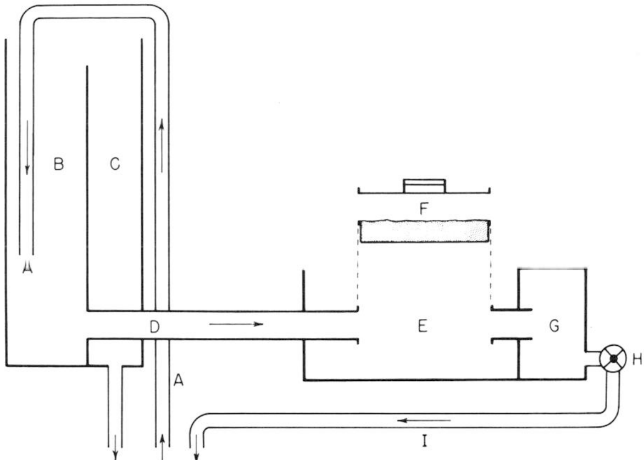

Fig. 2. Diagrammatic cross-section of a closed channel salt-water flume used to measure bottom erodability. A. Water supply pumped from reservoir. B. One-meter high head-tank. C. A spill-over tank receives excess water from head-tank and returns this water to the reservoir. D. One-meter long approach channel with a 100 m^2 cross-sectional area. E. Water bath tank in which the flume box core is inserted into the channel. F. Flume-box core shown in removed position. G. Valve chamber. H. Calibrated PVC ball valve. I. A discharge pipe returns effluent water to the reservoir.

corer withdrawn to the level of the bottom surface. At this position, the water-tight base plate is inserted, clamped in place, and the sample returned to the surface.

In the laboratory, the box core was inserted into the flume channel after the sediment surface was adjusted to match that of the approach channel. Before the flume treatment, two small surface sediment samples were withdrawn by pipette and preserved in 10% buffered formalin. Photomicrographs of these samples provided information on the nature of surface particles. Fecal pellet abundance, in particular, was estimated by counting and measureing pellets from enlarged photographs.

Particle transport was measured in the flume as follows: The operator observed particle behavior through a stereomicroscope (6X) at an oblique angle of 21°. Flow rate of water over the interface was controlled by opening a calibrated PVC ball valve on the downstream side of the flume channel (Fig. 2). Flow accelerations were on the order of 0.1 cm sec^{-2}. Measurements of particle motion were made at 1-cm intervals starting at a distance of 22 cm and extending to a distance of 31 cm as measured from the upstream end of the box core (N=10). As the flow accelerated from zero, two critical velocities were recorded: (1) the critical velocity at which a particle population of 10 or more in the field of view began to roll (critical rolling velocity); (2) critical suspension velocity at which grains were lifted into suspension. Flume water temperature ranged from 18-26°C and salinities from 32-35 °/oo. Before and after flume treatment, the recirculating water was filtered with a diatom and charcoal filter pump to remove particles.

After all flume runs were completed, the box was uncoupled from the flume channel, sediment removed, and washed through a 1-mm mesh sieve. Retained organisms are defined here as macrofauna. That part of the sample passing through the 1-mm screen was then washed through a 300-μm sieve. Retained organisms are defined as meiofauna.

X-ray Cores

Plexiglas core boxes 25-cm high, 30-cm wide and 2.5-cm thick were used to study biogenic and other sedimentary structures. These cores were taken in a similar fashion to the flume cores and represent a vertical section of bottom sediment 2.5-cm thick. Depending on the hardness of the bottom the depth of sampled sediment varies from 10-22 cm. Cores were x-rayed within several hours of collection by placing an 8" x 10" sheet of Kodak AA Industrial x-ray film on the back of the core box and exposing it at 60 kv. Animals occasionally form new burrow structures if a longer period of time is taken prior to x-raying.

Chemical Cores

Core boxes 25-cm high, 30-cm wide and 7.5-cm thick were used to study interstitial water and sediment chemistry. These cores, as well as the x-ray cores described above, have removable tops and bottoms. The tops are sealed by a rubber gasket during field sampling but are removed in the lab for processing of the core. Chemical cores were stored in a refrigerator (4°C) until processed, a period of 3-5 hr after collection. The depth of the redox discontinuity, buried erosional surfaces, and readily identified animal life were recorded--the side of the box was ruled at one-cm intervals from the sediment-water interface to within 3 cm of the base of the particular core being sampled. Water overlying the core was then rapidly removed using a vacuum line, the core top removed, and the entire core placed in a glove bag. This bag was purged several times with N_2 (O_2 free) and the core was subsequently sampled under a nitrogen atmosphere. Sediment was then removed at 1-cm intervals with plastic spoons, packed into 10-cm long sections of acetate tubing (4.5 cm I.D.), and sealed in the tubes with plastic end caps. Care was taken to avoid entrapment of N_2 in the sediment taken from each interval. Degrassing was apparently not a problem as shown by comparing values of H_2S concentrations obtained by this sampling procedure with other methods (Goldhaber et al., personal communication). The sediment in these sections was squeezed within a few hours for removal of interstitial water using the method of Kalil and Goldhaber (1973). Samples were stored at 5°C at times when they were not being handled. Glass fiber prefilters and 0.45-μm Millipore inline filters were used on pore water samples.

Chemical Analyses

Pore water analyses are reported here for NH_3 and $SO_4^=$. $SO_4^=$ was determined gravimetrically on 10-ml pore water samples immediately after squeezing by precipitation with $BaCl_2$ following heating and acidification to pH = 2-3. The precipitate was weighed after a digestion period of one to several days and $SO_4^=$ calculated from the weight of $BaSO_4$. These measurements are precise to within ± 0.5 mM. NH_3 was determined by a modification of the phenol hypochlorite method of Solorzano (1969). Filtered pore water for NH_3 analyses was placed immediately into a refrigerator at 4°C. NH_3 analyses were made, or samples were fixed with phenol (Degobbis 1973), within 24 hr of core collection. NH_3 values are precise to within 3%.

The depth of the redox potential discontinuity (RPD) was measured as the depth below the sediment surface where the sediment changed color from olive brown to grey or black. This depth was measured from the side of plexiglas cores and from sediment profile camera photographs.

RESULTS

Colonization Sequence

The dump surface was relatively barren of benthic macroinvertebrates during the spring and early summer of 1974. Recruitment of individuals, predominately polychaetes and bivalves, began during the summer and increased into November-December (Fig. 3). The total numbers of organisms at both dump stations increased exponentially and at approximately the same rate over this time period. After November, both dump stations leveled off in abundance. The northwest control had only minor changes in total numbers of organisms from July 1974-March 1975 and maintained densities of between 533 and 750 individuals per m^2.

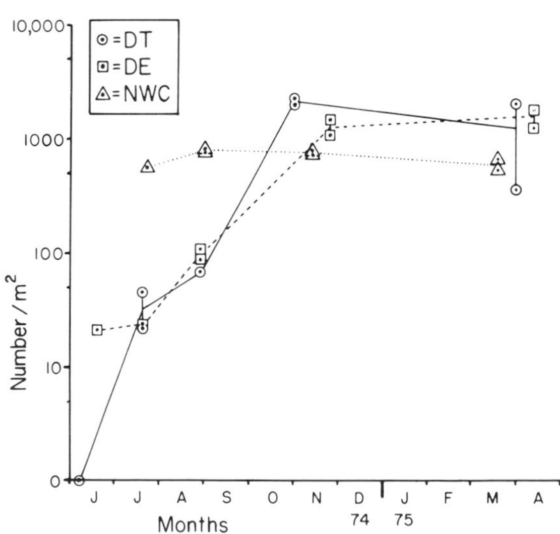

Fig. 3. Density of macrofauna (≥ 1 mm) at the dump-top (DT), dump-edge (DE), and northwest control (NWC) stations from June 1974 to April 1975. Over 80% of the organisms present are polychaetes and bivalves (see Fig. 8).

Polychaetes are the earliest colonizers of the dump (Fig. 4). The deep burrowing errant polychaete *Nephtys incisa* appears on the

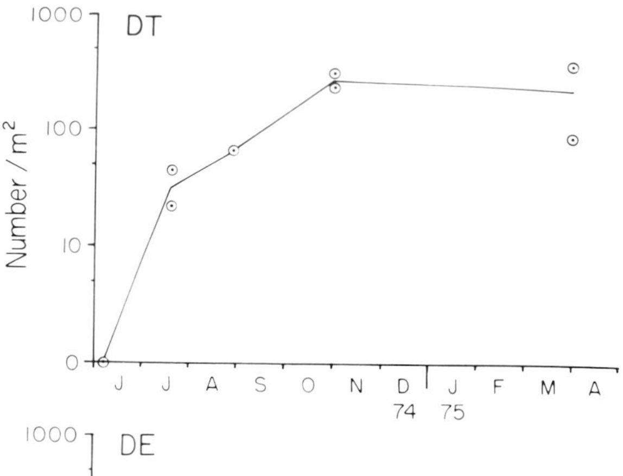

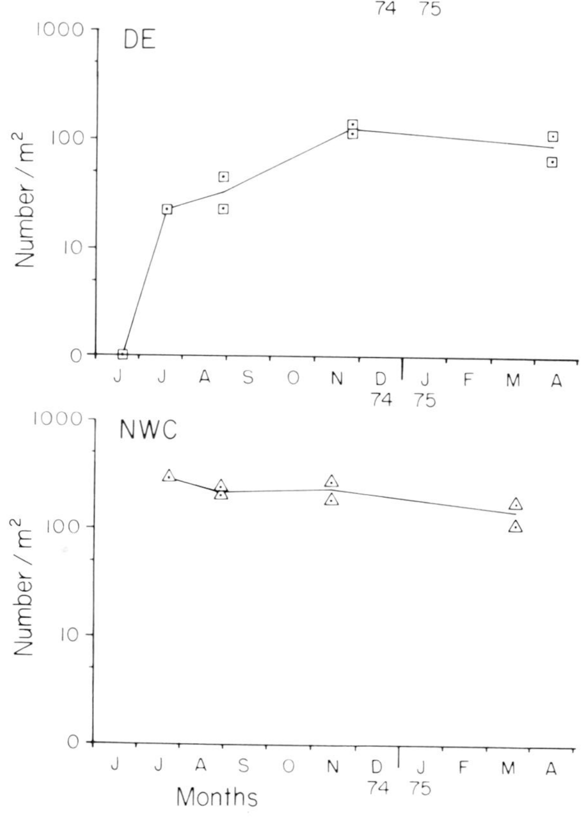

Fig. 4. Density of polychaetes at DT, DE, and NWC stations with time (see Fig. 8).

dump surface by late July. The tube-dwelling, deposit feeders, *Pectinaria gouldii* and *Owenia fusiformis*, appear on the dump-top in late summer and early fall. *Melinna cristata*, a surface deposit-feeding ampharetid appears at the NWC and DE in November samples. *Nephtys* numerically dominates the Polychaeta at the NWC and remains relatively constant in number over the sampling period.

Bivalves colonize the dump after polychaetes and occur in high abundance only in November and later samples (Fig. 5). The small size of individuals suggests that most arrived as larvae, although passive immigration of adults via tidal currents cannot be ruled out. The dump-top contains the most abundant and diverse molluscan fauna: 5 species of suspension feeders and two surface deposit-feeding

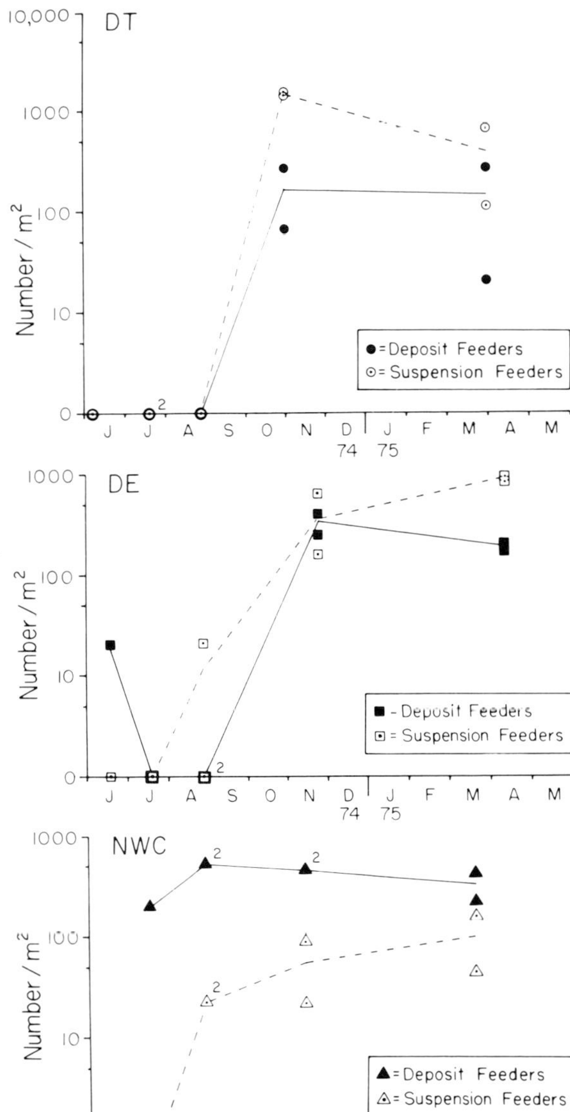

Fig. 5. Density of deposit-feeding and suspension-feeding bivalves at the DT, DE, and NWC stations with time (see Fig. 8).

tellinaceans. Bivalve abundance and diversity are less at the dump-edge. The northwest control is dominated by protobranch deposit feeders. Small populations of the suspension feeders, *Pitar morrhauna* and *Mulinia lateralis*, appear at the NWC in November.

If the numerically dominant taxa in our samples (Polychaeta, Amphipoda, and Bivalvia) are segregated into organisms that feed at or above the interface and those which feed at least one cm below the sediment surface, one can see that the dump-top is dominated by suspension and surface deposit feeders and the NWC by subsurface deposit feeders (Fig. 6). Initially the dump-edge was dominated by

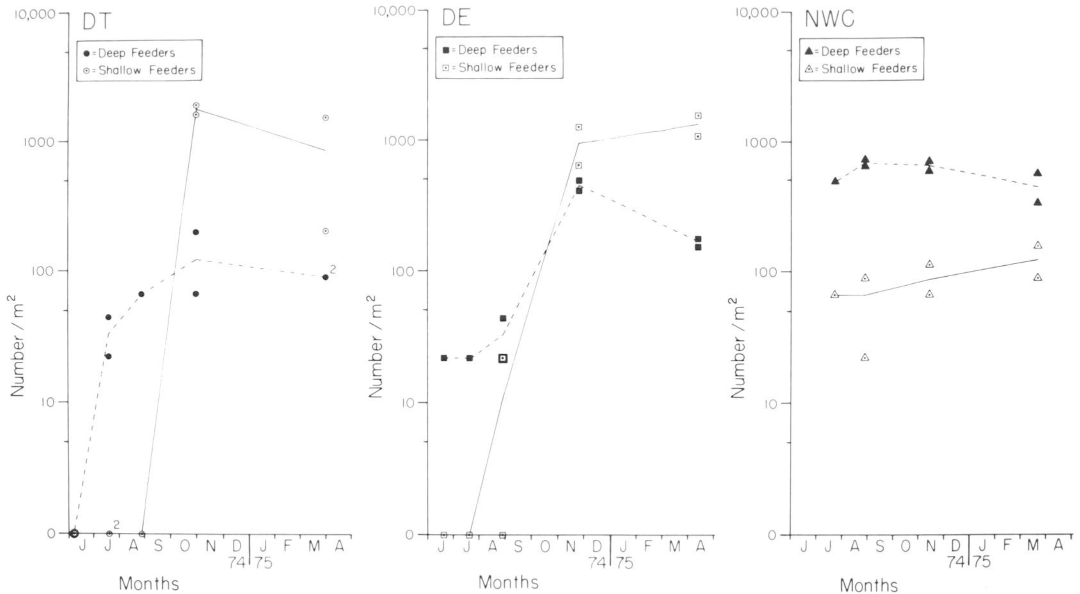

Fig. 6. Density of shallow and deep-feeding macrobenthos at the DT, DE, and NWC stations with time. Deep feeders are defined as those feeding ≥ 1 cm in depth. Shallow feeders feed near, or at, the interface. Suspension feeders are included in the latter group.

a single species of subsurface feeders (*Nephtys incisa* and later dominated by a variety of interface feeders following the fall settlement of bivalves. These observations confirm those of McCall (1975) who found that initial colonizers were closely associated with the sediment-water interface.

Meiofauna are here defined as those organisms within the size class <1000 to >300 μm. Figure 7 shows the temporal changes in abundance of foraminifera and of meiofauna minus forams and ostracods. Although ostracods are an important meiofaunal component in our samples, we have not yet examined this group. Benthic calcareous foraminifera (coiled forms) appear early on the dump surface, reaching peak abundance in late summer. Abundances on the dump surface converge with values on the NWC in November. Other meiofauna (minus ostracods) also peak in November, largely because of the appearance of juvenile bivalves and amphipods. The early July peak in meiofauna on the dump-top marks the appearance of benthic copepods. In late June a population of small gastropods (*Odostomia* sp) were recovered from one core. Foraminifera, juvenile molluscs, and amphipods dominate the NWC meiofauna.

In diagrammatic reconstructions of the dump and NWC assemblages during the fall (Fig. 8A, B), the late fall colonization stage on the dump clearly contains more species and trophic types than the equilibrium community at NWC. Further, the relative abundance of deep-feeders versus interface-feeders at these different stations is important in interpreting observations on pore water chemistry.

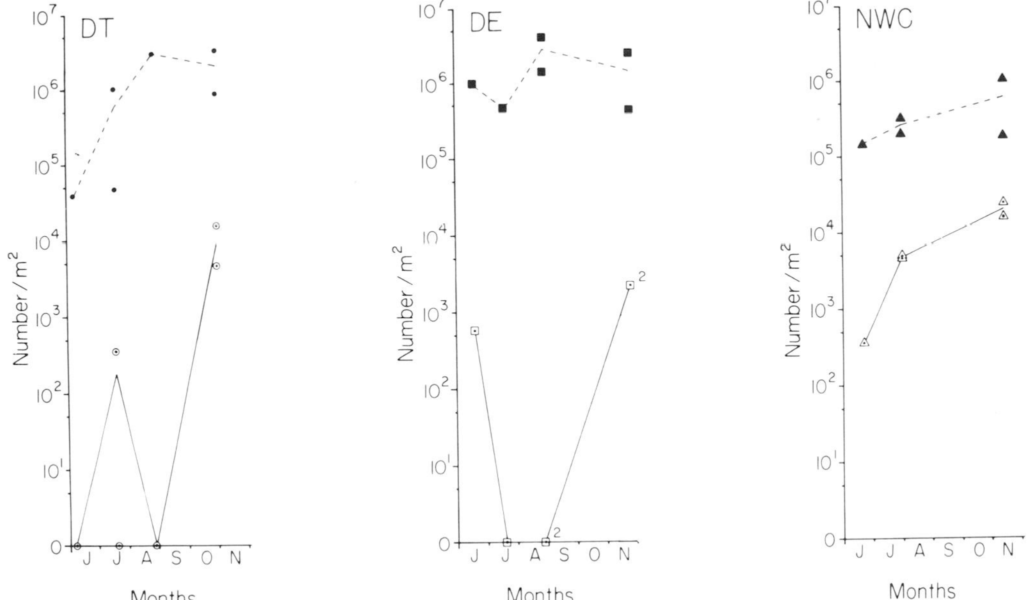

Fig. 7. Abundance of meiofauna at the DT, DE, and NWC station from June to November 1974. Solid symbols represent the abundance of foraminifera; open symbols represent other meiofauna (minus foraminifera and ostracods). The numeral 2 entered by some data points indicates values from two replicate samples are the same.

Biogenic Habitat Changes

Changes in physical-chemical properties of the sedimentary habitat resulting from benthic feeding and respiration were followed seasonally. Feeding activity, in part, is reflected in the changing abundance of fecal pellets at the sediment surface (Fig. 9). Most of these pellets are compact, fusiform in shape, and produced mainly by deposit-feeding polychaetes (e.g., *Owenia*). The abundance of fecal pellets per unit volume of sediment is controlled not only by the rate of production of pellets by macrobenthos but also by the rate of destruction presumably by grazing meiofauna, and disintegration of pellets by water turbulence. We are unable at this time to give absolute rates of production and destruction of pellets. However, relative rates of production and destruction (Fig. 9) may be inferred from the condition of pellet margins (sharp or diffuse).

Pellet abundance reaches a peak in July on the NWC. High production may well have preceded July but we have no earlier samples. Pellets present at the NWC in July have uniformly sharp margins. The standing crop of deposit feeders is high and water temperature approaches 17°C (Fig. 10). Peak pellet abundance on the dump surface is about one month later (August) and corresponds to the first significant population densities of deposit-feeding polychaetes at the dump stations.

Decline in pellet numbers and pellet margin sharpness at all stations in the fall probably indicates increased rate of pellet

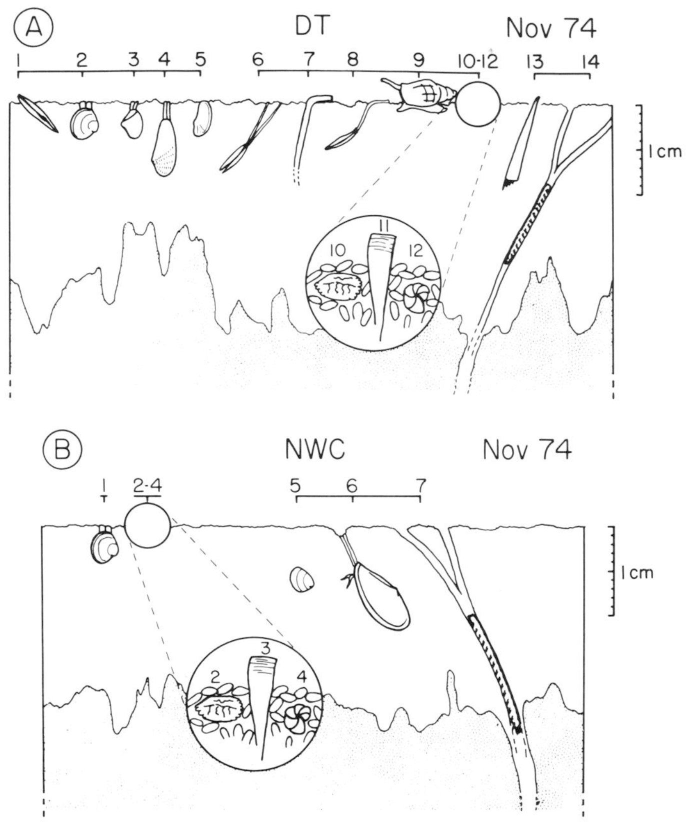

Fig. 8. Reconstruction of the dump-top and northwest control stations in November 1974. Shaded areas represent reducing sediment. A. Dump-top assemblage: I. Suspension feeders--(1) *Pandora gouldiana*, (2) *Pitar morrhuana*, (3) *Mulinia lateralis*, (4) *Petricola pholadiformis*, (5) *Lyonsia hyalina*. II. Surface deposit feeders--(6) *Tellina agilis*, (7) *Owenia fusiformis*, (8) *Macoma tenta*, (9) *Nassarius trivittatus*, (10) unidentified ostracods, (11) amphipods, (12) foraminifera. III. Deep deposit feeders--(13) *Pectinaria* sp., (14) *Nephtys incisa*. B. Northwest Control Assemblage: I. Suspension feeder--(1) *Pitar morrhuana*. II. Surface deposit feeders--(2) unidentified ostracods, (3) amphipods, (4) foraminifera. III. Deep deposit feeders-- (5) *Nucula annulata*, (6) *Yoldia limatula*, (7) *Nephtys incisa*.

Fig. 9. Abundance of fecal pellets at the DT, DE, and NWC stations from April to November 1974. Solid symbols represent pellet populations with sharp margins; open symbols diffuse margins. Partially solid symbols represent a mixture of sharp and diffuse margins. Mean pellet length over this period is about 100 μm, ranging from 25 to 350 μm.

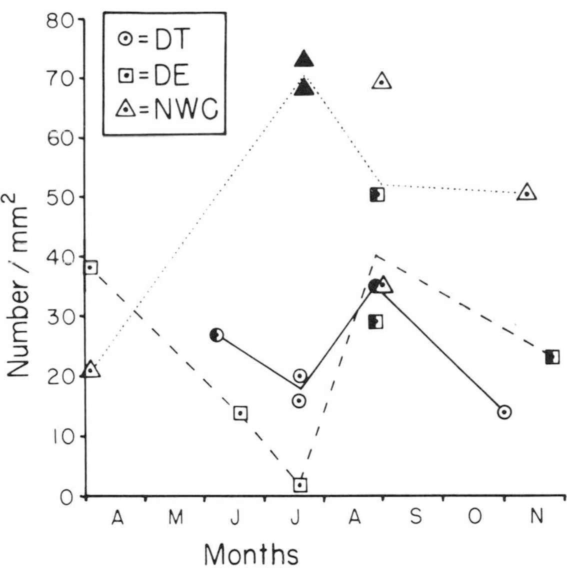

Fig. 10. Seasonal bottom water temperatures in central Long Island Sound.

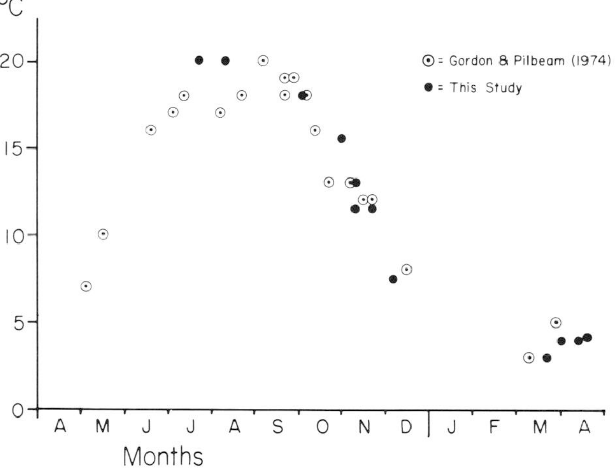

destruction rather than reduced production. It is unlikely that production rate falls off in the fall because water temperatures and faunal densities remain high. Biogenic reworking of sediments is also greatest during the fall and suggests rapid feeding and production of feces at this time (Aller and Cochran 1976).

The sedimentary manifestation of the competition between aerobic and anaerobic respiration may be seen in the color discontinuity (yellow-black) at depth in sediment often referred to as the redox potential discontinuity (RPD) (Hayes 1964; Fenchel and Riedl 1970). Figure 11 shows the depth of the RPD at the three sampling stations. The two dump stations have uniformly shallow RPD layers in June 1974 corresponding to what might be expected for the molecular diffusion distance of oxygen. The NWC has an RPD depth of over one cm at

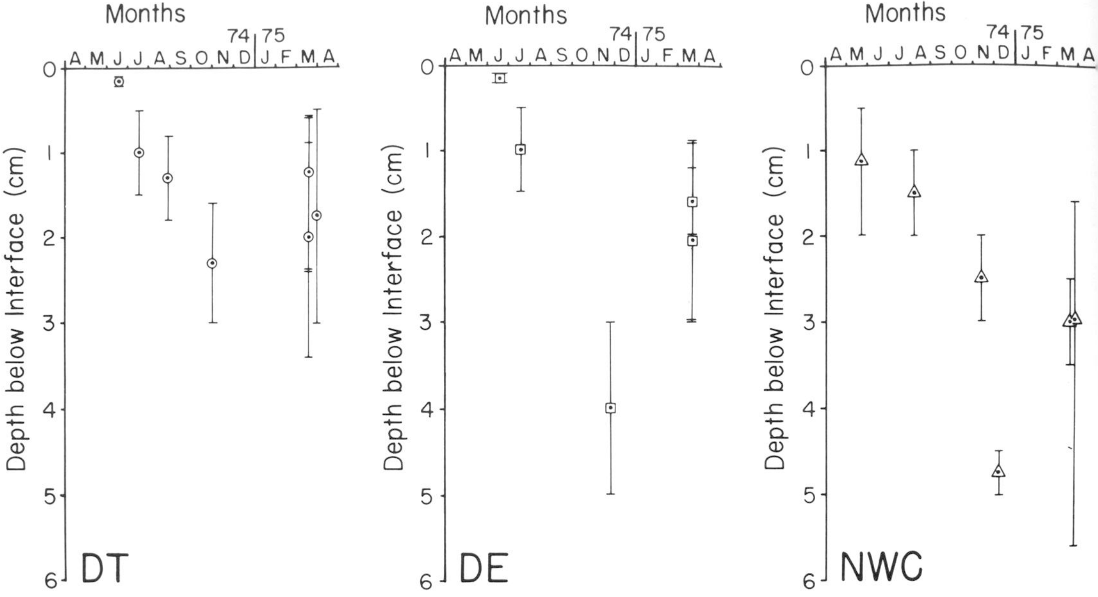

Fig. 11. Depth of the redox potential discontinuity (RPD) below the sediment-water interface at the DT, DE, and NWC stations from June 1974 to March 1975. The range and mid-range values are plotted for observations made on single core boxes from June 1974 through 19 March 1975 and for 1 April 1975 for the DT. Observations on 22 March 1975 are based on 19 measurements of the RPD depth from interface photographs. Means and ranges are plotted for this date.

this time. Maximum depression of the RPD appears to reach a peak between November and December at all stations. The NWC has the deepest RPD followed by the DE and DT stations. The color discontinuity migrates upward toward the interface slowly during the late winter.

Reworking of sediments by particle ingestion and irrigation may increase the total water content and porosity of a deposit. Figure 12 shows water content increasing at dump stations which have large numbers of deep burrowing macrofauna (DE2, DE3, DT3). The NWC maintains a well-defined profile of high surface water content over the sampling period. Meiofaunal bioturbation may also contribute to increased water content (Cullen 1973).

Bottom erodability

The resistance of bottom sediment to erosion by currents at each station was determined by recording the critical rolling and suspension velocities of sediment particles measured in the flume. Figure 13 shows these two critical velocities at the three sampling stations from June 1974 to April 1975. In early June 1974 the difference between rolling and suspension velocities at dump-top and dump-edge stations is large compared with subsequent times owing to changes in the nature of the sediment surface between early and late June. At

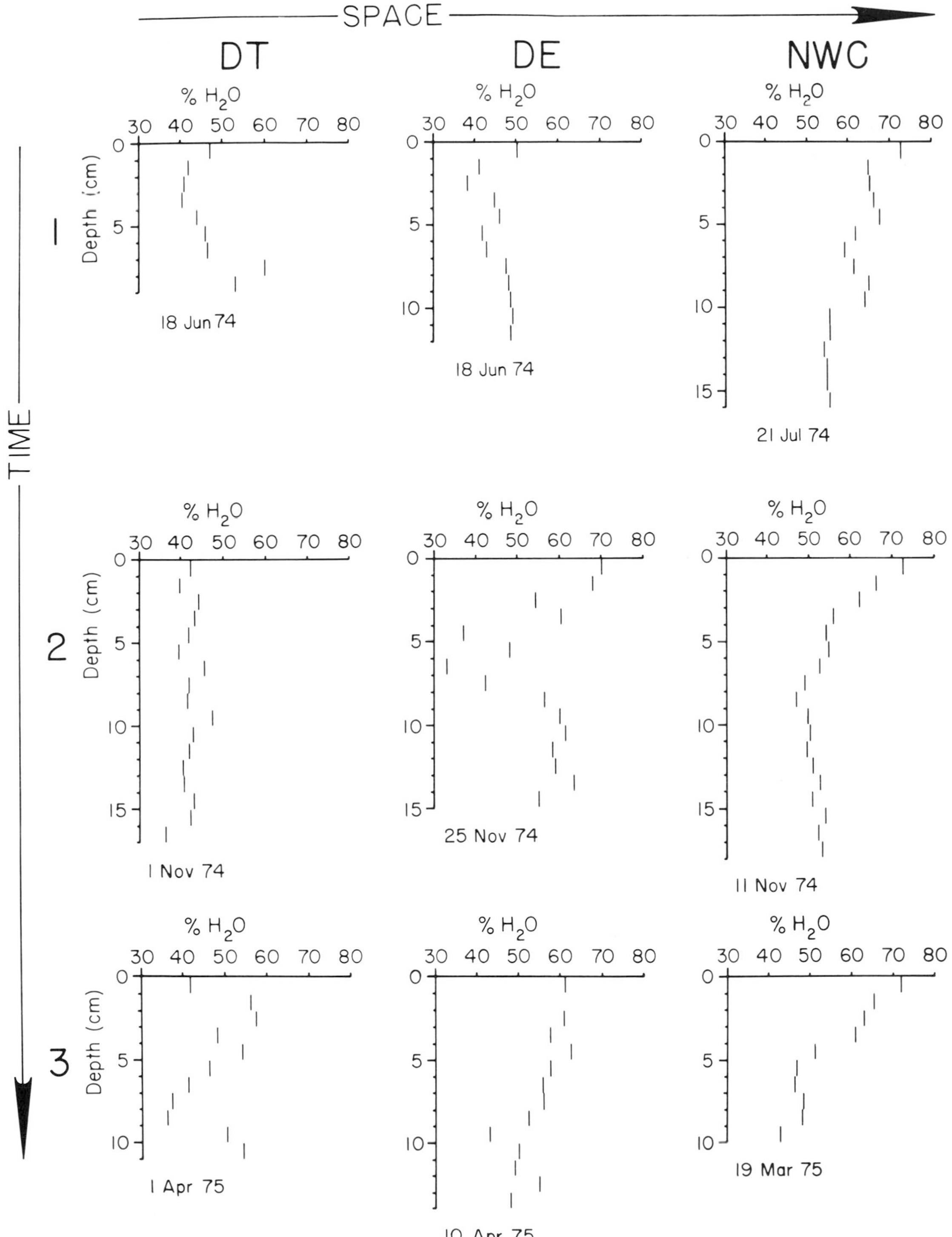

Fig. 12. Water content (Wt %) with depth in chemical box cores at the DT, DE, and NWC stations in summer, fall, and late winter 1974-1975. Low interface (1 cm) values at DT result from high sand content.

Fig. 13. Critical sediment transport velocities at the three sampling stations over time. The mean of ten measurements made on each flume core is plotted; the vertical bars represent ± one standard deviation. The lower curve at each station is mean critical rolling velocity; the upper curve the mean critical suspension velocity. Velocity values are those measured in the flume channel.

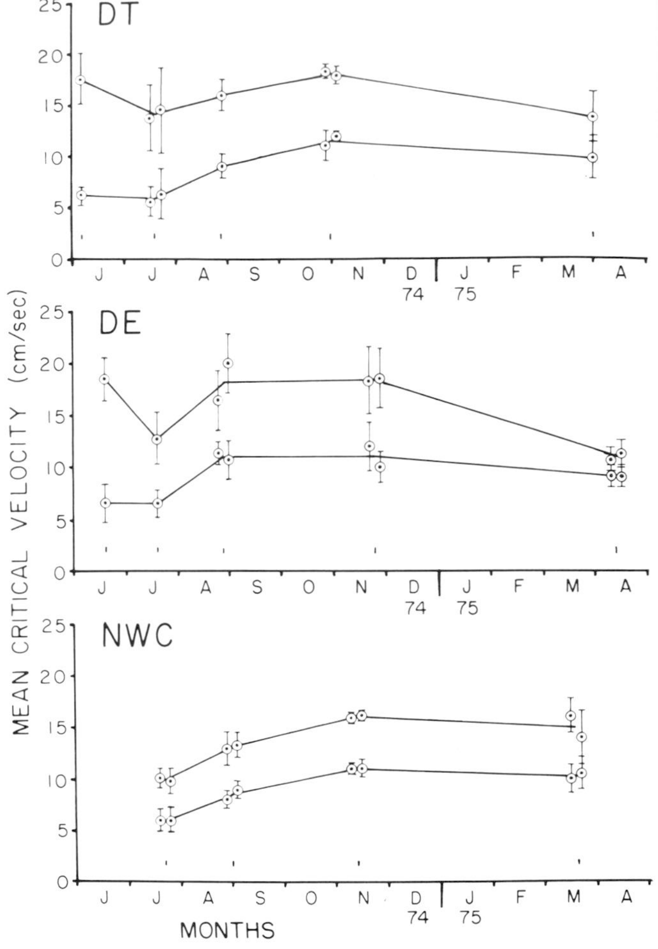

the end of the dumping operation the dump surface was capped with a relatively clean sand which required relatively high velocities to suspend silt and sand-sized mineral grains. By the end of June, the dump surface was covered with natural sediment from the ambient seafloor which formed a veneer of organic-rich silt. Critical suspension velocities in subsequent samples were therefore lower as the surface was covered with more easily suspended (low bulk density) organic-mineral aggregates. Some of these were fecal in origin.

From July through November the critical rolling velocity increased at all stations by about 5 cm/sec. All flume core samples taken on or after July 18 had their surfaces covered with a binding mucus-like material.

<u>Geochemistry</u>

Gravity cores taken in April 1974 on the dump-top showed low interface values for SO_4 (4-10 mM/1), high iron sulfides (0.16% S[FeS]), and high PO_4 and NH_3 (0.5-0.9 and 3-5 mM/1). Methane was present at saturation near the sediment-water interface (C. Martens personal communication). Many of these values normally occur at least several decimeters depth in Long Island Sound sediments. They indicate that the dumped material retained much, but not all, of its original composition during dredging and dumping and that the surface of the dump initially represented a diagenetically mature deposit. That is, although the dumping of material was a depositional event, the newly formed sediment-water interface corresponded chemically to a somewhat deeper deposit.

The sequence of change in natural bottom and dump site pore waters during this study can be represented in part by SO_4 and NH_3 data shown in Figures 14 and 15. Detailed modeling of these profiles is in progress and the relative contribution to each profile of diffusion, advection, consumption (inorganic or biogenic) and production (inorganic or biogenic) has not yet been fully evaluated. (Models used in describing pore water profiles are discussed by Berner 1974, 1975.) Preliminary calculations (not shown) demonstrate that NH_3 profiles (DT1, DT2, DT3, DE1, DE3, NWC3) and SO_4 profiles (DT1, DT2, and DE1) can be described by simple diffusion equations with relatively slight advection and production or consumption terms.

Ammonia profiles NWC1 and NWC2 are characterized by high production terms near the interface, as shown by the discontinuity between sediment (0.1-0.2 mM/1) and seawater (0.001-0.002 mM/1) NH_3 values and the NH_3 maximum near the interface in NWC1. Ammonia profile DE2 and sulfate profiles DE2, DE3, and DT3 show near-interface zones, 3-6 cm in depth, which lack a major concentration gradient; these are underlain by zones having profiles which can be described by simple diffusion. This upper zone has received SO_4 or lost NH_3 by an exchange process which is faster and less dependent on a concentration gradient than molecular diffusion. The shift of NH_3 background value from that of NWC1 to the lower value of NWC2 also cannot be accounted for by simple diffusion and represents an inorganic reaction or more probably a transport process other than diffusion.

The scatter in SO_4 profile NWC1 may reflect irregular consumption with depth, but may in part be due to bad analysis. SO_4 profiles NWC2, NWC3 show no concentration gradients with depth despite sulfate reduction, and SO_4 values are not significantly different from those of seawater.

DISCUSSION

Colonization of the two dump stations can be summarized by dividing the population events into three stages according to changing patterns of abundance and trophic structure. Stage I extends from our first sampling in June to July 1974. The dump surface is essentially barren with the exception of a few infaunal polychaetes (*Nephtys incisa*) and shallow burrowing suspension-feeding bivalves. Because all *N. incisa* are larger than 1 cm in size at this time, we believe that they were introduced with the dredge spoil or migrated

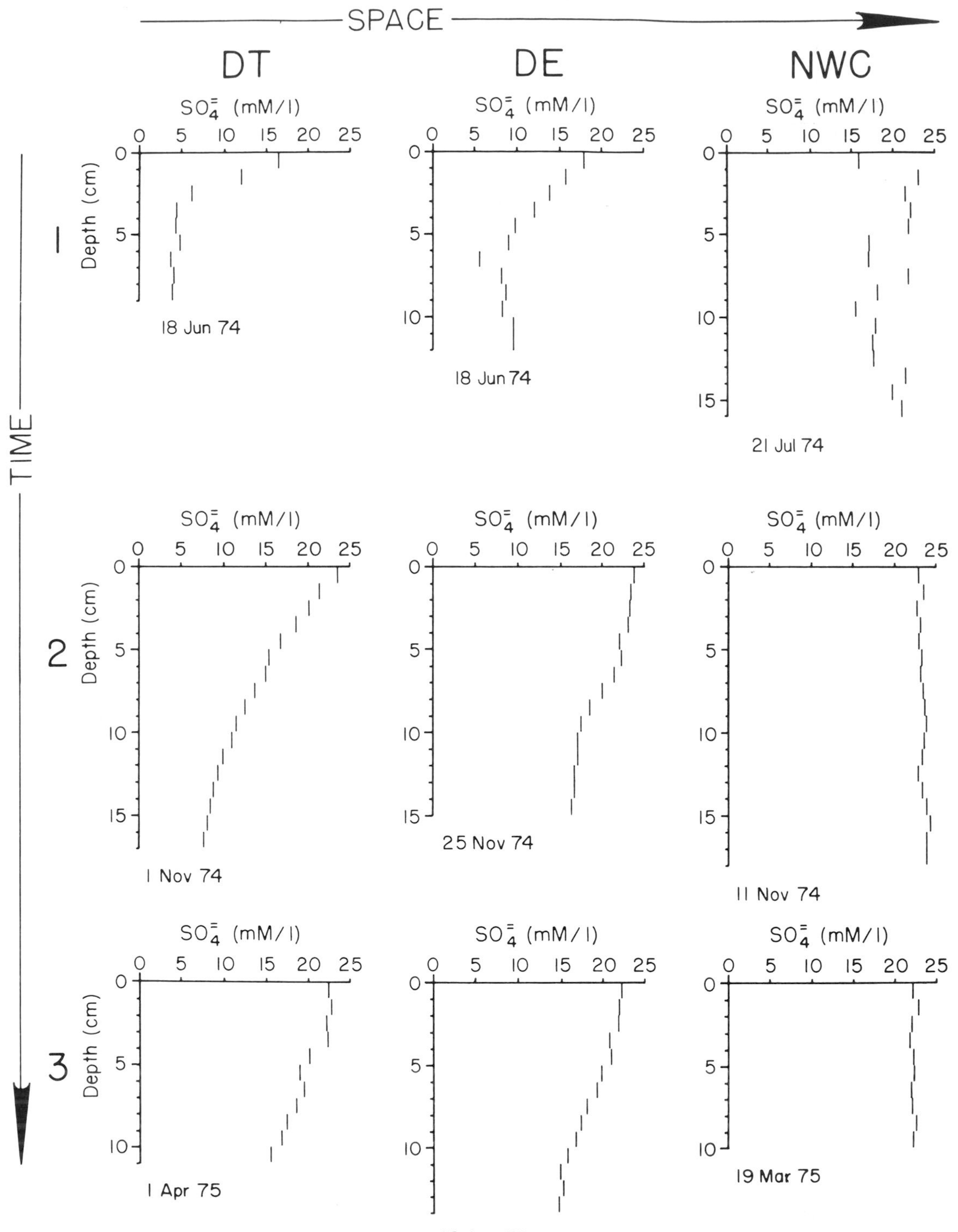

Fig. 14. Pore water profiles of $SO_4^=$ at the DT, DE, and NWC stations in summer, fall and late winter, 1974-1975. The net diffusion vector is in a downward direction.

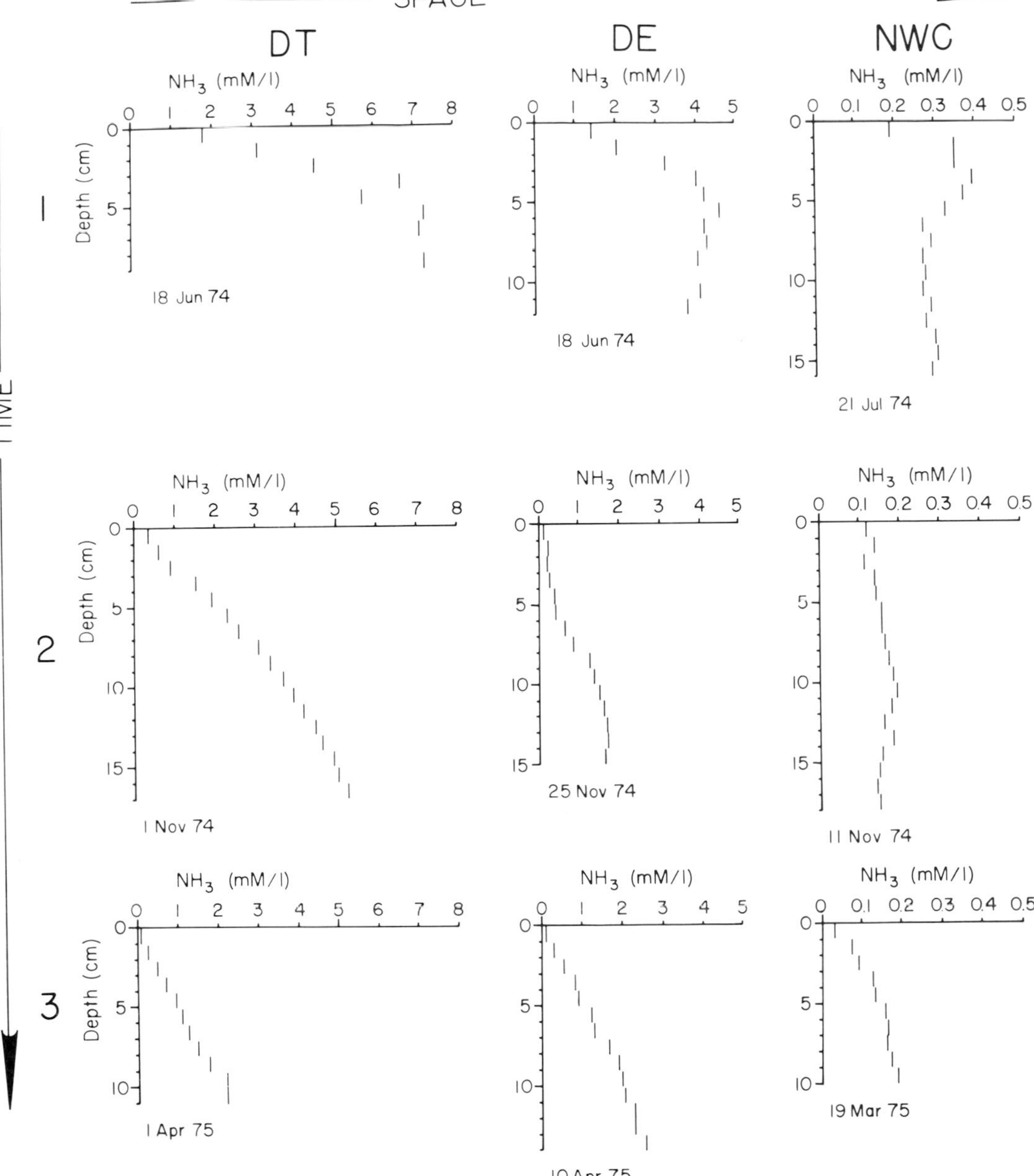

Fig. 15. Pore water profiles of NH_3 at the DT, DE, and NWC stations in the summer, fall, and late winter, 1974-1975. The net diffusion vector is in an upward direction.

onto the spoil pile from the surrounding seafloor. Meiofauna are already present on the dump at this time. Foraminifera dominate numerically.

Stage II extends from the August to November-December sampling dates. This is a period of exponential recruitment of both polychaetes and bivalves. Deposit-feeding bivalves and polychaetes increase in numbers but suspension feeders still dominate. Numbers of foraminifera level off in late summer but other meiofaunal populations show exponential growth.

Stage III extends from December to our last sampling in March and April 1975. During this period immigration rates are nil or balanced by death and (or) immigration rates. The assemblage growth curves level off. Meiofaunal data have not been worked up for this stage.

The above discussion of colonization does not describe the rather constant standing crop of deep-living deposit-feeding benthos at the NWC station over the entire sampling period. Only the shallow burrowing suspension-feeding bivalve *Pitar morrhuana* and meiofauna show a large increase in population size during stage II at the NWC.

One of the first sediment changes detected on the dump surface and NWC is the appearance of increasing abundances of fecal pellets at the surface in early summer. These pellets form a loose porous surface which may provide an important meiofauna habitat. Observations of flume cores indicate that meiofauna move over, or just below, the pelletal surface when the water flow is zero or very low. As water flow accelerated, meiofauna activity at the surface ceased. At this time, the meiofauna may move into the bottom to avoid being moved or displaced with the suspended surface--a layer 1-2 mm thick.

The appearance of abundant meiofauna may in turn play a role in pellet destruction as the surfaces of pellets are grazed and broken down. The finely divided pellet detritus may then be reingested by deposit feeders which otherwise might not be able to ingest the larger pellets. The partial destruction of the pelletal surface by meiofauna(?) grazing (habitat destruction) might account for the small decrease in foraminifera on the dump after August; or this decrease may be due to increased cropping by larger deposit feeders. Aside from these possibilities, the ecologic importance of changing pellet abundance is not understood. However, changing abundance patterns of these pellets clearly produce important textural changes in the upper few millimeters of the bottom. These biogenic particles probably play an important role in the observed faunal recolonization.

The low mean critical rolling velocities measured at all stations in June and July are probably related to the presence of a loosely bound and unpelletized surface. We hypothesize that microbial mucus binding is lowest at this time. The mucus-like material observed on the surfaces of all flume core samples after July 18 may be derived from bacterial exudates serving to agglutinate organic-mineral aggregates to the seafloor. The agglutination phenomenon probably explains the observed increases in critical velocities in late summer. Ullman (1975) has shown in studies with the same flume used here that marine microorganisms grown on beds of glass beads of silt to medium sand size can increase the mean critical rolling velocity up to 60% over that of "abiotic" glass spheres. The small decrease in critical velocities in late winter may be related to declining bacterial activity and/or biomass.

In late summer, the build-up of a pelletal surface together with increased microbial binding of the surface may contribute to the recruitment success of meiofauna and juvenile macrofauna. The binding phenomenon may be especially important for maintenance of suspension feeders on the dump as they rely on interface stability. For instance, only in late summer does one species of suspension feeder colonize the NWC (*P. morrhuana*). At other times, trophic group amensalism is probably active at this station excluding suspension feeders (Rhoads and Young 1970). Myers (1973) has shown similar seasonal changes in suspension- and deposit-feeder abundance related to intensity of bioturbation.

The depth of the RPD undergoes a well-defined seasonal migration having its maximum depression in late fall. The RPD reflects the level in the sediment at which anaerobic metabolism becomes dominant enough for iron sulfides to color the sediment black. The introduction of oxygen into sediment is important in determining the depth of the RPD. Oxygen availability to sediment over that provided by molecular diffusion results from reworking by macrobenthos (Rhoads 1974). The maximum RPD depth at NWC corresponds to the documented seasonal maximum in rates of biogenic particle reworking (Aller and Cochran, 1976). We think that irrigation activites of infaunal polychaetes should also reach maximum rates at this time and are especially important in determining the depth of the color change. The dynamics of this sedimentary feature may directly represent changing exchange rates of sedimentary material with overlying water, in this case oxygen resulting from macrobenthic and microbial activities.

Pore water analyses for SO_4 and NH_3 are also useful in following transfer processes across the sediment-water interface as well as metabolic activity within sediments because there are different major sources and sinks for these ions: $SO_4^=$ is supplied from overlying water and consumed in sediments by sulfate reducers; NH_3 is a metabolic product in sediments that becomes lost to overlying water or to diagenetic reaction (e.g., Goldhaber and Kaplan 1974).

Pore water profiles show that at low densities of deposit feeders, such as found initially at the dump stations, transfer of dissolved species ($SO_4^=$ and NH_4^+) into and out of sediments takes place primarily by molecular diffusion. As shown by the NH_3 data, winter profiles at all stations also appear to be diffusion controlled.

Early summer profiles at the control station indicate production (NH_3) and consumption ($SO_4^=$) of nutrients. Microbial activity increases rapidly near the sediment-water interface (Goldhaber et al. in preparation), producting the maximum in the NH_3 profile. This maximum is absent in the fall, when concentration gradients within the sediment are at a minimum. Interstitial production rates are still high during the fall, as shown by the discontinuity between sea and pore water NH_3 concentrations. We think this reduction in concentration gradients is due to a relative increase in biogenic mixing with respect to production rates in the fall. The result is noticeable in the biogenic exchange of pore water with seawater. This explanation also accounts for the low concentration gradient zones found at the dump edge in the fall and for the exchanged relict zones demonstrated by the winter sulfate profiles taken from the dump. Both dump stations developed these pore water features when biogenic sediment structures (burrows, tubes, bioturbated intervals), as observed in x-radiographs became abundant. The dump-edge and control station both show greater evidence of biogenic pore water exchange than the dump-top station.

These data suggest that sediment pore water chemistry near the interface is controlled during the summer and fall primarily by bacterial respiration and biogenic exchange of pore water with the overlying water. Microbial production and consumption of nutrients are prevalent during early summer while macroinfaunal activity is relatively dominant during the early fall. The winter profile is controlled by diffusion alteration of the late fall profiles; during this time biogenic reworking, although active, is near its yearly low (Aller and Cochran 1976). From the standpoint of sediment chemistry the year can be divided into a period of biological control and a short period of physical control.

We have seen that ventilation of the sediment by organisms depresses the RPD, increases sediment water content, and changes ionic diffusion profiles to biogenically exchanged profiles near the interface. Our data suggest that both the numbers and kinds of organisms present affect these processes. Sediments dominated by suspension and surface deposit-feeding organisms, such as the early dump and dump-top assemblages, are little affected below depths of 1-2 cm. However, when the sediment is dominated by deep-burrowing deposit feeders at densities $\geq$ 100 m^{-2} and at temperatures $\geq$ 10°C, major changes in sediment chemistry take place (NWC). This difference may be related to the behavior of deep-burrowing species which are vagile and continually bioturbate sediments, while members of the shallow-living assemblage are often sedentary, enclosed in shells or residing in permanent well-sealed burrows. Although burrows of all types act as pore water conduits, bioturbation by vagile infauna is probably more efficient in exchanging pore waters than exchange through permanent burrow structures. Bioturbation involves both particle and fluid transfer but the latter activity, termed irrigation, is probably most influential in pore water transport and modification of the sedimentary habitat at depth. Reported values for irrigation rates indicate that liters of seawater m^{-2} day^{-1} are pumped into and out of bottom sediments by sedentary deposit-feeding benthos at moderate population densities and at peak water temperatures (e.g., Wells 1949; Dales 1961; Mangum 1964). These values are probably applicable to vagile organisms as well. Most particle reworking rates are at least an order of magnitude lower volumetrically (e.g., Rhoads 1974).

By irrigating or otherwise reworking sediments, infauna promote a rapid return of mineralized nutrients such as NH_3 to overlying waters. Our data suggest that during the fall dissolved nutrients are rapidly released from sediments into the overlying water. (Direct measurements and modeling of these fluxes will be given in a later paper.) The $SO_4^{=}$ profiles illustrate the replenishment of depleted nutrients to the bottom sediments during this period as well. Both benthic microorganisms and phytoplankton may benefit by irrigation of the sediment nutrient reservoir.

Our study, and the earlier studies of McCall (1975), show that most early colonizers of new fine-grained sediments are surface deposit or suspension feeders. These organisms characteristically seal themselves off from surrounding sediment with well-defined tube dwellings or shells. A notable exception is the deep-living errant polychaete *Nephtys incisa*, a eurytypic species which apparently arrived on the dump as adults. The mobility and eurytypic nature of *N. incisa* have also been noted by McCall (1975). Most deep-burrowing fauna on the dump appear late in the colonization sequence. Our geochemical data show that in the presence of mobile infauna, the bioturbated zone has near sea water values for $SO_4^=$ and low NH_3 concentrations despite apparently strong interstitial production or consumption terms. This information, together with the data on biogenic activity and sediment stability, suggest a sequence of habitat modification and succession of major functional groups of benthos during recolonization of a naturally eroded or newly deposited (e.g., dump) seafloor.

Table 2 summarizes the colonization sequence as far as our study has progressed (April 1975). We have related each stage of colonization to observed changes in the sedimentary habitat. Faunal responses to these modifications are also listed. At this stage of the study, the list of faunal responses are working hypotheses. It remains to be seen if the colonization will revert to stage I or II in the early summer of 1975. We can assume that in subsequent years the colonizing species observed in 1974-1975 might be replaced, in part by other taxa, and that population growth rates and peak abundances might change from year to year. We also expect that colonization might be arrested or reversed by major disturbances such as renewed dumping activity, storm erosion, or intensive predation. We believe, however, that the general pattern of colonization and habitat modification set forth here will recur and prove to be predictable.

The full colonization sequence obviously has not been documented in this brief study. Assuming no reversals occur in the continued colonization, we expect that each successive summer's recruitment will cumulatively add deeper-feeding infauna to the dump assemblage, especially protobranch bivalves and *Nephtys incisa*. At some critical density of *N. annulata* and *Y. limatula*, their bioturbating activities will overcome the binding influence of microbial films and produce a loose sediment surface with low critical rolling and suspension velocities. Tidal resuspension of this surface may then serve to exclude many suspension feeders. Trophic-group amensalism will act to produce a low diversity assemblage of infaunal deposit feeders. The dump surface should then have faunal and sedimentologic properties identical with the NWC station.

Table 2. Relationship between colonization sequence (stages I-III) and habitat modifications on the dump top and dump edge stations. Faunal responses to habitat modifications are hypothetical.

Colonization Sequence	Habitat Modifications	Faunal Responses
Stage I (June-July): Low recruitment rate of surface-feeding and suspension-feeding macrobenthos.	Pellet production starts; RPD depressed to about 1 cm by feeding and respiratory activity.	Stimulation of microbial growth by irrigation of the bottom; recruitment of deeper living infauna following depression of RPD and exchange of pore water near surface.
Meiofaunal recruitment	Surface 'fluffing' by meiofaunal bioturbation. This may contribute to depression of the RPD.	Meiofauna crop microbial films, moving into the pelletal surface down to the RPD.
Stage II (Aug.-Nov.): Exponential recruitment of deeper feeding infauna. Attainment of maximum standing crops and high metabolic rates.	Pellet destruction by grazing meiofauna exceeds pellet production rates. Depression of RPD and sediment water content to 2-3 cm by particle reworking and respiratory irrigation. Pore water exchanged with sea water to 3-6 cm. Interstitial nutrients replenished, metabolites continually pumped out of sediment. Microbial binding of seafloor.	Some meiofaunal decline due to partial destruction of pellet layer; peak abundance of deep feeders. Stimulation of microbial and phytoplankton growth by nutrients pumped out of the bottom. Microbial binding of the seafloor maintains suspension feeders.
Stage III (Dec.-April): Recruitment nil. Some mortality. Metabolic rates decrease	Pelletal surface decays; RPD rebounds to 1-2 cm. Pore water profiles are diffusion-altered relicts of late fall metabolic activity. Microbial binding declines.	All populations level off or experience slight declines. Shallow-living organisms experience higher mortality than deep-living species.

REFERENCES

Aller, R. C. and J. K. Cochran. 1976. Th^{234}-U^{238} disequilibrium in near-shore sediment: particle reworking and diagenetic time scales. Earth Planet. Sci. Letters 29: 37-50.

Berner, R. A. 1974. Kinetic models for the early diagenesis of nitrogen, sulfur, phosphorus, and silicon in anoxic marine sediments, pp. 427-450. In E. D. Goldberg [ed.], The sea, v. 5, Marine chemistry. John Wiley.

_____. 1975. Diagenetic models of dissolved species in the interstitial waters of compacting sediments. Am. J. Sci. 275: 88-96.

Clements, F. E. 1904. Studies on the vegetation of the State III: Development and structure of vegetation. Nebraska Univ. Bot. Sem. Bot. Surv. Nebraska 7: 1-175.

Cowles, H. C. 1901. The physiographic ecology of Chicago and vicinity. A study of the origin, development, and classification of plant societies. Bot. Gax. 31: 1-73.

Cullen, D. J. 1973. Bioturbation of superficial marine sediments by interstitial meiobenthos. Nature 242: 323-324.

Dales, R. P. 1961. Oxygen uptake and irrigation of the burrow by three terebellid polychaetes: *Eupolymnia, Thelepus,* and *Neo-amphitrite.* Physiol. Zool. 34: 306-311.

Degobbis, D. 1973. On the storage of seawater samples for ammonia determination. Limnol. Oceanogr. 18: 146-150.

Fenchel, T. M. and R. J. Riedl. 1970. The sulphide system: A new biotic community underneath the oxidized layer of marine sand bottoms. Mar. Biol. 7: 255-268.

Fisher, J. B. 1973. The effect of environmental perturbations on benthic communities: an experiment in benthic recolonization and succession in Long Island Sound. Senior thesis, Yale Univ. 29 p.

Goldhaber, M. B. and I. Kaplan. 1974. The sulfur cycle, pp. 569-655. In E. D. Goldberg [ed.], The sea, v. 5, Marine chemistry. John Wiley.

Gordon, R. B. and C. C. Pilbeam. 1974. Environmental consequences of dredge spoil disposal in Long Island Sound: Geophysical studies, 1 October 1972-30 September 1973. Unpubl. Rpt. U.S. Army Corps of Engineers. New England Division, Waltham, MA.

Hayes, R. R. 1964. The mud-water interface. Oceanogr. Mar. Biol. Ann. Rev. 2: 121-145.

Johnson, R. G. 1972. Conceptual models of benthic marine communities, pp. 148-159. In T. J. M. Schopf [ed.], Models in paleobiology. Freeman, Cooper, & Co.

Kalil, E. K. and M. Goldhaber. 1973. A sediment squeezer for removal of pore waters without air contact. J. Sediment. Petrol. 43: 553-557.

McCall, P. L. 1975. The influence of disturbance on community patterns and adaptive strategies of the infaunal benthos of central Long Island Sound. Ph.D. thesis, Yale Univ. 198 p.

Mangum, C. 1964. Activity patterns in metabolism and ecology of polychaetes. Comp. Biochem. Physiol. 11: 239-256.

Mills, E. L. 1967. The biology of an ampeliscid amphipod crustacean sibling species pair. J. Fish. Res. Bd. Can. 24: 305-355.

Myers, A. C. 1973. Sediment reworking, tube building, and burrowing in a shallow marine subtidal community: rates and effects. Ph.D. thesis, Univ. Rhode Island. 117 p.

Rhoads, D. C. 1974. Organism-sediment relations on the muddy sea floor. Oceanog. Mar. Biol. Ann. Rev. 12: 263-300.

_____ and A. Michael. 1974. Summary of benthic biologic sampling in central Long Island Sound and New Haven Harbor (prior to dredging and dumping) July 1972-August 1973. Unpubl. Rpt. U.S. Army Corps of Engineers. New England Division, Waltham, MA.

_____ and D. K. Young. 1970. The influence of deposit-feeding organisms on sediment stability and community trophic structure. J. Mar. Res. 28 : 150-178.

Sanders, H. L. 1956. Oceanography of Long Island Sound, 1952-1954 X. The biology of marine bottom communities. Bull. Bingham Oceanogr. Coll. 15: 345-414.

Solorzano, L. 1969. Determination of ammonia in natural waters by the phenol hypochlorite method. Limnol. Oceanogr. 14: 799-801.

Ullman, W. 1975. Stabilization of the sediment-water interface by the presence of the extracellular products of microorganisms. Senior thesis, Yale Univ. 42 p.

Warming, E. 1918. Lehrbuch der Oekologischen. Pflanzengeographie. Gebruder Borntraeger, Berlin. 988 p.

Wells, G. P. 1949. Respiratory movements of *Arenicola marina* L.: Intermittent irrigation of the tube, and intermittent aerial respiration. J. Mar. Biol. Assoc. U.K. 28: 447-464.

Reestablishment of a Benthic Community Following Natural Defaunation

Joseph L. Simon and **Daniel M. Dauer**[1]
Department of Biology
University of South Florida
Tampa, FL 33620

ABSTRACT

During summer 1971, a massive outbreak of red tide resulted in the defaunation of a sandy, intertidal habitat in upper old Tampa Bay, Tampa, Florida. Colonization of the habitat was studied from August 1971 to July 1973. A transect composed of 4 stations running from just below mean high water to just below mean low water was quantitatively sampled each month for species composition, densities of individual populations, and distribution of age classes.

During the 24 months of sampling, 153 species of benthic infaunal invertebrates were identified. Species colonization and abundance patterns over time were studied for the entire macrofauna. In addition, five major taxonomic categories were examined separately: polychaetes, molluscs, amphipods, other crustaceans (isopods, cumaceans, shrimps, crabs, etc.) and miscellaneous phyla (amphioxus, phoronids, brachiopods, rhynchocoels, chaetognaths, oligochaetes, platyhelminths, and anemones).

The fauna made a rapid recovery in terms of species numbers and composition, returning to much the same assemblage as prior to the red tide. Polychaetes were the most rapid colonists both in terms of the number of species and number of individuals. Molluscs and amphipods were slower in appearance and also were significantly affected by seasonal patterns of reproduction, and thus dispersal. Only the polychaetes, other crustacea, and the total fauna showed species colonization patterns which indicated an approach to an equilibrium value. Species abundance patterns showed a variety of responses from strong seasonal influences (molluscs and amphipods) to a continuously increasing pattern (total fauna).

The demonstration of different colonizing abilities among major taxa leads to the conclusion that care should be used when interpreting environmental perturbation studies where only a single taxon has been examined.

[1] Present address: Department of Biology, Old Dominion University, Norfolk, Virginia 23508.

INTRODUCTION

During the summer of 1971, a serious outbreak of the Florida red tide organism, *Gymnodinium breve* (Davis), occurred along the Florida west coast and caused mass mortalities of both marine fishes and invertebrates (Steidinger and Ingle 1972). The benthic infauna of a sandy intertidal habitat in upper Old Tampa Bay, Tampa, Florida, was severely affected (Simon and Dauer 1972). In general, the number of infaunal invertebrate species was suddenly reduced 77% with a decrease of 97% in the total number of individuals. The kill was a localized phenomenon restricted primarily to intertidal areas where local current patterns were responsible for the greatest accumulation of dead fishes. The resulting anaerobic conditions were considered to be a major contributer to the mass mortalities. The study area, where the defaunation was most extensive, was 2.5 km (shoreline) by 120 m (intertidal range).

The sudden defaunation without physical disruption or, as near as is known, without the persistence of long-lasting toxins in the habitat, provided an opportunity to examine reestablishment of the benthic community. Since the area had been well studied previously (Bloom, et al. 1972), the fauna could be compared before and after various time periods. Studies of repopulation in the past have usually been based on man-made disasters (oil spills, dredging, etc.), all of which are known to not only kill or remove organisms, but also to drastically alter the environment. Seldom has there been a sufficient baseline of data prior to such disruptions for comparisons to be made.

The purpose of this paper is to present a general overview of the process of repopulation and to compare the responses shown by the total benthic infauna and separate major taxa.

We thank S. A. Bloom and S. L. Santos for their assistance in the computer handling and evaluation of the data. For taxonomic verifications and identifications, we thank William G. Lyons (molluscs) and David Camp (crustaceans) of the Florida Department of Natural Resources, Marine Research Laboratory; E. L. Bousfield (amphipods) of the National Museum of Canada; and Kris W. Thoemke (amphipods) and Ernest D. Estevez (isopods) of the University of South Florida. For aid in the collection and sorting of the samples, we thank W. Conner, K. Erwin, E. Estevez, M. Marshall, D. McKirdy, J. Miller, G. Pelsue, J. Rose, S. Santos, and T. Wilhelm.

This study was supported by the Oceanography Section, National Science Foundation, NSF Grant GA-31769.

MATERIALS AND METHODS

The study area was located on the south side of Courtney Campbell Causeway (State Road 60), Old Tampa Bay, Florida (Fig. 1). A

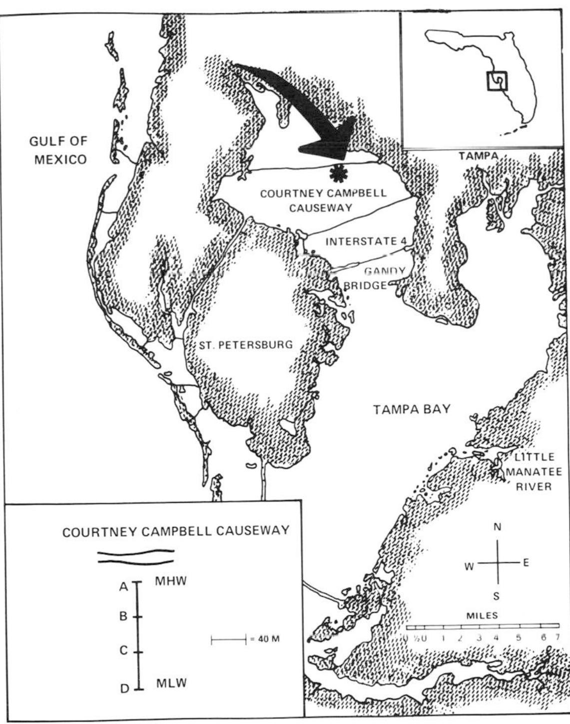

Fig. 1. Tampa Bay, Florida, U.S.A. Study area--Courtney Campbell Causeway. Station A--Just below mean high water, B, C, and D located at 40 m increments from A. Station D--just below mean low water.

transect, perpendicular to the shore and composed of four stations running from just below mean high water to just below mean low water was sampled monthly for 24 months (August 1971 to July 1973).

Samples were taken by a hand-held PVC coring device with a surface area of 0.008 m^2. The contents of five cores, taken to a depth of 25 cm, were pooled as a single sub-sample representing a surface area of 0.04 m^2. Five sub-samples were taken at each station, giving a total surface area sampled of 0.2 m^2. Previous studies (unpublished) have indicated that a sample size of 0.1 m^2 would have been adequate for statistical evaluation of the fauna existing prior to the red tide. Since the structure of the fauna after repopulation could not be predicted in advance, the previously known adequate sample size was doubled. Each sub-sample (of 5 cores) was sieved in the field through a 0.5-mm mesh screen. Reish (1959) has indicated a mesh of this size should yield close to 100% of the "macrofaunal" species. In the laboratory the organisms were relaxed in 0.15% propylene phenoxetol in sea water (McKay and Hartzband 1970), stained with rose bengal (Mason and Yevich 1967), preserved in 10% formalin, sorted to major taxon, and stored in 70% isopropyl alcohol. Species identifications and counts were subsequently made.

Temperature and salinity were measured during each sampling period by a hand-held thermometer and refractometer, respectively. Sediment samples were taken quarterly at each station and analyzed by wet-sieve techniques for particle size composition (Holme and McIntyre 1971). Sediment parameters (mean phi, median phi, sorting coefficient, skewness, kurtosis) were determined using the formulae of Inman (1952), and statistical analysis was performed to determine whether sediment parameters differed in space and time.

Colonization curves and species abundance curves were constructed by comparing species lists and density values from month to month. For the purposes of this paper, a general overview of the course of reestablishment of a benthic community, species have been summed over the entire transect and densities expressed as mean number m^{-2} for the entire transect. That is, the entire intertidal sandy habitat was treated as a single ecological unit (see Dauer and Simon 1975). Subsequent papers will discuss the distribution patterns along the intertidal gradient in greater detail.

Although 153 species (taxa) were noted during the 24 months, only the most abundant species (numerical dominants) or species of special interest will be discussed. A complete list of species may be obtained from the authors on request. In addition to total macrofauna, the fauna was examined as five major categories: polychaetes, molluscs, amphipods, other crustaceans (isopods, cumaceans, shrimps, crabs, etc.), and miscellaneous phyla (amphioxus, phoronids, brachiopods, rhynchocoels, chaetognaths, oligochaetes, platyhelminths, and anemones).

RESULTS

Defaunation

The defaunated area was well studied in 1968-1969 (Bloom et al. 1972) and in 1970 (unpublished). Although the sampling techniques used prior to the present study were different, in that a 1-mm mesh sieve was used, a general picture of the "before" fauna was available. Fifty-three species of infaunal invertebrates (over 1 mm) were known to be present. Sampling according to the above methods directly after the red tide outbreak (Month 1, August 1971) showed that at least 77% of the species numbers and 97% of the number of individuals in the area were destroyed (Table 1).

Although the vast majority of species were killed rapidly (during the red tide), several species appeared more resistant. For example, both *Pectinaria gouldii* (Verrill) and *Mulinia lateralis* (Say) took several months to completely die off; however, during this time they appeared unhealthy. *Pectinaria* lost its normal pink-red color and turned muddy-brown, while *Mulinia* was found lying on the sediment surface with its shell gaping and siphons extended. A number of species appeared to be completely unaffected by the red tide, their occurrence and densities remaining essentially constant in the "before" studies and "after" samples: *Phoronis architecta* Andrews, *Ophiophragmus filograneus* (Lyman), *Stylochus* sp., *Scolelepis texana* Foster, an oligochaete sp. and *Apanthura magnifica* Menzies and Frankenberg.

Environmental Parameters

Temperature and salinity during the study period are shown in Figure 2. The temperature varied from 8-13°C while the salinity

Table 1. A comparison of species (mean densities per m^2 along entire transect before (April 1970), immediately following (August 1971), and two years after (Month 24, July 1973) red tide induced defaunation. (? indicates species present but not counted.)

Taxon	Before*	Month 1	Month 24
POLYCHAETES			
Clymenella mucosa	13	0	23
Diopatra cuprea	78	0	1
Glycera spp.	16	0	28
Nereis succinea	33	7	14
Onuphis eremita oculata	273	0	3
Pectinaria gouldii	4	38	0
Polydora spp.	?	800	6
Prionospio heterobranchia	10	0	6
Scolelepis texana	15	13	31
Scoloplos foliosus	25	0	3
Scoloplos rubra	39	0	32
Travisia sp.	261	3	189
MOLLUSCA			
Ensis minor	34	0	22
Mulina lateralis	78	13	20
Nassarius vibex	26	0	0
Prunum apicinum	9	0	0
Tellina sp.	?	0	2436
AMPHIPODS			
Acanthohaustorius sp.	873	0	1694
Other amphipods	253	0	305
OTHER CRUSTACEANS			
Cumaceans	8	0	48
Apanthura magnifica	24	65	85
Pinnixa sayana	44	0	49
MISC. TAXA			
Branchiostoma caribaeum	203	0	85
Cerianthid anemone	2	0	0
Glottidia pyramidatum	67	10	1332
Phoronis architecta	3	1	23
Rhynchocoel spp.	8	0	34
Stylochus sp.	3	107	27

*Modified from Simon and Dauer, 1972.

Fig. 2. Salinity (°/₀₀) and temperature (C) at sampling site during the period of study (August 1971 to July 1973).

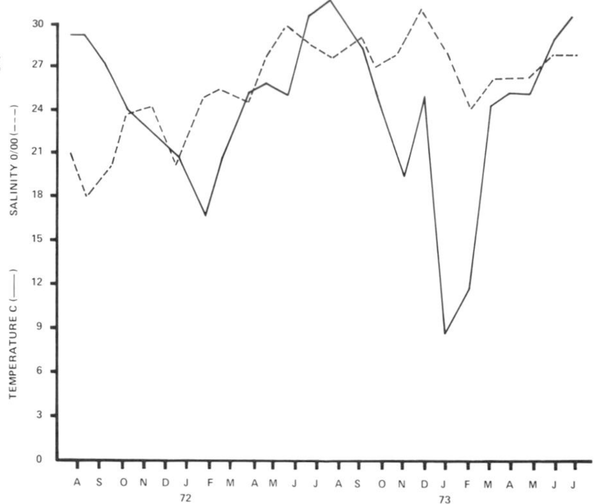

ranged from 18-29 °/₀₀. The average salinity during the second year of study was slightly higher than that of the first year.

Analysis of sediment parameters showed only one significant difference--Station A at the high tide line had a larger median grain size and higher average sorting coefficient (Md = 0.247 mm, σ_ϕ = 1.01) than the other stations (Md = 0.175 mm, σ_ϕ = 0.40).

<u>Recolonization--Species Numbers</u>

The species colonization curves for total benthic infauna and for the five major categories of taxa are shown in Figure 3.

The total fauna species curve (Fig. 3A) shows a rapid rise during Months 1-3 (August, September, October 1971), an additional peak at Month 6 (January 1972), a decline during Months 7-10 (February to May 1972), and a large rise at Month 11 (June 1972). The groups responsible for the peaks and troughs can be seen in Figure 3B-F and Table 2. The initial rise in species numbers (Months 1-3) was due primarily to the rapid appearance of polychaetes, with only minor contributions by other groups. The Month 6 rise was due primarily to increases in amphipods and molluscs. The decline during Months 7-10 was due to a reduction in other (non-amphipod) crustaceans.

The polychaetes (Fig. 3B) increased in species numbers more rapidly than any other group, and maintained a high level of species numbers throughout the last 12 months of study (28.9 ± 2 species). Amphipods, on the other hand (Fig. 3D), were very slow in colonizing. Over one-half of the total species did not appear until the last 8 months of study. Molluscs also showed a slow increase in species number for the first 10 months (Fig. 3C), followed by a sharp rise in species during Month 11 and again near the end of the study (Months 23-24). Other (non-amphipod) crustaceans showed a slight increase in species during the first two months, maintained that level more or less from Months 2-7, declined during Months 8-9, and rose to a maximum number of species in Month 11 (Fig. 3E). The miscellaneous phyla showed no great changes in species numbers throughout the study (Fig. 3F).

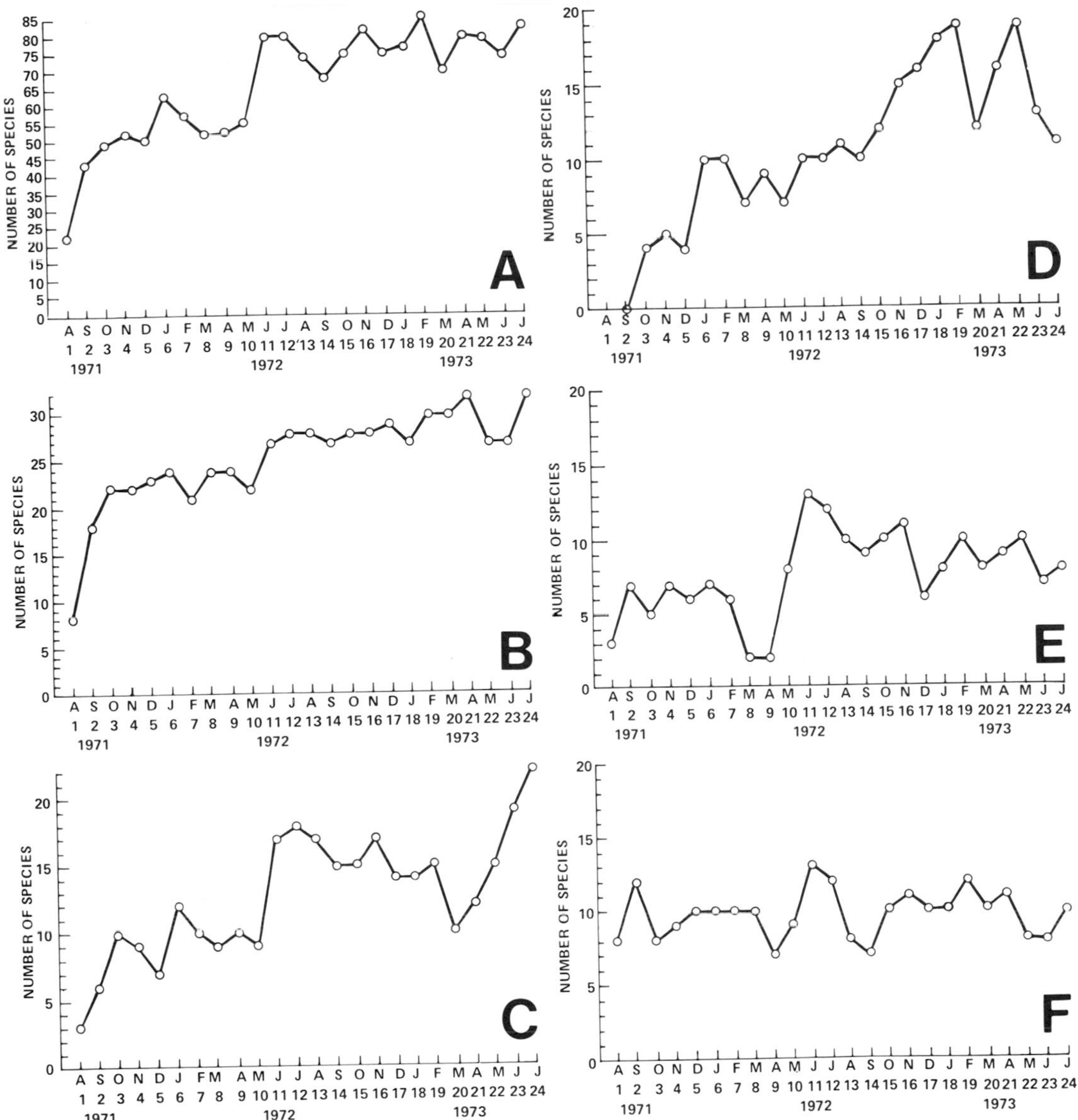

Fig. 3. Species colonization curves for total benthic infauna and various taxa during period of study (August 1971 to July 1973). A. Total benthic infauna, B. Polychaetes only, C. Molluscs only, D. Amphipods only, E. Other (non-amphipod) crustaceans only (isopods, cumaceans, shrimps, crabs, etc.), F. Miscellaneous Phyla (amphioxus, phoronids, brachiopods, rhynchocoels, chaetognaths, oligochaetes, platyhelminths, and anemones).

The percent contribution of the various taxonomic categories to the total number of benthic infaunal species (Table 2) illustrates the above patterns more clearly. Polychaetes made up from 34.1% to 47.2% of the total number of species present over the 24-month period, while the amphipods varied from 0% to a maximum of

Table 2. Number of species of five major taxa and percent of the total number of species (in parentheses) present along entire transect over 24 months (August 1971-July 1973).

Month	Polychaetes	Amphipods	Other Crustacean	Molluscs	Misc. Phyla	Total
1	8 (36.4%)	-0-	3 (13.6%)	3 (13.6%)	8 (36.4%)	22
2	18 (41.9%)	-0-	7 (16.3%)	6 (14.0%)	12 (27.9%)	43
3	22 (44.9%)	4 (8.2%)	5 (10.2%)	10 (20.4%)	8 (16.3%)	49
4	22 (42.3%)	5 (9.6%)	7 (13.5%)	9 (17.3%)	9 (17.3%)	52
5	23 (46.0%)	4 (8.0%)	6 (12.0%)	7 (14.0%)	10 (20.0%)	50
6	24 (38.1%)	10 (15.9%)	7 (11.1%)	12 (19.0%)	10 (15.9%)	63
7	21 (36.8%)	10 (17.5%)	6 (10.5%)	10 (17.5%)	10 (17.5%)	57
8	25 (47.2%)	7 (13.2%)	2 (3.8%)	9 (17.0%)	10 (18.9%)	53
9	25 (47.2%)	9 (17.0%)	2 (3.8%)	10 (18.9%)	7 (13.2%)	53
10	22 (40.0%)	7 (12.7%)	8 (14.5%)	9 (16.4%)	9 (16.4%)	55
11	28 (34.6%)	10 (12.3%)	13 (16.0%)	17 (21.0%)	13 (16.0%)	81
12	28 (35.5%)	10 (12.5%)	12 (15.0%)	18 (22.5%)	12 (15.0%)	80
13	28 (37.8%)	11 (14.9%)	10 (13.5%)	17 (23.0%)	8 (15.0%)	74
14	27 (39.8%)	10 (14.7%)	9 (13.2%)	15 (22.1%)	10 (13.3%)	68
15	28 (37.3%)	12 (16.0%)	10 (13.3%)	15 (20.0%)	10 (13.3%)	75
16	28 (34.1%)	15 (18.3%)	11 (13.4%)	17 (20.7%)	11 (13.4%)	82
17	29 (38.6%)	16 (21.3%)	6 (8.0%)	14 (18.7%)	10 (13.3%)	75
18	27 (35.0%)	18 (23.4%)	8 (10.4%)	14 (18.2%)	10 (13.0%)	77
19	31 (35.6%)	19 (21.8%)	10 (11.5%)	15 (17.2%)	12 (13.8%)	87
20	31 (43.7%)	12 (16.9%)	8 (11.3%)	10 (14.1%)	10 (14.1%)	71
21	32 (40.0%)	16 (20.0%)	9 (11.3%)	12 (15.0%)	11 (13.8%)	80
22	27 (34.2%)	19 (24.1%)	10 (12.7%)	15 (19.0%)	8 (10.1%)	79
23	27 (36.0%)	14 (18.6%)	7 (9.3%)	19 (25.3%)	8 (10.7%)	75
24	32 (38.6%)	11 (13.3%)	8 (9.6%)	22 (26.5%)	10 (12.1%)	83

24.1% (Month 22). Other crustaceans varied from 3.8% to 16.3%, while the molluscs ranged from 13.6% to 26.5%. The miscellaneous phyla after Month 9 showed an almost constant contribution to the total (e.g., Months 10-24 varied from 10.1% to 16.4%).

In general, the overall total infaunal species curve (Fig. 3A) shows a leveling off from Month 11 through the end of the study (Months 11-24 had a mean of 77.6 ± 5.1 species).

Recolonization--Density Patterns

The total benthic fauna density distribution over the 24-month period of study (Fig. 4A) showed a relatively small change from Month 1-10, and a marked increase during Months 11-13 (from about 2,000 to 10,000 individuals m^{-2}). The density patterns for major taxa (Fig. 4B-F) showed a wide variety of responses. The polychaetes exhibited a rapid increase during the first three months and during Months 11-21, with declines during Months 4-10 and again during Months 22-24 (Fig. 4B). Highest densities were found during the fall-winter-spring period, and lowest densities during the summer months. The other taxonomic categories (Figs. 4C-F) showed wide oscillations in density patterns--all related to brief or seasonal settlement of juveniles.

Table 3 shows the percent contribution of the major taxonomic categories to total densities. During the first six months of study,

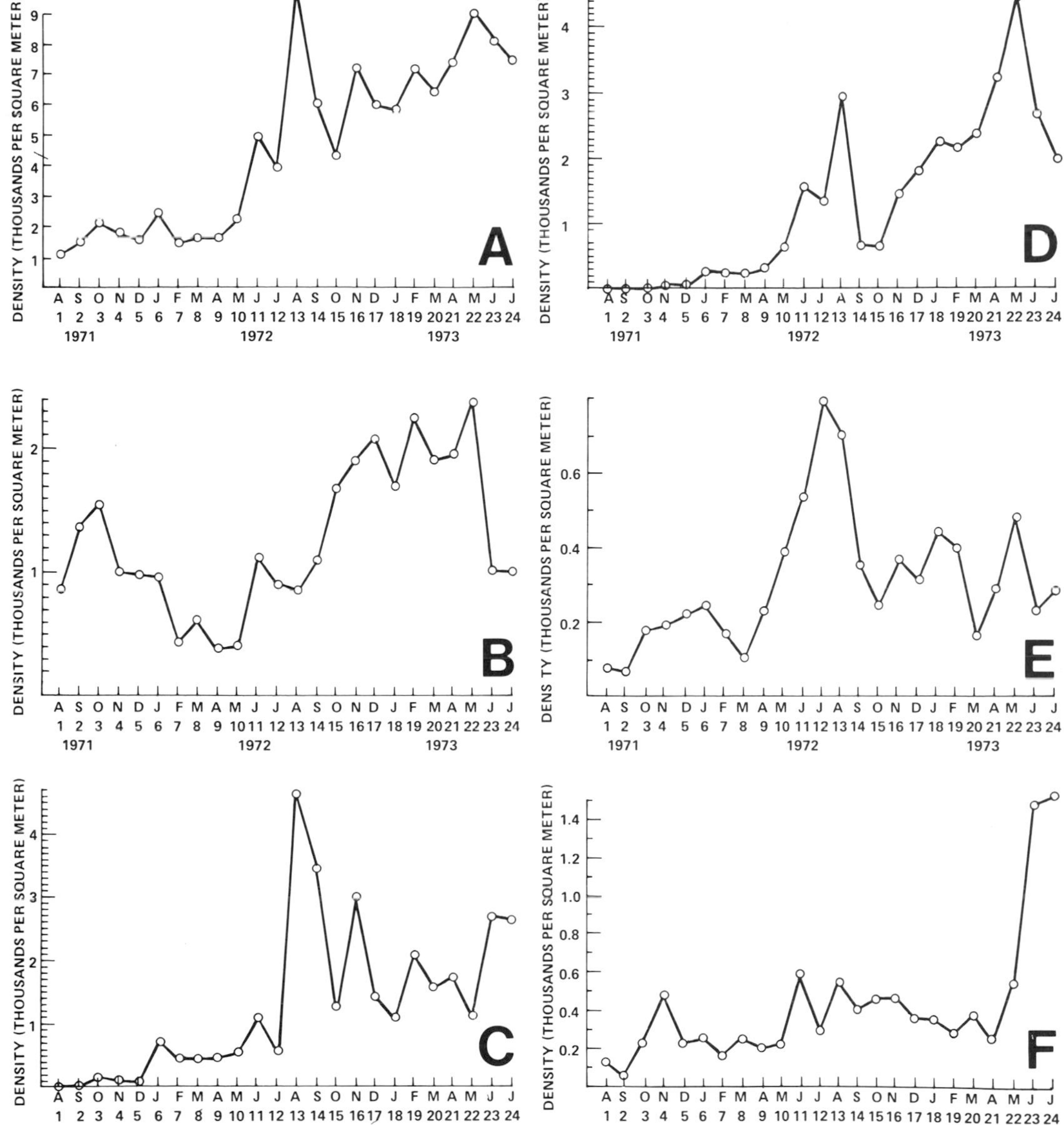

Fig. 4. Mean density (individuals m^{-2}) per transect for total benthic infauna and various taxa during period of study (August 1971 to July 1973). A. Total benthic infauna, B. Polychaetes only, C. Molluscs only, D. Amphipods only, E. Other (non-amphipod) crustaceans (isopods, cumaceans, shrimps, crabs, etc.), F. Miscellaneous phyla (amphioxus, phoronids, brachiopods, rhynchocoels, chaetognaths, oligochaetes, platyhelminths and anemones).

polychaetes dominated. After that time, the amphipods and molluscs became more important. Only during one month (12) did the (non-amphipod) other crustaceans comprise 20% of the total, and only during two months (4 and 24) did the miscellaneous phyla make up more than 20% of the total.

Table 3. Percent of total density made up by the five major taxa along entire transect over 24 months (August 1971-July 1973).

Month	Polychaetes	Amphipods	Other Crustaceans	Molluscs	Misc.Phyla
1	79.0	0	6.8	2.1	12.2
2	89.3	0	4.4	2.3	4.0
3	72.1	1.1	8.4	7.8	10.7
4	55.1	3.0	10.6	5.0	26.4
5	62.9	2.2	14.1	6.2	14.7
6	39.6	10.9	10.0	29.3	10.3
7	29.8	16.8	11.6	30.7	11.1
8	37.9	13.7	6.5	27.0	15.0
9	24.0	19.8	14.3	29.5	12.5
10	18.5	29.2	17.5	24.7	10.2
11	22.9	31.8	10.9	22.3	12.1
12	23.1	34.5	20.1	14.9	7.4
13	8.8	30.4	7.2	47.9	5.7
14	18.2	11.5	5.8	57.7	6.7
15	38.9	15.6	5.7	29.1	10.7
16	26.5	20.4	5.1	41.6	6.5
17	35.0	30.2	5.3	23.6	6.0
18	29.1	38.5	7.5	18.8	6.1
19	31.3	30.2	5.5	28.9	4.0
20	29.9	37.1	2.5	24.5	6.0
21	26.2	43.4	3.9	23.1	3.4
22	26.3	49.8	5.3	12.6	6.0
23	12.5	33.3	2.8	33.2	18.2
24	13.5	26.7	3.9	35.4	20.5

Initial Colonization Period (Months 1-3)

Five species (*Polydora ligni* Webster, *Polydora socialis* (Schmarda) *Apanthura magnifica*, *Stylochus* sp., and *Pectinaria gouldii*) made up 92% of the total number of individuals present Month 1 (Table 4). The total contribution of these five species had dropped to only 9.2% by Month 3, with only *Apanthura* making a major contribution. During Month 2, three additional species (*Nereis succinea* Frey and Leukart, *Eteone heteropoda* Hartman, and *Paraprionospio pinnata* (Ehlers) became dominant, contributing 21.7%, 29.7%, and 17.5% respectively. During Month 3, *Nereis* maintained its contribution to the total (20.1%), while *Eteone* and *Paraprionospio* both declined. During Month 3, a new group of species appeared (Table 4).

As already mentioned, of the species present initially three (*Apanthura*, *Pectinaria*, and *Stylochus*) were initially unaffected by the red tide, and thus cannot be considered colonizing species. Both *Polydora ligni* and *P. socialis*, however, must be considered colonizers. *Polydora ligni* has been discussed as an opportunistic species by Grassle and Grassle (1974), who ranked it second only to *Capitella*

Table 4. Species important as density dominants during the first three months of study (August 1971-October 1971), expressed as percent of total number of individuals and as mean density per m^2 along the entire transect (in parentheses).

Taxon	Month 1	Month 2	Month 3
Polydora ligni	69.2% (761)	1.4% (22)	0.05% (1)
Polydora socialis	3.6% (39)	0.8% (12)	0.05% (1)
Apanthura magnifica	5.9% (65)	3.1% (48)	6.9 % (148)
Stylochus sp.	9.7% (107)	0.9% (14)	0.6 % (13)
Pectinaria gouldii	3.5% (38)	1.5% (23)	1.6 % (35)
Nereis succinea	0	21.7% (333)	20.1 % (434)
Eteone heteropoda	0	29.7% (455)	11.6 % (250)
Paraprionospio pinnata	0	17.5% (269)	10.0 % (132)
Apoprionospio pygmaea	0	2.2% (34)	3.2 % (69)
Gyptis vittata	0	4.7% (72)	6.0 % (129)
Capitella capitata	0	1.5% (23)	1.5 % (33)
Magelona pettiboneae	0	0.7% (9)	13.0 % (280)
Haminoea succinea	0	0.2% (3)	3.5 % (76)
Branchiostoma caribaeum	0	0.2% (1)	2.3 % (50)
Mysella planulata	0	0	2.6 % (56)
Acanthohaustorius sp.	0	0	0.5 % (10)
Ampelisca verrilli	0	0	0.2 % (4)

capitata (Fabricius) in terms of its ability to colonize new or disturbed habitats. As in Grassle and Grassle (1974) and Reish (1962), during the present study this species rapidly built up large densities, then declined as other species moved in.

The apparent occurrence of large numbers of *Stylochus* during the initial month of study, as compared to its densities before and after that time (Table 1, 4), may be explained by its natural history. This species lives as a commensal in the tubes of other organisms. We assume, as a result of the red tide, that *Stylochus* left the tubes of their various host animals (mostly *Upogebia*) and were concentrated at the sediment surface.

The influx of high densities of *Nereis*. during Month 2 was due almost exclusively to the appearance of heteronereid forms, the swarming epitokes which swim near the surface of the water at night and retreat back into the sediment (if they have not spawned out) at dawn. During Month 2 about 75% of the *Nereis* present were heteronereids which were carried in from neighboring parts of the bay where defaunation did not occur. During Month 3, about 23% of the *Nereis* were juveniles, presumably the results of the previous months spawning.

The appearance of large numbers of *Eteone* during Month 2 is less easily explained. It is tempting to postulate that *Eteone*, a known predator of *Nereis* (Simon 1965), moved into the area in response to an increase in its preferred prey species, since when *Nereis* densities dropped, the *Eteone* density did likewise (Dauer 1974).

The second large increase in species numbers during Month 11 (June 1972) (Fig. 3A, Table 2) was due to the appearance of a variety of species (Table 5) which exhibit seasonality in reproduction, since the majority of individuals were juveniles.

Table 5. List of new species added between Month 10 (May 1972) and Month 11 (June 1972). Species in parentheses had appeared at some time prior to Month 10, but were absent during Month 10.

Polychaetes
Lepidonotus sublevis
Spiophanes bombyx
Sthenelais boa
(*Diopatra cuprea*)
(*Minuspio cirrifera*)
(*Pectinaria gouldii*)
(*Phyllodoce arenae*)
(*Prionospio heterobrancia*)
(*Spiochaetopterus costarum*)

Amphipods
Corophium sp. A
(*Caprella* sp.)
(*Cymadusa* sp. A)

Other Crustaceans
Lepidopa websteri
(*Ambidexter symmetricus*)
(*Leptalpheus forceps*)
(*Panopeus occidentalis*)
(*Squilla empusa*)

Molluscs
Epitonium sp.
Polinices duplicatus
Anadara transversa
Laevicardium mortoni
(*Haminoea succinea*)
(*Odostomia* sp.)
(*Branchiodontes exustus*)
(*Mercenaria campechiensis*)

Miscellaneous Phyla
Paranthus rapiformis
Spadella sp.
(*Anemone* sp.)
(*Edwarsia* sp.)

Species Responsible For the Month 13 Density Peak

The large density increase during Month 13 (Fig. 4A) was due primarily (71%) to reproduction of a few species (Table 6). The majority of individuals of the species listed were recently metamorphosed juveniles. The large reduction in numbers seen by Month 15 reflects a reduction in these juveniles (Table 6).

Other Species of Interest

The Month 16 increase in molluscs pointed out earlier (Fig. 4C) was due to the appearance of juveniles of *Mulinia*, *Tellina versicolor* DeKay, and *Mysella planulata* Stimpson.

The rise in amphipod densities during Months 21-23 (Fig. 4D) was due to reproduction and recruitment of *Acanthohaustorius* sp., *Ampelisca verrilli* Mills, and *Erichthonius brasiliensis* (Dana).

The change in density patterns of other (non-amphipod) crustaceans (Fig. 4E) was due to recruitment in *Apanthura* (Months 10-12) and the cumacean *Oxyurostylis smithi* Calman during Month 12.

Table 6. A comparison of species of importance in the Month 13 (August 1972) rise in density and Month 15 (October 1972) decline. Numbers are expressed both as mean density per m^2 and percent of total density (in parentheses) along the entire transect.

Species	Month 12	Month 13	Month 15
Molluscs			
Amygadalum papyria	3 (0.08%)	2824 (29.0%)	22 (0.5%)
Tagelus divisus	1 (0.03%)	345 (3.5%)	110 (2.5%)
Tellina versicolor	92 (2.30%)	297 (3.0%)	172 (3.9%)
Mysella planulata	359 (9.10%)	770 (7.9%)	775 (17.7%)
Amphipods			
Ampelisca verrilli	338 (8.60%)	1381 (14.2%)	142 (3.3%)
Rudilemboides naglei	346 (8.80%)	950 (9.8%)	9 (0.2%)
Misc. Phyla			
Glottidia pyramidatum	14 (0.40%)	159 (1.6%)	20 (0.5%)
Branchiostoma caribaeum	155 (3.90%)	215 (2.2%)	194 (4.4%)

Although the contribution of the miscellaneous phyla remained generally about the same (Fig. 4F), the rise during Month 4 was due to an increase in an oligochaete sp., the Month 12-15 increase to a set of juvenile *Glottidia pyramidatum* (Stimpson) and *Branchiostoma caribaeum* Sundevall, while the large peak during Months 23-24 was due to larval settlement of *Glottidia*.

Before/After Comparison

The "before" faunal species list included only 53 species, while the "after" species list included 153 species. This increase was related to the use of a 0.5-mm mesh size (after) rather than a 1.0-mm mesh size (before). A comparison of the species known to be present prior to the red tide and those present after (Month 24) (Table 1) showed that the fauna had not drastically changed in species composition as a result of defaunation. Given the fluctuations in density patterns shown during the present study (Fig. 4), it is perhaps surprising that many of the densities shown in Table 1 for Month 24 were as close to those species densities before defaunation. Several species which were at least conspicuous before, did not appear 24 months after repopulation (e.g., *Nassarius vibex* Say and *Prunum apicinum* Menke). Both of these species are gastropods which produce egg capsules and have "crawl away" young. One species which was dominant prior to defaunation (*Onuphis eremita* Hartman), was present in very low densities by Month 24. This species broods its young within the maternal tube and has no pelagic phase, and thus would, as the two gastropods above, be expected to be a slow colonizer.

DISCUSSION

Although a marked defaunation of benthic infaunal invertebrates was caused by the Florida red tide, the fauna made a rapid recovery in terms of species numbers and composition, returning to much the same assemblage as was present prior to the disturbance. Other analyses of the data (to be published elsewhere) indicate that an "equilibrium" level of species (sensu MacArthur and Wilson 1967) was reached by the 11th month.

The importance of polychaetes as initial colonizers was related to two facts. First, most of the 54 polychaete species present during the study exhibited year-round reproduction (Dauer 1974); thus for those species which produce planktonic larvae, a source of colonizers was available more or less continually. Secondly, polychaetes are now known to exhibit remarkable dispersal abilities as adults (Dauer 1974). The fact that in similar studies (Reish 1962; Dean and Haskin 1964; Rosenberg 1972) polychaetes appear to be the initial colonizers has led Grassle and Grassle (1974) to examine them as "opportunistic species."

The relatively slow appearance of molluscs and amphipods may be related to their lesser abilities of dispersal, and to the fact that most species in the Tampa Bay region appear to show marked seasonality of reproduction.

Thus, the rate of species colonization of some taxa was unaffected by seasonal variability (polychaetes, miscellaneous phyla), while the rate of colonization of other taxa (molluscs, amphipods, other crustacea) appeared to be greatly influenced by the time of the year when a perturbation in the community occurs.

Equilibrium in density patterns was more difficult to evaluate. The polychaetes showed an oscillating pattern which might be interpreted as a "neutrally stable" type of equilibrium (May 1971). The other taxonomic groups showed irregular patterns of change in density.

It thus appears that the sandy intertidal habitat studied has, since about the 11th month following defaunation, shown a relatively constant number of species, as have other study areas over both short and long periods (see Lie 1968; Lie and Evans 1973; Buchanan et al. 1974), while wide fluctuations in density patterns were common (see Jones 1961; Grassle and Sanders 1973; Buchanan et al. 1974).

The finding that different major taxa had different colonizing abilities should have implications for other studies attempting to assess man-made disturbances (e.g., environmental impact statements). Studies which are concerned only with a single taxon (e.g., the molluscs, the amphipods, or the polychaetes) can yield only a very narrow view of what happened to the total infaunal assemblage. Only by carefully and adequately examining the total benthic infauna can a true assessment of the repopulation of the sandy intertidal habitat be realized.

In addition, this study shows that if one were interested in understanding the most rapid response of the fauna to environmental perturbation, the polychaetes would be the group to examine carefully. On the other hand, if one were interested in whether the habitat was restored and at an "equilibrium" level of species, the molluscs and amphipods should be considered. Of course, these generalities should be interpreted with caution and considered representative of only a subtropical estuarine system such as Tampa Bay. Similar studies must be carried out in temperate systems in order to determine whether these conclusions are valid for all intertidal habitats.

LITERATURE CITED

Bloom, S. A., J. L. Simon, and V. D. Hunter. 1972. Animal-sediment relations and community analysis of a Florida estuary. Mar. Biol. 13: 43-56.

Buchanan, J. B., P. F. Kingston, and M. Sheader. 1974. Long-term population trends of the benthic macrofauna in the offshore mud of the Northumberland coast. J. Mar. Biol. Assoc. U. K. 54: 785-795.

Dauer, D. M. 1974. Repopulation of the polychaete fauna of an intertidal habitat following natural defaunation. Ph.D. thesis, Univ. S. Fla., Tampa. 66 p.

_____ and J. L. Simon. 1975. Lateral or along-shore distribution of the polychaetous annelids of an intertidal sandy habitat. Mar. Biol. 31: 363-370.

Dean, D. and H. R. Haskin. 1964. Benthic repopulation of the Raritan River Estuary following pollution abatement. Limnol. Oceanogr. 9: 551-563.

Grassle, J. F. and J. P. Grassle. 1974. Opportunistic life histories and genetic systems in marine benthic polychaetes. J. Mar. Res. 32: 253-284.

_____ and H. L. Sanders. 1973. Life history and the role of disturbance. Deep-Sea Res. 20: 643-659.

Holme, N. A. and A. D. McIntyre. 1971. Methods for the study of marine benthos. Blackwell Scientific Publications.

Inman, K. L. 1952. Measures for describing the size distributions of sediments. J. Sediment. Petrol. 22: 125-145.

Jones, M. L. 1961. A quantitative evaluation of the benthic fauna off Point Richmond, California. Univ. Cal. Publ. Zool. 67: 219-320.

Lie, U. 1968. A quantitative study of benthic fauna in Puget Sound, Washington, U.S.A. in 1963-1964. Fiskerldir. Skr. Ser. Havunders 14: 229-556.

_____ and R. A. Evans. 1973. Long term variability in the structure of subtidal benthic communities in Puget Sound, Washington, U.S.A. Mar. Biol. 21: 122-126.

MacArthur, R. H. and E. O. Wilson. 1967. The theory of island biogeography. Monographs in population biology, no. 1, Princeton Univ. Press. 203 p.

Mason, W. T., Jr. and P. O. Yevich. 1967. The use of phloxine B and rose bengal stains to facilitate sorting benthic samples. Trans. Am. Microsc. Soc. 86: 221-223.

May, R. M. 1971. Stability in model ecosystems. Proc. Ecol. Soc. Australia 6: 18-56.

McKay, C. R. and D. J. Hartzband. 1970. Propylene phenoxytol: narcotic agent for unsorted benthic invertebrates. Trans. Am. Microsc. Soc. 89: 53-54.

Reish, D. J. 1959. A discussion of the importance of the screen size in washing quantitative marine bottom samples. Ecology 40: 307-309.

_____. 1962. A study of succession in recently constructed marine harbors in Southern California, pp. 570-572. In First National Coastal and Shallow Water Res. Conf. Baltimore, Los Angeles, and Tallahassee.

Rosenberg, R. 1972. Benthic faunal recovery in a Swedish fjord following the closure of a sulfite pulpmill. Oikos 23: 92-108.

Simon, J. L. 1965. Feeding in the annelid *Eteone heteropoda*. Quart. J. Fla. Acad. Sci. 28: 370-372.

_____ and D. M. Dauer. 1972. A quantitative evaluation of red-tide induced mass mortalities of benthic invertebrates in Tampa Bay, Florida. Environ. Lett. 3: 229-234.

Steidlinger, K. A. and R. M. Ingle. 1972. Observations on the 1971 summer red tide in Tampa Bay, Florida. Environ. Lett. 3: 271-278.

Effect of *Schizoporella* (Ectoprocta) Removal on the Fouling Community at Beaufort, North Carolina, USA

John P. Sutherland
Duke University Marine Laboratory
Beaufort, NC 28516

ABSTRACT

The encrusting bryozoan, *Schizoporella unicornis*, was shown to inhibit the subsequent recruitment of other common organisms in the fouling community at Beaufort, North Carolina. Settling plates from which *Schizoporella* was experimentally removed on repeated occasions supported an assemblage of fouling organisms different from that found on control plates dominated by *Schizoporella*. The specific species suppressed depended on the year in which the experiment was initiated (April 1972 or 1973) because of annual differences in larval recruitment. Although *Schizoporella* resisted invasion and was one of the most long-lived members of the community, other species were gradually added to the *Schizoporella* monopolies.

Species were subtracted from the community as a result of senescence and urchin predation. The free space left behind usually was colonized by a species other than the previous occupant. Once occupied, the fate of that space depended on the species which occupied it and the regime of larval recruits, i.e., the degree to which the residents inhibited subsequent larval recruitment. Stable climax is not evident in this community and change is the rule rather than the exception.

In terrestrial plant communities there is often a reservoir of successional species in the soil which "prepare the way" for the climax species after perturbation. The fouling community at Beaufort has no such reservoir; colonization occurs by means of short-lived, even nonfeeding larvae. Furthermore, resident adults inhibit subsequent colonization and there is apparently no stable climax. Thus there is little evidence in support of the traditional view of succession in the fouling community at Beaufort.

INTRODUCTION

A community may be termed stable if "when the populations are perturbed, they in time return to their equilibrium values" (May 1973). In this context a "perturbation" is an event which results in a change in community structure. However communities are clearly resistant to some kinds of "perturbations" and not others (Sutherland 1974). Thus the same event may cause a structural change in one community but will have no visible effect on another. According to the above definition, such an event can be called a "perturbation" only if a structural change has been observed.

In order to understand the stability of natural communities it is equally important to know which events ("perturbations") cause no structural change, which cause only temporary structural changes, and which cause permanent structural changes. Thus the definition and identification of a perturbation must be separated from the community's response. I consider a perturbation to be any event which has the potential of altering community structure, whether or not it causes an observable structural change in a given community.

The fouling community at Beaufort is a complex mixture of sponges, hydroids, bryozoans, and tunicates (see McDougall 1943). In this community there are two major kinds of natural perturbations, those which may subtract, and those which may add individuals and species to the community. In the former category are urchin predation (Karlson 1975) and other types of adult mortality (Sutherland 1974; Sutherland and Karlson 1973 and in preparation), both of which provide unoccupied substrate. This substrate is most often recolonized by new recruits rather than occupied by the lateral growth of resident colonies (Sutherland and Karlson in preparation). I consider recruitment to be the process by which this system responds to the perturbations which subtract species. However, the recruitment process itself constitutes another type of perturbation which may add individuals and species to existing adult assemblages. Thus assemblages are stable if they resist the invasion (recruitment and growth) of larval recruits. Clearly the question "Is the community stable?" must always be answered with the question "With respect to what kinds of perturbations?"

For the past several years I have been following community development on newly submerged substrate at the Duke University Marine Laboratory in Beaufort, North Carolina. I view the submergence of unoccupied substrate as analogous to those disturbances which subtract individuals and species from the community. In addition I have been conducting removal experiments on selected species to determine their role in community development. In certain cases, these experiments have documented the effect of adults on subsequent larval recruitment.

This paper reports two such experiments involving the removal of the encrusting bryozoan, *Schizoporella unicornis*. I initiated these experiments in April 1972 and 1973 starting with newly submerged substrate. Thus the controls of each experiment were themselves a perturbation experiment which provided information on the way in which this community responds to the subtraction of individuals and species. In addition, the removal of *Schizoporella* provided information on the degree to which this species, which dominated both controls, was resistant to subsequent larval recruitment (addition of individuals and species). I therefore ask the question, "Is the fouling community at Beaufort equally resistant to both kinds of perturbations?" That is to say, does a stable climax exist in this community since, by definition, a climax must be resistant to natural perturbations which tend to add or subtract species?

This paper would not have been possible without the diligent help of many people. I would especially like to thank T. Fisher, P. Hooper, R. Karlson and W. Nelson. Financial support for this work was provided by the Office of Naval Research (Contract #N00014-67-A-0251-0006).

METHODS

The two experiments were initiated on 9 April 1972 and 10 April 1973, respectively. They were conducted on the lower surface of unglazed ceramic tile plates (232 cm^2) suspended horizontally on racks beneath the Duke University Marine Laboratory dock (see McDougal 1943; Maturo 1957). The plates were approximately 0.3 m below the low tide mark and remained continuously submerged. In each experiment, four of the newly submerged plates were randomly designated as controls (= no removals) and four as *Schizoporella* removal plates. On these latter plates, colonies of *Schizoporella* were removed as they appeared by scraping them off the plate with a small scalpel. These treatments were conducted as often as once a week during summer when *Schizoporella* recruitment was high. Colonies were generally removed while they were less than 5 mm in diameter. In the 1972 experiment, treatments were continued until March 1974, when they were stopped to see if *Schizoporella* would reinvade the community during the settlement season (summer) of 1974. Treatments on the 1973 experiment were continued until December 1974.

Individual plates were examined at 6-8 week intervals in a non-destructive manner to provide information on recruitment, growth and mortality for each species, and the resultant occupation of space by each species. At each census (and treatment), the plate was removed from the rack, brought to the laboratory, and examined in a small aquarium supplied with recirculating, aerated water and maintained within 5°C of ambient temperature. All organisms appeared healthy and unharmed by our handling procedure. Percent cover for each species was estimated by a point sampling technique. A plot of 75 random points was generated by computer on an area equal to that of the ceramic tile plate. These points were traced onto a glass pane which was suspended over the plate. A sighting device which reduced problems of parallax was used to identify species under each point. A different set of 75 random points was used for successive samples of the same plate.

Only the area occupied more or less exclusively by a species was allocated to that species. Canopies were not counted as occupying space; only the basal area of attachement was counted. Areas or points where species grew on top of other species were counted twice except when the lower species was a dead barnacle. (Dead barnacles were treated as empty space because organisms grew on them readily and they often persisted for months beneath a layer of tunicates or bryozoans.) Thus it was possible to estimate greater than 100% coverage because of epizooic overgrowth.

An attempt was made to study in detail "foundation species," "the group of critical species which define much of the structure of a community" (Dayton 1972). Operationally these were species (1) which were capable of occupying primary space (Dayton 1971), i.e., attaching to the plate itself--this ruled out most motile species and species which were only seen growing on top of others; and (2) which occupied at least 10% of the primary and/or secondary space at some time in the time interval considered here and on some plates in the overall study (not only those plates included in this paper.

Species fulfilling these criteria are listed in Table 1. Fish and sea urchins, *Arbacia punctulata*, were not included because fish are only occasionally important determinants of community structure (Sutherland 1974) and urchins did not invade the plates, which were suspended from above the high tide mark. The various species of

Table 1. Species included in the community. (Foundation species only - defined in text.) Numerals indicate species identification number in Figures 1, 2, 7, 8.

Porifera	Tunicata
1. *Microciona prolifera*	17. *Styela plicata*
2. *Mycale cecila*	18. *Ascidia interrupta*
3. *Haliclona* spp.	19. *Molgala manhattensis*
4. *Halichondria bowerbanki*	20. *Botryllus schlosseri*
	21. *Didemnum candidum*
Coelenterata	
5. *Bougainvillia* sp.	Polychaeta
6. *Hydractinia echinata*	22. *Hydroides dianthus*
7. *Eudendrium carneum*	
8. *Tubularia crocea*	Mollusca
9. *Pennaria tiarella*	23. *Ostrea equestris*
10. *Astrangia astreiformis*	
26. *Diadumene leucolena*	Arthropoda
	24. *Balanus* spp.
Bryozoa	25. *Corophium* spp.
11. *Bugula neritina*	
12. *Schizoporella unicornis*	
13. *Anguinella palmata*	
14. *Electra* spp.	
15. *Membranipora* sp.	
16. *Nollela* sp.	

barnacles common to the Beaufort area, *Balanus eburneus*, *B. amphitrite*, *B. tintinnabulum*, and *B. improvisus*, were not distinguished in this study. They were difficult to identify as juveniles and in mature assemblages they were frequently overgrown so that a specific identification was impossible.

Plates in the same experiment were not sampled simultaneously. Thus, data from a given plate often applied to a different time interval from that of other plates in the same experiment. Data within each experiment were "standardized" by a method described elsewhere (Sutherland 1970). I assumed that the events on each plate occurred uniformly throughout a sample interval. For example, if the percent cover of a species changed by 30% in 30 days, the rate of change was assumed to be 1%/day during each day of the interval. In a computer memory, an array was set aside for each species on each plate and numbered for each day after submergence. The appropriate rate of change (±) for each species was placed in the elements of the array representing a day in a given sample interval, e.g., from day 70 to day 100 after submergence. When this was done for all species on a given plate, the percentage cover of each species was estimated at arbitrary intervals (day 30, 60, 90, etc.) by summing the rate of change from day 1 (day of submergence). These arbitrary intervals thus coincided between plates submerged in the same year. When comparisons were necessary between plates submerged in different years, the time interval was similarly adjusted.

A number of calculations were done routinely on each group to describe the structural changes which occurred during the period of time covered in this paper.

Histograms--Percent cover for each species included in the study (Table 1) was plotted four times a year. I report data only for the mean species composition of each series, although I used information from each replicate for statistical comparisons (see below). Thus each bar in a histogram is the arithmetic mean of percent cover for a given species averaged over the four plates in the same treatment group. Times were adjusted to the 15th of March, June, September, and December, respectively.

Euclidean distance--It was impossible to include a measure of variability in the histograms without sacrificing their main advantage, that of being easy to read. I represent the variability in species composition between plates in the same treatment group with a modification of the squared Euclidean distance measure discussed by Williams and Lambert (1966). This measure is

$$\frac{\sum_{i=1}^{N} \sum_{j-1}^{M} (X_{ij} - \bar{X}_j)^2}{N}$$

where X_{ij} = percent cover of species j on plate i, $\bar{X}_j$ = mean percent cover of species j on the 4 plates in the group, M = number of species (=27), and N = number of plates in the treatment group (=4). This measure was calculated for each 30-day time interval and represents the degree to which the individual plates differed from the group centroid.

Diversity--The Standard Brillouin diversity index (Pielou 1969) was also calculated for each group at 30-day intervals using the arithmetic mean of percent cover as the measure of species abundance.

Community flux--This is a measure of the degree to which space is exchanged between species or given up altogether during a given 30-day time interval. The measure is

$$\sum_{j=1}^{M} \frac{X_{jt_1} - X_{jt_2}}{t_2 - t_1}$$

where X_{jt} is the percent cover of species j at time t and $t_2 > t_1$ (measured in days). These calculations were made on the arithmetic mean of percent cover averaged over the four plates in the group, the same data which appear in the histograms.

Statistical comparisons of Euclidean distance, diversity, and flux between experimental groups were made in the following manner. In each case calculations were made for individual plates at the same 30-day intervals as above. For Euclidean distance the measurement was

$$\sum_{j=1}^{M} (X_{ij} - \bar{X}_j)^2,$$

the distance of an individual plate from the group centroid at a given time. Diversity and flux were calculated as above for individual plates. These indices for each plate were then averaged over the calendar year, December to December (or from the beginning of the experiment to December). December was chosen as the dividing point because recruitment and growth were generally minimal at that time of year (Sutherland and Karlson in preparation). These individual plate averages, 4 for each experimental group, were then compared between groups by means of a Mann-Whitney U test (Siegel 1956).

Further details of data analysis will be discussed as necessary in the following sections.

RESULTS

April 1972 Experiment

Schizoporella dominated all four control plates throughout the observation period (Fig. 1). This species generally occupied at least 50% of the area until June 1974. In contrast, except for *Balanus* in June 1972 (18% cover), no other species occupied more than 10-13% of the area during the same period (Fig. 1). After June 1974, the abundance of *Schizoporella* dropped to 25-28% and by December several other species were moderately abundant, especially *Styela* (15% cover) and *Balanus* (15% cover) (Fig. 1).

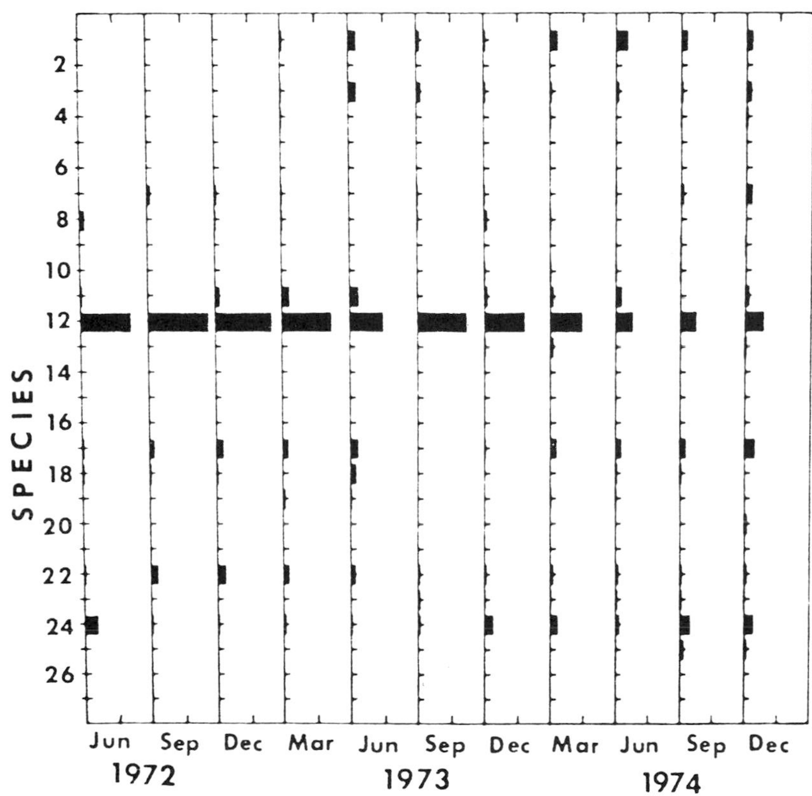

Fig. 1. April 1972 control. Percent cover for each species, 4 times a year. Each bar is the arithmetic mean of percent cover averaged over the 4 plates in the group. Distance across each column = 100%, tickmark = 50%. For species identification, see Table 1.

On the *Schizoporella* removal plates, *Balanus* abundance was variable, but was greater than 18% cover throughout the observation period, except for June 1973 (8% cover) and June and September 1974 (5% and 9% cover) (Fig. 2). By December 1972, *Mycale* disappeared during the spring of 1973 and was replaced briefly by *Styela* (33%

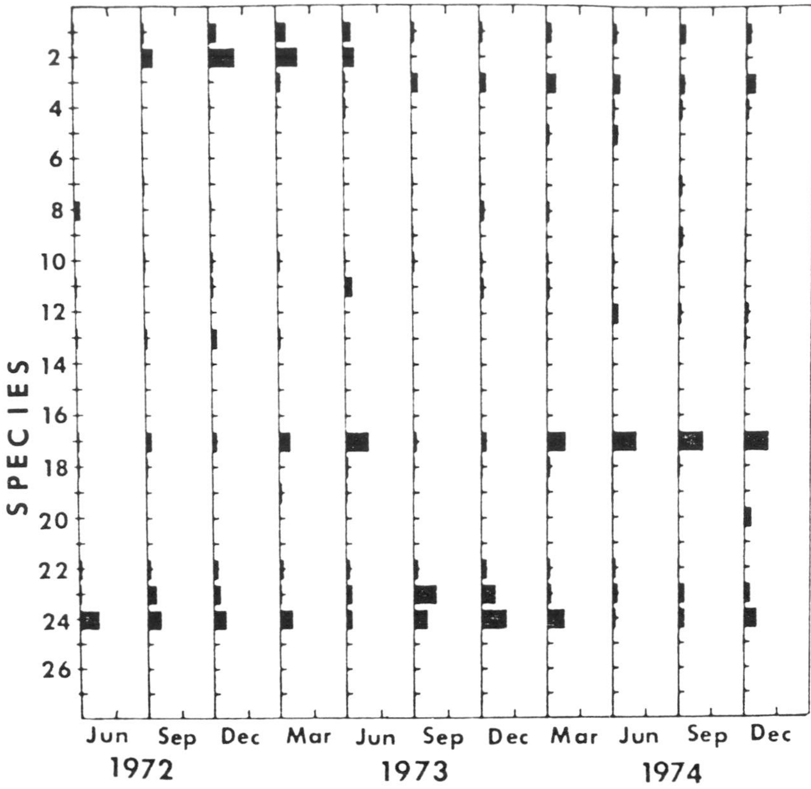

Fig. 2. April 1972 *Schizoporella* removal. For explanation, see caption for Figure 1.

cover in June 1973). However *Styela* almost disappeared during the summer of 1973 and *Balanus* and *Ostrea* collectively occupied 54% and 60% of the area on this series in September and December 1973, respectively. *Microciona* and *Haliclona* were common epizooic species on *Balanus* and *Ostrea* through most of the observation period (Fig.2). Finally, during 1974 *Styela* reinvaded and remained the dominant species. For some reason this species didn't disappear from these plates during the summer of 1974 as it did in 1973 (Fig. 2). By December 1974, species abundances on both control and removal plates were similar (Figs. 1, 2); treatments were stopped by March 1974 and the two series were "tested" by the same larvae during 1974. However, *Schizoporella* was still less abundant on the removal plates (Figs. 1, 2, Table 2).

Another effect of the treatment (*Schizoporella* removal) was to increase the amount of variation in species composition between replicate plates in the treatment group. Although initially comparable in treatment and controls, Euclidean distance was very much higher for the treatment group until the summer of 1973 (Fig. 3). Mann-Whitney U tests indicated that the annual averages for 1972 and 1973 were significantly higher in the treatment group ($p<0.29$). This was due largely to the differential invasion of the treatment

Table 2. Arithmetic means of percent cover which differed significantly ($p < 0.05$) between experimental groups. Differences were evaluated with one-way ANOVA after individual plate data were transformed with the angular transformation (Sokal and Rohlf, 1969). Data from the 1973 experiment marked with an "*". Rest of data from the 1972 experiment. Note that transformed means are not reported.

	Dec 72		Jun 73		Dec 73		Jun 74		Dec 74	
	Control	Sch Rem	Control	Sch Rem	Control	Sch Rem	Control	Sch Rem	Control	Sch Rem
Microciona	0	10								
Mycale	0	38	0	16						
Tubularia			11*	25*	6*	20*				
Schizoporella							27	9	26	6
Styela							8	36	10*	36*
Ascidia					0*	6*	1*	9*		
Hydroidea					2	8				
Ostrea	0	8	0	10	2	22			0	9
Balanus	1	17	1 5*	8 24*	12	38				

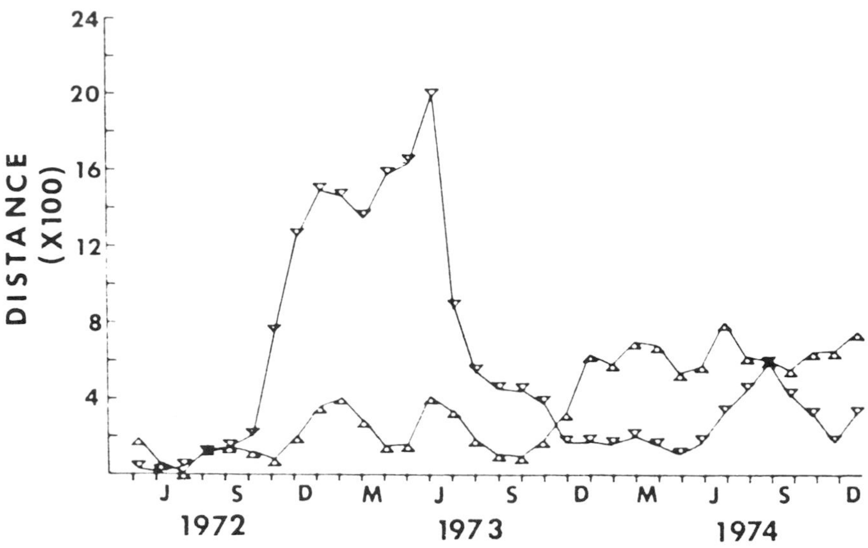

Fig. 3. Euclidean distance, April 1972 experiment. Δ=Control, ∇=*Schizoporella* removal. See text for explanation.

group by *Mycale* in the fall of 1972. *Mycale* occupied 81, 9, 55 and 7% of the area on the four plates respectively in December 1972. In the spring of 1973 the high variation between plates was caused by variation in the abundance of *Styela* on this group. In June 1973 *Styela* occupied 12, 41, 0, and 78% of the area on the four treatment plates, respectively. During 1972 and 1973, *Schizoporella* uniformly dominated the control group and the Euclidean distance between these plates was low (Fig. 3). Plates in the treatment group became more similar as *Styela* disappeared, and subsequent changes in species composition occurred more or less simultaneously; Euclidean distance remained relatively low in the treatment group after the fall of 1973 except for a small peak in September 1974 (Fig. 3). This peak was again due to variation in the abundance of *Styela* which occupied 63, 16, 30, and 45% of the area on the four treatment plates, respectively. During 1974, Euclidean distance was significantly higher for the control group (Mann-Whitney U test on annual averages, P=0.29) than for the treatment group (Fig. 3). This was due to variation in abundance of a number of species. For example, in June 1974 control plates 1 through 4 contained 19, 0, 0, and 52% *Microciona*, and 26, 41, 31, and 9% *Schizoporella*, respectively. In December 1974 the same plates contained 2, 6, 0, and 26% *Microciona*, 33, 39, 26, and 5% *Schizoporella*, 42, 2, 21, and 4% *Styela* and 8, 14, 3, and 29% *Balanus*.

Diversity increased rapidly on the *Schizoporella* removal treatment group and remained relatively high throughout the observation period (Fig. 4). In contrast, diversity on the control plates, dominated by *Schizoporella*, increased slowly and was not comparable to that on the treatment group until early 1974. In all three years the average annual diversity was significantly higher on plates in

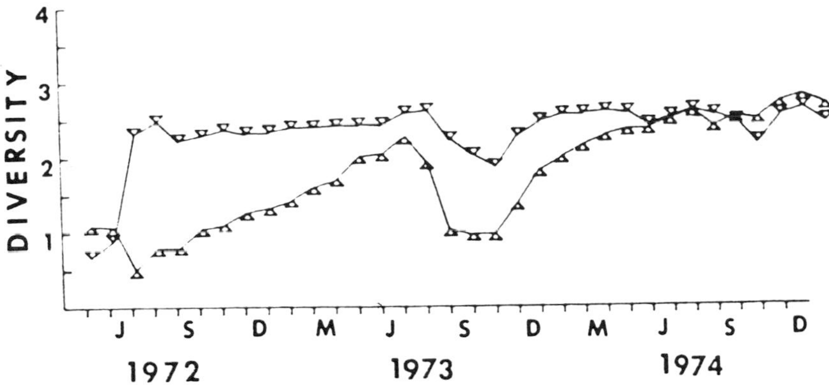

Fig. 4. Brillouin index of diversity, April 1972 experiment. Δ=Control, ∇=*Schizoporella* removal. See text for explanation.

in the treatment group (Mann-Whitney U test, p<.029). The drop in diversity in the fall of 1973 observed on both series was due to the simultaneous, almost total disappearance of *Bugula* and *Styela* from both groups during that period (Figs. 1, 2, 4).

Flux rates were initially high on both groups as the first recruits settled and grew (Fig. 5). However after the fall of 1972, flux rates were generally higher in the *Schizoporella* removal treatment group. The annual averages for 1972 and 1974 were not significantly different, but the average flux for 1973 was significantly higher on plates in the treatment group (Mann-Whitney U test, p = .014). There was a small peak in the flux rate for both groups in the fall of 1973 (Fig. 5) as *Bugula* and *Styela* generally disappeared (Figs. 1, 2). This coincided with the diversity drop for both groups (Fig. 4).

Flux rates were significantly higher during the latter part of 1972 on the treatment group (Mann-Whitney U test on average from August-December, p = 0.14). Removal of *Schizoporella* continually opened up new space (Fig. 6b) and larvae were able to invade this

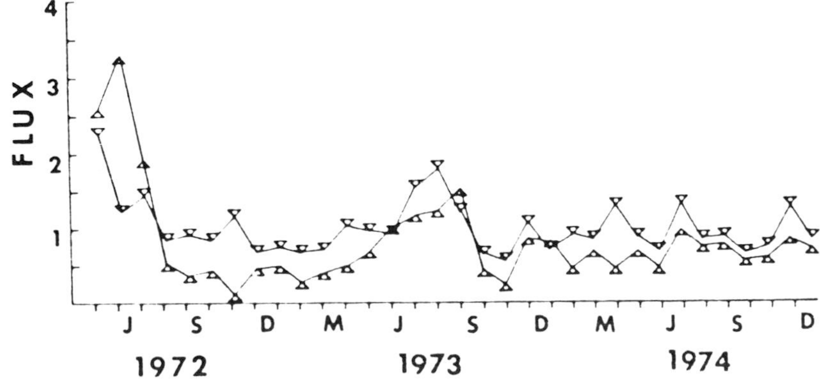

Fig. 5. Community flux, April 1972 experiment. Δ=Control, ∇=*Schizoporella* removal. See text for explanation.

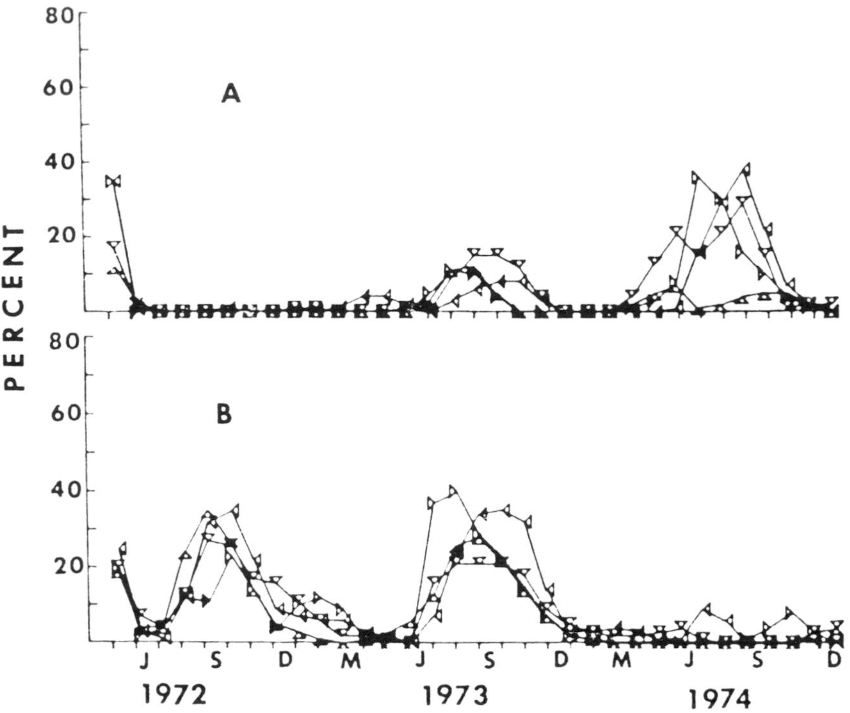

Fig. 6. Percent free space on each plate, April 1972 experiment. A=Control, B=*Schizoporella* removal. Δ=plate 1, ∇=plate 2, ▷=plate 3, ◁=plate 4.

group more easily. However, the higher rates during 1973 resulted largely from a progression of shorter lived species (than *Schizoporella*) rather than from the treatment itself (Fig. 2). The number of *Schizoporella* colonies removed during 1973 was very much less than for 1972 (Sutherland unpublished data).

During 1972 there was no free space on the control group after it was dominated by *Schizoporella* (Fig. 6A). In contrast, much space remained available on the treatment group during 1972 after an initial period when *Balanus* was very abundant (Fig. 6B). This availability of unoccupied space was probably the reason sponges invaded the treatment group, but not the control group during the fall of 1972 (Figs. 1, 2). *Styela* was also more abundant (except on plate 3) on the *Schizoporella* removal plates during the spring of 1973 (Fig. 1,2). *Schizoporella* probably resisted the invasion of *Styela* (see below). When *Styela* died and sloughed off both series in the fall of 1973 (along with *Bugula*), much more empty space was left behind on the *Schizoporella* removal plates than on the controls (Figs. 6A, B). This space on the treatment group was invaded by *Ostrea* and *Balanus*, and later by *Styela* (Fig. 2). *Styela* survived throughout 1974 and little free space was available on the treatment group during this time (Fig. 6B). In contrast there was considerable free space on 3 or the 4 plates in the control group in the fall of 1974 (Fig. 6A). The old *Schizoporella* colonies on this latter group began to flake off taking *Bugula* with them on plate 2 and *Microciona* on plate 4. Even though treatments in this experiment were terminated in March 1974, the "accidental" effects of the treatment continued to be important throughout the remainder of the year, e.g., much more free space was available on the control plates during 1974.

April 1973 Experiment

In 1973, *Schizoporella* was initially a relatively minor component of the control group (only 10% by June 1973), in contrast to the control group in 1972 (Figs. 1, 7). By June 1973, *Bugula*, *Styela*, and *Ascidia*, were more abundant than *Schizoporella* (Fig. 7).

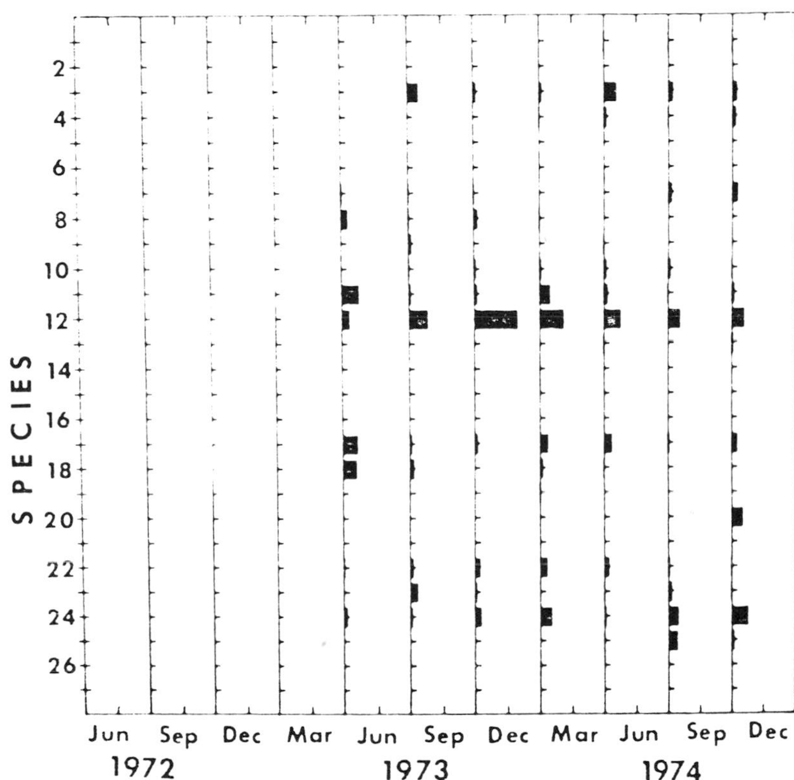

Fig. 7. April 1973 control. For explanation, see caption for Figure 1.

However, both species of tunicates declined dramatically during the summer and by September 1973, *Schizoporella* was dominant (28% cover) in the 1973 control group. *Schizoporella* continued to be one of the most abundant species of this group throughout 1974 (% cover > 19%) although *Haliclona*, *Bugula*, *Styela*, *Botryllus*, *Hydroides*, *Balanus*, and *Corophium* were also abundant (% cover > 10%) at times (Fig. 7).

The treatment group was initially very similar to the control group except for the absence of *Schizoporella*. However, there was significantly more *Tubularia* and *Balanus* by June 1973 (Fig. 7, 8, Table 2). *Styela* and *Ascidia* declined dramatically in the treatment

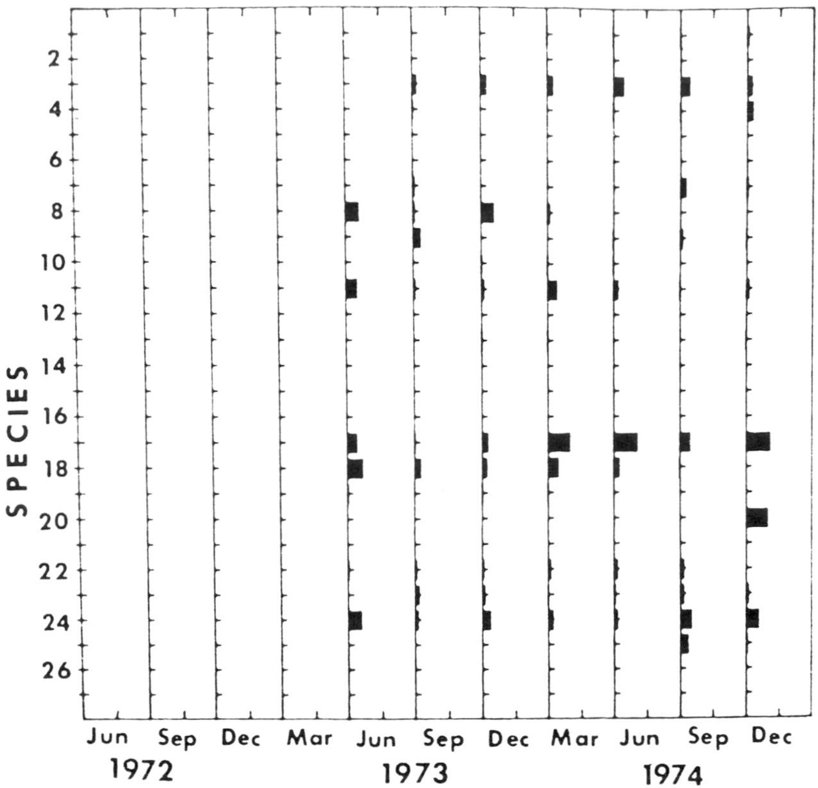

Fig. 8. April 1973 *Schizoporella* removal. For explanation see caption for Figure 1.

group as well as the control group during summer 1973, but *Schizoporella* was not allowed to invade the treatment group. By December *Tubularia* was the most abundant species (20% cover) but *Styela* was dominant throughout 1974 (% cover > 17%) (Fig. 8). *Haliclona, Eudendrium, Bugula, Ascidia, Balanus* and *Corophium* were periodically abundant (% cover > 10%) during 1974 as well, and by December *Styela* was covered with a layer of *Botryllus* (Fig. 8).

In the 1973 experiment, species replacements occurred more or less simultaneously on both control and treatment groups (Fig. 9); there were no dramatic peaks in Euclidean distance as in the 1972 treatment group (Fig. 3). However in this experiment the treatment group was less variable than the control during the winter and spring of 1973-1974 (Fig. 9), significantly so during 1973 (Mann-Whitney U test on annual averages, $p = 0.14$) although not during the entire year of 1974. This was in direct contrast to the results of the 1972 experiment (Fig. 3) owing to the replacement of *Schizoporella* by *Styela* on one of the control plates until June 1974. For example, by June 1974 there was 29, 60, 21, and 4% *Schizoporella* and 7, 0, 8, and 45% *Styela* on the four control plates respectively. Variations between the plates were reduced as *Styela* sloughed off plate 4 in June 1973, but increased again on the control group by

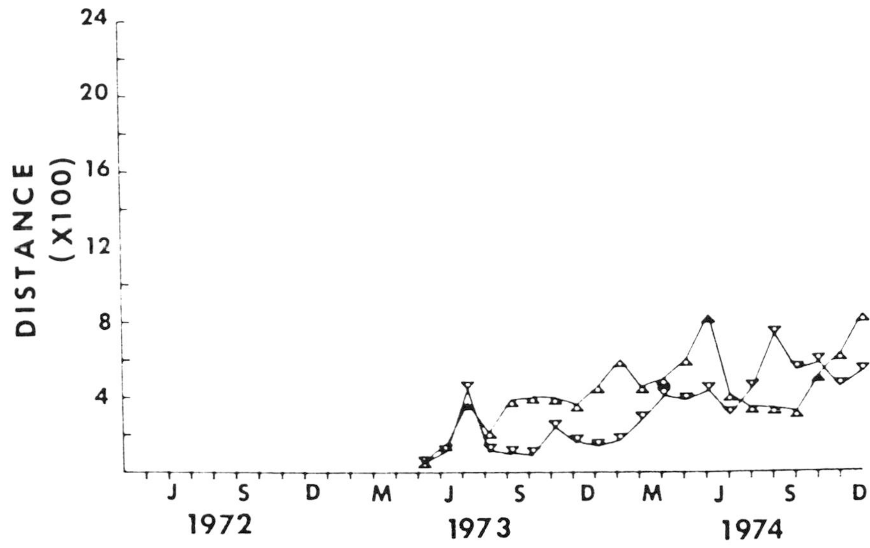

Fig. 9. Euclidean distance, April 1973 experiment. Δ=Control, ∇=*Schizoporella* removal. See text for explanation.

December (Fig. 9) because of the uneven densities of *Haliclona* (1, 0, 1, 25%), *Eudendrium* (1, 31, 5, 0%) and *Botryllus* (22, 2, 38, 13%). Euclidean distance was higher in the treatment group in August and September 1974 (Fig. 9) because of the uneven distribution of *Haliclona* (0, 26, 19, 5%), *Eudendrium* (3, 28, 5, and 12%), *Styela* (40, 29, 2, and 2%) and *Corophium* (5, 3, 29, and 13%).

Diversity was initially high on both treatment and control groups (Fig. 10), again in contrast to the 1972 experiment (Fig. 4). Diversity was slightly lower on the control group during the winter of 1973-1974 (Fig. 10) when this group was dominated by *Schizoporella* (Fig. 7). Except for this period, diversity was comparable for both groups throughout the observation period; Mann-Whitney U tests on annual averages showed no significant differences for 1973 and 1974.

Flux rates were also comparable for both groups in the 1973 experiment throughout the observation period (Fig. 11). There was no clear separation between treatments as in the 1972 experiment during 1973 (Fig. 5); Mann-Whitney U tests showed no significant differences for 1973 and 1974. In 1973 flux rates were generally higher on the 1973 experiment than the 1972 experiment (Figs. 5, 11) because of the growth and mortality of tunicates in 1973 followed by the growth of *Schizoporella* on the control group (Fig. 7) and of *Tubularia* on the treatment group (Fig. 8). Flux rates during 1974 were generally comparable for all four groups (Figs. 5, 11) except that *Botryllus* invaded the 1973 treatment group at a higher rate during the fall of 1974 (Figs. 8, 11).

In the 1973 experiment there was considerable empty space on both control and treatment groups during 1973 (Figs. 12A, B).

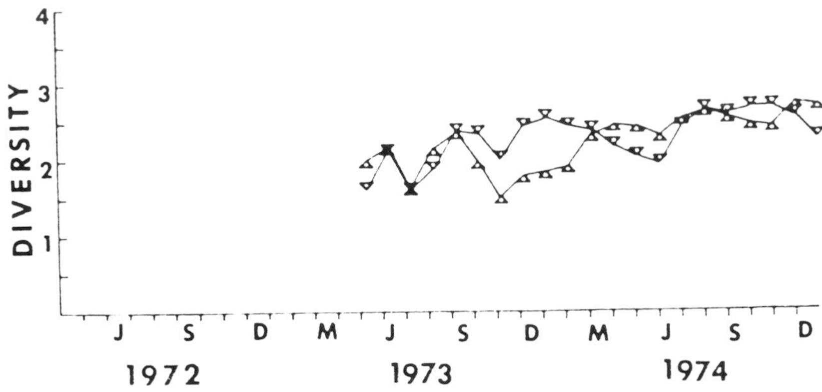

Fig. 10. Brillouin index of diversity, April 1973 experiment. Δ=Control, ∇=*Schizoporella* removal. See text for explanation.

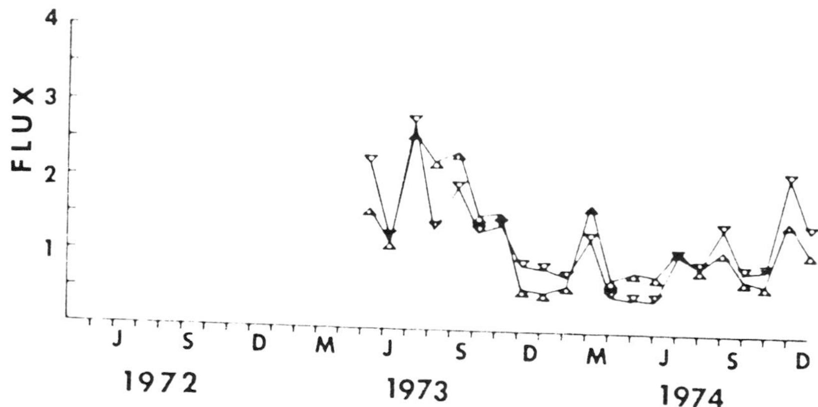

Fig. 11. Community flux, April 1973 experiment. Δ=Control, ∇=*Schizoporella* removal. See text for explanation.

However, empty space disappeared first from the control group which became dominated by *Schizoporella* in the fall of 1973 (Figs. 7, 12A). Virtually all of the tunicates sloughed off the control group in the fall of 1974 (Fig. 7) leaving considerable free space behind (Fig. 12A). The same was true only for plates 3 and 4 of the treatment group in the fall of 1974 (Figs. 8, 12B). With the continued removal of *Schizoporella*, the empty space on these latter plates was dominated again by *Styela*. *Styela* was significantly more abundant on the treatment group as compared to the control group by December 1974 (Figs. 7, 8, Table 2).

Differences in Species Composition

In each experiment one-way ANOVA was used to test for differences in the abundance of individual species between control and treatment groups. Percentage cover data for each species from each plate were normalized with the angular transformation (Sokal and

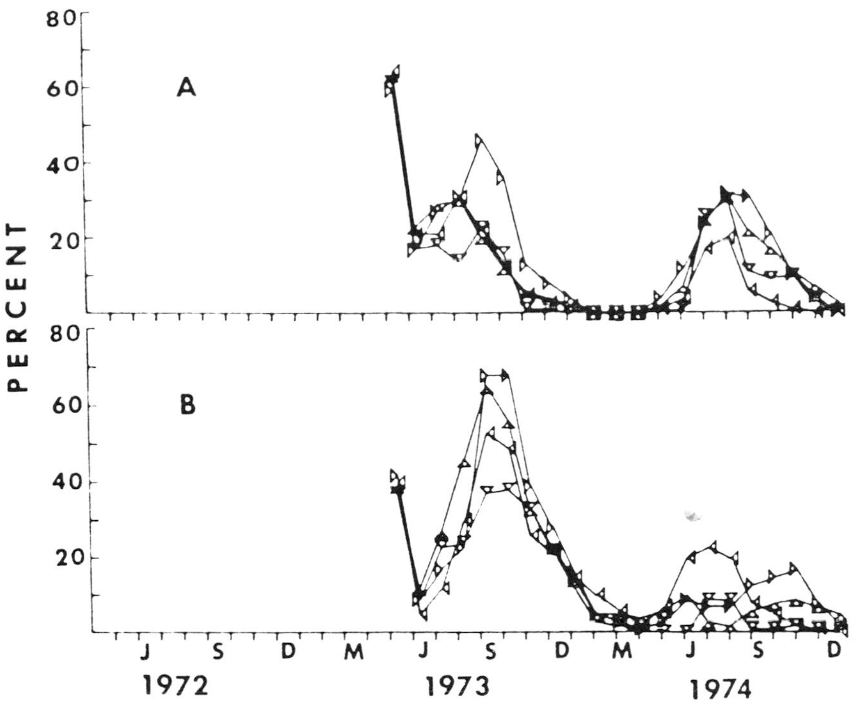

Fig. 12. Percent free space on each plate, April 1973 experiment. A=Control, B=*Schizoporella* removal. Δ=plate 1, ∇= plate 2, ▷=plate 3, ◁=plate 4.

Rohlf 1969). Tests were conducted biannually on all species except *Schizoporella*, starting with June 1972 and June 1973 for the 1972 and 1973 experiments, respectively. *Schizoporella* was included in the analysis for the 1972 experiment during 1974 because treatments in this experiment were terminated in March 1974. I have reported the arithmetic means of nontransformed data in Table 2 to indicate the direction of significant differences.

At some time during the observation period, *Schizoporella* had a significant effect on the abundance of many of the important community members (Table 2). This effect was generally to exclude other species from the space it occupied; when significant differences occurred a given species was always more abundant on the treatment group where *Schizoporella* was absent (Table 2). The only exception was for *Schizoporella* itself in 1974. It remained significantly less abundant on the treatment group even after treatments were terminated (Table 2). *Schizoporella* larvae were abundant during 1974 (Sutherland and Karlson in preparation) and did dominate newly submerged substrate during that time (Sutherland unpublished). Thus, while *Schizoporella* was able to exclude many species, it was itself excluded by other residents.

Cluster analysis--I have used single linkage cluster analysis (Davies 1971) to objectively illustrate the similarities and differences between the four experimental groups in the two experiments.

I have chosen this method because of its simplicity and because of the limited number of groups involved. Horn's (1966) index of overlap was used to calculate the similarity matrix. The arithmetic mean of percent cover within a group was used as the estimate of species abundance for that group. The analyses are time specific and were performed on data for mid-June and mid-December throughout the observation period (Fig. 13).

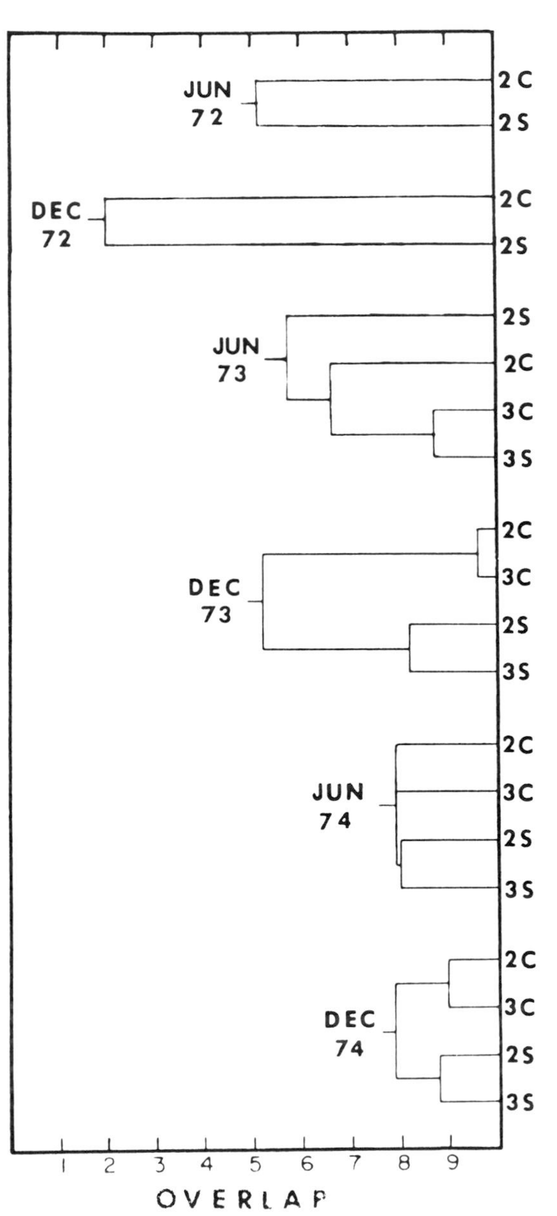

Fig. 13. Single linkage cluster analysis using Horn's (1966) index of overlap. The arithmetic mean of percent cover within a group (e.g., Fig. 1), was used as the estimate of species abundance for that group. 2C=April 1972 Control, 2S=April 1972 *Schizoporella* removal, 3C=April 1973 Control, 3S=April 1973 *Schizoporella* removal.

Schizoporella removal in 1972 produced a dramatic difference in community structure by June 1972 because the controls were dominated by *Schizoporella*. This difference increased by December of that year as the treatment group was invaded by sponges (Figs. 1, 3, 13).

In 1973, *Schizoporella* was initially not as abundant and the same treatment had produced little effect by June of 1973; the 1973 control and treatment groups were still quite similar at that time (Figs. 7, 8, 13). By December 1973, however, the 1973 control and treatment groups had diverged (Horn's index = .54) as *Schizoporella* replaced the tunicates on the controls (Figs. 7, 8). At this time the 1972 and 1973 controls were very similar, both being dominated by *Schizoporella* (Figs. 1, 7, 13). In the absence of *Schizoporella* both treatment groups were occupied by a mixture of sponges, hydroids, tunicates, oysters, and barnacles in December 1973 (Figs. 2, 8), and both were very different from the controls but reasonably similar to each other (Fig. 13).

There were no well-defined groups in June 1974 (Fig. 13). After the spring recruitment in 1974 all groups were more similar although no two groups were as similar as during the previous December. All groups were still as similar by December 1974 although the controls and treatments once again clustered out together (Fig. 13).

DISCUSSION

The presence of *Schizoporella* clearly inhibited the addition and/or subsequent increase of other species in the community (Table 2). As a result the relative abundance of species was different on the treatment groups as compared to the controls (Fig. 13). Different larvae were present in 1972 and 1973 (Sutherland and Karlson in preparation) so that the species inhibited by *Schizoporella* were different in each experiment. For example, by December 1972, *Schizoporella* had effectively resisted the invasion of *Microciona*, *Mycale*, *Ostrea*, and *Balanus* (Table 2). In the 1973 experiment *Schizoporella* had resisted the invasion of *Tubularia* and *Ascidia* by December 1973 (Table 2). Thus, the differences in species composition between experimental and control groups depended on the year in which the experiment was conducted (Fig. 13). Differences in larval recruitment also produced differences in the initial development of the two control groups (Figs. 1, 7). It is therefore not surprising that the patterns of community development described above (species composition, Euclidean distances, diversity, flux, and the availability of free space) were so different within and between years.

Even though *Schizoporella* was resistant to the invasion of many species, colonies were not immortal. New species were added gradually, lessening the difference between treatment and control groups (Fig. 13). *Schizoporella* is one of the more persistent species in the fouling community at Beaufort. On present evidence, only *Hydractinia echinata*, an encrusting hydroid, is better able to resist larval invasion (Karlson 1975; Sutherland and Karlson in preparation). This hydroid has monopolized the area on one plate for three years and is apparently "immortal." It is rare on the plates because its recrutiment rate is extremely low (Sutherland and Karlson in preparation). (Presently I do not know whether the persistence of *Schizoporella* and *Hydractinia* is a dynamic process of replacement or simply the result of being long lived.) *Styela* is another species which is resistant to larval invasion but generally does not persist for as long as *Schizoporella* because the adults die and do not replace themselves (Sutherland 1974). Finally, some species, such as *Balanus* and *Ostrea* are poor resistors. Thus while certain species can impart some degree of stability to the system by resisting larval invasion (for varying lengths of time depending on the resident and the regime of larval recruits), over a period of several years the system is generally not totally resistant to the addition and growth of new species.

Both control groups were very similar by December 1973 and remained more or less so during 1974 (Fig. 13). We might conclude on this evidence that the system was resistant to species subtraction (submerging new plates) because both controls eventually returned to the same point, a *Schizoporella*-dominated system. However, this conclusion is not justified for several reasons. First, the definition of adjustment stability requires that the system return to the previous equilibrium values following a perturbation (May 1973). In the study area we must assume that the "previous equilibrium values" were *Schizoporella*-dominated systems since the plates were new. Clearly, however, other initial conditions are possible; at various times since 1971, plates have been dominated by a wide variety of species (Sutherland 1974; Sutherland and Karlson 1973 and in preparation).

Second, it appears that the system has not (yet) returned to an equilibrium state. *Schizoporella* became less abundant from December 1973 to December 1974 (Figs. 1, 7). This decrease was significant ($p < .05$) on the 1973 controls (one-way ANOVA on data normalized with the angular transformation), but not on the 1972 controls because of a high initial variance. Thus the controls remained similar because they were undergoing similar changes, not because they had reached the same stable end-point.

Third, the "convergence" of the two controls appears to be a chance event, rather than a homeostatic event as implied by May's (1973) definition of stability. Tunicate monopolies (*Styela* and *Ascidia*) on plates submerged in the spring of 1971 were followed by a regrowth of *Tubularia* in the fall rather than by *Schizoporella* (Sutherland 1974; Sutherland and Karlson 1973 and in preparation). The convergence of the two controls in 1973 resulted from an early disappearance of tunicates in 1973, something which has not happened every year (e.g., Fig. 2, 1974). Thus, even though both controls were similar by December 1973 (Fig. 13), the evidence indicates that this is not a predictable event. I would expect the controls eventually to "converge" simply because the resident communities are being tested by the same larval recruits (Fig. 13, Sutherland and Karlson in preparation). The limits to this conversion are probably set by the inherent plate-to-plate variability in species composition which appears to vary inversely with the size of the plates (Sutherland and Karlson in preparation).

Finally, it is clear that the fate of newly available free space depends largely on which larvae are available in the plankton, a process over which the resident community has little control. After space is once occupied, subsequent changes depend on the resident species and regime of larval recruits, i.e., the longevity of the resident and the degree to which it is resistant to subsequent larval recruitment. Therefore, it seems reasonable to consider the community resistant to species subtractions only if the new resident is the same as the previous occupant. However, we observed extreme variability in initial community development on newly submerged substrate within and between years from 1971 to 1974 (Sutherland 1974; Sutherland and Karlson 1973 and in preparation). More important, the free space made available by the sloughing off of adults (e.g., Figs. 6, 12) has usually been colonized by new recruits rather than filled by the expansion of the resident colonies (Sutherland and Karlson in preparation). In 39 cases where new recruits could be determined from sequential photographs of plates, 82% of these differed from the previous occupant. I conclude that this community is not resistant to the subtraction or addition of species and that a stable climax is not found.

Terrestrial plant communities are traditionally thought to respond to perturbations (e.g., fires) by a community-controlled process called succession (Odum 1969). In at least some of these communities, viable seeds of successional species are present in the soil and germinate immediately after the climax species are removed (Marks 1974). These successional species "prepare the way" for the development of the climax community. In contrast, the fouling community has no such reservoir of "successional" species. Colonization is generally by animals which have short-lived, even nonfeeding larvae (Barnes 1968). Instead of "preparing the way" for subsequent larval recruitment, residents often inhibit it. Thus there is little evidence here in support of the traditional view of succession (e.g., Odum 1969), although similar processes have been documented for terrestrial plant communities by Drury and Nisbet (1973). The fouling community is not resistant to perturbations which alter abundances and there is no stable climax; change is the rule rather than the exception, change brought about by finite life spans, and larval recruitment.

REFERENCES

Barnes, R. D. 1968. Invertebrate zoology. W. B. Saunders Co.

Davies, R. G. 1971. Computer programming in quantitative biology. Academic Press.

Dayton, P. K. 1971. Competition, disturbance, and community organization: the provision and subsequent utilization of space in a rocky intertidal community. Ecol. Monogr. 41: 351-389.

_____. 1972. Toward an understanding of community resilience and the potential effects of enrichments to the benthos at McMurdo Sound, Antarctica, pp. 81-95. In B. C. Parker [ed.], Proc. Colloquium on Cons. Prob. in Antarct. Allen Press.

Drury, W. H. and I. C. T. Nisbet. 1973. Succession. J. Arnold Arboretum 54: 331-368.

Horn, H. S. 1966. Measurement of "overlap" in comparative ecological studies. Am. Nat. 100: 419-424.

Karlson, R. H. 1975. The effects of predation by the sea urchin, *Arbacia punctulata*, on a marine, epibenthic community. Ph.D. thesis, Duke Univ.

Marks, P. L. 1974. The role of pin cherry (*Prunus pennsylvanica* L.) in the maintenance of stability in northern hardwood ecosystems. Ecol. Monogr. 44: 73-88.

Maturo, F. J. S. 1957. A study of the bryozoa of Beaufort, North Carolina, and vicinity. J. Elisha Mitchel Sci. Soc. 73: 11-68.

McDougall, K. D. 1943. Sessile marine invertebrates at Beaufort, North Carolina. Ecol. Monogr. 13: 321-374.

May, R. M. 1973. Stability and complexity in model ecosystems. Princeton Univ. Press.

Odum, E. P. 1969. The strategy of ecosystem development. Science 164: 262-270.

Pielou, E. C. 1969. An introduction to mathematical ecology. Wiley-Interscience.

Siegel, S. 1956. Nonparametric statistics for the behavioral sciences. McGraw-Hill.

Sokal, R. R. and F. J. Rohlf. 1969. Biometry, the principles and practice of statistics in biological research. W. H. Freeman and Company.

Sutherland, J. P. 1970. Dynamics of high and low populations of the limpet, *Acmaea scabra* (Gould). Ecol. Monogr. 40: 169-188.

_____. 1974. Multiple stable points in natural communities. Am. Nat. 108: 859-873.

_____ and R. H. Karlson. 1973. Succession and seasonal progression in the fouling community at Beaufort, North Carolina, pp. 906-929. In Third Int. Cong. Mar. Corros. & Foul. Northwestern Univ. Press.

Williams, W. T. and J. M. Lambert. 1966. Multivariate methods in plant ecology. V. Similarity analyses and information-analyses. J. Ecol. 54: 427-445.

Temporal Adaptations in Sibling Species of *Capitella*

J. Frederick Grassle
Woods Hole Oceanographic Institution
Woods Hole, MA 02543

and

Judith P. Grassle
Marine Biological Laboratory
Woods Hole, MA 02543

ABSTRACT

Previously thought to be a single species, *Capitella capitata* is a complex of at least six sibling species. These species show virtually no genetic similarity at 10 loci studied electrophoretically. Close examination of the species in culture revealed life history differences and slight morphological differences between the types. As a result of life history differences the species partition the environment temporally, with each life history adapted to a somewhat different pattern of environmental uncertainty. The classification and evolution of temporal adaptations are discussed.

INTRODUCTION

From the sequence of events following an oil spill (Sanders et al. 1972; Grassle and Grassle 1974) we identified opportunistic species in marine benthos by (1) ability to increase rapidly in an unexploited environment, (2) large maximum population size, (3) early maturation and (4) high mortality. The most opportunistic species according to these criteria was *Capitella capitata*. This species has been widely regarded as a cosmopolitan indicator of pollution or environmental disturbance (Bagge 1969; Bellan 1967; Eagle and Rees 1973; Felice 1959; Halcrow et al. 1973; Henriksson 1969; Kitamori and Kobe 1959; Pearson 1972; Reish 1959; Rosenberg 1972; Tulkki 1968; Wade et al. 1972; Wass 1967). Our studies show that what we and others considered a single species, is actually a complex of at least six sibling species.

This finding raises a number of questions. How well separated are these species? How do these sympatric species with very similar food requirements subdivide the environment? How might they compare in rank on a scale of opportunism?

We gratefully acknowledge the skillful assistance of Judith Ashmore and Ann White. We thank R. Scheltema and R. Hoffmann for a number of valuable comments on the manuscript. Contribution no. 3580 from the Woods Hole Oceanographic Institution. This research was supported by NSF grants GA 35393, and GA 40144.

CAPITELLA SIBLING SPECIES

Table 1 lists some features of morphology and life history in the six sibling species of *Capitella* so far distinguished. Length

Table 1. A comparison of some morphological and life history features of six sibling species of *Capitella*.

Species	No. setigers with capillary setae	Shape of head	Shape of tail	Av. wet wt. mature worms (mg)	Egg diameter (μ)	No. eggs/ brood	Time larvae spend in plankton
I	7	prost. & perist. relatively short, prost. broadly triangular, head not depressed	plain	3-12	oval 216 x 180	30-400	several hrs
Ia	7	prost. & perist. largely fused, head depressed, sharply triangular	plain	10.1	75	200-2000	several days
II	7	prost. & perist. long, not distinctly separated, prost. broadly triangular, eyes somewhat ventral	lobed, with dorsal cleft	12.0	230	30-400	6-24 hrs
IIa	7	not distinguished from II	plain	11.9	-	-	-
III	3	prost. & perist. distinct. Prost. broadly triangular	flared with dorsal cleft	1-4	50	200-1000	up to 2 wks
IIIa	7	prost. & perist. partly fused not depressed	not flared, with dorsal cleft	1.7	∿250	30-50	none

of larval life was determined by observing the time from hatching to settlement of larvae which hatched spontaneously in the laboratory and were maintained at 20° over azoic mud. Type III larvae were also maintained in cultures free of sediment and were fed *Isochrysis* and *Phaeodactylum*, but successful settlement and metamorphosis were never observed. The number of eggs per brood is highly dependent on the amount of food available, and, for each species, the low end of the quoted range represents counts from starved laboratory individuals. The high end of the range for each species is representative of field-caught animals for which food is relatively abundant. Type III animals can readily be identified, but the other five species are very similar in morphology. However, each species is characterized by a set of enzymes with unique electrophoretic mobilities. Considering the eight loci most studied (PHI, XDH, PGM, IDH1, IDH2,

MDH1, MDH2, αGPDH)[1], only one allele is shared between any pair of species, that is the monomorphic PGM found in types I and Ia. More limited results on single esterase and leucine aminopeptidase loci also indicate that no alleles are common to all six species. The species in Table 1 have been numbered according to the relative mobilities of their most common PHI alleles using bovine serum albumin as a standard: I (.48), Ia (.50), II (.29), IIa (.36), III (.18), and IIIa (.16). A complete description of the electrophoretic results is in preparation.

The discovery of six species in *Capitella capitata* leads us to modify our interpretation of electrophoretic results described earlier for two MDH loci (Grassle and Grassle 1974).

At the faster locus (MDHI) the three bands identified are monomorphic homozygotes characterizing type I (the band with the slowest migration), type II and type III (the band with the fastest migration) *Capitella*. Most of the field results and all of the field experiments described in Grassle and Grassle (1974) apply to type I *Capitella* (Table 2), the type normally most common in intertidal marsh environments. Reexamination of the MDH gels previously described indicates that 46% of the Wild Harbor population in April 1971, then classified as heterozygotes at MDH1, were type III *Capitella* The December 1969 and July 1970 samples (from Stations II and IV respectively in Wild Harbor) were composed entirely of type I worms. Winter collections from Station IV in the years subsequent to 1971 indicate that type III *Capitella* reach peak population densities in the months of December and January, when they are also reproducing. The results of our sampling indicate that the oil spill prevented settlement and reproduction in the type III worms in 1969-70 and perhaps caused late settlement in 1970-71.

Table 2. Frequency of Type I *Capitella*, and percent Type I *Capitella* null homozygotes at MDH2 locus in collections from Wild Harbor and greater Sippewissett marshes following the Wild Harbor oil spill (Grassle and Grassle, 1974).

Location and Date	Total Number of Individuals	Percent Type I	Percent Type I in Null Homozygote Class at MDH2
Wild Harbor Station II December 1969	76	100	62
Wild Harbor Station IV July 1970	41	100	100
Wild Harbor Station IV April 1971	28	54	40
Gr. Sippewisset Marsh August 1970	182	99	77

At the slow locus (MDH2), the gel pattern previously classified as Type 2 is characteristic of type III *Capitella*. That is, 46% of the April 1971 Wild Harbor population are type III *Capitella*. In December 1969 all the worms were type I and there were two gel patterns at the MDH2 locus: 38% of the individuals with a single main band (and two conforming bands) were classified as either homozygotes or heterozygotes for the active allele; 62% of the individuals, with

[1]PHI, phosphohexose isomerase; XDH, xanthine dehydrogenase; PGM, phosphoglucomutase; IDH, isocitrate dehydrogenase; MDH, malate dehydrogenase; αGPDH, α-glycerophosphate dehydrogenase.

no activity at the MDH2 locus, belonged to the null homozygote class. In the July 1970 sample all individuals were type I and 100% were homozygous for the null allele. The August 1970 Sippewissett control samples had 77% of the type I individuals in the null homozygote class. In Wild Harbor, April 1971, 40% of the type I individuals were in this class. At the MDH2 locus the null allele was selected for by conditions associated with the oil spill. Our interpretation of the significance of the null allele in the type I worms needs to be confirmed by further breeding studies.

Samples of *Capitella* populations collected at different times of the year at seven different locations in Massachusetts have shown dramatic changes in the percent contribution of the six sibling species. For example, samples collected subtidally at the Woods Hole sewer outfall show five of the six species living sympatrically, although the contribution of a given species does not remain constant throughout the year. Temporal fluctuations in the percent composition of the different *Capitella* species have been found at all stations sampled for more than one year. A comparison of two subtidal samples collected on the same date at Gloucester at two localities separated by one mile, showed three species in one and two species in the other. In the first, 90% were type IIIa, in the second, 90% were type Ia, indicating that the proportions of the different species vary greatly over short distances.

Before the electrophoretic results conclusively demonstrated the existence of several species, we made many attempts (more than 200 crosses between individual males and females) to cross breed pairs of types I with Ia, II and III, and II with III, without success. This lack of success is hardly surprising considering the lack of common alleles between any two species (with the single exception of the PGM in types I and Ia). Table 1 shows that although these separate species in general lack differentiating morphological features, they exhibit marked differences in reproductive modes, particularly in the degree to which the larvae are dispersed. Species IIIa has only males and females (gonochoristic), species I, Ia, and II have males, females and protandrous hermaphrodites (which in type I can be selfing), and species III is an obligate outcrossing protandrous hermaphrodite. The length of planktonic larval life ranges from zero for the benthic larvae produced by type IIIa, to several weeks (or possibly longer) for type III.

TEMPORAL ADAPTATION AND DISPERSAL

In unpredictable environments niche separation is likely to result from differences in length of life cycle relative to the period of environmental change (Hutchinson 1965, Southwood et al. 1974). Hutchinson (1965) indicated that such temporal adaptation is likely to be particularly important for terrestrial and freshwater invertebrates. In an environment of a given average predictability (Grassle 1972), length of life cycle relative to the period of environmental change places each species in an environment of slightly different predictability--i.e., temporal adaptation renders the environment variously predictable to the species. Schoener's (1974) generalization about resource partitioning, that "Habitat dimensions are important more often than food-type dimensions which are important more often than temporal dimensions," may not apply in highly unpredictable environments. In such environments closely related, relatively opportunistic species such as the *Capitella* species will be separated by temporal adaptations based on life history differences.

Studies of temporal adaptation are scarce, in part, because the data are difficult to obtain. Where populations of closely related species have been intensively studied, life history adaptations to differing temporal regimes have been found. Among the best examples are the temporal adaptations occurring in a wide spectrum of species of *Drosophila* (Carson 1965; Dobzhansky 1965; Levins 1965). Perhaps the best example of a group of closely related species in which niche separation results from differences in temporal adaptation to environments are the nine species of the genus of water striders, *Gerris*, studied by Vepsäläinen (1974). In these species wing length determines dispersal ability, and dispersal ability is correlated with the degree of uncertainty and evanescence of the environment that the species are exposed to.

We believe the six species of *Capitella* represent several distinct temporal adaptations based partly on the dispersal capability of the larval stages. There are benthic larvae, larvae with a planktonic life of several days, and larvae that can remain in the plankton at least 14 days. Some of the species (e.g., Ia and III) seem to have relatively short breeding seasons limited to the winter or early spring, while others (e.g., I and II) breed throughout the year. Despite the enormous differences in life history features, all of the *Capitella* species may be considered to be relatively opportunistic. The differences in colonizing ability reflect differences in the environmental variability of their respective local habitats. Unlike the species of *Gerris*, the species of *Capitella* with the greatest powers of dispersal (types III and Ia) occur in the less variable, subtidal habitats. The species with the most rapid response to disturbed environments is type I. Although it has relatively limited dispersal ability, this is the species with the largest rate of increase, largest maximum population size, and highest mortality (Grassle and Grassle 1974).

The most opportunistic polychaetes brood their young (Grassle and Grassle 1974), and yet good dispersal ability is a requisite for colonization of the short-lived, unpredictable habitats where they become abundant. A distinction can be made between species which spend the greater part of their embryonic development in the plankton, and those which are brooded to a stage capable of either immediate settlement or dispersal over relatively short distances. Species with primarily planktonic development (e.g. *Capitella* species Ia and III), must adapt to local conditions through short-term selection every generation. The heaviest mortality in these species (which in *Capitella* have the highest number of eggs per brood) occurs in the plankton chiefly from predation (Mileikovsky 1971; Thorson 1946), but their relatively wide dispersal allows the selection of potentially more favorable habitats. Consequently, the postlarval phase of their life history appears less opportunistic. The mussel, *Mytilus edulis*, is this kind of opportunistic species (Koehn and Mitton 1972). In species where the offspring may settle adjacent to the adult (e.g., *Capitella* species I and IIIa, adaptation to local environments can occur by selection through several generations.

The distinction between adaption in species with large outcrossing populations and in species divided into subpopulations is somewhat similar to the distinction between adaptation in central and peripheral populations (Frank 1974). In species with a number of separate subpopulations there is, in addition to differential response to selection, a high incidence of local extinction which may occur as a result of a variety of unpredictable events. However, the resultant interdemic selection probably will contribute only to long-term evolutionary changes in the species.

LEVELS OF ORGANIZATION AND TIME SCALES OF TEMPORAL ADAPTATION

A simple gradient of degree of opportunism is not sufficient to explain the subtle differences in life histories which may reflect differences in temporal adaptation (see Wilbur et al. 1974). Every species adapts to the environment at a combination of levels of organization, each being appropriate for a different time scale of environmental variation (Haldane 1956; Lewontin 1957; Thoday 1953). Each unique life history is adapted to the pattern of environmental change in a unique way e.g. a species which has a life cycle of one year and breeds once during a two-week period will interact differently with seasonal and other environmental changes than a species in which individuals have a life span of four months and breed continuously for three of those four months. To clarify this concept levels of organization are presented in Table 3 along with time scales of adaptation and significant life history features.

To illustrate how the Table might be used, we may consider the observation that body size and degree of opportunism are related (Fenchel 1974; Pianka 1970). Large animals, because they are generally better regulators than small animals, usually adapt at the level of the individual rather than the population. An environmental change not included in the range of tolerance of every individual is likely to have an unpredictable effect and adaptation will be at the ecological or genetic level. This argument may be applied to the observation of Selander and Kaufman (1973) that invertebrates have higher genetic variability than vertebrates. The vertebrates they studied were homeotherms except for a fish with relatively high genetic variability. Selander and Kaufman explained the differences in genetic variability by saying that the environment of vertebrates is more fine grained because of their larger body size, greater mobility and greater homeostatic control. From Table 3 we would say that vertebrates are better physiological (and behavioral) regulators, so

Table 3. Levels of organization and time scales of adaptation.

Level of organization:	behavioral and physiological	developmental	genetic	ecological	evolutionary
Unit of adaptation:	individual	individual life cycle	populational	spatial inter-populational	temporal inter-populational
Type and frequency of environmental change relative to length of life cycle:	frequent	on same scale (usually seasonal)	unpredictable and infrequent	localized unpredictable and infrequent	gradual autocorrelated
Life span, (if adaptation primarily at this level)	long	same	short	short	very short
Population size: (If adaptation primarily at this level)	small	intermediate	large	spatially separated large	small
Genetic variability: (If adaptation primarily at this level)	low	intermediate	high additive	high, not necessarily additive	small
Selection: (If adaptation primarily at this level)	normalizing	normalizing	diversifying-temporal model	diversifying-spatial model and interdemic	long term directional

that adaptation is more at the level of the individual than the population.

For consideration of temporal resource partitioning the important parts of Table 3 are labeled genetic and ecological to avoid coining new terms. Benthic species with obligate planktonic dispersal have less of a spatial interpopulational component to the adaptation. Diversifying selection is important to these species but the temporal model, where different genotypes are selected at different times in an unpredictably varying environment, is more appropriate (Haldane and Jayakar 1963). The temporal model is somewhat less effective in maintaining genetic variation than the spatial model (Hedrick 1974), where different alleles are favored in each local environment and the genetic variability remains high as a result of limited gene flow between subpopulations (Levene 1953; Soulé 1971). Habitat selection and loss of alleles through founder effects would also contribute to genetic differentiation of local populations (see Levins 1970).

Spatial interpopulational adaptation is a significant component of adaptation in the most opportunistic species (Grassle and Grassle 1974). In benthic invertebrates, such as type I *Capitella*, the possibility for immediate settlement results in more spatial subdivision and allows the population in a local environment to respond to selection through several generations without being swamped by immigrants from surrounding populations. Short-term selection (see Williams 1975) is likely to be an important part of adaptation regardless of the degree of spatial subdivision. Marine benthic species with greatest powers of dispersal will undergo genetic differentiation only through intense selection from a large planktonic gene pool every generation. Perhaps equally important is the fact that species without planktonic larvae or with the possibility for almost immediate settlement will have the greatest rate of population increase since planktonic dispersal is always accompanied by heavy mortality. For example, most of the type I, type II and type IIIa *Capitella* which can settle soon after hatching will form part of the rapid population increase in a local area (with only the occasional larva being widely dispersed). Every larva of types Ia and III *Capitella* colonizes a new environment so that rapid local population increases will be made up of larvae selected from a number of source populations each generation.

SPECIATION

Enormous differences in life history frequently occur in very closely related species. Species of the genus, *Littorina* (Heller 1975; Mileikovsky 1975), or *Crepidula* (Coe 1949), are good examples in gastropods. *Drosophila* species can range from rare, narrow-habitat species of the tropical forest to very widely dispersed species adapted to the unpredictable habitats formed by man-made disturbance. Species with a large number of geographically separated subpopulations are more likely to speciate than those with larger breeding units (Carson 1960; Levins 1965).

In large genera that include opportunistic species the taxonomic unit that survives through evolutionary time may be a metaspecies in which species are continually becoming extinct and being formed. This is similar to the metapopulational equilibrium described by Levins (1970). In groups of asexually reproducing organisms it is frequently difficult to say whether the evolutionary unit represents a metaspecies or metapopulational equilibrium. Weeds, weevils (Suomalainen and Saura 1973), aphids (Hille Ris Lambers 1966) and brine shrimp (Barigozzi 1974) all provide good examples of opportunistic organisms where a large number of biotypes appear to form a complex that functions as an evolutionary unit (see Simpson 1961; Sokal 1974). Some members of nearly all the parthenogenetic groups maintain sexual reproduction (White 1973). The asexually reproducing lines may evolve repeatedly from sexually reproducing ancestors.

A complex of species may be the unit that survives through evolutionary time in sexually reproducing species where speciation may frequently occur through chromosomal events in isolated, founder populations (Mayr 1963). The very low allelic similarly in the *Capitella* species is not typical of groups of sibling species. About one-half to two-thirds of the loci among sibling species of *Drosophila* have alleles in common (Ayala et al. 1970; Zouros 1973). The extreme differences in *Capitella* electrophoretic patterns are more like those described for biotypes of weevils (Suomalainen and Saura 1973).

Opportunistic genera are often represented by groups of sibling species. In the well-known example of r-selection, one biotype of dandelion is favored over another biotype as a result of differences in temporal adaptation to habitats of different predictability (Gadgil and Solbrig 1972; Solbrig and Simpson 1974). The opportunistic marine species chosen for genetic studies because of short life histories and ease of culturing are representives of sibling groups. The isopod species group, *Jaera albifrons*, includes five species, each with different chromosome numbers (Staiger and Bocquet 1956;

Bocquet 1972). The copepod genus, *Tisbe,* includes a number of sibling species each with somewhat different life histories (Volkmann-Rocco 1972; Volkmann-Rocco and Battaglia 1972). The situation most like that found in *Capitella* occurs in the polychaete genus, *Ophryotrocha,* studied by Åkesson (1973) and Bacci (1965). *O. labronica* may be similar in many ways to our type I *Capitella* since, although it is usually gonochoristic, selfing hermaphrodites have been found in one of the populations (Parenti 1960; Zunarelli 1962; Zunarelli-Vandini 1967). *O. puerilis* is like our type III *Capitella* in being a protandrous hermaphrodite. Both *O. labronica* and *O. puerilis* are considered pollution indicator species (Åkesson 1973). Some species of *Ophryotrocha* have brood protection and others do not. One species is viviparous. Twelve of the species may be put into three groups on the basis of chromosome number.

SUMMARY

Niche separation in the *Capitella* species results from temporal adaptations based on differences in dispersal ability. The various life history features of the *Capitella* species cannot be classified along a simple gradient of environmental predictability since dispersal ability and the extent of spatial division into subpopulations must be considered. The most opportunistic *Capitella* species, type I, has relatively limited dispersal ability, which is compensated for by the possibility of responding to selection through several generations in each local environment.

Sibling groups of opportunistic species show little tendency to exploit different habitats or foods and a variety of life history patterns are likely to evolve many times. The whole complex survives through evolutionary time as a unit with new adaptive modes continually being formed and becoming extinct.

REFERENCES

Åkesson, B. 1973. Reproduction and larval morphology of five *Ophryotrocha* species (Polychaeta, Dorvilleidae). Zool. Scripta 2: 145-155.

Ayala, F. J., C. A. Mourão, S. Perez-Salas, R. Richmond, and T. Dobzhansky. 1970. Enzyme variability in the *Drosophila willistoni* group, I. Genetic differentiation among sibling species. Proc. Natl. Acad. Sci. U.S.A. 67: 225-232.

Bacci, G. 1965. Sex determination. Pergamon Press.

Bagge, P. 1969. Effects of pollution on estuarine ecosystems. 1. Effects of effluents from wood processing industries on the hydrography, bottom and fauna of Saltkällefjord (W. Sweden). 2. The succession of the bottom fauna communities in polluted estuarine habitats in the Baltic-Skagerrak region. Meer. jukl., Suomi 228: 1-130.

Barigozzi, C. 1974. *Artemia:* a survey of its significance in genetic problems. Evol. Biol. 7: 221-262.

Bellan, G. 1967. Pollution et peuplements benthiques sur substrat meuble dans la région de Marseille. 2ème partie. L'ensemble portuaire marseillais. Rev. int. Océanogr. méd. 8: 51-95.

Bocquet, C. 1972. La speciation des *Jaera albifrons*. État présent des connaissances et des problèmes. Fifth Europ. Mar. Biol. Symp., Piccin Editore, Padova. 348 pp.

Carson, H. L. 1960. Genetic conditions which promote or retard the formation of species. Cold Spring Harbor Symp. Quant. Biol. 24: 87-105.

_____. 1965. Chromosomal morphism in geographically widespread species of *Drosophila*, p. 503-531. In H. G. Baker and G. L. Stebbins [eds.], The genetics of colonizing species. Academic Press.

Coe, W. R. 1949. Divergent methods of development in morphologically similar species of prosobranch gastropods. J. Morphol. 84: 383-399.

Dobzhansky, T. 1965. "Wild" and "domestic" species of *Drosophila*, p. 533-546. In H. G. Baker and G. L. Stebbins [eds.], The genetics of colonizing species. Academic Press.

Eagle, R. A. and E. I. S. Rees. 1973. Indicator species--a case for caution. Mar. Pollut. Bull. 4: 25.

Felice, F. P. 1959. The effect of wastes on the distribution of bottom invertebrates in the San Francisco Bay estuary. Wasmann J. Biol. 17: 1-17.

Fenchel, T. 1974. Intrinsic rate of natural increase: the relationship with body size. Oecologia 14: 317-326.

Frank, P. 1974. The regulation of populations, p. 81-102. In W. H. Johnson and W. C. Steere [eds.], The environmental challenge. Holt, Rinehart and Winston.

Gadgil, M. and O. T. Solbrig. 1972. The concept of r- and k-selection: evidence from wild flowers and some theoretical considerations. Am. Nat. 106: 14-31.

Grassle, J. F. 1972. Species diversity, genetic variability and environmental uncertainty. Fifth Europ. Mar. Biol. Symp., Piccin Editore, Padova. 348 pp.

_____, and J. P. Grassle. 1974. Opportunistic life histories and genetic systems in marine benthic polychaetes. J. Mar. Res. 32: 253-284.

Halcrow, W., D. W. Mackay, and I. Thornton. 1973. The distribution of trace metals and fauna in the Firth of Clyde in relation to the disposal of sewage sludge. J. Mar. Biol. Assoc. U. K. 53: 721-739.

Haldane, J. B. S. 1956. Time in biology. Science Progress 44: 385-402.

_____, and S. D. Jayakar. 1963. Polymorphism due to selection of varying direction. J. Genet. 58: 237-242.

Hedrick, P. W. 1974. Genetic variation in a heterogeneous environment. I. Temporal heterogeneity and the absolute dominance model. Genetics 78: 757-770.

Heller, J. 1975. The taxonomy of some British *Littorina* species, with notes on their reproduction (Mollusca: Prosobranchia). Zool. J. Linn. Soc. 56: 131-151.

Henriksson, R. 1969. Influence of pollution on the bottom fauna of the Sound (Öresund). Oikos 20: 507-523.

Hille Ris Lambers, D. 1966. Polymorphism in Aphididae. Ann. Rev. Entomol. 11: 47-78.

Hutchinson, G. E. 1965. The ecological theater and the evolutionary play. Yale Univ. Press.

Kitamori, R. and Z. Kobe. 1959. The benthic community in polluted coastal waters. IV. Kanzaki River. Bull. Island Sea Res. Biol. Station 12: 223-226.

Koehn, R. K. and J. B. Mitton. 1972. Population genetics of marine pelecypods. I. Ecological heterogeneity and evolutionary strategy at an enzyme locus. Am. Nat. 106: 47-56.

Levene, H. 1953. Genetic equilibrium when more than one ecological niche is available. Am. Nat. 87: 311-313.

Levins, R. 1965. Theory of fitness in a heterogeneous environment. V. Optimal genetic systems. Genetics 52: 891-904.

_____. 1970. Extinction, p. 77-107. In Some mathematical questions in biology, v. 2. American Mathematical Society.

Lewontin, R. C. 1957. The adaptation of populations to varying environments. Cold Spring Harbor Symp. Quant. Biol. 22: 395-408.

Mayr, E. 1963. Animal species and evolution. Harvard Univ. Press.

Mileikovsky, S. A. 1971. Types of larval development in marine bottom invertebrates, their distribution and ecological significance: a re-evaluation. Mar. Biol. 10: 193-213.

_____. 1975. Types of larval development in Littorinidae (Gastropoda: Prosobranchia) of the world ocean and ecological patterns of their distribution. Mar. Biol. 30: 129-135.

Parenti, U. 1960. Self-fertilization in *Ophryotrocha labronica*. Experientia 16: 413-414.

Pearson, T. H. 1972. The effect of industrial effluent from pulp and paper mills on the marine benthic environment. Proc. Roy. Soc. Lond. B 180: 469-485.

Pianka, E. R. 1970. On r- and k-selection. Am. Nat. 104: 592-597.

Reish, D. J. 1959. The use of marine invertebrates as indicators of water quality, p. 92-103. In E. A. Pearson [ed.], Waste disposal in the marine environment. Berkeley.

Rosenberg, R. 1972. Benthic faunal recovery in a Swedish fjord following the closure of a sulphite pulp mill. Oikos 23: 92-108.

Sanders, H. L., J. F. Grassle, and G. R. Hampson. 1972. The West Falmouth oil spill I. Biology. Woods Hole Oceanographic Inst. Tech. Rpt. 72-20. Unpublished manuscript.

Schoener, T. W. 1974. Resource partitioning in ecological communities. Science 185: 27-38.

Selander, R. K. and D. W. Kaufman. 1973. Genic variability and strategies of adaptation in animals. Proc. Natl. Acad. Sci. U.S.A. 70: 1875-1877.

Simpson, G. G. 1961. Principles of animal taxonomy. Columbia Univ. Press.
Sokal, R. R. 1974. The species problem reconsidered. Syst. Zool. 22: 360-374.
Solbrig, O. T. and B. B. Simpson. 1974. Components of regulation of a population of dandelions in Michigan. J. Ecol. 62: 473-486.
Soulé, M. 1971. The variation problem: the gene flow-variation hypothesis. Taxon 20: 37-50.
Southwood, T. R. E., R. M. May, M. P. Hassell, and G. R. Conway. 1974. Ecological strategies and population parameters. Am. Nat. 108: 791-804.
Staiger, H. and C. Bocquet. 1956. Les chromosomes de la super-espèce *Jaera marina* (F.) et de quelques autres Janiridae (Isopodes Asellotes). Bull. Biol. 90: 1-32.
Suomalainen, E. and A. Saura. 1973. Genetic polymorphism and evolution in parthenogenetic animals. I. Polyploid Curculionidae. Genetics 74: 489-508.
Thoday, J. M. 1953. Components of fitness. Symp. Soc. Exp. Biol. 7: 96-113.
Thorson, G. 1946. Reproduction and larval development of Danish marine bottom invertebrates with special reference to the planktonic larvae in the Sound (Öresund). Med. Komm. Danmarks Fisk.-og. Havundersogelser. Ser. Plank. 4: 1-533.
Tulkki, P. 1968. Effect of pollution on the benthos off Gothenburg. Helgolander wiss. Meersunters. 17: 209-215.
Vepsäläinen, K. 1974. The life cycles and wing lengths of Finnish *Gerris* Fabr. species (Heteroptera, Gerridae). Acta Zool. Fennica 141: 1-73.
Volkmann-Rocco, B. 1972. Species of *Tisbe* (Copepoda, Harpacticoida) from Beaufort, North Carolina. Archo. Oceanogr. Limnol. 17: 223-258.
_____, and B. Battaglia. 1972. A new case of sibling species in the genus *Tisbe* (Copepoda, Harpacticoida). Fifth Europ. Mar. Biol. Symp., Piccin Editore, Padova. 348 pp.
Wade, B. A., L. Antonio, and R. Mahon. 1972. Increasing organic pollution in Kingston Harbour, Jamaica. Mar. Pollut. Bull. 3: 106-111.
Wass, M. L. 1967. Biological and physiological basis of indicator organisms and communities. Section II. Indicators of pollution p. 271-283. In T. A. Olson and F. J. Burgess [eds.], Pollution and marine ecology. Wiley, Interscience.
White, M. J. D. 1973. Animal cytology and evolution. Cambridge Univ. Press.
Wilbur, H. M., D. W. Tinkle, and J. P. Collins. 1974. Environmental certainty, trophic level, and resource availability in life history evolution. Am. Nat. 108: 805-817.
Williams, G. C. 1975. Sex and Evolution. Princeton Univ. Press.
Zouros, E. 1973. Genic differentiation associated with the early stages of speciation in the *mulleri* subgroup of *Drosophila*. Evolution 27: 601-621.

Zunarelli, R. 1962. Il differenziamento citosessuale di tre specie di *Ophryotrocha*. Boll. Zool. 29: 417-423.

Zunarelli-Vandini, R. 1967. Azione reciproche sulle gonadi in coppie omeospecifiche ed eterospecifiche di *Ophryotrocha puerilis siberti* ed *Ophryotrocha labronica*. Archo zool. ital. 52: 179-192.

Ecology of Shallow Water Deposit-Feeding Communities Quisset Harbor, Massachusetts

Jeffrey S. Levinton
Department of Ecology and Evolution
State University of New York
Stony Brook, NY 11794

ABSTRACT

The deposit-feeding macrofauna of muddy sand communities of Quisset Harbor, Massachusetts were studied by means of bottom-sampling, SCUBA diving, and laboratory analysis of interspecies interaction. Two communities are defined: a shallow (1-4 m) eel grass muddy sand community, characterized by habitat heterogeneity, relatively high environmental stress, diverse fauna, and patchiness in faunal distribution; and a Channel sandy mud (4-7 m) community that is more homogeneous in physical characteristics and faunal distributions. Species richness is greater in the eel grass community but equitability (J') is less.

Field and laboratory x-ray studies show that biogenic reworking of the substratum determined the distribution and abundance of deposit-feeding species. Sediment-conditioning caused an increase in water-content of the sediment, and an increase in the average grain size of sedimentary particles through fecal pellet formation. These substratum modifications, plus physical displacement of sedimentary grains during burrowing, were sufficient to cause interference between different deposit-feeding species. Also, direct physical interference between mobile deposit-feeding bivalves was regularly observed in the laboratory.

The distribution and abundance of deposit-feeding species in these two communities suggest that the dominant species are resource-limited and that competitive interactions control species presence in a given microhabitat. Exploitation rates and regional distributions in Buzzards Bay support these hypotheses. Physical interference between deposit-feeding species mediated through sediment modification is a major determinant of competitive exclusion. Food exploitation is probably important as well.

INTRODUCTION

Sanders' (1968) model depicting a gradient of soft-bottom communities from shallow to deep water suggested that communities residing in very shallow water are controlled primarily by the physical environment, whereas those in deep water stable habitats are controlled by biological factors or accommodation. Levinton (1972*a*) pointed out, however, that this model is overly simplistic and neglects contrasting feeding strategies, independent of water depth. He suggested that suspension-feeders live under a more fluctuating trophic regime than deposit feeders (Levinton 1972*a*). Dayton and Hessler (1972) also criticized Sanders' hypothesis by pointing out that predation affects stabilization of diversity. All these studies lacked data on interspecies interactions in soft-bottom marine invertebrate communities, and we still know little of the mechanisms by which soft-bottom benthic species compete for limiting resources (but see Rhoads and Young 1970; Woodin 1974; Fenchel 1975). The purpose of this study, therefore, was to: (1) map in detail a discrete assemblage of deposit-feeding benthic species, (2) determine the processes that control population size and the importance of interspecific competition, and (3) assess how deposit-feeding species affect their sedimentary environment, and each other.

Mechanisms of interspecific interactions were studied by direct observations of species behavior and interspecies interactions in the laboratory, while the question of biological accommodation was studied through the analysis of spatial pattern and niche structure of two deposit-feeding benthic communities in lateral contact. The communities are defined as recurrent groups of species. The question raised was: can those species that consistently co-occur be assigned to a suite of contiguous niches? I examined the dimensions of the niche related to feeding and living positions within the sediment. If individuals of species requiring the same resource were observed to interact, and if a community was composed only of species which do not compete significantly and occupy contiguous niches with respect to living position and food supply, then biological interactions were thought to play an important role in the structure of multispecies assemblages. Of course, any postulated competitive advantage was predicated on a species' relative superiority in exploiting a limiting aspect of the physical or biotic environment. Therefore, this study concentrated on those parameters which are known to influence the distribution of deposit-feeding benthos, especially sedimentary characteristics which strongly limit benthic deposit-feeders. I also attempted to relate these characteristics to the outcome of postulated competitive interaction of pairs of species.

Deposit-feeding species, or species which ingest sediment to extract food, are ideal subjects for studying interspecific interactions and niche structure in soft-bottom communities. They are relatively little affected by sudden changes in plankton in the overlying water, and they exert significant and measurable physical changes on the sediment in which they live (Rhoads and Young 1970).

I am grateful to D. C. Rhoads for advice and H. L. Sanders for laboratory space. Gail Levinton, J. Howard and Donald Allen assisted me in the field. K. W. Flessa, R. T. Paine, and S. A. Woodin read drafts of this manuscript. Supported by grants-in-aid from the

Geological Society of America, Sigma Xi, and a National Science Foundation predoctoral fellowship, this report is adapted from part of a Ph.D. thesis (Yale University). Contribution number 145 from the Program in Ecology and Evolution at the State University of New York at Stony Brook.

AREA OF STUDY

Quisset Harbor is a small (1.2-km long) embayment on the southeastern portion of Buzzards Bay, Massachusetts, about 2 km northeast of Woods Hole (Fig. 1). Extensive tidal flushing makes salinities similar to those of Buzzards Bay (29.5-32.5 °/oo).

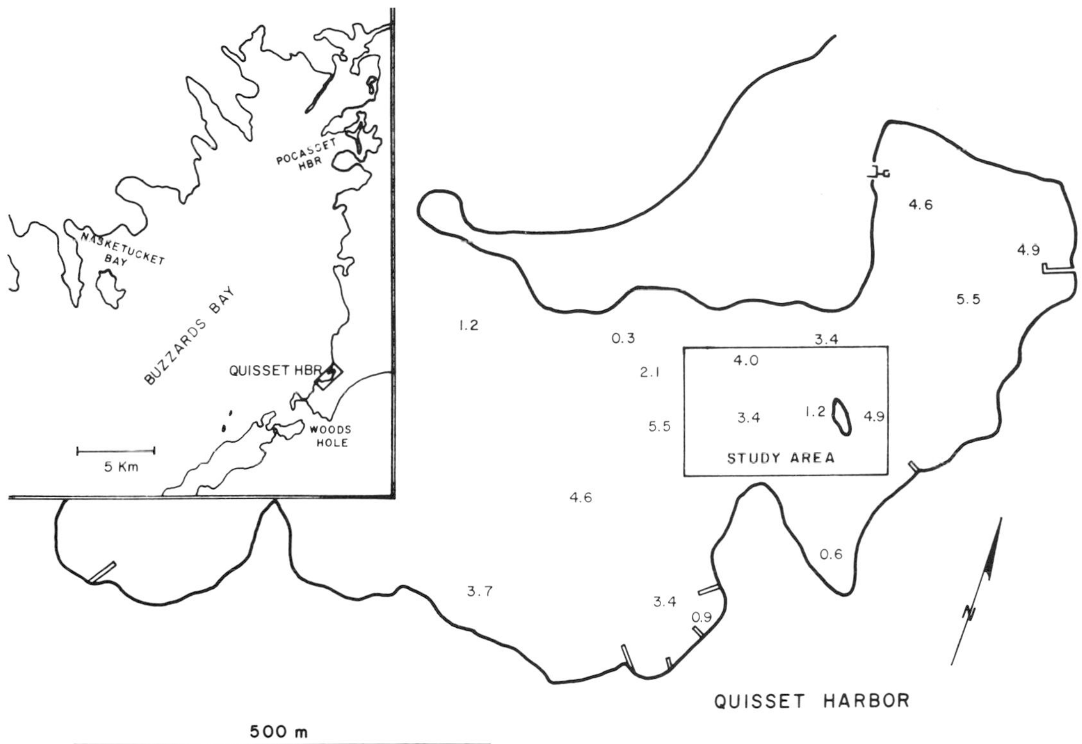

Fig. 1. Map of Quisset Harbor, showing location of Buzzards Bay, Massachusetts (inset) and Study Area. Depths of scattered locations are given in meters.

Faunal collections (summers of 1968, 1969) were taken from an area 2 to 6 m deep, just east of an island in the narrows area of the harbor (Fig. 2). Sediments contain 20-80% silt-clay (by weight). The shoreward portion of the study area is rich in eel grass (*Zostera marina*), and is areally heterogeneous with respect to eel grass cover, sediment and currents (Fig. 2), relative to the more homogeneous channelward area. The study area, a shallow water eel grass community and a deeper water channel community--was delineated on the basis of faunal, floral and sediment differences documented in a 1967 pilot study.

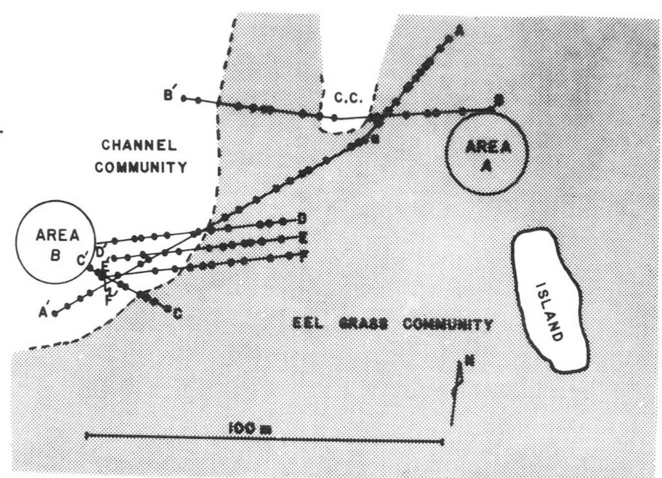

Fig. 2. Study area, with areal distribution of eel grass and channel "communities", location of transects, and smaller sampling areas.

MATERIALS AND METHODS

All collecting was done by SCUBA to ensure accurate location of sampling sites and to minimize variation in size and quality of samples obtained with ship-deployed sampling gear. Direct observations and underwater photography allowed *in situ* documentation not available to studies based solely on dredge and bottom grab samples.

Faunal samples were collected from an aluminum or fiberglas frame of either 0.25 m^2, 0.04 m^2, 0.03 m^2, that was pushed into the bottom to a depth of approximately 25 cm below the sediment-water interface; sediment was carefully transferred to covered buckets which were brought to the surface. A short sediment core was taken adjacent to each faunal sampling station, the top 7 cm being kept for textural analysis. Undisturbed 7-cm core samples were usually higher in silt-clay content than excavated or mixed samples, probably because of vertical grading of sediments by organisms (Rhoads and Stanley 1965).

Faunal samples were sieved in the field through a 0.5-mm mesh screen and fixed in a 5% buffered formalin in sea water solution, stained with rose bengal and then transferred to 70% ethanol. Samples were resieved in the laboratory through a 2.0-mm mesh screen and all benthic animals were picked, identified and counted. The 2.0-mm screen size was selected because no abundant new species were found in the 0.5-mm mesh, and I wished to avoid newly settled individuals. Animals were identified with the aid of a key to marine invertebrates of Woods Hole (Smith 1964), and Pettibone's (1963) description of New England polychaetes.

Particle size distribution was measured by disaggregating wet sediment with an electric blender and sieving through a 0.062-mm mesh. The dry weight percent of sediment passing through the screen was defined as percent silt-clay. The sand-sized fraction was further fractionated using a Wentworth graded series of sieves.

I estimated bottom sediment stability by measuring the vertical core water-content (Moore 1931; Rhoads and Young 1970). Undisturbed sediment cores were collected underwater and brought to the surface in their original orientation, then frozen and extruded. These cores were sliced with a sharp knife, at 5-mm intervals, perpendicular to the long axis of the core. Slices were then weighed wet, dried at 50°C for 12 hours, and weighed dry, together with deposited salts. The difference between the wet weight and the dry weight, divided by the wet weight, was taken as the percent water-content. Water-content was determined at increasing depths below the sediment-water interface. Photographs of the sediment-water interface were used to further investigate sedimentary properties. The sediment-water interface camera, suggested by Rhoads and Young (1970), was employed for this procedure. X-radiography of thin aquaria was used to study interspecies interactions and sediment modification by deposit-feeders in the laboratory.

In the summer of 1968, transects A-A', B-B' and C-C' were established to examine variation within and between the Eelgrass and Channel communities (Fig. 2). End points and turning points were located using sextant sights horizontal to shore locations. From a given end point a line was stretched along the bottom with previously attached, randomly spaced tags indicating each 1/4 sq m sample. Sampling density was high, samples being as little as 2 m apart. In the summer of 1969, the approximate intercommunity boundary was located, and three parallel transects, D-D', E-E' and F-F', were made across this boundary. Three 0.03-m^2 samples were collected at each station, each sample located randomly about the tag, in a manner similar to that of Sanders et al. (1962).

Spatial distribution within each community was investigated in a series of 0.04-m^2 samples taken within Areas A and B in an areally random sampling pattern. Samples were taken from a circle approximately 25 m in diameter. Spatial distribution was investigated on a smaller scale by taking 0.03-m^2 samples randomly spaced on seven 1.8-m long transects. These transects were parallel; intertransect distance was 30 cm. The Eelgrass series was taken at point a (Area N) whereas the Channel series was taken at point C' (Fig. 2, Area P).

SEDIMENT DISTRIBUTION

Many studies have documented the effects of sedimentary properties on the distribution of deposit-feeding infauna. Sanders (1958) demonstrated that the abundance of deposit-feeders strongly correlated with the silt-clay fraction of the sediment. He related this correlation to food supply. In addition, the deposit-feeding infauna exerts strong changes in the grain size properties and stability of the sediment (Rhoads and Young 1970). These changes may prohibit the presence of certain species, or may be necessary before certain other species can be present (Rhoads and Young 1971). This study therefore found it necessary to assess the properties of the bottom sediments of the Eelgrass and Channel biotopes as a framework for faunal data.

1. Sand and silt-clay content of sediments.--Silt-clay content decreases going from the deeper water channel bottoms towards the shallow water eelgrass bottoms, along transect A-A' (Fig. 3). The mean percent silt-clay for samples of area A (Eelgrass) was 36.1 ± 1.93 (± s.e., N = 36), whereas the mean percent silt-clay for area B (Channel) was 57.4 ± 1.55 (N = 36). However, silt-clay decreases locally from eelgrass to channel bottoms at the eelgrass-to-bare-bottom transition, in transect D-D', E-E' and F-F' (Figs. 4, 5). In the eelgrass bottoms systematic areal changes are evident in silt-clay abundance (Fig. 6), in 36 samples taken in an area of

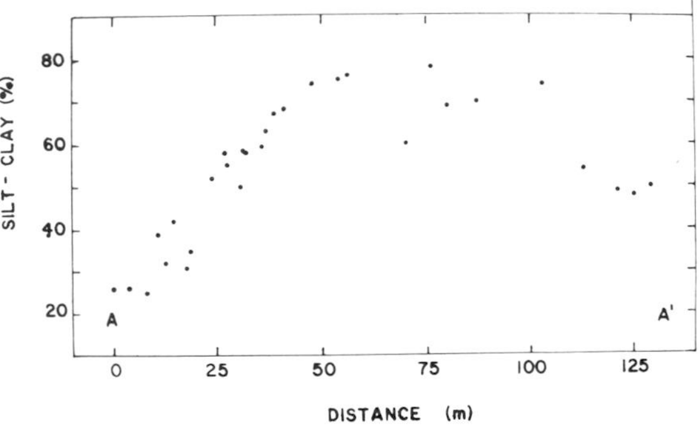

Fig. 3. Distribution of sediment silt-clay content along transect A-a-A'. Note increase of silt-clay from Eelgrass (A) to Channel habitats. Silt-clay decreases towards other end of transect (A') because of reapproach towards Eelgrass sediments (see Fig. 2).

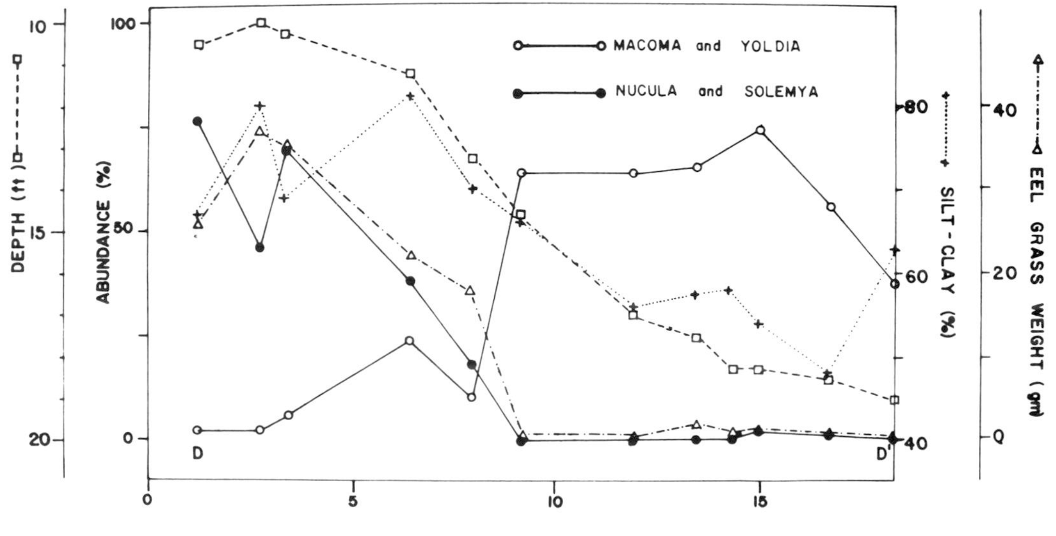

Fig. 4. Distribution of dominant bivalve species, water depth, dry weight of Eelgrass (per 0.1 m^2), and sediment silt-clay percentage along transect D-D'.

Fig. 5. Distribution of dominant bivalve species, water depth, dry weight of Eelgrass (per 0.1 m^2), and sediment silt-clay percentage along transect C-C'.

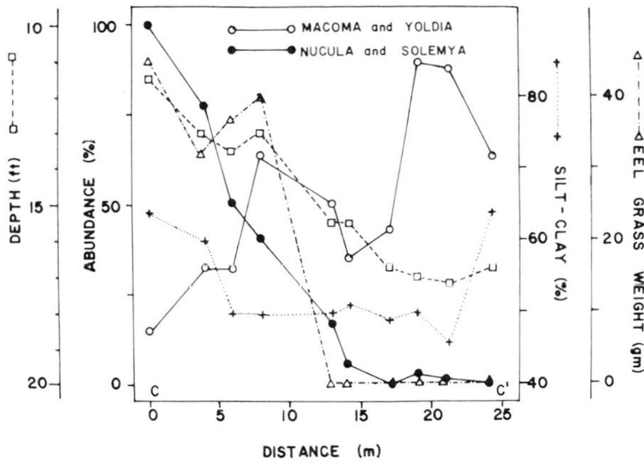

Fig. 6. Distribution of the tellinacean bivalves, *Tellina agilis* and *Cumingia tellinoides*, in Eelgrass Area A (see Fig. 2). Percent silt-clay contours are shown.

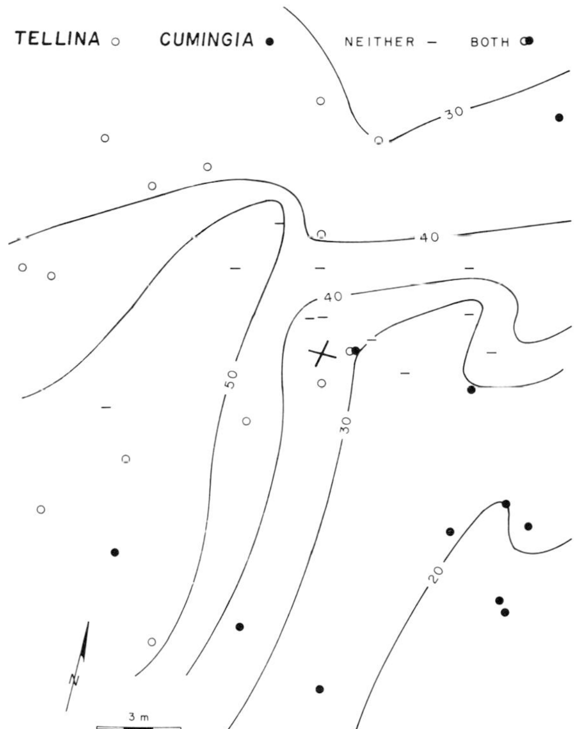

490 sq m. However, in the Channel area B patterns with the same sampling were not visually detected. Consistent with this observation was the greater variation observed during cursory examination of the Eelgrass area A samples for abundance of benthic diatoms, eelgrass detrital particles, and clumps of organic detritus less than 2 mm in diameter. Three randomly selected microscope slides of surface eelgrass sediment and standard geological thin-section comparison charts indicated that fecal pellets compromise 40-50% of the sediment and are fine sand in size. Channel sediments appeared uniform, diatoms being generally uncommon, and other benthic algae rare. Aggregates of organic detritus were smaller in size.

The sediment is predominantly composed of sand and fecal pellets. The latter have smaller size distribution in Channel bottoms than in Eelgrass bottoms (Fig. 7), as measured in samples from core tops by wet sieving. However, I found little variation in the relative abundance of the sand-sized fractions (Fig. 8). Modally the sand fraction is a fine sand (ca. 0.5 mm).

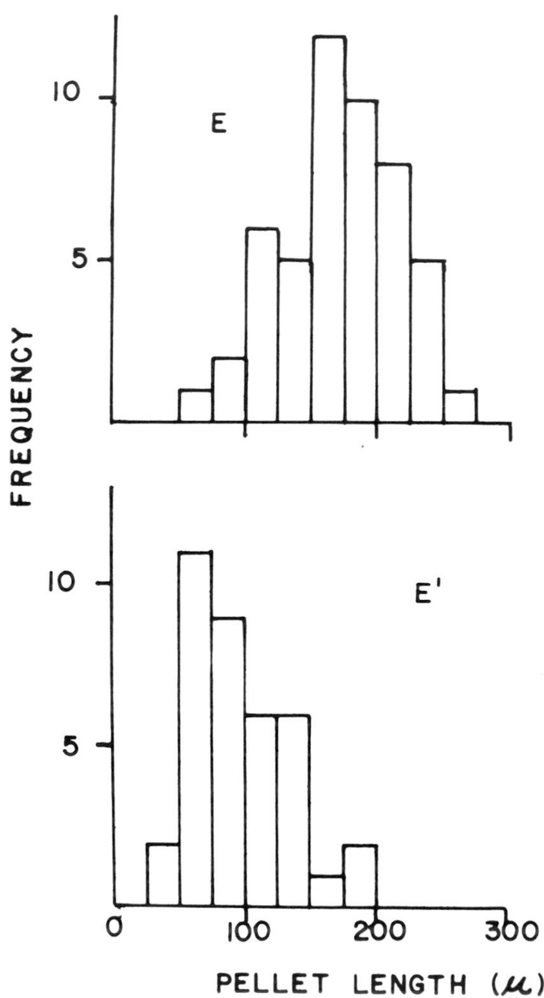

Fig. 7. Length frequency distribution of fecal pellets taken from Eelgrass (E) and Channel (E') bottoms (see transect E-E' in Fig. 2).

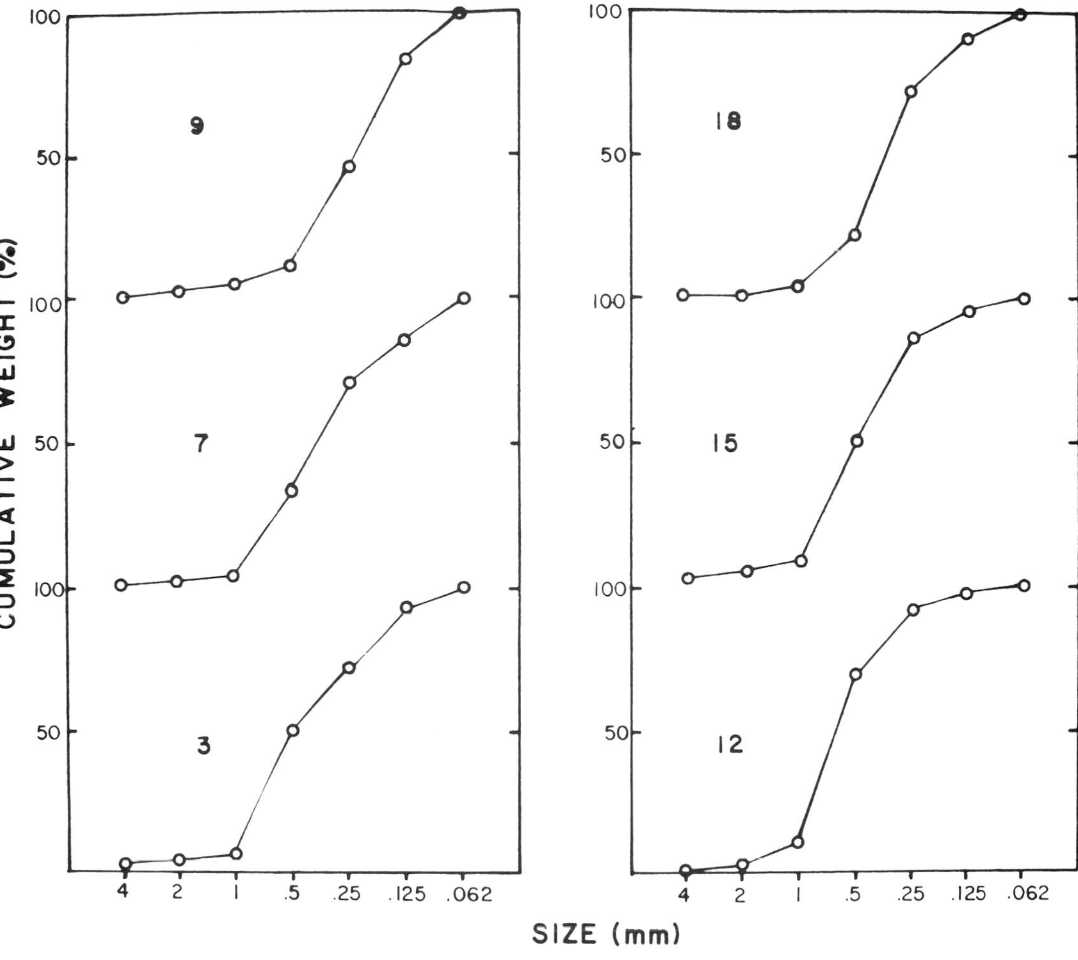

Fig. 8. Cumulative weight distributions for sand-size sediment fractions of samples distributed along transect A-a-A' (sample number 3 is the third sample from point A, Fig. 2, number 18, the eighteenth, etc.).

2. Sediment water-content.--Three stations were established: an Eelgrass biotope station (point D), a Channel biotope station (D') and an intermediate station midway along the transect. The water-content of the Eelgrass sediment is greater at all depths than that of the Channel biotope station (Fig. 9). In all three samples water-content decreases with depth; however most of the decrease in the Channel sample occurs in the upper 5 mm.

3. Sediment-water interface.--Cross-sections of Eelgrass biotope sediments are homogeneous with depth. The sediment appears to be granular in structure with only one recognizable interface, the sediment-water interface (Fig. 10). Cross-sections of Channel biotope sediments reveal a distinct interface 5-10 mm below the sediment-water interface. Fairly well-compacted sediment is found below this interval, whereas a layer of relatively loosely packed

sediment is evident above (Fig. 10). A similar sedimentary profile was developed when populations of the common channel bivalve, *Macoma tenta*, were maintained in thin-walled aquaria at naturally occurring densities (Fig. 11). Similarly, the Eelgrass biotope cross-sections were closely matched by populations of the eelgrass bivalve, *Nucula proxima*, maintained in eelgrass sediment (Fig. 11).

4. Turbidity.--Figure 12 shows turbidity differences above the sediment-water interface between stations at either end of transect D-D'. Note the significantly higher turbidity near the sediment-water interface over the Eelgrass bottom.

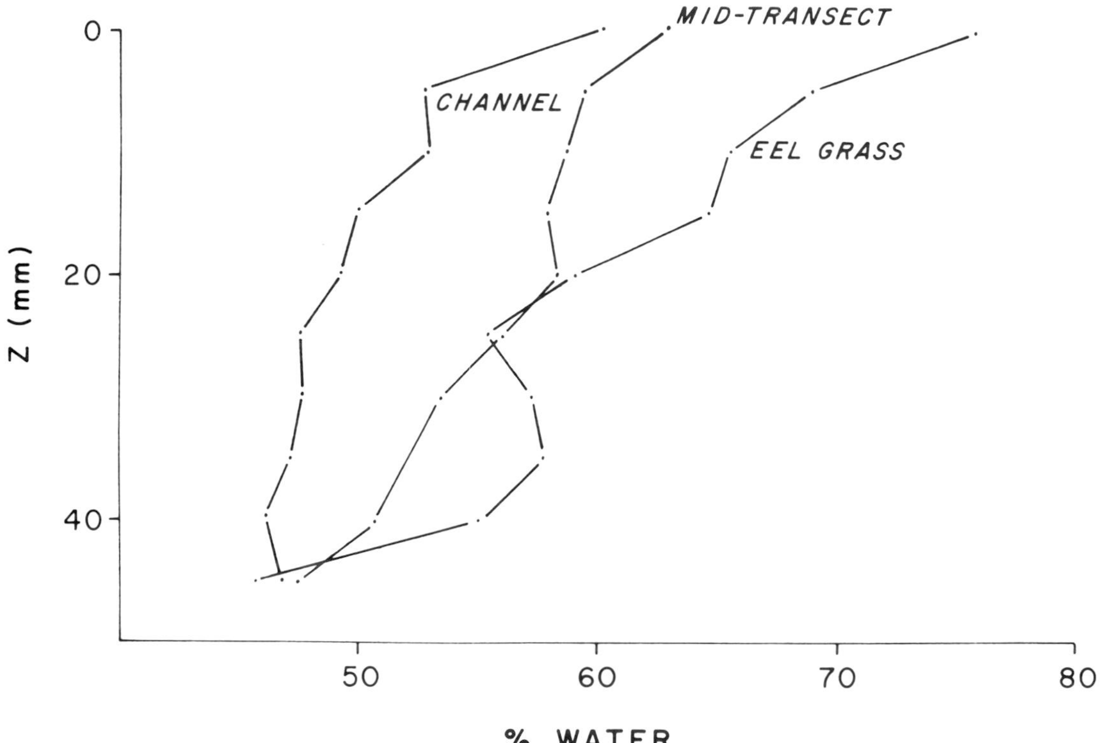

Fig. 9. Percent water-content with depth(z) below the sediment-water interface.

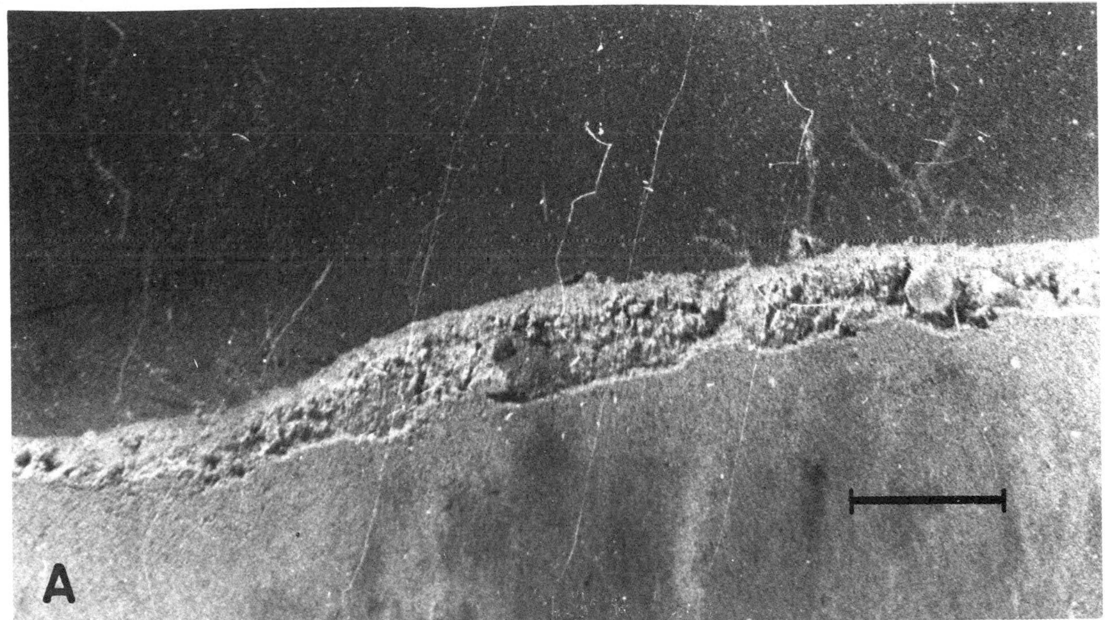

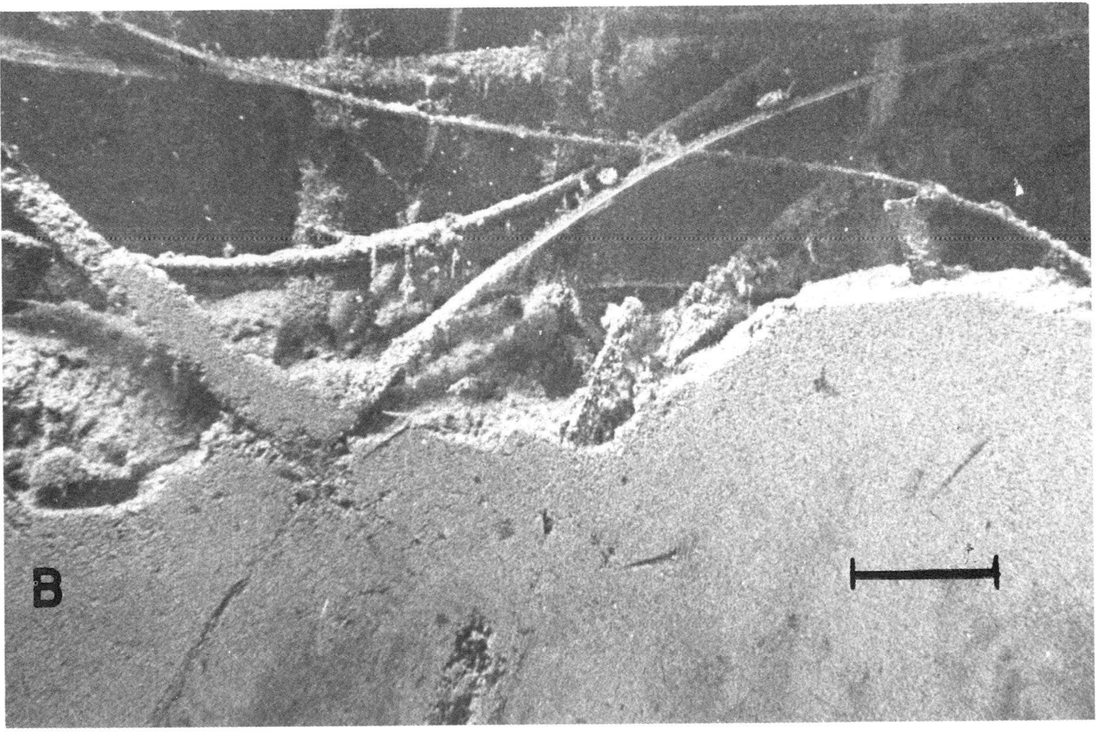

Fig. 10. Sediment-water interface photograph of Channel habitat (A) and Eelgrass habitat (B). A sediment-water interface camera was employed, as described in Rhoads and Young (1970). Scale is 2 cm. Note layer of fecal pellet-rich material overlying distinct interface in Channel photograph A.

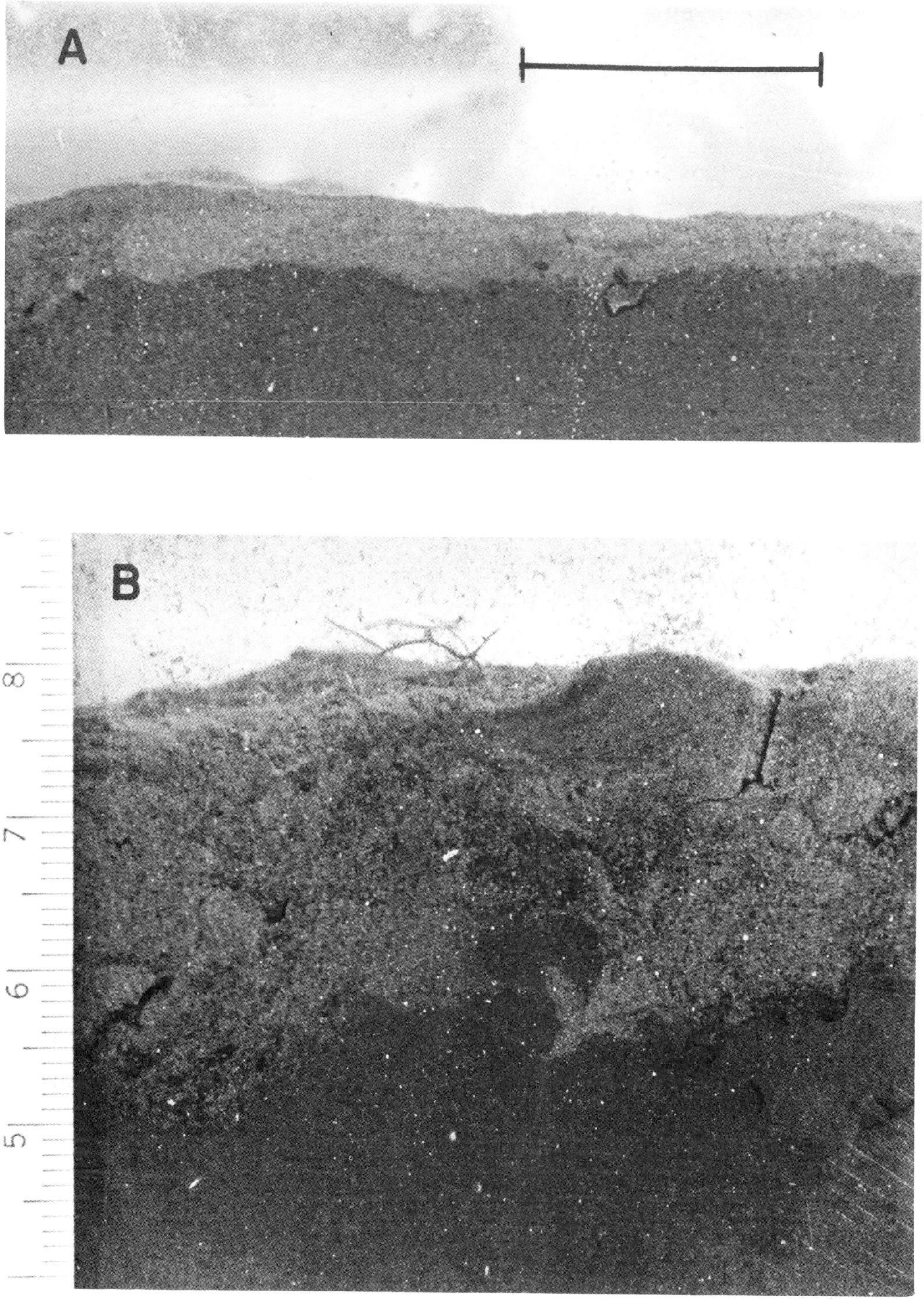

Fig. 11. Side-views of thin aquaria, showing sediment structure generated by *Macoma tenta* (A) and *Nucula proxima* (B) in the laboratory. Scale in (A) is 2 cm.

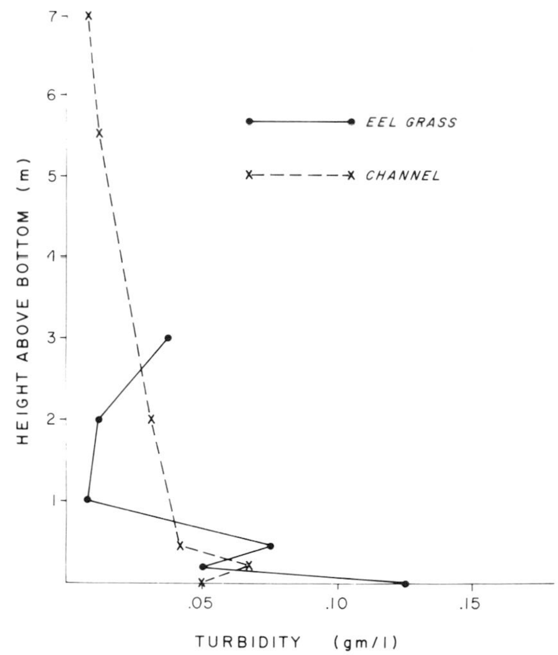

Fig. 12. Turbidity relative to height above the sediment-water interface in the Eelgrass and Channel habitats (each point is a mean of five measurements). Measurements at "0" m were taken 10 cm above the sediment-water interface.

AUTECOLOGY

The dominant deposit-feeding species of the Eelgrass and Channel biotopes are figured in Levinton (1971) and Levinton and Bambach (1975). In summary, the Eelgrass community is dominated by the surface deposit-feeding tellinacean bivalves, *Cumingia tellinoides* and *Tellina agilis*, the near-surface feeding protobranch bivalve, *Nucula proxima*, and the deeper fine-grained deposit-feeding protobranch, *Solemya velum*. The Channel community is dominated by the surface feeding tellinacean bivalve, *Macoma tenta*, the deeper feeding protobranch bivalve, *Yoldia limatula*, and the still deeper maldanid polychaete, *Clymenella troquata*. Life habits and abundances are summarized in Table 1.

Eelgrass Community

1. Surface deposit-feeders.--*Cumingia tellinoides* and *Tellina agilis* are abundant as surface-feeders, both feeding with a separate inhalent siphon which rapidly moves about and draws in aggregates of bottom detritus as it makes contact with the bottom. Area A (Fig. 6) contains both species, but they almost never co-occur. In Area A, *C. tellinoides* is found in sediments of 20-40% silt-clay, whereas *Tellina* is found in 40-50% silt-clay. However, this transition point occurs in sediments of higher silt-clay content in other parts of the study area (transects D-D', E-E', and F-F'). In some other areas of Quisset Harbor out of the study area, both species co-occur

Table 1. Densities, feeding depth below sediment-water interface, feeding classification and major constituents of gut contents.

Species	No./m^2	Feeding Depth (mm)	Feeding Type	Gut Contents
Nucula proxima	499 (Area A)	7.9 ± 3.9[a] (N = 40)	palp proboscide feeder (Yonge 1939)	sand, silt, finely divided organic detritus; some diatoms
Solemya velum	154 (Area A)	42.5 ± 1.6[a] (N - 26)	crude suspension feeder (?) on organic detritus	fine-grained organic detritus, < 10 microns
Cumingia tellinoides	51 (Area A)	0-5[d]	siphon deposit-feeder (plucker)	aggregates of organic detritus, diatoms, sand; some algal filaments and ciliates
Tellina agilis	58 (Areas A & B)	0-5[d]	siphon deposit-feeder (plucker)	sand, diatoms, organic detritus
Macoma tenta	54 (Area B)	0-5[c]	siphon deposit-feeder (vacuum cleaner)	fine sand, fine-grained organic detritus, some diatoms.
Yoldia limatula	150 (Area B)	23.7 ± 1.3[a] (N = 20)	palp proboscide feeder (Stanley 1971)	fine sand, fine-grained organic detritus
Clymenella torquata	258 (Area B)	38.5 ± 4.3[b] (N = 90)	swallower (Mangum 1964)	sand, fine-grained organic detritus
Nephtys incisa	69 (Area B)	variable; not measured	facultative deposit-feeder (Sanders 1960)	empty (4) or sand and organic detritus (6)

[a]Measured from X-radiographs of thin aquaria, mean ± standard error
[b]Measured from lengths of relaxed specimens
[c]Range of depth inferred from observations of sediment reworked by this species
[d]Range determined from observations of feeding animals in trays of sediments

in fair abundance. Generally *Cumingia* is more abundant in sediments of lower silt-clay, to the west of the island (Fig. 6). Further west, towards the Channel habitat, *Tellina agilis* become the dominant species.

2. Shallow-depth feeders.--The nuculid bivalve, *Nucula proxima*, is common in muddy sand sediments of Buzzards Bay. It is small, variable in living position and constantly moves about in an aquarium. Feeding is accomplished with a palp proboscide which conveys sediment to the palp, and thence to the mouth (Drew 1899; Yonge 1939). Densities correlate with the percent silt-clay of the bottom sediment and with the abundance of eelgrass (Table 2). Partial product-moment correlation coefficients reveal that both of these parameters correlate with *Nucula* abundance significantly (Table 3).

Observations of laboratory populations in aquaria show that biogenic reworking of this species converts the sediment to approximately 50% fecal pellets, by volume. Mean pellet dimensions are 179 ± 9.03 μ long and 90.5 ± 4.34 μ in width (N = 51). The pellets tend to give the substratum a fine sand texture (Rhoads 1967).

Table 2. Correlations between animal abundance and either eelgrass dry weight or percent silt-clay of sediment. Product-moment currelation coefficient (r) is employed.

*n*th	Samples	N	r	p
Nucula - silt-clay percent				
	D-D', E-E' + F-F'	36	.46	< .005
	A-a	14	.31	< .25
	A-a (less 1 sample)	13	.62	< .025
	a-A'	16	.59	< .01
	Area A	29	-.12	n.s.
Solemya - silt-clay percent				
	A-a	14	.40	< .10
	A-a (less 1 sample)	13	.64	< .01
	a-A'	19	.40	< .05
	Area A	29	.37	< .025
Yoldia - silt-clay percent				
	Area B	35	.36	< .025
Nucula - eelgrass dry weight				
	A-a	14	.52	< .05
	a-A'	15	.73	< .005
	B-B'	16	.81	< .005
Solemya - eelgrass dry weight				
	A-a	14	.46	< .05
	a-A'	15	.63	< .01
	B-B'	16	.55	< .025

Table 3. Partial and full correlation coefficients relating silt-clay percent, dry weight of eelgrass, and numerical abundance of *Nucula proxima* in transect a-A'[a].

Correlation	d.f.	r	p
r_{12}	12	.75	$< .01^{**}$
r_{23}	12	.76	$< .005^{***}$
r_{13}	12	.83	$< .001^{***}$
$r_{12.3}$	11	.32	$< .5$
$r_{13.2}$	11	.61	$< .05^{*}$
$r_{23.1}$	11	.38	$< .5$

[a]variable 1: percent silt-clay of sediment; variable 2: number of *Nucula proxima* per 1/4 square meter; variable 3: dry weight of eelgrass per 1/4 square meter.

Because *Nucula proxima* is active, its spatial patterns might be determined by active selection of substratum type. Two shallow trays were prepared, one control with uniform sediment of 90% silt-clay. In the other tray, one-half contained fine sand and the other half silt-clay, as in the control. Twenty-four individuals were evenly spaced in each tray. After twelve days a significant shift occurred in the two-sediment tray, with no shift in the one-sediment tray (2 x 2 contingency test, $p < 0.05$). This experiment was repeated using sediment from the Eelgrass biotope (30% silt-clay) and the Channel biotope (60% silt-clay), with similar results. Therefore, though the abundance of *Nucula proxima* correlated positively with silt-clay content <u>within</u> the Eelgrass biotope, individuals actively selected sandier sediments.

3. <u>Deeper feeder</u>.--*Solemya velum* lives in a y-shaped burrow, the plane of the <u>y</u> being vertical (Frey 1968; Stanley 1971). X-radiographs reveal that the animal lies with its long axis horizontal at the intersection of the arms of the <u>y</u>. The feeding habits of this species are poorly understood. *Solemya velum* has a diminutive gut, and only the very finest particles of detritus can be ingested (Yonge 1939; Owen 1961). *Solemya* introduces sediment from the burrow walls into the mantle cavity by muscular contraction. Ciliary currents are relatively unimportant in bringing detritus to the gills (Yonge 1939; Beedham and Owen 1961). The palps are not long, as in the deposit-feeding nuculidae, and do not feed directly upon the substratum. Instead they pick off material that has been conveyed by the ciliary tracts of the ctenidia (Yonge 1939). In most preserved specimens large amounts of mud and organic detritus have been found in the mantle cavity.

There is some confusion as to whether *Solemya* maintains an open or closed burrow. If the burrow were closed in mud substrata, then suspension-feeding would be a less likely mode of feeding than deposit-feeding. Some investigators have found no trace of an opening to the overlying water (Yonge 1939; Owen 1961), whereas others have reported that *Solemya* maintained a permanent burrow with well-defined openings to the sediment-water interface (Frey 1968). Frey found that *Solemya velum* burrows were permanent and coated with a rust-colored substance which agglutinated the walls. In this study, experiments performed in plexiglas aquaria showed that *Solemya velum* moved laterally every few days when placed along with *Nucula proxima* in Eelgrass biotope sediment of 30-40% silt-clay. Experimental densities were similar to area A and movements were detected with x-radiography of 3 experimental aquaria. Burrow walls in this more muddy substratum were never cohesive, in contrast to those in fine sand. While diving I found that one-third of the animals (greater than 2 mm in length) in the sediment were observable by burrow openings to the sediment-water interface. Therefore, functionally, *Solemya velum* is probably a crude suspension-feeder (Stanley 1971); and in sandy sediments devoid of silt and clay, its diet may be similar to some eulamellibranch suspension-feeders. However, in the Eelgrass biotope, its food derived from fine-grained detritus cannot be distinguished from that of a deposit-feeder. The lateral movement typical of this species in biogenically reworked muddy substrata may be solely due to interference from other animals; but its net effect is to allow more complete exploitation of available food and space within the bottom.

Channel Community

1. Surface deposit feeders.--The inhalent siphon of the common tellinacean, *Macoma tenta*, is slowly withdrawn and ingests bottom material from the upper 2 to 5 mm in contrast with the darting motions of the inhalent siphon of *Tellina agilis* (Table 1). *Macoma tenta* was never observed to be suspension-feeding as have some members of the genus *Tellina* and other species of *Macoma* (McIntyre and Eleftheriou 1968; Reid and Reid 1969). Apparently *Macoma tenta* is an obligate surface deposit-feeder in this habitat.

The feeding activities of *Macoma tenta* produce a layer of sediment rich in fecal pellets that is 5-10 mm thick. This species more commonly feeds at night, possibly to avoid fish predation (Levinton 1971).

2. Near surface feeders.--*Yoldia limatula* is an active deposit-feeding bivalve, feeding by means of palp proboscides, like *Nucula proxima*. Lateral movement regularly occurs, and burrowing is very rapid in this smooth-shelled, laterally compressed species (Stanley 1971). Contrary to the observations of Drew (1899), x-radiography shows that it lives well below the sediment-water interface, connecting to the surface with siphons (Stanley 1971). Feeding therefore is below the sediment-water interface (Table 1). Two experiments similar to those done on *Nucula proxima* revealed no significant behavioral sediment preference.

Burrowing activities, pseudofeces and fecal pellets (which vary from 80-150 μ in length in Quisset Harbor) convert the sediment texture from a silt-clay to a fine sand and increase the water-content of the sediment (Rhoads 1967; Rhoads and Young 1970).

Nephtys incisa was judged to be a deposit-feeding polychaete by Sanders (1960) and was the fourth most abundant macroinvertebrate in area B in 1968. However, in the summer of 1969 the population had virtually disappeared. It is therefore regarded a transient in this habitat relative to the other dominants. *N. incisa* is the most common polychaete species in shallow water muddy bottoms of the New England coast (Pettibone 1963). Its sediment preferences are generalized and it can live in environments of low dissolved oxygen (Pettibone 1963). It is probably an opportunistic species in Quisset Harbor.

3. Deeper feeders.--A deposit-feeding maldanid polychaete, *Clymenella torquata* is common in intertidal and shallow subtidal and high silt-clay bottoms of the Woods Hole region (Mangum 1964). Residing in a tube head down, it feeds from the lower end. It ingests sedimentary particles 1 mm and less and egests undigested material on the sediment surface (Mangum 1964). In sandy habitats, biogenically graded beads are usually produced by popualtions of *Clymenella* (Rhoads and Stanley 1965). Although individuals can be up to 20-cm long (Sanders et al. 1962; Rhoads), they were never more than 14-cm long in the Channel community. The feeding depth below the sediment-water interface (Table 1) was estimated from body lengths of specimens relaxed with propylene phenoxytol. In area B, there was no significant correlation between percent silt-clay and abundance of *Clymenella* ($r = -0.14$, $N = 35$).

Experiments on Interspecies Interactions

Table 4 summarizes a series of experiments on inter-individual interactions of deposit-feeding bivalves. Most experiments consisted of placing individuals of different species together, with subsequent time-lapse x-ray photography of sediment trays. Some interactions were neutral, but the extent of direct interspecies interference among the Protobranch bivalves (*Nucula, Solemya, Yoldia*) was surprising. A good example is the *Yoldia-Solemya* interaction. Five individuals of *Yoldia limatula* were added to an aquarium in which 5 individuals of *Solemya velum* had been placed one day before. The living position of the body of a large *Yoldia* is deeper and overlaps that of *Solemya*. Thus, when an individual of *Yoldia* overlapped that of *Solemya*, the latter's burrow became disrupted and it would burrow downward (Fig. 13). This interaction explains the negative association of these two species in Quisset Harbor. In contrast, individuals of *Nucula proxima* are attracted to the burrow openings, but do not burrow deeply enough to directly disrupt the living position of *Solemya*; this behavior may account for their coexistence in the lab and in the field. These and other observations (Table 4) demonstrate that interactions that represent competition for space are of paramount importance to soft-bottom deposit-feeding bivalvia. A similar conclusion has been reached for Polychaeta (Woodin 1974).

Table 4. Observations of positive or negative interactions between dominant bivalve species. Types of experiments are symbolized as follows: (a) nearest neighbor analysis of X-radiographs (areal view) of sediment trays (see Levinton 1972b), (b) time-lapse X-ray photography of thin aquaria with sediment plus bivalves (cross-sectional view), (c) visual observations of animals in sediment trays.

Species	Interactions With Other Species and Individuals of Same Species	
Nucula proxima	1. *Nucula proxima*	Tendency towards random spatial distributions (a, 5 experiments).
	2. *Solemya velum*	Disrupts burrow openings and causes lateral movement and reestablishment of burrows every 2 to 5 days (b, 4 experiments).
	3. *Yoldia limatula*	Increases sediment water-content and makes sediment unstable for *Yoldia* juveniles, resulting in increased juvenile mortality (Levinton and Bambach 1972).
	4. Tellinacea	No detected effects on *Cumingia tellinoides*, *Tellina agilis* or *Macoma tenta* (b, 1 experiment for each species; c, 2 experiments per species).
Solemya velum	1. *Solemya velum*	Some inter-individual interaction to avoid overlap of y-shaped burrows (b, 6 experiments).
	2. *Nucula proxima*	Attracts individuals to proximity of burrow openings (b, 3 experiments).
	3. *Yoldia limatula*	Possible (?) attraction to burrow (b, 1 experiment).
	4. Tellinacea	No detected effects (casual observations).
Yoldia limatula	1. *Yoldia limatula*	Spatial distribution random (a, 3 experiments).
	2. *Nucula proxima*	Causes avoidance. Individuals of *Yoldia* placed in a tray of sediment with *Nucula* result in areas with *Yoldia* surrounded by several cm of empty space ("cruising" area) along with areas of *Nucula* patches (a, 3 experiments).
	3. *Solemya velum*	Overlap of living position disrupts burrow, causing movement and relocation of burrow (b, 3 experiments; overlap observed in one experiment).
	4. Tellinacea	No detected effects on *Macoma* or *Tellina* (b, 1 experiment for each species).
Macoma tenta	1. *Macoma tenta*	Reduction of siphon-feeding radius under crowded conditions (c, 5 experiments).
	2. *Yoldia limatula*	No effect (a, 2 experiments).
	3. *Tellina agilis*	No detected effect (c, 1 experiment).
Tellina agilis	1. *Tellina agilis*	Uniform spatial distribution (a, see Gilbert 1968).

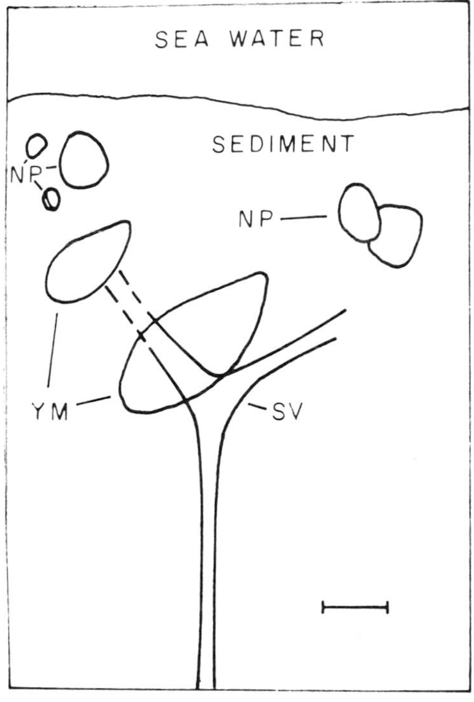

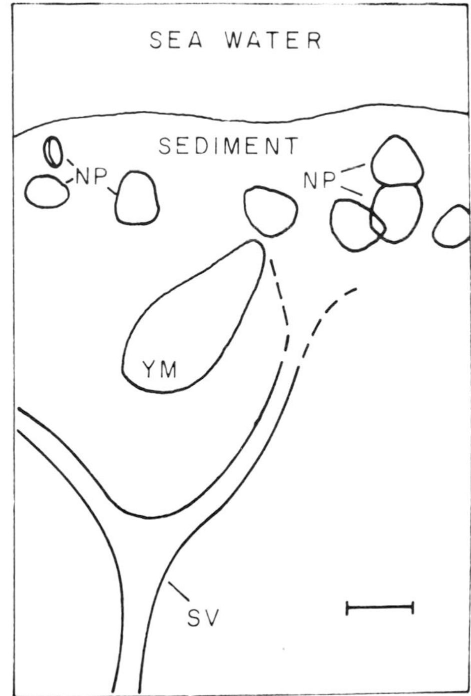

Fig. 13. Tracing of x-radiographs involving interactions between *Yoldia limatula*, *Solemya velum* and *Nucula proxima*. Note the avoidance response of *S. velum* when confronted with *Y. limatula*.

Two other spatial interactions connoting interspecific competition were inferred from laboratory experiments employing time-lapse x-radiography. One was an apparent negative spatial interaction between *Nucula* and *Yoldia* (Fig. 14). These two species tended not to overlap areally in experimental trays (as in the field). Second was the attraction of *Nucula proxima* to the siphon holes of the bivalve *Mercenaria mercenaria* (Fig. 15). Individuals congregating around siphon holes resulted in sediment destablilization and therefore excessive turbidity at the sediment-water interface, which was strongly inhibitory to a suspension-feeder such as *Mercenaria* (Rhoads and Young 1970). This attraction may explain the relative rarity of *Mercenaria* in the Eelgrass habitat, despite its abundance in non-*Nucula* sandy bottoms nearby.

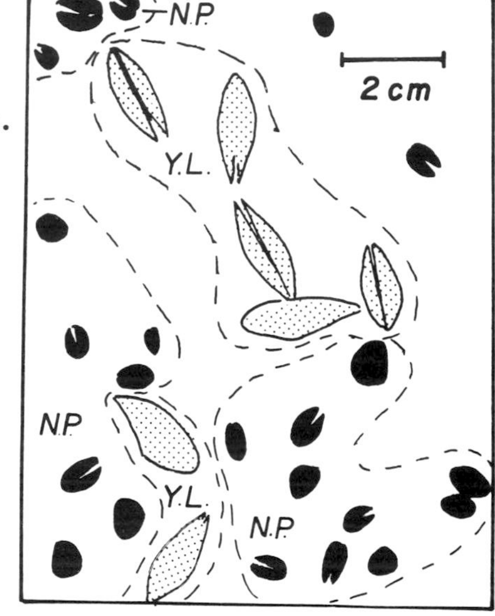

Fig. 14. Avoidance response between *Nucula proxima* and *Yoldia limatula*. Positions of animals traced from x-radiograph of aquarium (top view). Response is inferred from non-overlap of patches of each of the two species.

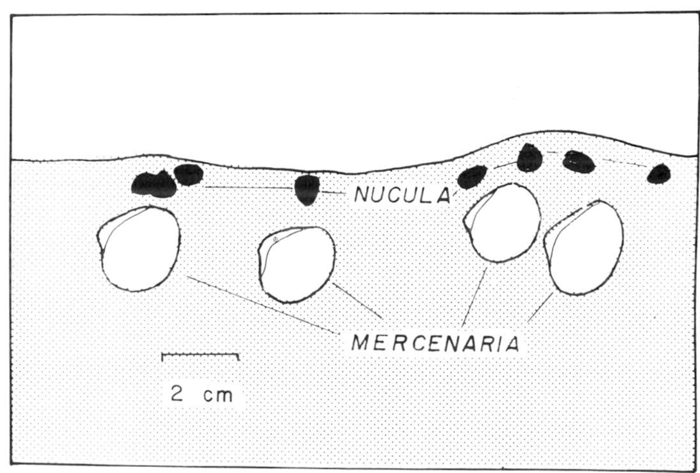

Fig. 15. Attraction of *Nucula proxima* to siphon holes of *Mercenaria mercenaria*. Tracing of x-radiograph of thin wall aquaria (side-view).

The burrowing efficiency of *Nucula proxima* was examined in different substrata that were biogenically reworked by different species. The time and number of burrowing "thrusts" required to bury the shell were observed. Essentially, no advantage in burrowing speed was gained in biogenically unreworked Eelgrass habitat sediments, relative to unburrowed Channel habitat sediments (Table 5). More surprising was that *Nucula proxima* increased burrowing speed in both burrowed Eelgrass sediments and burrowed Channel sediments. I conclude that the presence of reworked sediment not the presence of a given species, determines burrowing speed.

Table 5. Burrowing speeds of *Nucula proxima* and *Yoldia limatula* in different experimental substrata. Significant differences between different conditions are determined from 95% confidence limits of means.

Sediment Type	Number of Observations	Number of Thrusts (± s.e.)	Time Until Burial (seconds ± s.e.)
Nucula proxima			
Eelgrass, unburrowed	28	8.2 ± 0.23	32.6 ± 1.55
Channel, unburrowed	30	7.6 ± 0.24	33.1 ± 1.99
Eelgrass, unburrowed	7	6.0 ± 0.08	25.7 ± 1.19
Channel, unburrowed	9	5.7 ± 0.06	20.7 ± 2.89
Yoldia limatula			
Channel, unburrowed	16	8.2 ± 0.35	6.6 ± 0.36
Eelgrass, unburrowed	15	8.4 ± 0.34	6.7 ± 0.37

Contrast	Time	Thrusts
Nucula proxima		
Unburrowed eelgrass vs channel	n.s.	n.s.
Burrowed eelgrass vs channel	n.s.	n.s.
Eelgrass burrowed vs unburrowed	$p < .05$	$p < .05$
Channel burrowed vs unburrowed	$p < .05$	$p < .05$
Yoldia limatula		
Unburrowed eelgrass vs channel	n.s.	n.s.

SYNECOLOGY

Both faunas are dominated by mollusks and polychaetes (Table 6). Deposit-feeders comprise 75% by number of the Eelgrass community (area A) and 77% of the Channel fauna (area B). Suspension-feeders comprise 9.7% of the Eelgrass and 1.9% of the Channel fauna. Although amphipods (*Ampelisca*) and holothurians (*Leptosynapta*) are locally abundant, these taxa are patchily distributed and show no recurrent dominance patterns over the entire study area sampled.

Spatial Variation

Spatial distributions of the dominant species were estimated

Table 6. Data for Areas A (Eelgrass, 36 samples, sample area = 0.04 m^2, area sampled = 19.3 m^2), B (Channel, sampling same as for A), N (Eelgrass, 25 samples, sample area = 0.03 m^2, area samples = 3.2 m^2), and P (Channel, sampling same as for N). Number of individuals in samples (I), percentage of samples in which a given species was present (II), mean numerical abundance per sample (III), and Morisita's I_δ (IV) are given.

	I Number of Individuals				II Percentage of Samples in Which Species is Present				III Mean Abundance Per Sample (no. m^{-2})				IV Morisita's I_δ *: $p < 0.05$, **: $p < 0.01$ ***: $p < 0.005$			
	A	N	B	P	A	N	B	P	A	N	B	P	A	N	B	P
BIVALVIA																
Nucula proxima	539	585	11	2	100	100	25	8	375.0	780.0	7.5	3.3	1.18***	1.03***		
Solemya velum	166	81	1	4	97	96	3	16	112.5	253.3	0.8	3.3	1.20	1.06		
Laevicardium mortoni	33	37	2	2	47	68	6	8	22.5	50.0	2.5	3.3	2.93***	1.65***		
Cumingia tellinoides	55	191	0	0	31	96	0	0	37.5	253.3	0.0	0.0	3.83***			
Tellina agilis	47	8	78	26	39	20	81	56	32.5	10.0	55.0	33.3	4.93***		1.27*	1.46*
Yoldia limatula	8	0	162	110	14	0	100	100	5.0	0.0	112.5	146.7			1.14*	1.00
Macoma tenta	9	0	58	185	17	0	81	100	7.5	0.0	40.0	246.7			1.48	1.24**
Mulinia lateralis	0	0	30	17	0	0	47	40	0.0	0.0	20.0	23.2			1.90	1.42
Corbula contracta	3	1	2	0	3	4	6	0	2.5	1.3	2.5	0.0				
Petricola pholadiformis	3	1	0	0	3	4	0	0	2.5	1.3	0.0	0.0				
Aequipecten irradians	0	1	0	0	0	4	0	0	0.0	1.3	0.0	0.0				
Mercenaria mercenaria	4	6	0	0	11	24	0	0	2.5	6.7	0.0	0.0				
Astarte sp.	0	0	1	0	0	0	3	0	0.0	0.0	0.8	0.0				
POLYCHAETA																
Clymenella torquata	39	7	279	95	42	24	97	100	1.1	0.3	8.0	3.8	3.16***		1.26***	1.33**
Maldanopsis elongata	0	0	20	16	0	0	37	40	0.0	0.0	0.6	0.6			1.84	1.46
Pectinaria gouldii	52	25	14	22	56	40	29	52	1.4	0.7	0.4	0.9	2.50***	4.74***		1.19
Nephtys incisa	0	0	75	40	0	0	86	76	0.0	0.0	2.1	1.6			1.26	1.12
Lumbrinereis tenuis	28	35	0	0	58	88	0	0	0.8	1.4	0.0	0.0	0.67	0.84		
Stauronereis rudolphi	26	12	5	6	32	36	9	4	0.7	0.5	0.1	0.2	4.10***			
Nereis greyi	13	0	3	0	22	0	8	0	0.4	0.0	0.1	0.0				
Nereis pelagica	1	0	0	0	3	0	0	0	0.03	0.0	0.0	0.0				
Lepidametria commensalis	22	74	0	0	36	92	0	0	0.6	3.0	0.0	0.0	1.71	1.01		
Amphitrite ornata	9	3	0	0	22	8	0	0	0.3	0.1	0.0	0.0				
Amphitrite cirrata	0	0	18	3	30	10	39	12	0.0	0.0	0.5	0.1				
Capitellid	5	0	2	0	8	0	6	0	0.1	0.0	0.1	0.0				
Sabella micropthalma	4	0	0	0	8	0	0	0	0.1	0.0	0.0	0.0				
Lepidonotus squamatus	3	9	0	0	6	24	0	0	0.1	0.4	0.0	0.0				
Dorvillea sp.	2	0	0·	0	3	0	0	0	0.1	0.0	0.0	0.0				

with Morisita's (1964) index because it is relatively independent of distribution type, mean density, and number of samples (Southwood 1966). In addition, a simple variance ratio (F) test can be employed to test for significance. Quadrat size often affects measured indices of spatial distribution, so that nearest neighbor techniques, where possible, are preferable (Levinton 1972b). Since quadrat size is essentially the same for all species in both communities, relative spatial patterns were examined within the two communities.

In 36 samples taken randomly over 80 sq m in the Eelgrass biotope (area A), 8 out of 11 of the examined species were found to have significantly aggregated dispersion patterns (Table 5). Such results can be expected in this habitat owing to marked spatial changes in sediment composition and floral cover.

In 25 samples taken over 3.2 sq m (area N), only 3 out of 7 species were significantly aggregated. The clumped distribution of *Cumingia* is explained by the patchiness of the many juveniles in this small area; the 2-mm sieve size was not adequate to sample a small-size juvenile.

In the Channel biotope, 36 samples taken randomly over approximately 700 sq m (area B), reveal only 3 out of 7 significantly aggregated distributions. One of these is a species principally associated with the Eelgrass biotope (*Tellina agilis*). The relatively lower occurrence of patchiness correlates with the relative uniformity of the sedimentary environment and lack of floral cover. This trend is continued in the smaller 3.2-sq-m area P (Table 6), where only 3 out of 9 examined species show significantly aggregated patterns. One is *Macoma tenta*, which can be explained by concentrations of juveniles. Patchiness of juveniles vs randomness of adults is commonly observed in marine benthos (Buzas 1968; Gilbert 1968; Jackson 1968).

Diversity and Environmental Complexity

Species richness was examined in bivalves, polychaetes and gastropods of the Eelgrass and Channel communities. In order to detect the presence of habitat heterogeneity, the small areas (3.2 m^2) of each biotope were compared to their corresponding larger areas (80 m^2).

In the Eelgrass community, polychaete species numbers increase two-fold from the small to the large area. However, neither bivalves nor gastropods increase (Table 7). In the more homogeneous Channel community, polychaete species numbers increase only slightly with an increase in area, as do the bivalves (Table 8). The rate of change of S (number of species) with the number of individuals per sample is greater for polychaetes than for bivalves in all samples. This too indicates the relative heterogeneity of polychaete species occurrence and abundance, as opposed to the homogeneity of molluscan occurrence (see McIntyre and Elftheriou 1968).

Table 7. Species numbers in the eelgrass (smaller area N and larger area A), and channel (smaller area P and larger area B) communities.

Site	Area	Polychaetes	Bivalves	Gastropods
Eelgrass	N	10	9	4
	A	19	10	3
Channel	P	12	7	3
	B	14	9	3

Table 8. Equitability, or evenness, in relative abundances of eelgrass and channel community mollusks. Equitability (J') in $H'/\log_{10}S$, where $\log_{10}S$ is the largest value H' can obtain for a given S.

Site	Area	S	H'	J'
Eelgrass	N	13	1.7	0.46
	A	13	1.9	0.51
Channel	P	10	2.0	0.60
	B	12	2.5	0.70

In both large and small areas sampled in the Eelgrass and Channel habitats the H' diversity index (Pielou 1969) is adequately estimated with about 15-20 samples added cumulatively (Figs. 16,17). This indicates that the total number of samples added together sufficiently estimates diversity (Pielou 1966). In both communities, the small areas (N and P) are less diverse than the larger ones (A and B), but the difference is greater in the Channel community. The

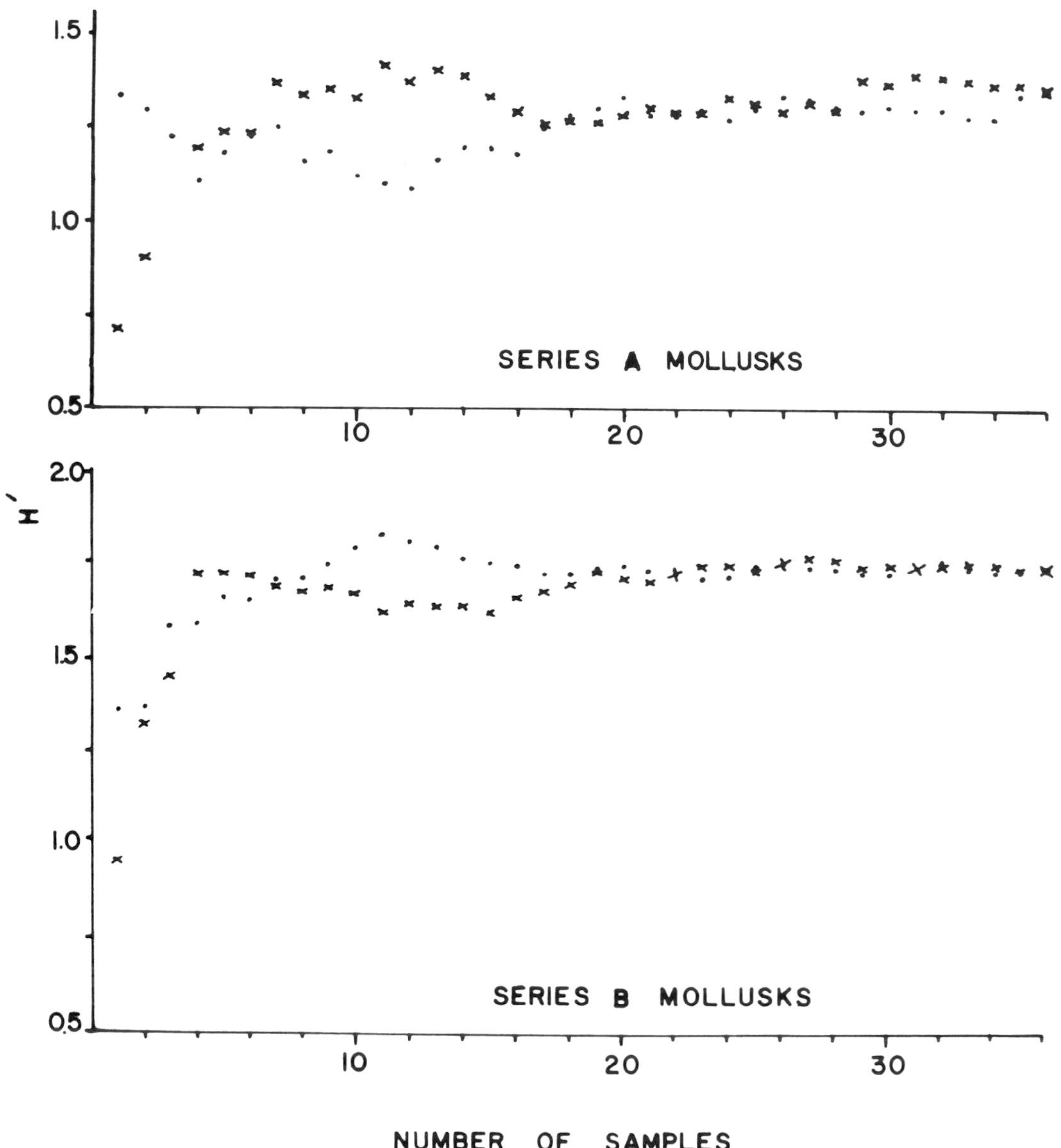

Fig. 16. Mollusk diversity (H') as a function of cumulative number of samples in Eelgrass (series A) and Channel (series B) communities. Crosses and dots indicate two different randomizations of sample order.

Fig. 17. Diversity (H') as a function of cumulative number of samples in Area N (series N) and Area P (series P) mollusks.

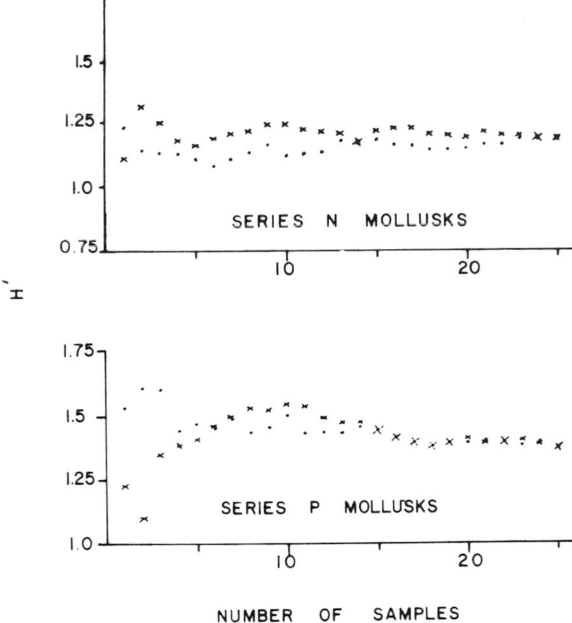

Channel community is clearly more diverse than the Eelgrass community. In these samples, H' for the larger Eelgrass area A approximately equals H' for the smaller area P of the Channel biotope. The overall greater H' in the Channel community is explained by greater evenness of species numbers (equitability), since there are more molluscan species in the Eelgrass community than in the Channel community. This difference is readily seen where evenness, J', is calculated for the samples (Table 8).

TRANSECT DATA

Figure 18 shows trends in abundance of dominant species from the Eelgrass biotope to the Channel biotope. Abundance varies with each community, but the increase of Channel community species coincides with a decrease in Eelgrass community species along the transects. However, Channel community species penetrate far into the area of Eelgrass and vice versa.

Trends in the Eelgrass community and Channel community species abundance (as indicated by the sum of the two dominant bivalve species) vs changes in depth, silt-clay content of the sediments and eelgrass are plotted in Figures 4 and 5. These transects extend from the point just where the Eelgrass species are 100% of the fauna, to the corresponding point in the Channel habitat. In all cases, the curves of abundance for the animals of each community cross at a zone which corresponds with a maximum change in water depth with lateral distance, and with the disappearance of eelgrass.

Figure 18 shows animal abundances calculated by summing subsample data from each station. This approach suggests that there

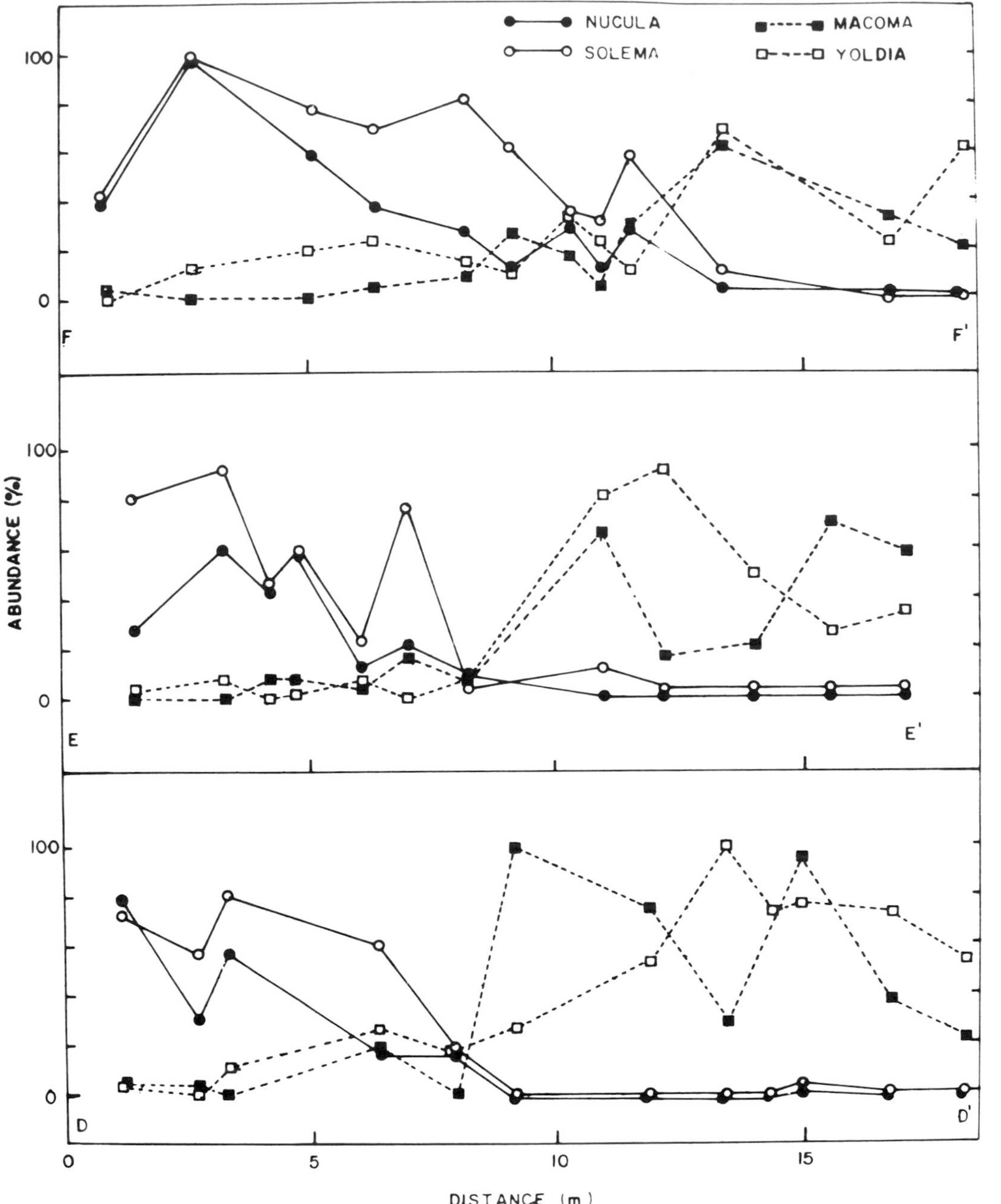

Fig. 18. Trends in abundance of dominant bivalve mollusk species along transects from the Eelgrass (points D, E, and F) to Channel (points D', E', and F') habitats. Abundance axis is percent of maximum observed abundance.

is a continuous decline of Eelgrass habitat species into the Channel habitat, and therefore supports the ecotone concept of soft-bottom marine communities. The sampling scheme includes three parallel transects (D-D', E-E', and F-F') with three replicates per station. Therefore the data can be treated in a two-way analysis of variance, with replicates. It can be determined whether there are station differences along the transects, or interactions between transect and station location. This type of analysis was carried out for 4 of the common deposit-feeding species (Table 9). As expected, when whole transects were considered strong differences existed between stations for all species. However, if a transect was divided in two subtransects, each corresponding to the area of each habitat type, no statistically significant differences were found along a subtransect between stations, or for a species within its "own" habitat, except for *N. proxima*. This observation supports the hypothesis that each community is statistically homogeneous on a small scale, with minor ecotonal effects blurring the community boundary. Thus, although small numbers of an Eelgrass species, such as *Solemya velum*, penetrate into the Channel habitat, populations of this species within its habitat type are statistically homogeneous. It was also found that although *Nucula proxima* and *Solemya velum* show no significant between-transect differences within their habitat, the Channel species *Macoma tenta* and *Yoldia limatula* show significant between-transect differences. Apparently, abundance decreases from transect D-D' to E-E' to F-F'. Thus a gradient of

Table 9. Analysis of variance of species abundances in transects D-D', E-E' and F-F'. Left column shows analyses of whole Eelgrass-Channel transects. Right shows analyses of transects in which species in question is abundant.

Source of Variation	Whole Transects				Half Transects (within species "own" habitat)			
	d.f.	s.s.	m.s.	Fs	d.f.	s.s.	m.s.	Fs
Nucula proxima								
Between transects	2	113.4	56.7	2.1	2	50.8	25.4	1.1
Between stations	11	2509.3	228.1	8.3[c]	5	921.3	184.3	7.9[c]
Interaction	22	803.1	36.5	1.3	10	741.3	74.1	3.2[b]
Error	72	1970	27.4		36	834.7	23.2	
Solemya velum								
Between transects	2	30.9	15.5	3.5[a]	2	36.9	18.5	2.3
Between stations	11	626.4	56.9	12.6[c]	5	80.7	16.1	2.0
Interaction	22	231.4	10.5	2.3[b]	10	150.0	15.0	1.9
Error	72	322.7	4.5		36	286.0	7.9	
Macoma tenta								
Between transects	2	30.5	15.3	3.4[a]	2	77.8	38.9	5.4[b]
Between stations	11	259.8	23.6	5.2[c]	6	40.0	6.7	0.9
Interaction	22	275.2	12.5	2.8[c]	12	223.5	18.6	2.6[b]
Error	72	325.7	4.5		44	314.7	7.2	
Yoldia limatula								
Between transects	2	66.8	33.4	11.1[b]	2	84.0	42.0	7.0[b]
Between stations	11	417.8	38.0	12.7[c]	5	67.0	13.5	2.3
Interaction	22	193.0	8.8	2.9[c]	10	201.6	20.2	3.4[b]
Error	72	215.3	3.0		36	216.7		

[a]Significance: $p < 0.05$
[b]Significance: $p < 0.01$
[c]Significance: $p < 0.001$

species abundance is approximately perpendicular to the intercommunity boundary. Therefore, trends in Channel species abundance are somewhat independent of the Eelgrass community, despite the fact that Eelgrass species penetrate into the channel habitat. The above makes the dangers of single transects apparent. The single transect sampling scheme presupposes unidimensional variation along a preconceived gradient, and does not allow for the complex two-dimensional variation that apparently is characteristic of both the Eelgrass and Channel habitats.

DISCUSSION

Deposit-Feeding Dominance

The dominance of deposit-feeders in silt-clay sediments has long been recognized by many investigators to be a major characteristic of marine benthic communities (e.g., Davis 1925; Jones 1950; Sanders 1956, 1958; Savilov 1957; Thorson 1957; McNulty et al. 1962). I suggest that the abundance of deposit-feeders is due to the presence of abundant digestible microorganisms associated with organic matter.

The high silt-clay content of the substratum, in combination with biogenic reworking of sediments by deposit-feeders, causes high turbidity at the sediment-water interface, and makes the upper layers of sediment high in water-content and physically unstable (Rhoads and Young 1970). Weak bottom currents tend to resuspend this sediment. These effects suffocate suspension-feeding organisms and prevent juveniles from maintaining a stable living position. The attraction of mobile deposit-feeders, such as *Nucula*, towards the siphon holes of suspension-feeding bivalves, such as *Mercenaria mercenaria*, enhances the interference process (Fig. 15).

Substrate Conditioning by Deposit-Feeders

The substratum in both habitats is strongly modified by the deposit-feeding infauna. First, fecal pellets modify the texture of the sediment from a silt to a fine sand. Secondly, the behavior and feeding depths below the sediment-water interface of different species determine such characteristics as grain size and water-content. I infer that the siphon-feeding activities of *Macoma tenta* determine the high water-content in the upper 5-10 mm of the Channel habitat sediment. All oxygen-requiring animals that live below this reworked zone must maintain some connection with the surface for respiration (e.g., siphons of *Yoldia limatula*).

The Eelgrass bottom interface photographs, when compared with laboratory-produced sediment structures, indicate that the burrowing activities and fecal pellet formation of *Nucula proxima* strongly affect the water-content and grain size of the sediment. As demonstrated by the light brown (anoxic sediments are black) color of sediment in aquaria, the burrowing of this species allows oxygen to exist several cm into the sediment. The small size, more constant activity and greater abundance of *Nucula proxima* result in the higher water-content of Eelgrass sediment, relative to Channel sediments. The relatively large size and low densities of Channel species such as *Yoldia limatula* probably are responsible for the lower water-content. Because *Macoma tenta* feeds at night (Levinton 1971) whereas the water-content samples were taken during the day, water-content in near-surface sediments of the Channel habitat may undergo a diurnal cycle, and may increase at night.

Niche Structure of Deposit-Feeders

When the exploitation ranges of dominant species are combined, we see that the available spectrum of feeding depths is exploited in the communities, each species being approximately contiguous in its feeding preference with some other species, or pair of species (Fig. 19). In the Eelgrass community a tellinacean bivalve feeds on aggregates of organic detritus on the sediment surface in which many diatoms are concentrated. This species may be *Tellina agilis* or *Cumingia tellinoides*. These two species usually do not co-occur. Further down into the sediment, the bivalve *Nucula proxima* feeds indiscriminately on the sediment, probably digesting the bacterial flora that colonizes organic detritus, as has been determined for a detritus-feeding amphipod (Genchel 1970). Still deeper in the sediment, *Solemya velum* probably exploits the very fine-grained material that is again colonized by bacteria. In order to accept this hypothesis, we must acknowledge that this species is functionally a suspension-feeder which, in muds, derives much of its food from the

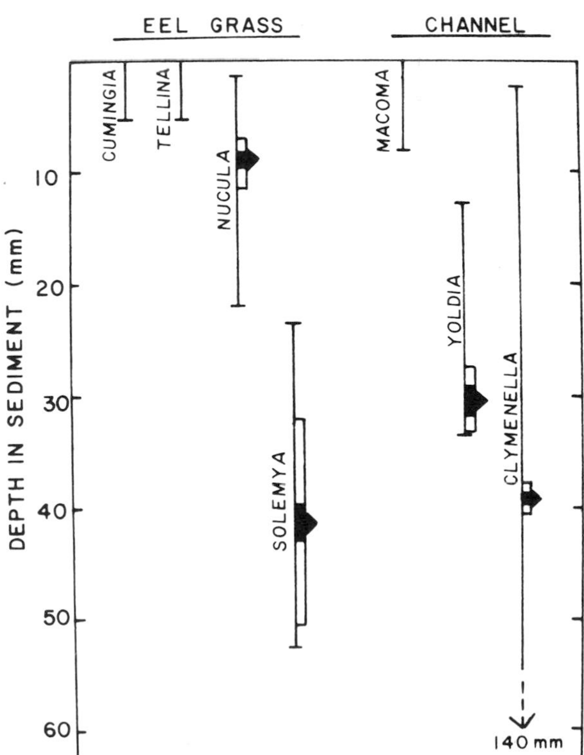

Fig. 19. Feeding depths of deposit-feeding species that occur most frequently in samples from the Eelgrass and Channel Habitats. *Cumingia* and *Tellina* rarely co-occur in the same sample. See Table 1 for details. Line is total range of feeding depths; black portion of bar is one standard error on either side of the mean. White bar is one sample standard deviation on either side of the mean; mean indicated by black arrow.

fine-grained material near its living position on the walls of its burrow. We are not concerned with feeding behavior but food sources.

Similarly in the Channel community, we find zonation of feeding depths, which might be termed stratification (Turpaeva 1957). *Tellina agilis* feeds at the surface by plucking aggregates of organic detritus and feeding on the resident diatoms. In some areas, the absence of this species indicates the lack of benthic diatoms, the presence of some detrimental physical factor, predation, or perhaps competition with *Macoma tenta*. Unlike *T. agilis*, *Macoma tenta* draws sediment indiscriminately into its siphon and mantle cavity, and therefore depends on much the same food as *Nucula proxima*, namely bacteria living on organic detritus.

Feeding deeper into the sediment is *Yoldia limatula*, whose gut contents, like those of *Nucula proxima*, are very similar to the sediment. This similarity is also evident in *Y. hyperborea* (Turpaeva 1953). Feeding deeper than *Y. limatula* is the polychaete *Clymenella torquata*. In much smaller numbers, *Maldanopsis elongata* lives similarly to *C. torquata*.

Although a series of contiguous niches of dominant species can be based on spatial separation, feeding behavior and feeding level within the sediment and living space, many species present in relatively small numbers overlap broadly with the dominant species in food requirements and space utilization. Also, the spatial feeding ranges of the dominant species may not be perfectly contiguous but may overlap to varying degrees. In some species, feeding level below the sediment-water interface is highly age-dependent. For example, the deposit-feeding polychaete *Clymenella torquata* feeds at successively greater depths as it matures and grows longer. Similarly, juvenile *Tellina agilis* depends upon finer-grained detrital particles than adults. Consequently the form of competition, where present, might continually change owing to differential exploitation with different age.

Food Limitation

All of the deposit-feeders, with the exception of the diatom-feeding tellinaceans (*Tellina agilis* and *Cumingia tellinoides*) probably depend upon bacteria as a primary source of food (Zhukova 1963; Newell 1965; Brinkhurst and Chua 1969; Fenchel 1970; Hargrave 1970). Bacteria are very abundant in fine-grained sediments and probably control rate of food production for deposit-feeders (Zobell 1938). Because bacteria may act upon both organic detritus delivered by currents and upon animals and plants dying on the bottom, turnover of organic matter in the bottom is extremely important in the determination of food abundance for deposit-feeders (Fenchel 1972; Levinton 1972a). There is some question as to whether bacteria depend upon dissolved organic matter exclusively for nutrients, and use bottom sediment particles as a substratum for attachment; or whether the organic particles in the sediment also provide nutrients for bacteria. Changes in the organic nitrogen content of fecal pellets of benthic invertebrates suggest that these changes are directly related to populations of bacteria colonizing the pellets (Newell 1965). These particles are nevertheless a necessary condition for significant bacterial populations, if only for space for attachment (Jannasch and Pritchard 1972). Therefore, resuspension of fecal pellets, so common in muddy bottoms populated by deposit-feeding benthic invertebrates (Rhoads and Young 1970; Young 1971), may be a means of importing organic matter into the bottom. Space for attachment of bacteria may be the first limiting factor for bacterial population size in sediments. Recent evidence suggests that deposit-feeding oligochaete species may differentially utilize the available diversity of bacterial flora (Wavre and Brinkhurst 1971). Studies of the interactions of these factors are urgently needed before we can construct a convincing model of deposit-feeding trophic dynamics.

Many of the species present in Quisset Harbor deposit-feeding communities are known to rework the sediments at a rapid rate. As mentioned above, *Nucula proxima* and *Yoldia limatula* populations can rework the sediments completely several times per year. The polychaete, *Pectinaria gouldii*, may assimilate all labile organic matter available to it in one month (Gordon 1966). Young (1971) found that the population of *Nucula annulata* at station R (Sanders 1960) could rework the amount of sediment represented by permanent annual deposits 1 to 5 times/day. Thus, it is entirely plausible that available food is completely exploited by the benthic deposit-feeding populations. The coprophagy prevalent in deposit-feeding organisms indicates the ingestion of all possible sources of food (Johannes and Satomi 1966; Frankenburg and Smith 1967). Finally, the significant amount of sediment transfer occurring in the bottom, such as transport of fine sediments to the surface by *Clymenella torquata* during feeding, permits complete exploitation of any organic matter that may have not been assimilated into living organisms when first deposited on the sediment surface. This transfer creates conditions for extensive interspecific dependence in deposit-feeding communities.

Possible Role of Interspecific Competition

Interspecific competition for space, which ultimately is governed by food requirements of a given population, may be said to affect the structure of deposit-feeding communities. Regional data tend to support this hypothesis. As mentioned above, two sibling species of *Nucula* live in the Buzzards Bay area. *Nucula annulata* lives in deeper water fine-grained oozes whereas *Nucula proxima* (present in the Eelgrass community) lives in shallow water sand and sandy-mud sediments (Hampson 1971). However, in intermediate sediments of about 50 to 80% silt-clay content and water depths of 4 to 20 m *Macoma tenta* and *Yoldia limatula* are dominant. Why can the genus *Nucula*, in Buzzards Bay, exploit two end members of a habitat-type but not an intermediate? Competition with *Macoma tenta* and *Yoldia limulata* is probably the reason for this anomaly.

A similar argument can be proposed for the *Cumingia tellinoides*-

Tellina agilis zonation discussed above. *Tellina agilis* is usually abundant in fine sands in the intertidal zone and shallow subtidal waters (Sanders et al. 1962; Gilbert 1968; W. H. Gilbert personal communication). Therefore it might be expected to occur in sandier sediments of low silt-clay content. But in sediments of lower silt-clay in the Eelgrass habitat (Area A), we find the ecological equivalent of this species, *Cumingia tellinoides*. *Tellina agilis* does not become dominant until sediments have at least 35-40% silt-clay content. *Cumingia tellinoides* is well adapted to muddy sand in bottoms with eelgrass and swift currents (Grave 1927). In its optimal habitat it can competitively exclude *Tellina agilis* and include it only in a suboptimal habitat.

Although competitive control of areal distribution is not widely reported among benthic species, McIntyre and Eleftheriou (1968) noted that where the normally intertidal *Tellina tenuis* is absent, the normally subtidal *Tellina fabula* is capable of changing its depth zone and invades the intertidal zone. Furthermore, Segerstrale (1960, 1962, 1965) has documented the contiguous but non-overlapping distributions of the tellinacean bivalve, *Macoma balthica*, and the amphipod *Pontoporeia affinis*. The disjunct distributions observed are apparently due to interspecific interference. More recently, Woodin (1974) carefully demonstrated competitive interactions between infaunal polychaete species and Fenchel (1975) documented competition and character displacement in two competing species of *Hydrobia*.

Possible mechanisms of competition probably include both exploitive abilities and interference (Miller 1967). Interference mechanisms are those processes by which individuals of one species directly prohibit individuals of another species from exploiting a given resource. Exploitation mechanisms are those by which one species excludes another because it more efficiently exploits a given resource than another species, reproduces faster, and displaces that species. Both types of processes seem to occur in the Eelgrass-Channel community complex.

Interference is probably common owing to the extensive modifications of the sediments caused by deposit-feeding species. The sediment-modification activities of *Nucula proxima* in sediments of medium to high silt-clay content tend to exclude *Yoldia limatula*. *Yoldia limatula* juveniles show poor survival, probably because of siphon and ctenidial clogging relative to adults in sediments strongly reworked by *Nucula proxima* (Levinton and Bambach 1970). Thus, *Yoldia* is abundant only in sediments of intermediate silt-clay where *Nucula* is absent. It is also uncommon in station R, where *Nucula* is a dominant of the community (Sanders 1960; Rhoads 1963). As it does not employ a siphon for respiration, *Nucula proxima* can exist in considerably turbid bottoms near the sediment-water interface. Thus, we may conclude that siphonate and non-siphonate protobranch bivalves, when both occur in great densities, should not coexist (Levinton and Bambach 1975). In low to moderate densities *Nucula*-like species might not increase the water-content of the sediments sufficiently to exclude siphonate nuculanid bivalves such as *Yoldia limatula*.

A second example of interference is the *Solemya-Yoldia* interaction observed in the laboratory. The avoidance response of *Solemya* probably indicates that this species could not exist with large densities of *Yoldia*. This prediction is borne out by field observations.

The relative exploitative efficiencies of coexisting deposit-feeding species can be used to predict competitive effects. If we assume that the rate of biogenic reworking of sediments is related to the rate of feeding, then we may conclude that *Yoldia limatula* will exploit a given sediment sample more quickly than *Nucula annulata*, the latter being dominant in deeper water mud bottoms of station R (Sanders 1960). Data on rates of sediment reworking from Rhoads (1963) and Young (1971) indicate that an average natural population of *Yoldia limatula* (150 m^{-2} in the Channel community) can rework 2355 ml of sediment per year, whereas a typical population of *Nucula annulata* at station R can only rework 910 gm $year^{-1}$. Assuming the sediments of station R are approximately 65% quartz and 35% illite (Moore 1963), and the density of such sediments is approximately 2.7, then the above-mentioned *Yoldia* population would rework 6359 gm of sediment per year. Thus, its rate of exploitation would be about 7 times faster than a population of *Nucula annulata*.

I conclude that a combination of interference and exploitation differences have resulted in the sediment specializations of Buzzards Bay deposit-feeding bivalves. The interaction between 2 sibling species of *Nucula* in Buzzards Bay with *Yoldia limatula* and *Macoma tenta* led one *Nucula* species to specialize on sandy sediments and the other to restrict itself to sediments of high silt-clay content. In Quisset Harbor, the sandy (Eelgrass community) sediments have sufficiently large amounts of silt and clay to allow *Nucula* to exclude *Yoldia* by interference. On the other hand, *Yoldia limatula*, and *Macoma tenta*, through their faster reworking (exploitation) rates, exclude *Nucula proxima* (sand species) from intermediate silt-clay bottoms. In deep water muds of Buzzards Bay, we find that *Yoldia limatula* decreases sharply with a concomitant increase in either *Nucula annulata* (silt-clay species), or large populations of small individuals of *Macoma tenta*. In these cases, *Yoldia* is excluded because of high sediment water-content generated by these large populations (Rhoads and Young 1970), or because there is little available food several cm below the sediment-water interface. Biotic interactions may be said to strongly regulate boreal shallow-water soft-bottom biotas that have been characterized as physically controlled.

LITERATURE CITED

Beedham, G. E. and G. Owen. 1965. The mantle and shell of *Solemya parkinsoni*. Proc. Zool. Soc. London 145: 405-430.

Brinkhurst, R. O. and K. E. Chua. 1969. Preliminary investigation of the exploitation of some potential nutritional resources by three sympatric tubificid oligochaetes. J. Fish. Res. Bd. Can. 26: 2659-2668.

Buzas, M. A. 1968. On the spatial distribution of Foraminifera. Contr. Cushman Found. Foram. Res. 19: 1-11.

Davis, F. M. 1925. Quantitative studies on the fauna of the sea bottom. II. Southern North Sea. Great Britain Fish. Invest., Ser. II 8: 1-50.

Dayton, P. K. and R. R. Hessler. 1972. Role of biological disturbance in maintaining diversity in the deep sea. Deep Sea Res. 19: 199-208.

Drew, G. A. 1899. Some observations on the habits, anatomy and embryology of members of the Protobranchia. Anatom. Anz. 15: 493-519.

Fenchel, R. 1970. Studies on the decomposition of organic detritus derived from the turtle grass *Thalassia testudinum*. Limnol. Oceanogr. 15: 14-20.

_____. 1972. Aspects of decomposed food chains in marine benthos. Verh. d. Dtsch. Zool. Ges. 65: 14-22.

_____. 1975. Character displacement and coexistence in mud snails (Hydrobiidae). Oecologia 20: 19-32.

Frankenberg, D. and K. L. Smith, Jr. 1967. Coprophagy in marine animals. Limnol. Oceanogr. 12: 443-450.

Frey, R. W. 1968. The lebensspuren of some common marine invertebrates near Beaufort, North Carolina. I. Pelecypod burrows. J. Paleontol. 42: 570-574.

Gilbert, W. H. 1968. Distribution and dispersion patterns of the dwarf tellin clam, *Tellina agilis*. Biol. Bull. 135: 419-420.

Gordon, D. C. 1966. The effects of the deposit-feeding polychaete, *Pectinaria gouldii*, on the intertidal sediments of Barnstable Harbor. Limnol. Oceanogr. 11: 327-332.

Grave, B. H. 1927. The natural history of *Cumingia tellinoides*. Biol. Bull. 53: 208-219.

Hampson, G. R. 1971. A species pair of the genus *Nucula* (Bivalvia) from the eastern coast of the United States. Proc. Mal. Soc. Lond. 39: 333-342.

Hargrave, B. T. 1970. The utilization of the benthic microflora by *Hyalella azteca* (Amphipoda). J. Anim. Ecol. 39: 427-438.

Jackson, J. B. 1968. Bivalves: spatial and size frequency distributions of two intertidal species. Science 161: 479-480.

Jannasch, H. W. and P. H. Pritchard. 1972. The role of inert particulate matter in the activity of acquatic microorganisms. Mem. 1st. Ital. Idrobial. Suppl. 29: 289-308.

Johannes, R. E. and M. Satomi. 1966. Composition and nutritive value of fecal pellets of a marine crustacean. Limnol. Oceanogr. 11: 191-197.

Jones, N. S. 1950. Marine bottom communities. Biol. Rev. 25: 283-313.

Levinton, J. S. 1971. Control of Tellinacean (Mollusca: Bivalvia) feeding behavior by predation. Limnol. Oceanogr. 16: 660-662.

______. 1972a. Stability and trophic structure in deposit-feeding and suspension-feeding communities. Amer. Natur. 106: 472-486.

______. 1972b. Spatial distribution of *Nucula proxima* Say: an experimental approach. Biol. Bull. 143: 175-183.

______ and R. K. Bambach. 1970. Some ecological aspects of bivalve mortality patterns. Am. J. Sci. 268: 97-112.

______ and R. K. Bambach. 1975. A comparative study of Silurian and recent deposit-feeding bivalve communities. Paleobiol. 1: 97-124.

McIntyre, A. D. and A. Eleftheriou. 1968. The bottom fauna of a flatfish nursery ground. J. Mar. Biol. Assoc. U. K. 48: 113-142.

McNulty, J. K., R. C. Work, and H. B. Moore. 1962. Some relationships between the infauna of the level-bottom and the sediment in South Florida. Bull. Mar. Sci. 12: 322-332.

Mangum, C. P. 1964. Studies on speciation in Maldanid polychaetes of the North American Atlantic Coast. II. Distribution and competitive interaction of five sympatric species. Limnol. Oceanogr. 9: 12-26.

Miller, R. S. 1967. Pattern and process in competition. Adv. Ecol. Res. 4: 1-74.

Moore, H. B. 1931. The muds of the Clyde Sea area. III. Chemical and physical conditions, rate of sedimentation and fauna. J. Mar. Biol. Assoc. U. K. 17: 325-358.

Moore, J. R. 1963. Bottom sediment studies, Buzzards Bay, Massachusetts. J. Sediment. Petrol. 33: 511-558.

Morisita, M. 1964. Application of I-index to sampling techniques. Res. Popul. Ecol. 6: 43-53.

Newell, R. 1965. The role of detritus in the nutrition of two marine deposit-feeders, the prosobranch *Hydrobia ulva* and the bivalve *Macoma balthica*. Proc. Zool. Soc. Lond. 144: 25-45.

Owen, G. 1961. A note on the habits and nutrition of *Solemya parkinsoni* (Protobranchia: Bivalvia). Quart. J. Micros. Sci. 102: 15-21.

Pettibone, M. H. 1963. Marine polychaete worms of the New England region. U.S.N.M. Bull. 227: 356 p.

Pielou, E. C. 1966. The measurement of diversity in different types of biological collections. J. Theor. Biol. 13: 3-144.

______. 1969. An introduction to mathematical ecology. Wiley-Interscience.

Reid, R. G. and A. Reid. 1969. Feeding processes of members of the genus *Macoma* (Mollusca: Bivalvia). Can. J. Zool. 47: 649-657.

Rhoads, D. C. 1963. Rates of sediment reworking by *Yoldia limatula* in Buzzards Bay, Massachusetts, and Long Island Sound. J. Sediment. Petrol. 33: 723-727.

______. 1967. Biogenic reworking of intertidal and subtidal sediments in Barnstable Harbor and Buzzards Bay, Massachusetts. J. Geol. 75: 61-76.

_____ and D. J. Stanley. 1965. Biogenic graded bedding. J. Sediment. Petrol. 35: 956-963.

_____ and D. K. Young. 1970. The influence of deposit-feeding organisms on sediment stability and community trophic structure. J. Mar. Res. 28: 150-178.

_____ and _____. 1971. Animal-sediment relationships in Cape Cod Bay, Massachusetts. II. Reworking by *Molpadia oolitica* (Holothuroidea). Mar. Biol. 11: 255-261.

Sanders, H. L. 1956. Oceanography of Long Island Sound, 1952-1954. X. Biology of marine bottom communities. Bull. Bingham Oceanogr. Coll. 15: 345-414.

_____. 1958. Benthic studies in Buzzards Bay. I. Animal-sediment relationships. Limnol. Oceanogr. 3: 245-258.

_____. 1960. Benthic studies in Buzzards Bay. III. The structure of the soft bottom community. Limnol. Oceanogr. 5: 138-158.

_____. 1968. Marine benthic diversity: a comparative study. Am. Nat. 102: 243-282.

_____, E. M. Goudsmit, E. L. Mills, and G. R. Hampson. 1962. A study of the intertidal fauna of Barnstable Harbor, Massachusetts. Limnol. Oceanogr. 7: 63-79.

Savilov, A. I. 1957. Biological aspect of the bottom fauna groupings of the North Okhotsk Sea, p. 67-136. In B. N. Nikitin [ed], Marine Biology, Trans. Inst. Oceanol. 20. 302 p.

Segerstrale, S. G. 1960. Fluctuations in the abundance of benthic animals in the Baltic Sea. Soc. Scient. Fenn., Comm. Biol. 23: 1-19.

_____. 1962. Investigations on Baltic populations of the bivalve *Macoma balthica* (L.). Part II. What are the reasons for the periodic failure of recruitment and the scarcity of *Macoma* in the deeper waters of the inner Baltic? Soc. Scient. Fenn., Comm. Biol. 24: 1-26.

_____. 1965. Biotic factors affecting the vertical distribution and abundance of the bivalve, *Macoma balthica* (L.) in the Baltic Sea. Bot. Gothoburgensia 3: 195-204.

Smith, R. I. 1964. Keys to marine invertebrates of the Woods Hole region. Contr. no. 11, Systematics-Ecology Program, Mar. Biol. Lab., Woods Hole, 208 p.

Southwood, T. R. E. 1966. Ecological methods. Methuen.

Stanley, S. M. 1971. Relation of shell form to life habits of the Bivalvia (Mollusca). Geol. Soc. Am. Mem. 125. 296 p.

Thorson, G. 1957. Bottom communities, p. 461-534. In J. W. Hedgepeth [ed.], Treatise on marine ecology and paleoecology, v. 1, Ecology. Geol. Soc. Am. Mem. 67. 1296 p.

Turpaeva, E. P. 1953. Feeding and trophic classification of benthic invertebrates. Trudy Inst. Okeanol. 7: 259-299 [in Russian].

_____. 1957. Food interrelationships of dominant species in marine benthic biocoenoses, p. 171-185. In B. N. Nikitin [ed.], Marine biology. Trans. Inst. Oceanol. 20. 302 p.

Wavre, M. and R. O. Brinkhurst. 1971. Interactions between some tubificid oligochaetes and bacteria found in the sediments of Toronto Harbour, Ontario. J. Fish. Res. Bd. Can. 28: 335-341.

Woodin, S. A. 1974. Polychaete abundance patterns in a marine soft-sediment environment: the importance of biological interactions. Ecol. Monogr. 44: 171-187.

Yonge, C. M. 1939. The protobranchiate mollusca; a functional interpretation of their structure and evolution. Phil. Trans. R. Soc. Lond. Ser. B. 230: 79-147.

Young, D. K. 1971. Effects of infauna on the sediment and seston of a subtidal environment. Vie Milieu Suppl. 22: 557-571.

Zhukova, I. A. 1963. On the quantitative significance of microorganisms in nutrition of aquatic invertebrates, p. 699-710. In C. H. Oppenheimer [ed.], A symposium of marine microbiology. C. C. Thomas.

Zobell, C. E. 1938. Studies on the bacterial flora of marine bottom sediments. J. Sediment. Petrol. 8: 10-18.

Competition, Coexistence and Character Displacement in Mud Snails (Hydrobiidae)

Tom Fenchel
Institute of Ecology and Genetics
University of Århus
DK-8000 Århus C
Denmark

ABSTRACT

The distribution patterns of four species of closely related deposit feeding prosobranchs (Hydrobiidae) were studied in a patchy estuarine environment off Jutland. Although these species tolerate wide ranges in salinity, their habitat selection in the study area was related to salinity gradients as well as to interaction of competition, migration, habitat size, extinction, colonization, and local microevolutionary changes.

Stable coexistence of these species may have been initiated by the interaction of competition and migration between habitats. Coexisting hydrobiids showed character displacement in terms of adjustment in body size, which correlated with particle size range of ingested material. This adaptation was sometimes sufficient to explain stable coexistence. Coexisting hydrobiids were also found to have restricted (and nonoverlapping) breeding periods as compared to allopatrically occurring populations.

Several findings in this study support the theory of island biogeography.

INTRODUCTION

Within the last decade, theoretical understanding of the distribution of organisms in nature has advanced considerably, as has our knowledge of ecological niche and the limiting similarity of coexisting species (Diamond 1973; MacArthur 1972; MacArthur and Wilson 1967; May 1973). These ideas, which explained observed distribution patterns on the basis of habitat selection, competition, migration, and extinction of local populations, so far have had little impact on the study of marine animals.

The objective of this study was to examine the distribution of four closely related species in a patchy estuarine environment and to compare the findings with theories on the distribution of animal species, particularly in marine bottom communities. The deposit feeding prosobranchs belonging to the family Hydrobiidae are well suited for this kind of study owing to their wide distribution and well known general biology and taxonomy. These closely related species show habitat selection but no differences in their resource utilization. While most localities harbor only one of the four species, two and sometimes three of the species coexist in some localities. One of the main objectives of the study has therefore been to investigate how this coexistence is maintained. Further details of the study are described in Fenchel (1975a, b).

THE GENERAL BIOLOGY OF HYDROBIID SNAILS

Mud snails (Hydrobiidae) are among the most important deposit feeders in Northern European estuaries and lagoons and occur on nearly all kinds of substrate (exposed beaches and sulfide containing muds excepted) with densities often exceeding 50,000 m^{-2}. Four species are found in Danish waters: *Potamopyrgus jenkinsi*, *Hydrobia ventrosa*, *H. neglecta* and *H. ulvae* (Fig. 1). Various aspects of their biology are described in detail in Fenchel et al. (1975). Hylleberg (1975), Hylleberg and Lassen (in preparation), Kofoed (1975a, b), Muus (1967) and papers cited therein.

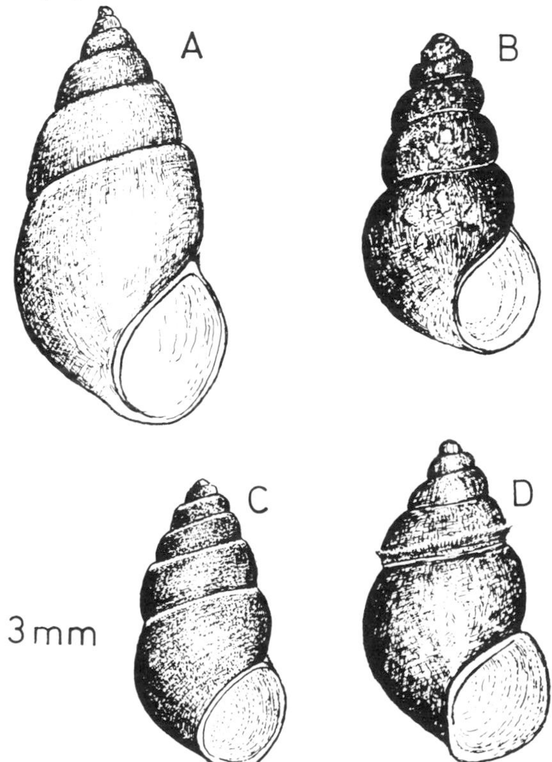

Fig. 1. Typical shells of hydrobiids. A: *Hydrobia ulvae*, B: *H. ventrosa*, C: *H. neglecta*, and D: *Potamopyrgus jenkinsi*.

All four species are deposit feeders which utilize the microflora attached to ingested mineral and detrital particles. At times the animals float in the water surface; they may then trap bacteria with excreted mucus which is later engulfed.

Potamopyrgus jenkinsi is parthenogenetic and viviparous, and males are not found. In the *Hydrobia* spp. males are present and the females deposit egg capsules. In *H. ulvae* the capsules contain about 20 eggs which develop into short-lived pelagic larvae. *H. neglecta* and *H. ventrosa* capsules contain 1-2 eggs which develop directly into small snails. The hydrobiids are believed to reach an age of 1.5-2 years (Fish and Fish 1974).

Species are easily identified by the shape of the penis in males or by shell morphology and pigmentation of the living animal. Since the species are often polymorphic within populations as well as among different populations with respect to these characters, identification of the females or of dead animals is difficult. However, the species do not hydridize in the field, nor can they be made to do so in the laboratory (Lassen unpublished results).

Laboratory experiments show small differences among the species with respect to their tolerance of extreme temperatures, dessication and anoxia. Habitat selection is most obvious with regard to salinity preference. The optimum salinity increases in order from *P. jenkinsi*, *H. ventrosa*, *H. neglecta*, to *H. ulvae*. Hylleberg (1975) found that the 3 latter species have optimum salinities at approximately 20, 25 and > 30 °/₀₀, respectively. However the tolerance ranges of the species are wide and overlap considerably.

Muus (1967) found *P. jenkinsi*, *H. ventrosa*, *H. neglecta*, and *H. ulvae* in the field at 0-15, 6-20, 10-24 and 10-33 °/₀₀, respectively, in Danish estuaries and lagoons. He noted that two or more species rarely occur at any one locality. He also concluded that salinity alone does not control the distribution of the species because the boundary between two particular species may occur at different salinities in different estuaries. He attributed this variation to other, in part hypothetical, physical factors. He stressed water turbulence as an important factor because he found *H. ventrosa* and *H. neglecta* only in sheltered localities, whereas *H. ulvae* also occurred in more exposed habitats. Since strong wave action is usually correlated with fairly high salinity in inner Danish waters, this interpretation is not easily discounted. However, it is rendered unlikely by the fact that in the inner Baltic Sea *H. ventrosa* and *H. ulvae* are often found together, not only in soft sediments but also on exposed sands, rocks and *Fucus* (Koli 1961). This habitat of competition from other gastropods (rissoids, littorinids) which cannot live in the brackish Baltic Sea (5-6 °/₀₀).

AREA OF STUDY

The main study area was the Limfjord, a 140-km long, shallow sound cutting through Northern Jutland. In the open, western parts salinity is > 30 °/₀₀, decreasing eastward to < 20 °/₀₀ at the eastern inlet. In the many bays, lagoons, and coves, and seaward of marsh, salinities are considerably lower and may fluctuate owing to ground-water seepage and stream flow in conjunction with the absence of lunar tides in the Limfjord. This water system thus constitutes a very complex and patchy estuarine environment. The system is of special interest since it is only 150 years old in its present state. Prior to 1825 the western entrance to the North Sea was closed and the fjord consisted primarily of a number of large, interconnected freshwater lakes. Following a storm the western inlet broke open and it has since been kept open artificially. Thus, establishment of the present marine fauna and its distribution patterns, as well as microevolutionary changes of local populations, have all taken place within the last 150 years.

During the present investigation 100 localities along the shores of the Limfjord were regularly sampled during 1974 in order to study the composition of the hydrobiid fauna. In addition, samples were taken from 27 localities along a 28-kg long estuary (Randers Fjord) on the east coast of Jutland, a fjord with a relatively stable salinity gradient. Additionally, samples from 6 localities in the Baltic Sea off Tvärminne, Finland have been considered in the present study. All these localities are described in more detail in Fenchel (1975a, b). Altogether, the present study is based on about 26,000 identified and measured hydrobiids.

THE DISTRIBUTION PATTERNS

Data from all the Limfjord localities clearly indicate a correlation between salinity and distribution (Fig. 2). However, a particular salinity gradient alone may not necessarily indicate the presence or absence of any particular species.

H. ulvae is the most widespread species, and is the only species in 32 out of 91 localities in the Limfjord. It occurs with *H. neglecta* in one locality and with *H. ventrosa* in 23 localities. *H. neglecta* is much rarer; it is the only species in one locality, and in 14 other localities it coexists with *H. ventrosa* or *H. ulvae*, or both. *H. ventrosa* is found in 51 localities; in 12 of these it is the only species and in the remaining localities it coexists with one or two of the other hydrobiid species. *P. jenkinsi* is found in 9 localities, together with *H. ventrosa* in 3 of these.

Certain features of Figure 2 indicate that competitive interactions affect the distribution of hydrobiids. Thus localities with *H. neglecta* are relatively sparse in spite of the fact that

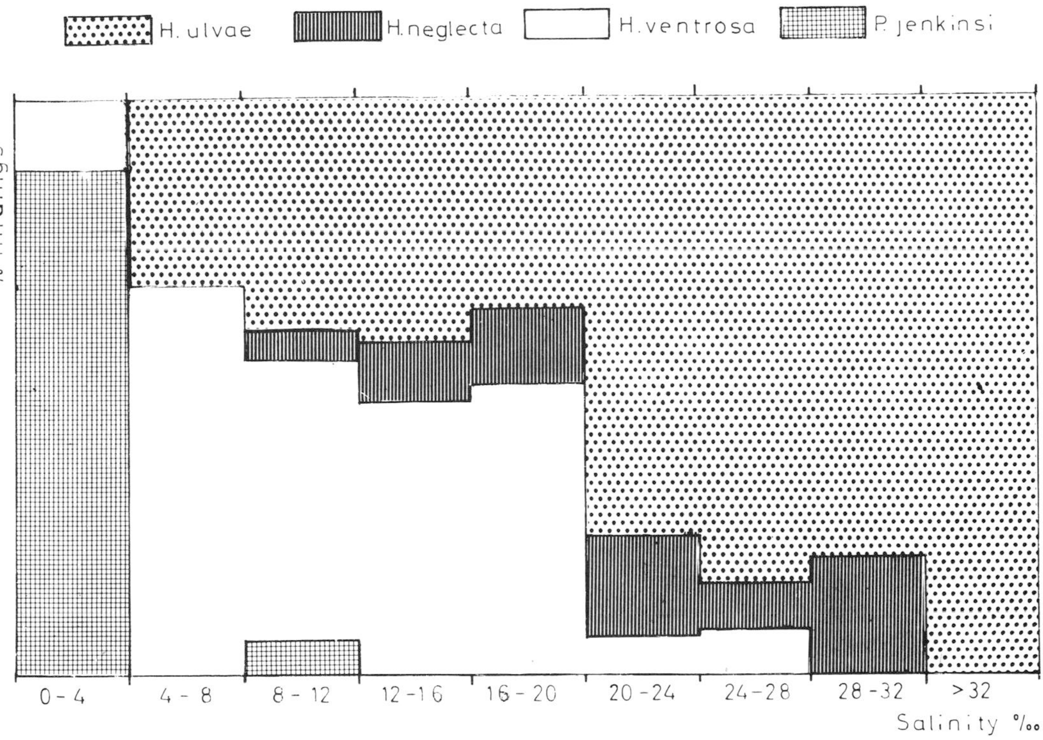

Fig. 2. The percentage of the four hydrobiids in 73 Limfjord locatities with different salinities.

the majority of the sampled localities have salinities at around the optimum for this species. *H. ventrosa* is most common at salinities below the optimum for this species, as determined by laboratory experiments.

The local distribution patterns can be understood at least qualitatively in the light of the theoretical model described by Fenchel (1975<u>a</u>). This model investigates two competing species in which the populations follow the Lotka-Volterra equations and it is assumed that one of the species can always exclude the other in a homogenous environment. Two habitats are considered in the model. Each of the species is competitively superior in one of the habitats, but both species can sustain populations in both habitats in the absence of the other species. It is finally assumed that individuals migrate in a certain pattern from one habitat to the other. On the basis of this model the following can be shown formally. (1) If one of the species has a relatively high migration rate from the habitat in which it is superior into the other habitat, it may exclude the other species in the total system, including the habitat in which the latter species is a superior competitor. This is likely to happen when one of the species is confined to a small habitat which is surrounded by a large habitat more suitable for the other species, and the small habitat is not protected by migration barriers. (2) If there is a moderate migration between the two habitats, or if the two habitats (and thus the populations) are about equally large, a stable coexistence between the two species in the system will occur. (3) If the habitats are sufficiently large for the migration rate of individuals to be a function of distance, a gradient in the species composition will occur between the habitats. The position and steepness of this transition between the species will not only be a function of the change in relevant environmental factors which determine the outcome of competition, but also a function of the migration rates of the two species.

This model cannot yet be applied quantitatively to the present material. Although carrying capacities and coefficients of competition can be estimated roughly for the hydrobiids, no quantitative data on migration rates are available. The model does, however, explain many distribution patterns qualitatively. Some of these patterns are shown in Figures 3-5.

In accordance with its salinity preference, *H. ulvae* is generally the only species found in the open areas of the Limfjord, whereas the other species are confined to isolated populations along certain stretches of the shore, especially in bays and lagoons. Since *H. ulvae* has by far the largest and most widely distributed populations it may undergo a considerable rate of migration into the brackish lagoons and bays. If the latter habitat types are small and not protected by migration barriers (causeways, narrow inlets), they cannot sustain populations of the other species but harbor only *H. ulvae* even in the very dilute brackish water (e.g., see Figure 3 showing the distribution of hydrobiids in a large bay of the fjord system).

The southeastern part, which is separated by a sluice, has very low salinity (< 1 °/∘∘) and is populated only by *Potamopyrgus jenkinsi*. The remaining part of the bay harbors only populations of *H. ulvae* (occasionally a few specimens of the two other *Hydrobia* spp.), although the localities in the innermost parts of the bay have low salinities (15 °/∘∘ or less) and are sheltered. The absence of *H. ventrosa* and *H. neglecta* is due to the absence of migration barriers between these localities and the open, more saline northern parts of the bay, which sustain large populations of *H. ulvae*. The only exception is the small locality in the southwestern arm of the bay which is separated by a causeway. Although salinity and other factors seem to be nearly identical inside and outside of the causeway, a population of *H. ventrosa* is found inside. The causeway was built in the 1960's, and since then *H. ventrosa* has probably colonized the locality and been able to sustain a population where it is somewhat protected from *H. ulvae* migration.

In larger bays and coves with salinity gradients, gradual transitions from one species to another are found. However, often *H. neglecta*, and more rarely also *H. ventrosa* are absent; probably they have been squeezed out by a combination of competition and migration from both sides (Figs. 3,5). *H. neglecta* is especially

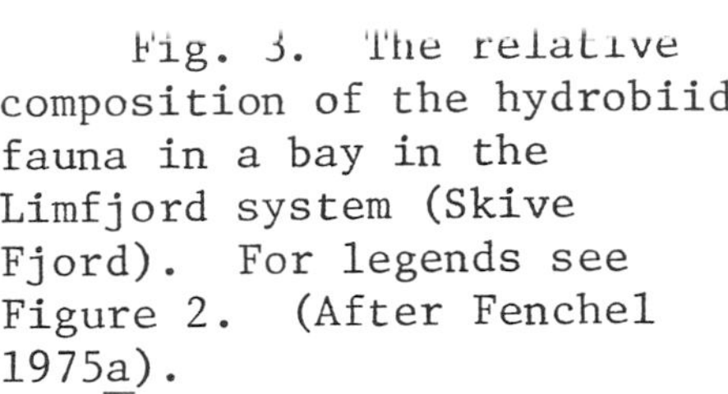

Fig. 3. The relative composition of the hydrobiid fauna in a bay in the Limfjord system (Skive Fjord). For legends see Figure 2. (After Fenchel 1975a).

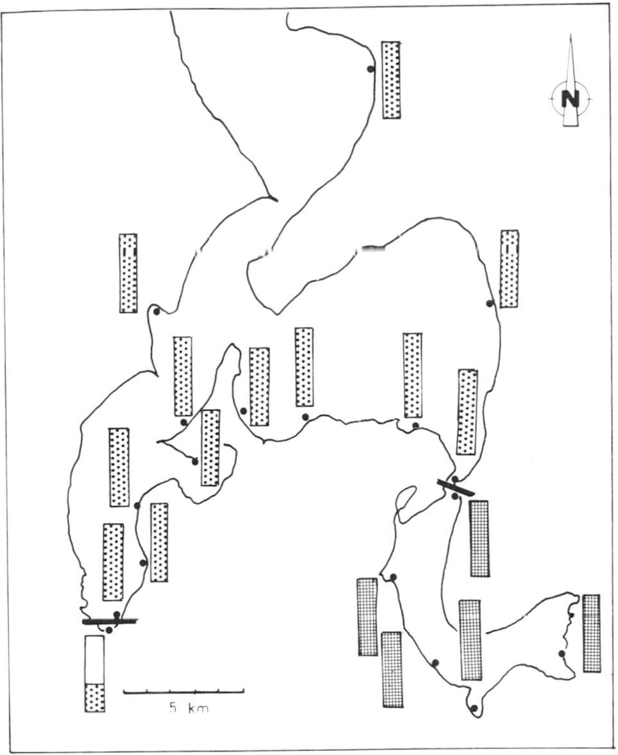

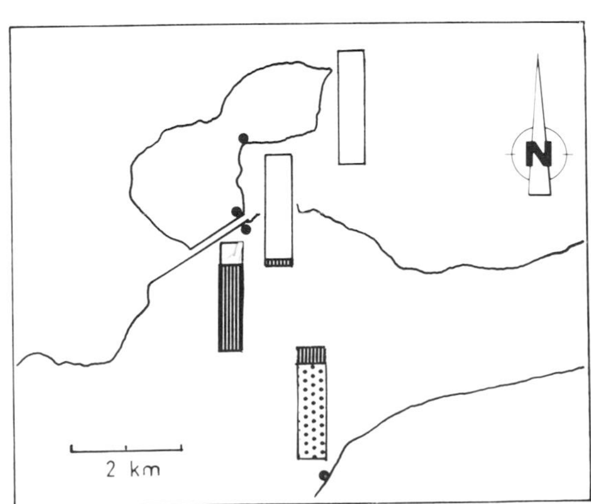

Fig. 4. The relative composition of the hydrobiid fauna on either side of a causeway separating a lagoon with dilute brackish water. *H. neglecta* and *H. ventrosa* coexist on each side of the causeway. For legends see Figure 2. (After Fenchel 1975a).

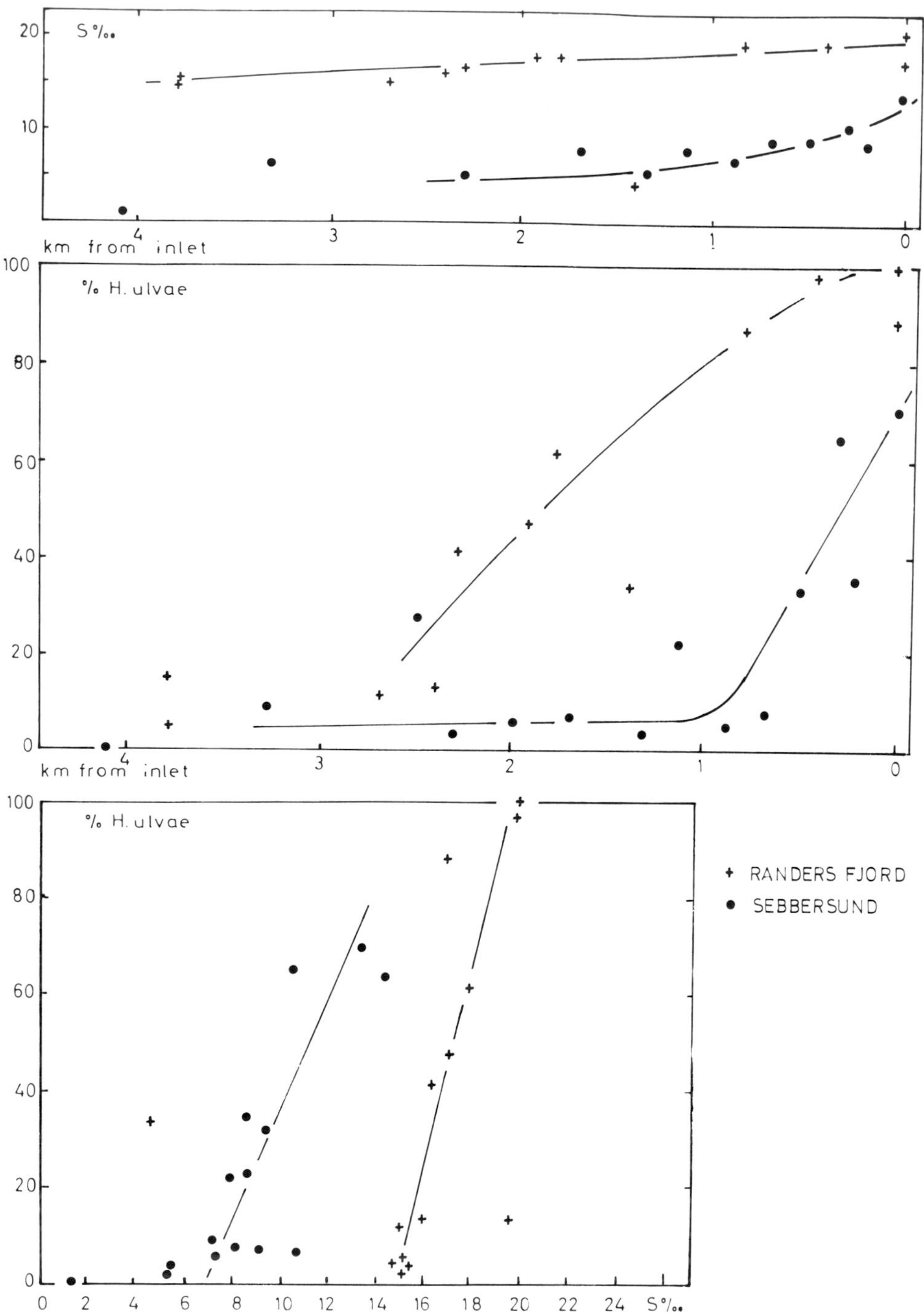

Fig. 5. The salinity gradients and the percentages of *H. ulvae* of the total hydrobiid population (*H. ulvae* and *H. ventrosa*) as a function of distance from the inlets and as a function of salinity in two estuaries. (Altered after Fenchel 1975a).

vulnerable having to compete with *H. ulvae* and *H. ventrosa* from both sides in salinity gradients. Thus, *H. neglecta* is confined mainly to areas along the shoreline with optimum salinity and only where it is exposed to competition with one of the other *Hydrobia* spp. As discussed below, the competition between *Potamopyrgus genkinsi* and the *Hydrobia* spp. is probably less intense than the competition between the different *Hydrobia* spp. *H. ventrosa* is therefore in a less vulnerable position than *H. neglecta* and is more widely distributed.

Figure 5 shows the transition between *H. ulvae* and *H. ventrosa* in salinity gradients of two systems: Randers Fjord and a smaller lagoon in the Limfjord system (Sebbersund). In both systems the total density of hydrobiids is approximately the same in the different localities. There are no obvious changes in other environmental factors (sediment, vegetation etc.) along the area of species transition. Although there is a clear correlation between salinity and distribution, *H. ulvae* extends its range toward lower salinities in the steeper gradient of the smaller lagoon where the migration distance is shorter. Thus the distribution patterns of the species appear to be combined functions of competition and migration. The one point from the Randers Fjord which deviates strongly from the others in Figure 5 is from a locality close to the estuary mouth but with a stream outlet and therefore a lower salinity. Here *H. ulvae* constitutes a larger proportion of the snails than would be expected from salinity alone; its abundance may be due to the proximity of other large *H. ulvae* populations.

CHARACTER DISPLACEMENT IN COEXISTING HYDROBIIDS

Stable coexistence of competing hydrobiid species can be established and maintained through a low migration rate. At the same time, even closely located populations of the species may show genetic differences (Lassen unpublished data; Muus 1967). Microevolutionary changes in sympatric species which tend to relax interspecific competition, i.e., character displacement sensu Brown and Wilson (1956) and Hutchinson (1959), might therefore be expected.

Figure 6 shows the shell length of *H. ulvae* and of *H. ventrosa* from 15 localities where they coexist and from 17 localities where only one or the other of the two species are found. When the species occur allopatrically they are within the same size range (3-3.5 mm), but when they coexist *H. ulvae* is always considerably larger than *H. ventrosa*. The average ratio of lengths of the two species when they coexist is 1.53 and ranges from 1.23 to 1.95 as based on 30 samples from 15 localities (Fig. 6). Although the average size of the populations varies somewhat through the year, owing to changes in age structure, the size ratio between a pair of coexisting species remains relatively constant. Only snails

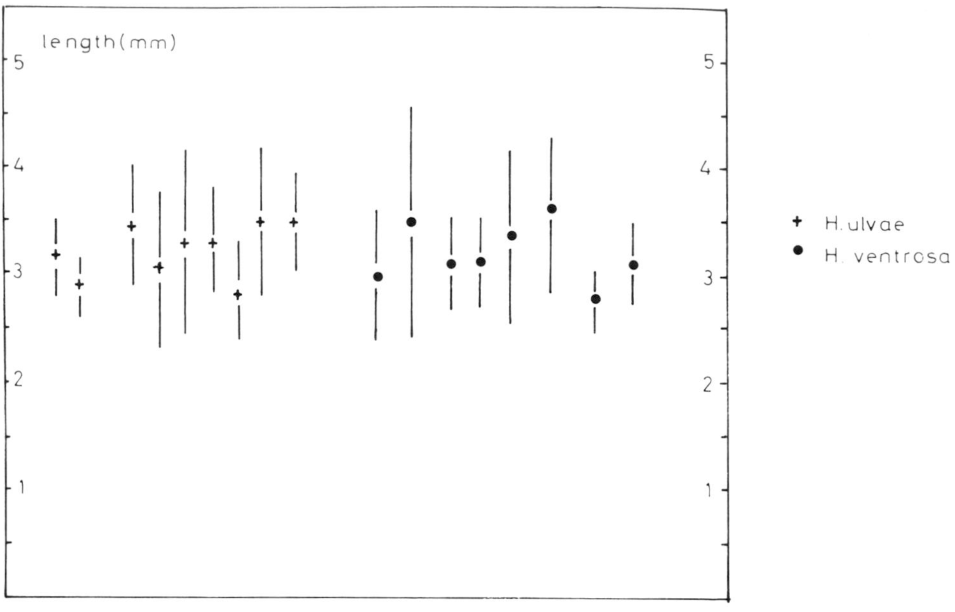

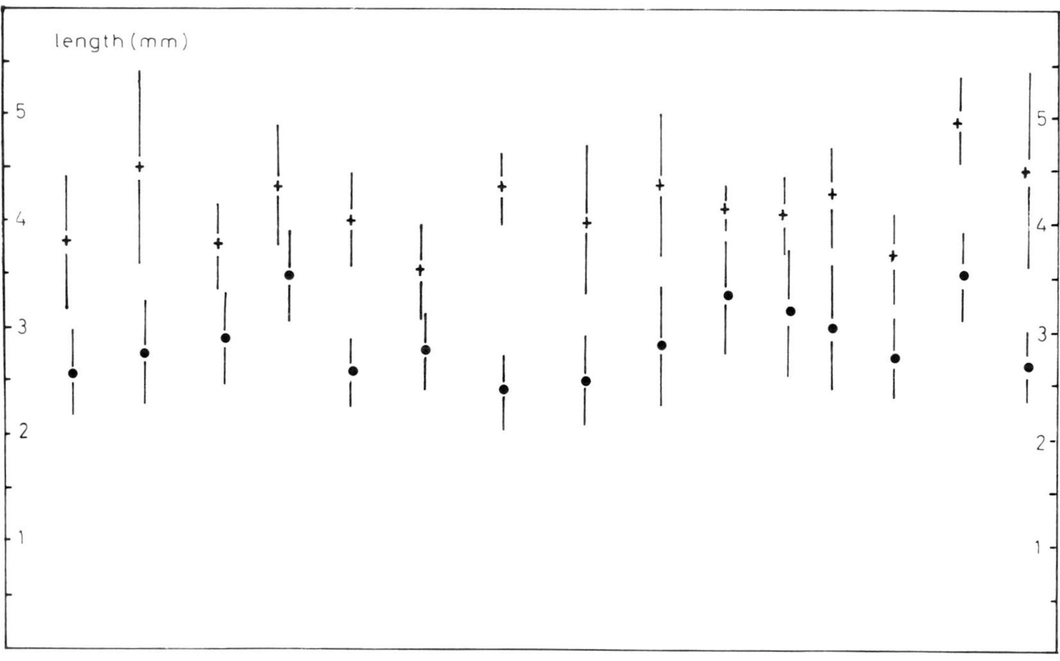

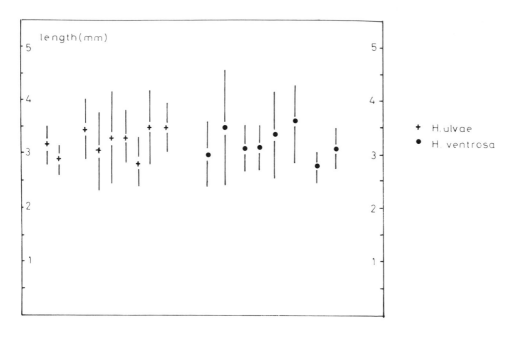

Fig. 6. The average shell lengths of *H. ulvae* and of *H. ventrosa* from 15 localities where they coexist (below) and from 17 localities where one of the species are found allopatrically. The bars indicate 1 standard deviation. (After Fenchel 1975b).

$>$ 1.5 mm were considered when the average shell length was calculated. The examples shown in Figure 6 are all from June-July, when the size distributions are usually unimodal. However, even earlier and later in the season, when the size distributions may be bimodal, the slight overlap in size of coexisting populations is evident, whereas allopatrically occurring populations usually deposit eggs throughout the summer, coexisting populations of *H. ulvae* and *H. ventrosa* have relatively short, nonoverlapping reproductive periods. The exact period of reproduction, however, seems to vary somewhat from locality to locality (Fenchel 1975b).

H. neglecta also shows a similar fixed size relationship to *H. ulvae* and to *H. ventrosa* when coexisting with these two species. *H. neglecta* is nearly always larger than coexisting *H. ventrosa* and always smaller than coexisting *H. ulvae*. The length ratio between coexisting *H. Neglecta* and *H. ventrosa*, however, is smaller than that of other pairs of coexisting *Hydrobia* spp.: i.e., 1.13 (1.06-1.22) as based on the Limfjord localities. Since *H. neglecta* is rarer and seldom occurs alone, this species is difficult to analyse.

In the Finnish localities *H. neglecta* is absent. In the inner Baltic the salinity is constantly 5-6 ‰, which is close to the lower tolerance limit for both *H. ventrosa* and *H. ulvae*; salinity does not affect habitat selection in this area and the two species are usually found coexisting in most localities (also together with *P. jenkinsi*). The size ratio between the two *Hydrobia* spp. in this area is 1.32 (1.2-1.47).

In the Randers Fjord system character displacement in terms of size is also found along the stretch of the estuary where *H. ventrosa* and *H. ulvae* coexist. However, the size ratio is smaller (1.17 and ranging from 1.13 to 1.23) than in the Limfjord. This is reasonable since in this open estuary migration rates are probably higher than in Limfjord localities where *H. ulvae* and *H. ventrosa* coexist. The latter localities are mostly lagoons with narrow inlets or closed by causeways or dikes so that gene flow from surrounding allopatric populations is more restricted.

Potamopyrgus jenkinsi does not show any fixed size ratio with coexisting *Hydrobia* spp. in the Danish or in the Finnish localities.

Hutchinson (1959) found empirically that size ratios (length) of whole animals or of some trophic organ (mainly bill dimensions of birds) of about 1.3 (i.e., a weight ratio of about 2) permit the coexistence of congeners. This empirical number was further supported by MacArthur (1972) and Schoener (1965). It may be asked whether this size ratio, which apparently is also valid for *Hydrobia* spp., can be explained in terms of current ideas on resource partitioning and coexistence.

Theoretical considerations as well as empirical findings indicate that when two competing species are limited by only one type of resource, a modal distance between utilization functions allows stable coexistence (MacArthur 1972; May 1973).

The hydrobiids feed mainly on diatoms and on mineral and detrital particles, utilizing primarily the attached microorganisms.

Figure 7 shows a nearly linear relation between the modal particle sizes ingested and the shell length. Furthermore, *Potamopyrgus jenkinsi* ingests particles which are about 3 times larger than those ingested by similar sized *Hydrobia* spp. The competition for food particles between *P. jenkinsi* and the *Hydrobia* spp. is therefore probably less intense than the competition between the different *Hydrobia* spp.

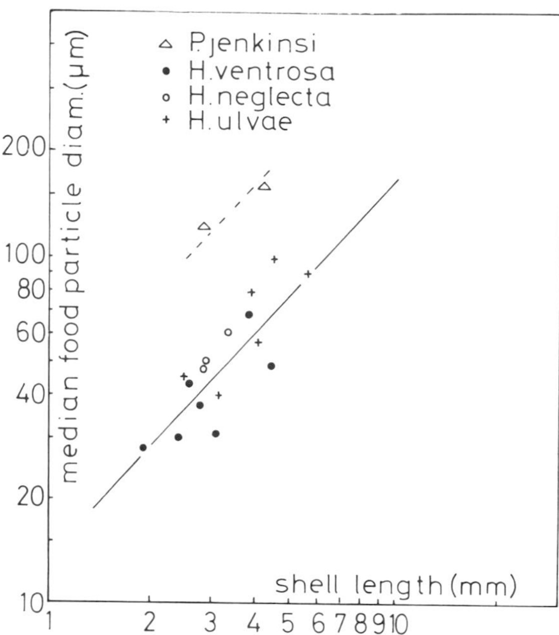

Fig. 7. The median particle size of ingested material as a function of shell length for four species of hydrobiids. (After Fenchel 1975b).

The resource utilization function, or niche width with respect to the particular resource, will be a function of the variance of the resource qualities consumed by the individuals and the variance among the different individuals due to genotypic or environmental variation. In the case of the *Hydrobia* spp. the standard deviation of particles ingested by an individual is about 0.4 $\log_2$ units, and the standard deviation of the shell lengths within populations is about 0.1 $\log_2$ units (ingested particles as well as the shell lengths of a population fit log-normal curves reasonably well; see Fenchel 1975b). The relation between shell length and ingested particle size is linear; thus, in order to have resource utilization functions spaced 1 standard deviation along the resource axis, the ratio in shell length would have to be $(0.4^2 + 0.1^2)^{\frac{1}{2}}$ $\log_2$ units, or a factor of about 1.4. These rough calculations show that stable coexistence may be explained by size ratios of the magnitude reported. Figure 8 shows the particle size frequency distribution of ingested material of populations of coexisting *H. ulvae* and *H. ventrosa*, and of two allopatric populations.

Most cases of character displacement previously reported involve either size differences or temporal differences in resource utilization (e.g. breeding time), whereas changes in other adaptive characters have been less frequently recorded; there are probably

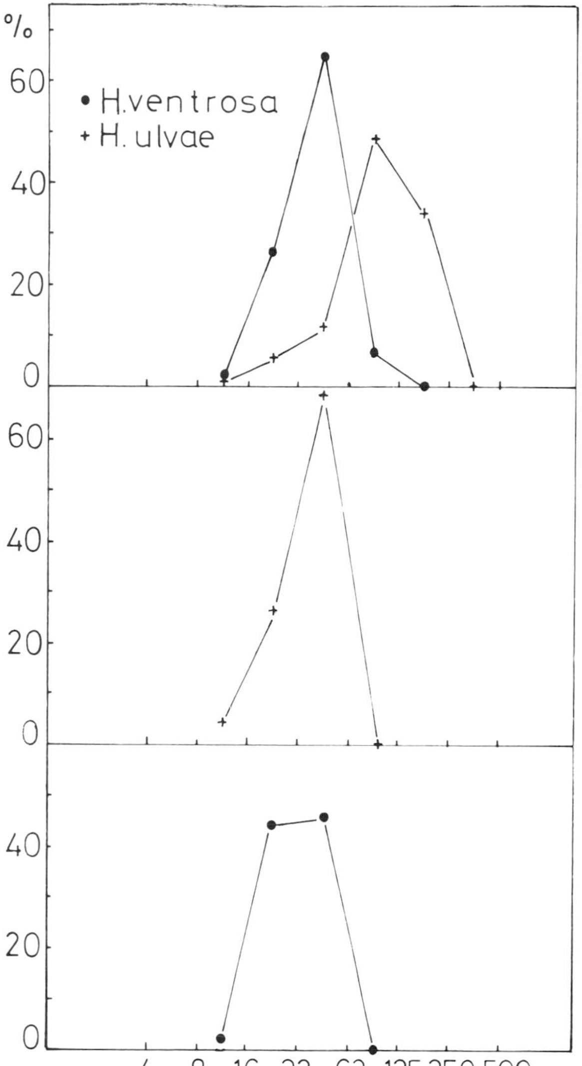

Fig. 8. The particle size distribution of ingested mineral particles of populations of *H. ventrosa* and *H. ulvae* from a locality where they coexist and from two allopatric populations. (After Fenchel 1975b).

several reasons for this. First, in most cases where congeners have been brought together, habitat selection rather than resource partitioning has occurred (MacArthur 1972). Among the possible changes which could lead to resource partitioning, size differences are of course easy to detect and quantify. Finally, it is probably significant that body size can be changed quickly by selection compared to other adaptive characters. As previously mentioned, the Limfjord is only 150 years old as a marine habitat. The observed differences in sizes and in breeding periods (as well as local differences in isozymes, pigmentation and shell morphology, characteristics which cannot yet be interpreted ecologically) have all evolved independently in many more-or-less isolated populations within this short time period. Local selection pressures and how they balance with migration, and thus gene flow from neighboring populations, remain to be studied.

DISCUSSION

The present study shows that in a patchy environment such as the Limfjord a species may consist of a large number of more or less isolated subpopulations in which microevolution may take place. This possibility for change may explain the great variability of many estuarine animals and the difficulties in finding constant diagnostic characters for distinguishing closely related congeners. Muus (1967) and Rasmussen (1973) considered these features to be characteristic for many estuarine genera.

While the classical view of animal communities did not ignore biotic interactions, it did imply that given certain environmental factors in a habitat and a given pool of species, a unique community would develop following a characteristic sucession. This view also lies behind the concept of marine bottom communities developed by Thorson (1957). As a result many community studies suggest that if a sufficient number of factors are quantified, community composition can be predicted.

The present findings do not support this concept. The distribution patterns observed in the study area result from an interplay between habitat selection, competition, migration, extinctions and colonizations and local microevolutionary changes, factors dependent in part on "macro-geographical" structures (habitat sizes, migration barriers and distance and sizes of surrounding populations of other species) and on local environmental factors.

In many respects the picture off Jutland supports the theory of island biogeography (MacArthur and Wilson 1967; Simberloff 1974). This theory also includes factors such as migration, colonization, extinction, local microevolution, the importance of habitat size for the number of coexisting, competing species, and the possibility of alternative species assemblages in habitats with a given set of environmental factors.

REFERENCES

Brown, J. and E. O. Wilson. 1956. Character displacement. Syst. Zool. 5: 49-64.

Diamond, J. M. 1973. Distributional ecology of New Guinea birds. Science 179: 759-769.

Fenchel, T. 1975a. Factors determining the distribution patterns of mud snails (Hydrobiidae). Oecologia (Berl.) 20: 1-17.

_____. 1975b. Character displacement and coexistence in mud snails (Hydrobiidae). Oecologia (Berl.) 20: 19-32.

_____, L. H. Kofoed, and A. Lappalainen. 1975. Particle size selection of two deposit feeders: the amphipod *Corophium volutator* and the prosobranch *Hydrobia ulvae*. Mar. Biol. 30: 119-128.

Fish, J. D. and S. Fish. 1974. The breeding cycle and growth of *Hydrobia ulvae* in the Dovey Estuary. J. Mar. Biol. Ass. U. K. 54: 685-697.

Hutchinson, G. E. 1959. Homage to Santa Rosalia or why are there so many kinds of animals? Am. Nat. 93: 145-159.

Hylleberg, J. 1975. The effect of salinity and temperature on egestion in mud snails (Gastropoda: Hydrobiidae): a study on niche overlap. Oecologia (Berl.) 21: 279-289.

______ and H. H. Lassen (in preparation). The effect of abiotic factors on activity, respiration and survival in mud snails (Gastropoda: Hydrobiidae).

Kofoed, L. H. 1975a. The feeding biology of *Hydrobia ventrosa* I. The assimilation of different kinds of food. J. Exp. Mar. Biol. Ecol. 19: 233-241.

______. 1975b. The feeding biology of *Hydrobia ventrosa* II. The allocation of the parameters of the carbon budget and the significance of the secretion of dissolved organics. J. Exp. Mar. Biol. Ecol. 19: 243-256.

Koli, L. 1961. Die Molluskenfauna des Brackwasserbebietes bei Tvärminne. Ann. Zool. Soc. Vanamo 22: 1-22.

MacArthur, R. H. 1972. Geographical ecology. Harper and Row.

______ and E. O. Wilson. 1967. The theory of island biogeography. Princeton University Press.

May, R. M. 1973. Stability and complexity in model ecosystems. Princeton University Press.

Muus, B. J. 1967. The fauna of Danish estuaries and lagoons. Med. Danm. Fisk.-Havunders., N.S. 5: 1-316.

Rasmussen, E. 1973. Systematics and ecology of the Isefjord marine fauna (Denmark). Ophelia 11: 1-495.

Schoener, T. W. 1965. The evolution of bill size differences among sympatric congeners species of birds. Evolution 19: 189-213.

Simberloff, D. S. 1974. Equilibrium theory of island biography and ecology. Ann. Rev. Ecol. Syst. 5: 161-182.

Thorson, G. 1957. Bottom communities. Mem. Geol. Soc. Am. 67: 461-534.

Community Regulation

A New Look at the Zonation of Benthos Along the Estuarine Gradient

Donald F. Boesch
Virginia Institute of Marine Science
Gloucester Point, VA 23062

ABSTRACT

The zonation of macrobenthos along a homoiohaline estuarine gradient in the Chesapeake Bay and a seasonally poikilohaline estuarine gradient in the Brisbane River estuary, Australia, was investigated by assessing assemblage similarity and patterns of species distributions. The faunal change along the homoiohaline gradient is gradual and relatively uniform, with zones of acelerated change broadly occurring around the boundaries of the Venice System salinity zones. The more abrupt change along poikohaline gradients is governed by low salinity conditions. These patterns of estuarine zonation can be explained in terms of the distribution and abundance of stenohaline marine, euryhaline marine, euryhaline opportunistic, estuarine endemic and freshwater species.

INTRODUCTION

Biological features of the transition zone between the sea and fresh water have long attracted the interest of marine biologists. Consequently, the biotic changes and depression of species richness which occur in estuaries are familiar to us all. Although some workers have referred to the estuarine habitat as an ecotone between marine and freshwater habitats (Burbanck et al. 1956), most agree that it has its own unique characteristics (Carriker 1967). The biotic change along the estuarine complex-gradient is best referred to as a "coenocline", or community gradient, and the estuarine ecosystem gradient as an "ecocline" (Whittaker 1967).

Early estuarine benthic ecologists found it useful to classify segments of the estuarine ecocline into zones of similar biotic composition and to relate these zones to the distribution of salinity. Classification schemes were developed, particularly in northwestern

Europe, by investigators working in large homoiohaline brackish systems, e.g., the Baltic and the Zuiderzee (reviewed by Segerstraale 1959; Remane 1971). The proliferation of classification schemes resulted in a symposium convened in 1958 to consider brackish water classification. The concensus classification adopted is the "Venice System" (Symposium on the Classification of Brackish Waters 1958). Carriker (1967) further expanded the Venice System by incorporating Day's (1964) physiographic subdivisions and biotic distributional classes based on observations in South African estuaries (Table 1).

Table 1. Classification of estuarine zones relating the Venice System classification to distributional classes of organisms (after Carriker 1967).

Divisions of Estuary	Venice System: Salinity ranges $^{o}/oo$	Venice System: Zones	Ecological Classification: Types of organisms and approximate range of distribution in estuary, relative to divisions and salinities				
River	0.5	limnetic	↑	limnetic			↑
Head	0.5-5	oligohaline		oligohaline	↑	↑	
Upper Reaches	5-18	mesohaline	mixohaline				
Middle Reaches	18-25	polyhaline			true estuarine (estuarine endemics)		
				↑			
Lower Reaches	25-30	polyhaline					
Mouth	30-40	euhaline	↓	stenohaline marine	↓	euryhaline marine	migrants

The Venice System classification, particularly the designation of euhaline, polyhaline, mesohaline and oligohaline, has been widely used by benthic ecologists working in large homoiohaline brackish water systems in northwestern Europe: the Baltic region (Bagge 1969; Muus 1967), German estuaries (Caspers 1959; Riemann 1966), and Holland (Den Hartog 1971). However, the last-mentioned application to estuaries in the Dutch Delta area has been criticized by Wolff (1973) who concluded that either clear-cut faunal discontinuities did not occur along the estuarine gradient, or that such breaks coincided with physiographic changes rather than salinity levels. The Venice System classification has also been applied to North American estuaries: San Francisco Bay system (Kelley 1966), Pamlico Sound system, North Carolina (Tenore 1972), and the Chesapeake Bay (Boesch 1972, 1974; Wass 1972).

Implicit in the concepts of estuarine segmentation is the existence of biotic discontinuities, or zones of more abrupt biotic change, coinciding with the salinity limits of the zones, i.e., 30, 18, 5, and 0.5 $^{o}/oo$, and relative biotic homogeneity within the zones (Wolff 1973). The existing concepts of brackish water classification and estuarine segmentation reflect subjective experience of European ecologists and are based mainly on patterns of species ranges along estuarine gradients. However, ecological estuarine segmentation implies similarity of community composition, structure and function within zones. The time seems right to have a new, more objective look at zonation of the estuarine ecocline based on changes in biotic assemblages rather than species ranges, and to examine the applicability of classification schemes to estuaries outside of northwestern Europe.

I have examined zonation in the macrobenthic coenocline of the Chesapeake Bay system, a remarkably large and relatively homoiohaline estuary with gradual salinity gradients. I have compared with this the preliminary results of a similar investigation in the Brisbane River estuary in eastern Australia, which, although long and well developed, is seasonally greatly poikilohaline.

My understanding of estuarine gradients has been enhanced by helpful discussions with Wim J. Wolff, Robert J. Diaz and Marvin L. Wass. I thank them for sharing their experience.

Contribution No. 743 from the Virginia Institute of Marine Science. This research was supported in part by a Fulbright-Hays research fellowship and by the Environmental Protection Agency Grant R-803599-01-0.

STUDY AREAS

The Chesapeake estuarine gradient runs from the mouth of the Chesapeake Bay through the York River and into the Pamunkey River (Fig. 1). The limit of tidal influence in the Pamunkey is over 150 km from the mouth of the Bay, but salinity seldom exceeds that of the freshwater discharge more than 120 km from the Bay mouth. Because the freshwater discharge into the York system is relatively small, the isohalines in the estuary are nearly evenly spaced. Thus salinity distribution of the York estuary is reasonably representative of that in Chesapeake Bay proper, which is over 300 km long. Salinity does not fluctuate widely during a tidal cycle or seasonally (Fig. 2) and is typically lowest in spring and highest in fall, although the rare passage of hurricanes or tropical storms during the summer (e.g., August 1969) can drastically reduce salinity.

The Brisbane River flows into Moreton Bay (Fig. 3) and is tidal for over 85 km above its mouth; measurable salinity is seldom found more than 70 km upestuary. The subtropical Brisbane estuary is strongly poikilohaline seasonally (Fig. 3), with salinities in excess of 25 $^{o}/_{oo}$ found over 30 km from the mouth during low flow conditions (winter and spring); however, freshwater commonly extends to within 20 km of the mouth during the summer months following the passage of cyclones (Bayly 1965; Stephenson 1968).

METHODS

Both estuaries were sampled in a similar fashion. Macrobenthos (>1.0 mm) was sampled at 10 sites positioned along the estuarine gradient in mud or sandy-mud bottoms. However, sediments at sites at the mouths of both estuaries were predominantly sand. Stations

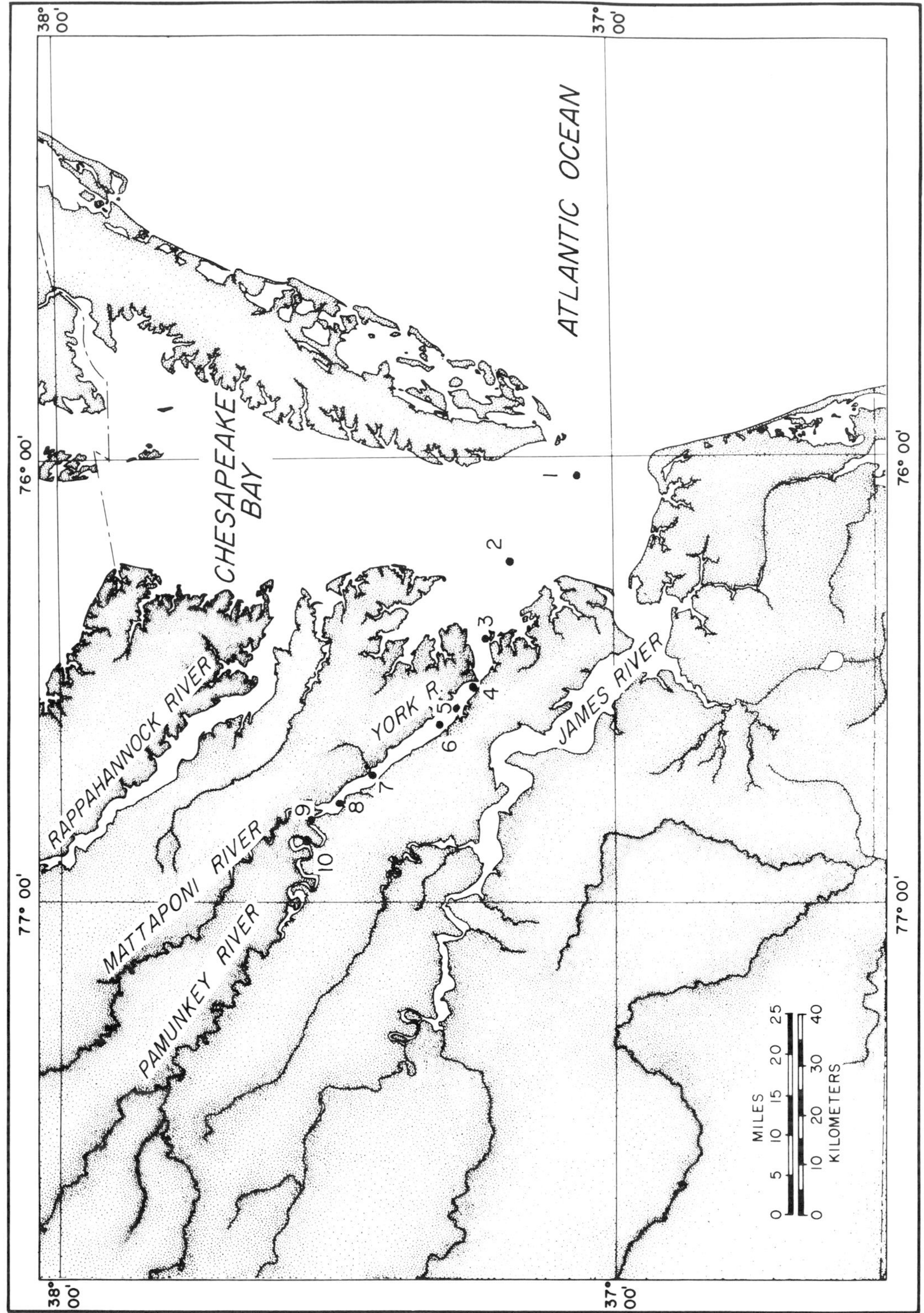

Fig. 1. Lower Chesapeake Bay showing location of the 10 sampling sites in the lower Bay and York and Pamunkey rivers.

in the Chesapeake-York estuary were in 8-10 m of water on the slopes of channels, and in the Brisbane estuary were in 2-6 m of water near shore. The deeper bottoms of the Brisbane estuary are current scoured and covered with coarse sand and gravel. In both cases a total of

Fig. 2. Variation in salinity for a 2 1/2 year period (1968-1970) along the Chesapeake-York estuarine gradient.

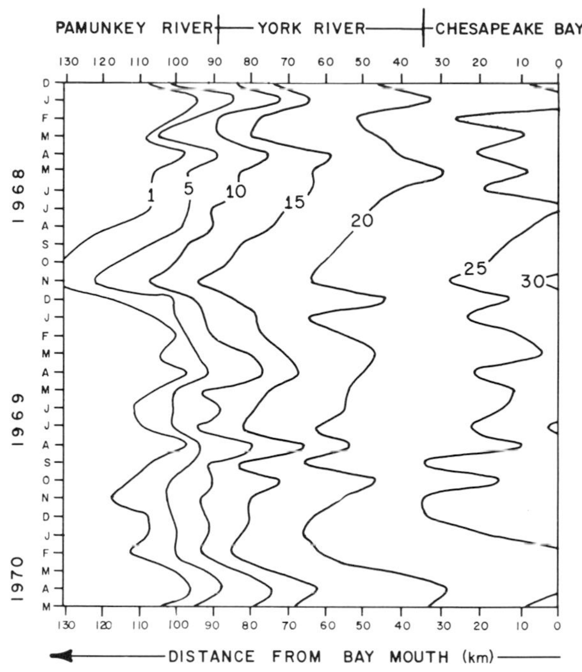

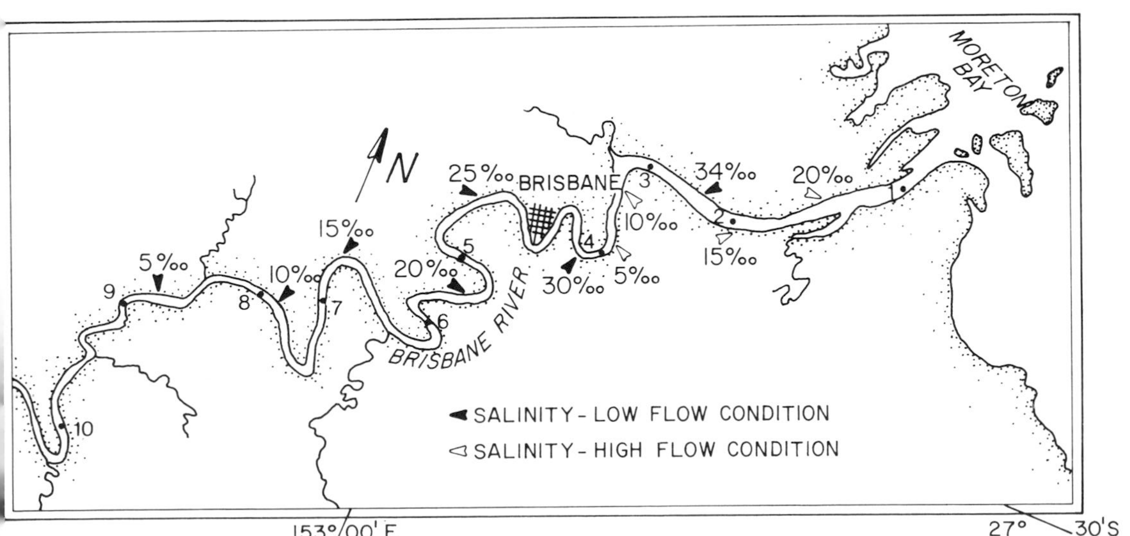

Fig. 3. Brisbane River estuary showing location of the 10 sampling sites and salinity distribution typical of low flow and high flow conditions.

0.2 m^2 of bottom was sampled at each site four times during one year.

Classification (cluster analysis) of sites along the estuarine gradient was rejected because it would impose divisions in the coenocline regardless of whether such divisions naturally exist. Similarly, ordination was rejected because recent analyses show that even model coenoclines are distorted by indirect ordination techniques (Whittaker and Gaugh 1973). The main method of analyzing biotic change along the gradients was coenocline similarity projection (CSP, Boesch in prep.) which is a modification of a technique used by Terborgh (1971) to study an avian coenocline along a montane gradient. This simple graphical technique projects a between-site similarity matrix as a series of curves plotted for sites ordered along an environmental gradient.

Qualitative (species presence or absence) similarity was measured in all species collected by the Sørensen coefficient

$$S_S = 2a/2a{+}b{+}c,$$

where a, b and c are the standard elements of the presence-absence contingency (Goodall 1973). Quantitative similarity was measured using the 75 "characteristic" (defined as having a minimum level of constancy at any one of the sites) species from the Chesapeake-York estuary and the 37 most frequent species from the Brisbane estuary collections using measure variously known as the Czekanowski or the Bray-Curtis coefficient,

$$S_c = 1 - \frac{\Sigma|x_i - y_i|}{\Sigma(x_i + y_i)},$$

where x_i and y_i are the log-transformed abundance values of the i th species in the two samples being compared (Goodall 1973).

Inverse classifications of all species were performed by Czekanowski similarity matrix computed for log-transformed abundance values (Chesapeake-York), or a Sørensen similarity matrix (Brisbane), and flexible sorting with the cluster intensity coefficient $\beta = -0.25$ (Lance and Williams 1967).

RESULTS

Chesapeake-York Estuary

Whether arranged on an abscissa of distance or salinity, the coenocline similarity projections (CSP's) show a gradual and continual change in assemblage along the estuarine complex-gradient (Fig. 4). The gradualness is evidenced by the lack of abrupt downward inflections in the individual similarity curves, which would indicate a sharp break or ecotone in the coenocline (Terborgh 1971), and the more or less parallel nature of the tails of the curves. The

Fig. 4. Coenocline similarity projections of quantitative similarity (S_c) along the Chesapeake-York estuarine gradient for August 1969, plotted on an abscissa of distance (a) and on an abscissa of salinity (b). Hypothetical intra-site similarity set at 0.8.

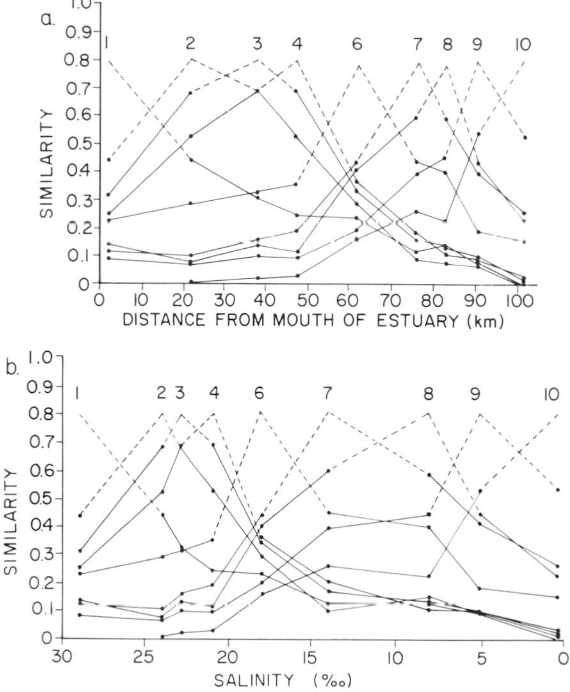

continuity is reflected in the virtual lack of crossing over of curves projecting in the same direction. Note, however, that the tails of curves for some proximal stations fall in a restricted envelope (e.g., the upestuary tails of curves for Stations 2, 3 and 4), but there may be a hiatus between the envelope and the curve for an adjacent station (e.g., upestuary tails of curves for Stations 4 and 6). This suggests an increased rate of change.

CSP's for the summer 1969 sampling are presented in Fig. 4. Only quantitative similarity (S_c) is shown, as qualitative similarity projections were very similar. The CSP's demonstrate that the rate of change in the benthic coenocline of the Chesapeake-York estuarine gradient is greater between Stations 1 and 2, Stations 4 and 6 (Station 5 was not sampled during this period), and Stations 8 and 9 than elsewhere. Faunal and sediment data indicate that biotic changes between Stations 1 and 2 are mainly the result of considerable differences in substrate; sediments at Station 1 were almost totally sand whereas sediments at the remaining stations were muddy. Most of the species collected at Station 1 are found at least into the lower York River on similar sandy substrates.

As further indication of rate of coenocline change, the average slopes of all projected similarity curves may be computed for each between-site interval. Whether expressed as change in similarity per unit distance or per unit salinity, the computed indices again indicate greatest change between Stations 4 and 6 and 8 and 9. Thus during the summer period the "faunal breaks" in the estuary coincide with salinity changes of 21-18 $^{o}/oo$ and 8-5 $^{o}/oo$, which is basically as indicated by the Venice System classification. It must be stressed, however, that these boundaries are in no way discontinuities. For example, although the biotic change between Stations 4 and 6 is relatively great, so is the change between Stations 6 and 7 (Fig. 4). The tails of the similarity projection for Station 6 are intermediate between curve envelopes of proximal upestuary and downestuary sites. Instead of a sharp break occurring at 18 $^{o}/oo$, the transition between polyhaline and mesohaline conditions occurred broadly between 21 and 14 $^{o}/oo$ (Stations 4 and 7).

Although the gradualness and continuity of the coenocline was apparent from CSP's for the other sampling periods, variations in the rates and zones of change did occur from season to season. For example, in spring 1970, when salinity was lowest throughout most of the estuary, quantitative similarity change appeared rather constant throughout the coenocline, although more pronounced changes in qualitative similarity did occur between Stations 2 and 3 and 6 and 7 (Fig. 5).

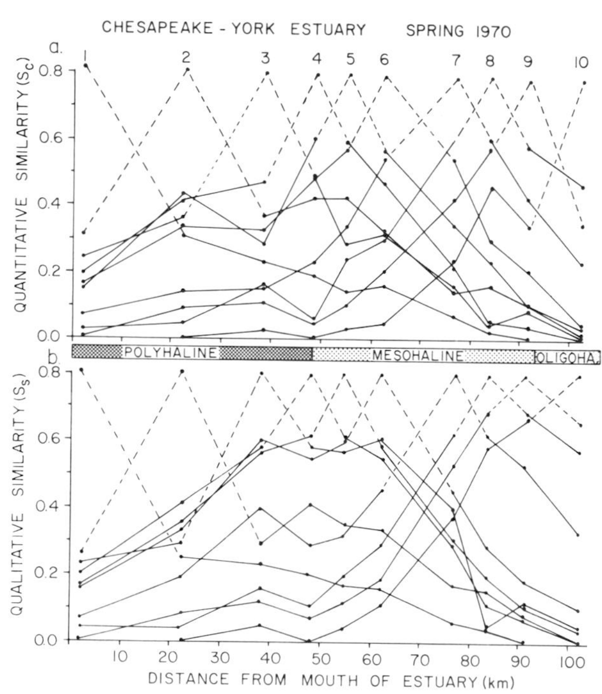

Fig. 5. Coenocline similarity projections of quantitative similarity (a) and qualitative similarity (b) along the Chesapeake-York estuarine gradient for May 1970. Hypothetical intra-site similarity set at 0.8.

The pivotal nature of the coenocline segment around Station 6 is demonstrated in Figure 6, in which the similarity projections for Station 6 are superimposed for each of the four sampling periods. The similarity curve can be skewed upestuary (e.g., quantitative similarity in winter), skewed downestuary (e.g., qualitative similarity in spring) or nearly symmetric (e.g., quantitative similarity in summer or spring). Complex dynamics of species recruitment and survival are the underlying causes of these variations. For example,

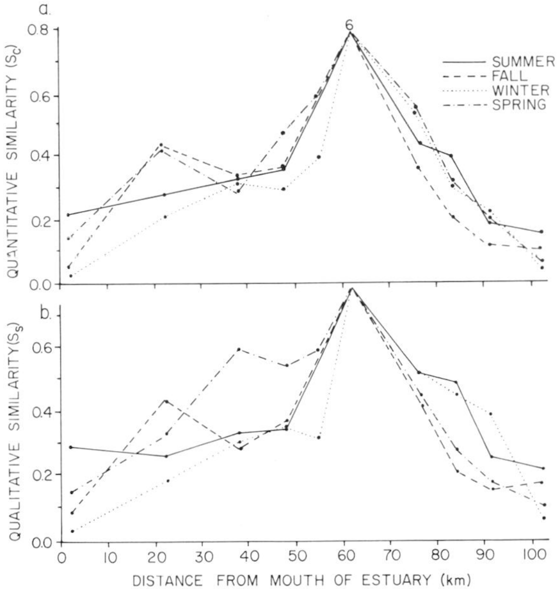

Fig. 6. Projected quantitative (a) and qualitative (b) similarities for Station 6 on the Chesapeake-York estuarine gradient for each of the four sampling periods.

recruitment, survival and dominance of "lower salinity" species and extinction of "higher salinity" species account for the shift in both quantitative and qualitative similarity upestuary from fall to winter. Recruitment of "higher salinity" species during spring, when reproductive dispersal of many species is more intense, caused a great shift in qualitative similarity downestuary but a lesser shift in quantitative similarity as "lower salinity" forms remained dominant.

Further insight can be gained by analysis of species distribution patterns along the estuarine complex-gradient. The classification based on the quantitative similarities of distribution of 75 characteristic species produced 18 species groups (Table 2). The distribution of species group constancy (Boesch 1973) over the ten sites is illustrated in Figure 7. Species groups with very high constancy at Station 1 (Groups 1, 2 and 3) are composed of psammophiles, most of which actually extend further than indicated along the estuarine gradient in suitable sandy substrates. The remaining species groups show a pattern of increasing penetration of the estuary, and thus increasing euryhalinity, to the point of ubiquity over all 10 sites (*Edotea triloba* and *Neomysis americana*, Species Group 16). Finally, two groups are composed almost entirely of "true estuarine" (Carriker 1967; Remane 1971) or estuarine endemic species which were not found downestuary of Station 6.

Many euryhaline marine species were not found above Station 5 or 6 (Fig. 7). Of the 192 species collected during this study, 52 found as far upestuary as Stations 4 or 5 were not found at Station 6, and 25 found as far upestuary as Station 6 were not found at Station 7. An inventory of collection records for nearly 400 species of non-colonial macrobenthos from the Chesapeake Bay (Wass 1972) also indicates that, although most of these species are found in the lower

Table 2. Species groups formed following classification of 75 "characteristic" species from the Chesapeake-York estuarine transect.

GROUP 1
- *Trichophoxus epistomus* (A)
- *Magelona papillicornis* (P)
- *Paranthus rapiformis* (An)
- *Aglaophamus verrilli* (P)
- *Nucula proxima* (B)

GROUP 2
- *Tellina agilis* (B)
- *Spiophanes bombyx* (P)
- *Owenia fusiformis* (P)

GROUP 3
- *Ampelisca verrilli* (A)
- *Clymenella zonalis* (P)

GROUP 4
- *Glycera dibranchiata* (P)
- *Macoma tenta* (B)
- *Turbonilla interrupta* (G)
- *Acteon punctostriatus* (G)

GROUP 5
- *Nephtys magellanica* (P)
- *Ampelisca vadorum* (A)
- *Melinna maculata* (P)
- *Spiochaetopterus oculatus* (P)

GROUP 6
- *Corophium acherusicum* (A)
- *Anadara transversa* (B)
- *Glycera americana* (P)

GROUP 7
- *Ensis directus* (B)
- *Mitrella lunata* (G)
- *Lepidonotus sublevis* (P)
- *Polydora ligni* (P)

GROUP 8
- *Asabellides oculata* (P)
- *Mytilus edulis* (B)

GROUP 9
- *Tubulanus pellucidus* (N)
- *Diopatra cuprea* (P)
- *Batea catharinensis* (A)

GROUP 10
- *Nassarius vibex* (G)
- *Mulinia lateralis* (B)
- *Sigambra tentaculata* (P)

GROUP 11
- *Nephtys incisa* (P)
- *Pseudeurythoe* sp. (P)
- *Heteromastus filiformis* (P)
- *Acteocina canaliculata* (G)
- *Phoronis* spp.

GROUP 12
- *Micropholis atra* (Op)
- *Tharyx setigera* (P)
- *Cirriformia grandis* (P)
- *Harmothoe* sp. A (P)

GROUP 13
- *Edwardsia elegans* (An)
- *Ceriantheopsis americanus* (An)
- *Palaeonotus heteroseta* (P)
- *Clymenella torquata* (P)
- *Pectinaria gouldii* (P)
- *Loimia medusa* (P)
- *Cerapus tubularis* (A)
- *Listriella clymenellae* (A)
- *Ancistrosyllis jonesi* (P)
- *Sarsiella zostericola* (Os)

GROUP 14
- *Ogyrides limicola* (D)
- *Ampelisca abdita* (A)
- *Scoloplos fragilis* (P)
- *Eteone heteropoda* (P)
- *Peloscolex gabriellae* (Ol)

GROUP 15
- *Paraprionospio pinnata* (P)
- *Glycinde solitaria* (P)
- *Streblospio benedicti* (P)
- *Leucon americanus* (C)
- *Nereis succinea* (P)

GROUP 16
- *Edotea triloba* (I)
- *Neomysis americana* (M)

GROUP 17
- *Corophium lacustre* (A)
- *Gammarus daiberi* (A)
- *Peloscolex* sp. C (Ol)
- *Cyathura polita* (I)
- *Chiridotea almyra* (I)

GROUP 18
- Nemertean A
- *Scolecolepides viridis* (P)
- *Monoculodes edwardsii* (A)
- *Macoma mitchelli* (B)
- *Macoma balthica* (B)
- *Peloscolex heterochaetus* (Ol)

A=amphipod; An=anthozoan; B=bivalve; C=cumacean; D=decapod crustacean; G=gastropod; I=isopod; M=mysid; N=nemertean; Ol=oligochaete; Op= ophuroid; Os=ostracod; P=polychaete.

Fig. 7. Distribution and average constancy at each station of species groups from Chesapeake-York estuary (Table 2).

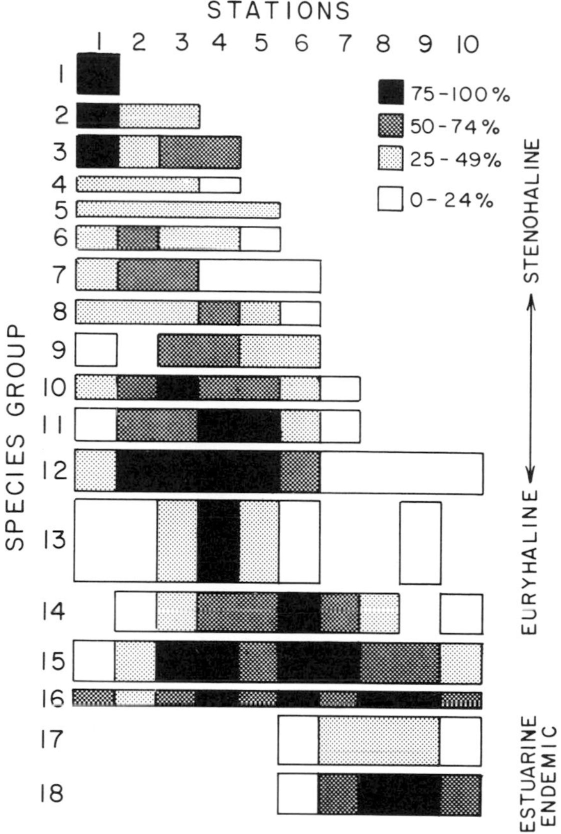

York estuary 40-50 km from the Bay mouth, a large portion has not been found more than 60-70 km from the Bay mouth. This attenuation in species richness of the benthic fauna in this segment of the estuary is also apparent in the drop-off of within-habitat species diversity (Boesch 1972, 1974).

Large changes occur in the typically dominant species in this transition from "polyhaline" to "mesohaline" conditions. The dominant species at Stations 2 to 5 were marine species which are mildly to moderately euryhaline and mostly members of Species Groups 11 and 12. Although several of these species were also abundant at Station 6, moderately to strongly euryhaline species (mostly members of Species Groups 14 and 15), which were not particularly abundant downestuary, dominanted at Stations 6 and 7. These "euryhaline opportunists" are characteristically abundant in salinities of 10-20 $^{o}/oo$ throughout the Chesapeake Bay system but are usually not as abundant in higher salinities, except in shallow water habitats or following disturbances. The euryhaline opportunists are mostly annelids (the polychaetes, *Nereis succinea*, *Eteone heteropoda*, *Glycinde solitaria*, *Heteromastus filiformis*, *Scoloplos fragilis*, *Paraprionospio pinnata*, and *Streblospio benedicti*, and the oligochaete, *Peloscolex gabriellae*) and include several well-known opportunistic species (Grassle and Grassle 1974). Estuarine endemic species become numerically important at Station 7 and are virtually the only dominants at Stations 9 and 10.

Brisbane Estuary

The CSP for qualitative similarity (all sampling periods combined) along the benthic coenocline of the Brisbane estuary (Fig. 8b) also shows continual and gradual change. Zones of more accelerated change were found between Stations 1 and 2, and to a lesser

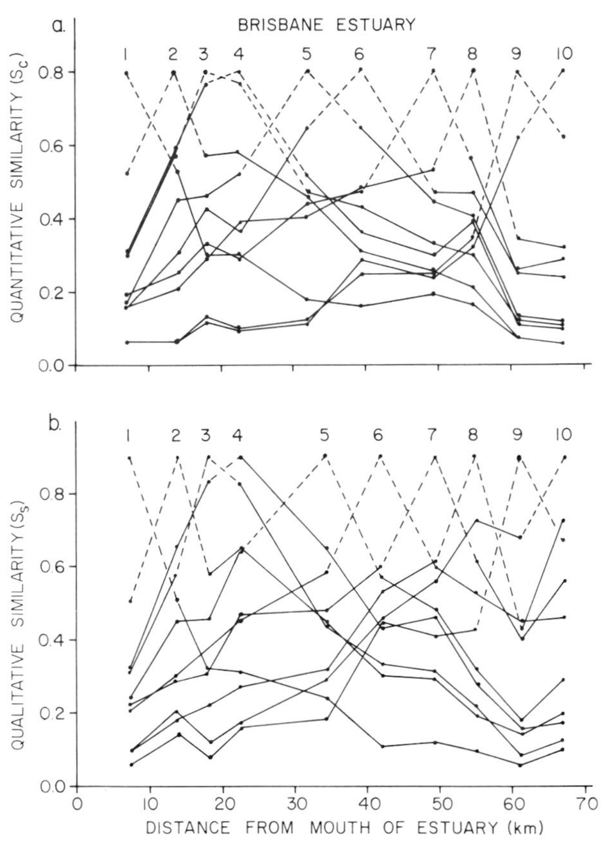

Fig. 8. Coenocline similarity projections of qualitative similarity for all sampling periods combined (b) and quantitative similarity for May 1972 (a) along the Brisbane estuarine gradient. Hypothetical intrasite similarity set at 0.8 in (a) and 0.9 in (b).

degree between Stations 5 and 6. The apparent reversal in the coenocline between Stations 9 and 10 (i.e., Station 10 has greater down-estuary similarities than Station 9) is due to the low species richness and reduced sampling effort at Station 9. The CSP for quantitative similarity shows a somewhat different pattern as exemplified by the May (fall) 1972 sampling (Fig. 8a). Although a major change is likewise evident between Stations 1 and 2, an equally large change is indicated between Stations 8 and 9. Somewhat accelerated change is also suggested between Stations 4 and 5.

The segment of greatest coenoclinal change along this estuarine gradient occurred in the lower reaches of the estuary where salinities were above 34 $^{o}/oo$ for most of the year. The difference in salinity between Station 1 and Station 2 was most often less than 1 $^{o}/oo$. However the high river discharge experienced during January 1972 lowered the salinity at Station 2 to 20 $^{o}/oo$ while the salinity at Station 1 remained 25-30 $^{o}/oo$. Heavy rainfall and flooding in the drainage basin of the Brisbane River due to the passage of a cyclone in February 1972 reduced the salinity in the lower reaches of the estuary even more. Surface salinities were nearly zero at low tide, but salinities at the 4-6 m depths at which the sampled bottoms were located remained above 10 and 15 $^{o}/oo$ at Stations 2 and 1, respectively. Although the substrate at Station 1 was somewhat sandier than at the other stations, and undoubtedly accounted for some of the faunal differences, additional sampling on a variety of substrates suggests the accelerated coenoclinal change between Stations 1 and 2 is mainly a response to the estuarine (salinity) complex-gradient. A large portion (58%) of those species recorded from Station 1 were not found as far upestuary as Station 2, and the attenuation of within-habitat species diversity and richness is greatest in this zone (Boesch 1974).

The second zone of accelerated change occurred between Stations 4 and 6. Overall qualitative change was greater between Stations 5 and 6 because several euryhaline species abundant downestuary were occasionally found at Station 5 (see below); but quantitative change was greatest between Stations 4 and 5 because these euryhaline marine forms were never abundant at Station 5. This zone of change is coincident with a salinity change of 30-18 $^{o}/oo$ during low flow conditions, but experiences salinities below 5 $^{o}/oo$ during high flow conditions.

The third zone of accelerated change occurred between Stations 8 and 9 and marks a transition to high constancy and dominance of freshwater species, although several estuarine species were common at Stations 9 and 10. During the study period the salinity did not exceed 2 $^{o}/oo$ above Station 9. Several estuarine benthic species (peracarid crustaceans in particular) were found virtually to the limit of tidal influence, almost 20 km above Station 10, and actually above the limit of tidal influence in some of the tributaries. Bayly (1965) has commented on the high chloride ion content (brought through the atmosphere from the sea) of the freshwater runoff in the Brisbane drainage basin which apparently allows deep penetration of the estuary by some species.

Despite the extreme seasonal poikilohalinity of the Brisbane estuary, the basic patterns described above remained relatively constant throughout the study period. Sampling just after the flood in February 1972 showed the displacement of a few euryhaline species from Station 3 and 4, but considering the magnitude of the salinity reduction and the increased current velocities that accompanied it, the flood had surprisingly little impact on the macrobenthos of the estuary. This is in marked contrast to the pattern described by Sandison and Hill (1966) for Lagos Lagoon in West Africa, where monsoonal freshening of an estuary caused decimation of attached epifauna, only to be followed by extensive repopulation when salinity escalated again. On the other hand, Hailstone (1972) detected a substantial effect of an earlier flood on macrobenthos at the mouth of the Brisbane River below Station 1.

Analysis of the distribution of the 37 species classifed (Table 3, Fig. 9) helps in explaining the pattern of coenocline change just described. Species in Group 1 were restricted to Station 1 (as were a number of those less frequent species not classified). There continues a transition in species penetrating increasingly farther into the estuary as far as Station 5; furthermore, a number of very

Table 3. Species groups formed following classification of 37 most frequent species from the Brisbane estuarine transect.

GROUP 1
- *Phyllodoce malmgreni* (P)
- *Sigambra parva* (P)
- *Diopatra dentata* (P)
- *Lumbrineris latreilli* (P)
- *Magelona* sp. (P)

GROUP 2
- *Peloscolex* sp. (O)
- *Armandia lanceolata* (P)
- **Owenia fusiformis* (P)
- **Barantolla lepte* (P)
- *Spio* sp. (P)
- *Parcanassa ellana* (G)
- *Myadora* sp. (B)

GROUP 3
- Nemertean (salmon)
- *Polydora* sp. (P)

GROUP 4
- **Prionospio* sp. (P)
- **Laonome* sp. (P)
- *Phoronopsis albomaculata* (Ph)
- **Notospisula trigonella* (B)
- *Soletellina donacioides* (B)
- *Macoma* sp. (B)
- **Eriopisa australiensis* (A)

GROUP 5
- **Boccardia* sp. (P)
- **Grandidierella* sp. (A)
- *Rhopalophthalmus brisbanensis* (M)

GROUP 6
- Tubificid A (O)
- **Ceratonereis erythraeensis* (P)
- **Marphysa sanguinea* (P)
- **Notomastus* sp. (P)
- *Exosphaeroma* sp. (I)
- *Brachyambylopus* sp. (F)

GROUP 7
- **Apseudes estuarius* (T)

GROUP 8
- *Geoloina coaxans* (B)
- *Gastrosaccus dakini* (M)
- *Cyathura* sp. (I)
- *Melita* sp. (A)
- *Corophium* sp. (A)
- *Leme mordax* (F)

GROUP 9
- **Limnodrilus hofmeisteri* (O)
- **Branchiura sowerbyi* (O)
- **Corbiculina* sp. (B)
- *Plotiopsis* spp.
- Tendepedid A. (D)

*Dominant species; A=amphipod; B=bivalve; D=dipteran; F=fish; G=gastropod; I=isopod; M=mysid; O=oligochaete; P=polychaete; Ph=phoronid; T=tanaid.

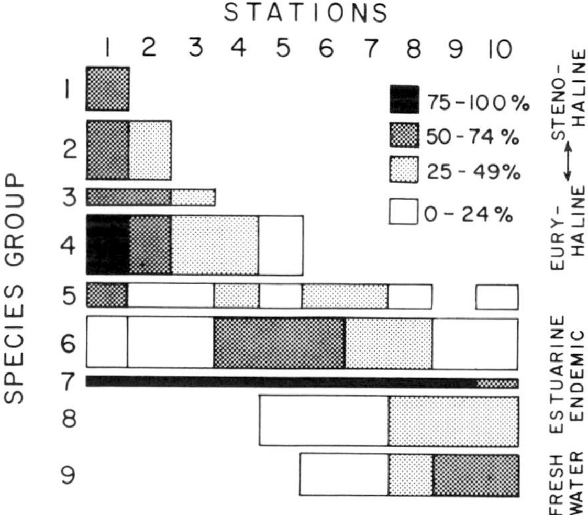

Fig. 9. Distribution and average constancy at each station of species groups from Brisbane estuary (Table 3).

euryhaline marine species and estuarine endemics occurred throughout the estuary. Finally, several estuarine endemic (Species Group 8) and freshwater species were restricted to the upper reaches of the estuary.

The tanaid, *Apseudes estuarius*, is an estuarine endemic which was a dominant (overwhelmingly so in the middle reaches) throughout the portion of the estuary studied, although it apparently was not taken by Hailstone (1972) who sampled just downestuary from Station 1. The other dominants in the lower estuary are primarily members of Species Group 4 and were found abundantly upestuary to Station 4. These species may be best considered as analogs of the euryhaline opportunists discussed for the Chesapeake estuary because they are apparently rather uncommon and only sporadically abundant in Moreton Bay (Hailstone 1972; Stephenson et al. 1974; Raphael 1974). Several estuarine endemic species (members of Species Groups 5 and 6) were also abundant at the lower estuary sites but these were most characteristic of the region between Sites 4 and 8. Freshwater species, chiefly tubificid oligochaetes, were dominant at Stations 9 and 10.

DISCUSSION

Comparison of Chesapeake Bay and Brisbane Estuary

Interesting differences and similarities exist between the macrobenthic coenoclines of the Chesapeake-York and Brisbane estuaries. The differences are mainly attributable to the relative homoiohalinity of the former and poikilohalinity of the latter, although I must advance the qualification that important differences exist in the geomorphology, sedimentology, hydrography, anthropogenic modification and biogeography of the two estuaries.

The Chesapeake Bay is large and relatively homoiohaline, much like those brackish water bodies in northwestern Europe for which estuarine classification schemes were developed. The macrobenthic coenocline of the Chesapeake estuary is gradual and relatively constant. Zones of somewhat accelerated change occur in the 20-15 °/oo range and in the 8-3 °/oo range, and these need not be coincident with geomorphological changes as suggested by Wolff (1973) for estuaries in the Dutch Delta. This suggests that there may be some objective basis for classification of segments of relatively homoiohaline estuaries and that the Venice System may extrapolate well to large eastern North American estuaries. It must be remembered, however, that the boundaries of the estuarine "zones" are not sharp but are themselves broad zones of accelerated change superimposed on a gradient of continuous change.

The benthic coenocline of the Brisbane estuary appears to be controlled by the boundary condition of seasonally minimum salinity, rather than by average conditions. The coenocline change in the Brisbane estuary is much more abrupt than in the Chesapeake Bay and the benthic habitats throughout most of the estuary are inhabited by estuarine endemic forms. Thus the zonation patterns along the estuarine gradient do not relate in any meaningful way to existing estuarine classification schemes such as the Venice System. Designation of portions of the estuary as polyhaline, mesohaline, oligohaline, etc., seems futile.

Unfortunately, my work in the Chesapeake Bay and Brisbane River sheds little light on zonation patterns at the marine (euhaline) end of the estuarine spectrum because overwhelming changes in sediment habitats occur at the mouths of both estuaries. Such a habitat transition to inner continental shelf conditions is a common feature of many estuaries (e.g., the Delta of Holland, Wolff 1973) and may itself be an important criterion in classificatory segmentation of particular estuarine systems.

Similarities can be found between the two estuaries in terms of classes of species distribution patterns. Both estuaries have what can be termed euryhaline marine species, euryhaline opportunists, and estuarine endemics, although here, too, we run the risk of arbitrary classification of a continuum of distribution patterns. A general model of estuarine zonation can be developed on the basis of these species distributional classes (Fig. 10). In a homoiohaline estuary the dominant and characteristic species of macrobenthos progress from stenohaline marine species on the continental shelf to a diverse assemblage of euryhaline marine species in the lower reaches of the estuary. Many of the euryhaline species, although they are

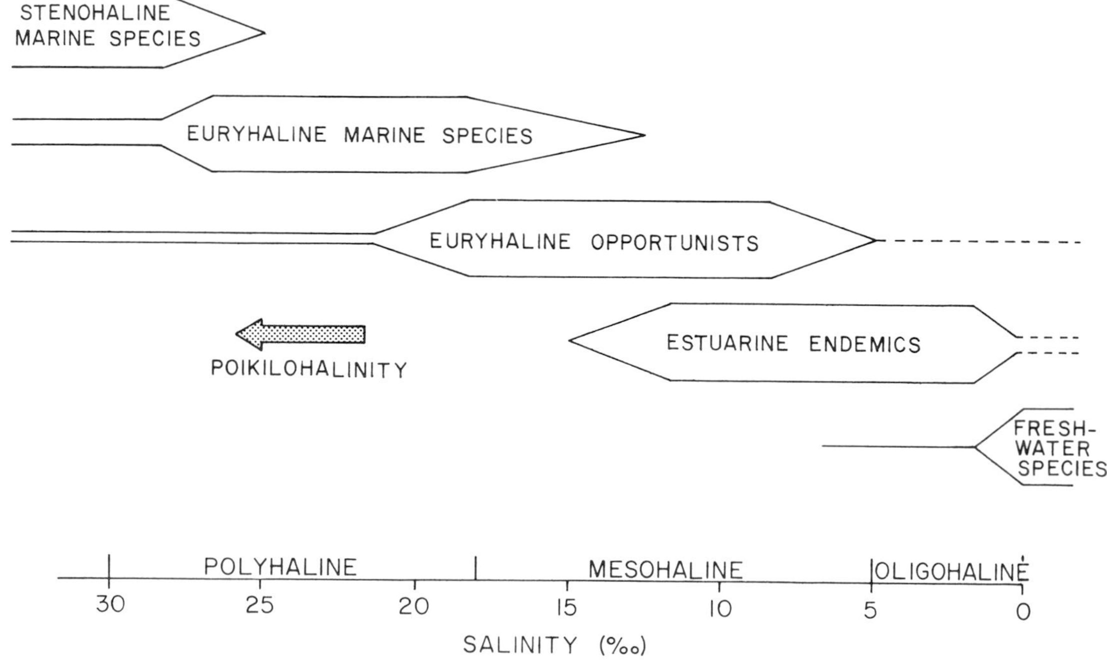

Fig. 10. Schema of the distributional classes of species in a homeohaline estuary.

known from fully marine habitats, are much more common and abundant in the lower estuary. These species tend to be "equilibrium" species (Grassle and Grassle 1974) relative to the opportunistic species dominant in lower salinity zones. The coenocline further grades into domination by opportunistic euryhaline species and estuarine endemics broadly around a salinity of 18 °/oo. The euryhaline opportunists decline in importance and number upestuary as their salinity tolerance limits are reached and give way, broadly at a salinity of 5 °/oo, to virtually complete domination by estuarine endemics. The estuarine endemics decline in numbers and importance entering tidal fresh water, but may remain important in freshwater areas which periodically experience brackish water conditions. The effect of poikilohalinity is to displace the "equilibrium" euryhaline species as well as the opportunistic euryhaline species downestuary, allowing the domination of much of the estuary by estuarine endemic forms.

Comparison with Other Estuaries

Comparison of my results with those of the many other studies of estuarine zonation is encumbered by the lack of published data to which similar methods of analysis can be applied. An interesting comparison can be made with a study by Sanders et al. (1965) of the small tidally poikilohaline estuary of the Pocasset River in New England. Projections for quantitative and qualitative similarity using the same methods of analysis as this study are given in Figure 11. Quantitatively, the coenocline is very gradual from the mouth of the estuary to Station 5, followed by a much more accelerated change from Station 4 to the head of the estuary at Station 1. Qualitatively, the coenocline is also very gradual to Station 5 but is accelerated between Stations 3 and 4 and Stations 1 and 2. Sanders et al. pointed out an abrupt faunal break at about Station 3 and while this site is

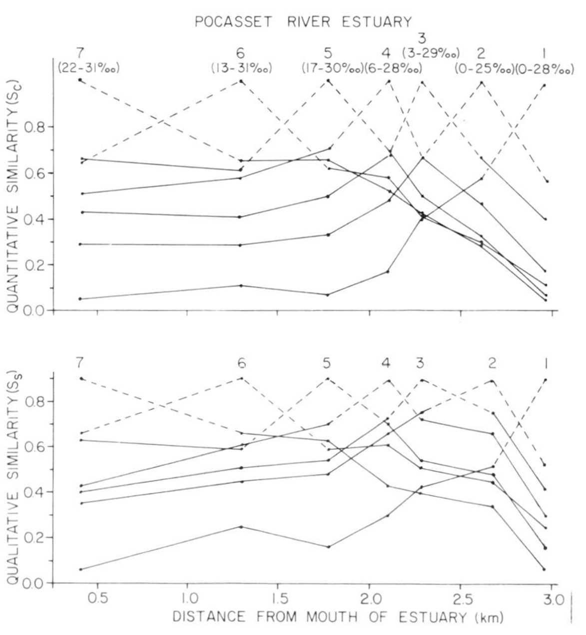

Fig. 11. Coenocline similarity projections of quantitative similarity (a) and qualitative similarity (b) along the Pocasset River estuarine gradient based on the data of Sanders et al. (1965). Hypothetical intra-site similarity set at 0.8.

certainly located in a zone of rapid change, the "transition zone" of the estuary appears much broader than they suggest. The transition is one of declining numbers and importance of euryhaline marine species versus an increase in estuarine endemic species. Euryhaline opportunists dominate the lower portion of this shallow estuary and are important from Station 3 downestuary. Estuarine endemic forms are important from Station 3 upestuary. As Sanders et al. demonstrated, the interstitial salinity, which is relatively homoiohaline, is more important in determining the distribution of many species than is salinity of the overlying water, which varies greatly during a tidal cycle. They pointed out that sediment salinities in the transition region varied from 19-22 ^{o}/oo. Furthermore, minimum bottom water salinity at the start of the accelerated transition at Station 5 was 17 ^{o}/oo, whereas at Station 4 minimum salinity was 6 ^{o}/oo.

Wolff's (1973) evaluation of the application of estuarine classification to the macrobenthos of the relatively homoiohaline estuarine area of the Rhine, Meuse and Scheldt rivers has already been mentioned. Basically, he found a continuum of faunal change along estuarine gradients, except where geomorphological changes in the estuary resulted in variable hydrographic conditions (i.e., increased poikilohalinity). Wolff concluded that there are no discontinuities in the species-salinity curve and that a classification of brackish waters cannot be based on the fauna, because "the fauna does not behave as an entity in its reactions to salinity".

In contrast, Riemann (1966) found pronounced changes in the meiobenthos of the Elbe estuary from the polyhaline zone to the mesohaline zone, although the transition from the mesohaline zone to the oligohaline zone was not as well defined. However the border between the polyhaline and mesohaline zones lies at the mouth of the Elbe, where changes in geomorphology and poikilohalinity also occur. The Sacramento-San Joaquin estuary of the San Francisco Bay system is tidally homoiohaline and its seasonal poikilohalinity is intermediate between that of the Chesapeake Bay and the Brisbane River. Painter (1966) described a faunal break in the eastern Carquinez Strait where the salinity ranged from 5-15 ^{o}/oo, but it is difficult to apply a Venice System classification to this estuarine coenocline. However, the biota of the extensive low salinity zones of Suisun Bay and the Delta is very similar to that of the oligohaline zones of Chesapeake Bay, the Baltic and other large estuarine systems.

The many small British estuaries which have been studied tend to be tidally poikilohaline (see Boyden and Little 1973). Although they vary slightly in degree of penetration of euryhaline marine forms and other characteristics, these estuarine coenoclines resemble that of the Pocasset River in many respects. In the tidally poikilohaline estuary of the Heathcote River in New Zealand, Estcourt (1967) found an abrupt transition from dominance by euryhaline marine polychaetes to estuarine endemic polychaetes of the genera *Scolecolepides* and *Nicon*. Application of the Venice System classification to tidally poikilohaline estuaries does not seem meaningful.

Causes of Zonation of The Estuarine Coenocline

In general, the upestuary limits of marine and estuarine organisms are set by tolerance of low salinity. Similarly, the downestuary limits of freshwater species are generally set by tolerance of high salinity. In addition to salinity tolerance of adult individuals, larval and juvenile tolerances and the effect of salinity on reproduction may also determine distributional limits along the estuarine coenocline. The physiological implications of tolerance of reduced and fluctuating salinity have been extensively reviewed by Kinne (1971) and Schlieper (1971).

The factors affecting the downestuary distribution of euryhaline marine and estuarine endemic species are not as well understood. Euryhaline opportunistic species which dominate in the mesohaline reaches of the Chesapeake Bay are only sporadically abundant in the deeper bottoms of the polyhaline zone. They are abundant in shallow water polyhaline habitats and in deeper habitats which have been disturbed by low oxygen conditions, dredging or toxic pollution (Boesch 1973). A similar pattern of restriction of euryhaline opportunistic species to intertidal or shallow water habitats (which tend to be more poikilohaline) under polyhaline conditions have been shown by Wolff (1973), e.g., *Nereis diversicolor*, and Painter (1966), e.g., *Streblospio benedicti*. Euryhaline opportunists have many of the characteristics of opportunistic species listed by Grassle and Grassle (1974) and are apparently disfavored in "equilibrium" polyhaline habitats by biotic interaction.

The distribution of estuarine endemic species presents somewhat of an enigma for they are very rarely found in salinities which remain above 15 $^{o}/oo$ in homoiohaline brackish waters. Probability dictates that if they were excluded from higher salinity zones by pressures of competition or predation, they would have been collected more often than they have been in the course of our intensive and long-term sampling of the polyhaline York River. On the other hand, most estuarine endemic or "true estuarine" species are known to be able to survive for long periods in high salinity. The work of Cain (1972) on reproduction and development of *Rangia cuneata*, a mactrid bivalve generally not found in salinities above 15 $^{o}/oo$, provides some provocative insight into mechanisms which might be restricting the distribution of estuarine endemics. Cain found that a change of salinity either up from 0 $^{o}/oo$ or down from 10-15 $^{o}/oo$ was necessary to induce spawning in *Rangia*, and that embryos and early larvae survive only in salinities between 2 and 10 $^{o}/oo$. It is apparent that the distributional limits of estuarine endemic species are maintained through behavioral and physiological adaptations, evolved to assure maintenance of estuarine populations, coupled with biological exclusion downestuary.

In many respects the estuarine coenocline is an analog of the intertidal coenocline of rocky shores where biotic interactions have been well studied (Connell 1972). Biotic interactions largely set lower (downestuary) distributional limits and physiological tolerances set upper limits along both coenoclines. Both habitat gradients are characterized by many opportunistic species adapted to exploit space and resources following disturbances. Specialized organisms physiologically adapted to mitigate stress--but at the expense of competitive advantage--and displaying behavioral mechanisms which enhance repopulation have evolved to occupy the extremes of the gradients, the high intertidal and the low salinity zones. Manipulative field experiments, employed so successfully in intertidal ecology, offer promise of elucidating the complex interplay of physiological tolerance and biotic interaction which result in the distribution patterns observed in estuaries.

REFERENCES

Bagge, P. 1969. Effects of pollution on estuarine ecosystems. II. The succession of the bottom fauna communities in polluted estuarine habitats in the Baltic-Skagerak region. Merentutkimus lait. Julk. Havsforskningsinst. Skr. 228: 119-130.

Bayly, I. A. E. 1965. Ecological studies on the planktonic Copepoda of the Brisbane River estuary with special reference to *Gladioferens pectinatus* (Brady) (Calanoida). Aust. J. Mar. Freshw. Res. 16: 315-350.

Boesch, D. F. 1972. Species diversity of marine macrobenthos in the Virginia area. Chesapeake Sci. 13: 206-211.

_____. 1973. Classification and community structure of macrobenthos in the Hampton Roads area, Virginia. Mar. Biol. 21: 226-244.

_____. 1974. Diversity, stability and response to human disturbance in estuarine ecosystems, p. 109-114. In Proc. First Intern. Congr. Ecol. Pudoc, Wageningen, The Netherlands.

Boyden, C. R. and C. Little. 1973. Faunal distributions in soft sediments of the Severn estuary. Estuar. Coast. Mar. Sci. 1: 203-223.

Burbanck, W. D., M. E. Pierce, and G. C. Whiteley, Jr. 1956. A study of the bottom fauna of Rand's Harbor, Massachusetts: an application of the ecotone concept. Ecol. Monogr. 26: 213-243.

Cain, T. D. 1972. The reproductive cycle and larval tolerances of *Rangia cuneata* in the James River, Virginia. Unpublished Ph.D. thesis, Univ. Virginia, Charlottesville. 120 p.

Carriker, M. R. 1967. Ecology of estuarine benthic invertebrates: a perspective, p. 442-487. In G. H. Lauff [ed.], Estuaries. American Association for the Advancement of Science Publ. 83.

Caspers, H. 1959. Die Einteilung der Brackwasser-Regionen in einem Ästuar. Archo. Oceanogr. Limnol. 11 (Suppl.): 153-169.

Connell, J. H. 1972. Community interactions on marine rocky intertidal shores. Ann. Rev. Ecol. Syst. 3: 169-192.

Day, J. H. 1964. The origin and distribution of estuarine animals in South Africa. Monogr. Biol. 14: 159-173.

Den Hartog, C. 1971. The border environment between the sea and the freshwater, with special reference to the estuary. Vie et Milieu, Suppl. 22: 739-750.

Estcourt, I. N. 1967. Ecology of benthic polychaetes in the Heathcote estuary, New Zealand. New Zealand J. Mar. Freshwat. Res. 1: 381-394.

Goodall, D. W. 1973. Sample similarity and species correlation, p. 105-115. In R. H. Whittaker [ed.], Ordination and classification of communities. Junk, The Hague.

Grassle, J. F. and J. P. Grassle. 1974. Opportunistic life histories and genetic systems in marine benthic polychaetes. J. Mar. Res. 32: 253-284.

Hailstone, T. S. 1972. Ecological studies of the subtidal benthic macrofauna at the mouth of the Brisbane River. Unpublished Ph.D. thesis, Univ. Queensland, Brisbane, Australia.

Kelley, D. W. 1966. Ecological studies of the Sacramento-San Jaoquin estuary. Description of the Sacramento-San Jaoquin estuary. Fish. Bull. Calif. Dep. Fish Game 133: 8-17.

Kinne, O. 1971. Salinity. Invertebrates, p. 800-995. In O.Kinne [ed.], Marine Ecology, v. I, Part 2. Wiley-Interscience.

Lance, G. N. and W. T. Williams. 1967. A general theory of classificatory sortin strategies. I. Hierarchical Systems. Comput. J. 9: 373-380.

Muus, B. J. 1967. The fauna of Danish estuaries and lagoons. Distribution and ecology of dominating species in the shallow reaches of the mesohaline zone. Medd. Danmarks Fish. Havundersøg., (n.ser.) 5: 1-316.

Painter, R. E. 1966. Ecological studies of the Sacramento-San Joaquin estuary. Zoobenthos of San Pablo and Suisun Bays. Fish. Bull. Calif. Dep. Fish Game 133: 40-56.

Raphael, Y. I. 1974. The macrofauna of Bramble Bay, Moreton Bay, Queensland. Unpublished M. Sc. thesis, Univ Queensland, Brisbane, Australia.

Remane, A. 1971. Ecology of brackish water. Die Binnengewasser 25: 1-210.

Riemann, F. 1966. Die interstitielle Fauna in Elbe-Aestuar. Verbreitungund Systematik. Arch. Hydrobiol. 31 (Suppl. Elbe-Aest., 3): 1-279.

Sanders, H. L., P. C. Mangelsdorf, Jr., and G. R. Hampson. 1965. Salinity and faunal distribution in the Pocasset River, Massachusetts. Limnol. Oceanogr. 10 (Suppl.): R216-R226.

Sandison, E. E. and M. B. Hill. 1966. The distribution of *Balanus pallidus stutsburi* Darwin, *Gryphaea gascar* [(Adanson) Pautzenberg], *Mercierella enigmatica* Fauvel and *Hydroides uncinata* (Philippi) in relation to salinity in Lagos Harbor and adjacent creeks. J. Anim. Ecol. 35: 235-250.

Schlieper, C. 1971. Physiology of brackish water. Die Binnengewasser 25: 211-350.

Segerstraale, S. G. 1959. Brackish water classification, a historical survey. Archo. Oceanogr. Limnol. 11(Suppl.): 7-33.

Stephenson, W. 1968. The effects of a flood upon salinities in the southern portion of Moreton Bay. Proc. Roy. Soc. Queensland 80: 19-34.

Stephenson, W., W. T. Williams, and S. D. Cook. 1974. The benthic fauna of soft bottoms, southern Moreton Bay. Mem. Qld. Mus. 17: 73-124.

Symposium on the Classification of Brackish Waters. 1958. The Venic System for the classification of marine waters according to salinity. Oikos 9: 311-312.

Tenore, K. R. 1972. Macrobenthos of the Pamlico River estuary, North Carolina. Ecol. Monogr. 42: 51-69.

Terborgh, J. 1971. Distribution on environmental gradients: Theory and a preliminary interpretation of distributional patterns in the avifauna of the Cordillera Viacabamba, Peru. Ecology 52: 23-40.

Wass, M. L. 1972. A checklist of the biota of lower Chesapeake Bay. Virginia Inst. Mar. Sci. Spec. Sci. Rept. 65, 290 p.

Whittaker, R. H. 1967. Gradient analysis of vegetation. Biol. Rev. 42: 207-264.

Whittaker, R. H. and H. G. Gaugh, Jr. 1973. Evaluation of ordination techniques, p. 289-321. In R. H. Whittaker [ed.], Ordination and Classification of Communities. Junk, The Hague.

Wolff, W. J. 1973. The estuary as a habitat. An analysis of data on the soft bottom macrofauna of the estuarine area of the Rivers Rhine Meuse, and Scheldt. Zool. Verhandel. 126: 1-243.

A Benthic Food Budget for the Grevelingen Estuary, The Netherlands, and a Consideration of the Mechanisms Causing High Benthic Secondary Production in Estuaries

W. J. Wolff
Netherlands Institute for Sea Research
P. O. Box 59
Texel, The Netherlands

ABSTRACT

An annual food budget for the zoobenthos of a tidal estuary of 140 km^2 in The Netherlands is constructed. Although this budget is partly based on several questionable assumptions, the following observations seem reliable. Primary production *in situ* and import of organic detritus from the coastal sea appear to be the most important food sources. Detritus imported from salt marshes or other terrestrial systems is relatively unimportant.

This type of food budget, which also has been found in the Dutch Wadden Sea, is very different from the benthic food budgets of American estuaries where the benthos depend primarily on salt marsh or mangrove detritus and primary production *in situ*.

The mechanisms causing high benthic secondary production in estuaries are reviewed and categorized into three types (1) those in which the supply of dissolved nutrients from various sources causes high primary production; (2) those with supply of particulate organic matter from various sources to estuarine waters; and (3) those in which the shallow nature of the estuary causes rapid sinking of particulate organic matter, as well as rapid transport of particulate organic matter by turbulent diffusion.

INTRODUCTION

Estuaries are well known for their high benthic secondary production, and throughout the world they sustain important shell-fish cultures and fisheries. Their high benthic production is also reflected in the role estuaries play as nursery grounds for juvenile fishes and other nektonts, and in the multitude of shorebirds that feed in these areas.

The high benthic production of estuaries has been attributed to a number of food sources, primarily detritus from various macrophytes (Schelske and Odum 1961; Odum 1971; De la Cruz 1973; Day et al. 1973). However, during a study of a Dutch estuary we found high benthic production in a water body with insignificant salt marshes and eelgrass beds. Apparently other mechanisms may also cause high benthic production values.

In this paper I propose a food budget in the form of a particulate organic carbon budget for the benthos of the Grevelingen estuary. In comparing this budget with similar budgets for other estuaries, the discussion centers on differences between these waters and the mechanisms causing high benthic secondary production in various estuaries.

I gratefully acknowledge the help of my colleagues at the Delta Institute who made some of their unpublished data available and who criticized an earlier draft of the manuscript, as did Prof. Dr. H. Postma (Texel). The Ministry of Roads and Waterways kindly supplied hydrographical information, and the Ministry of Agriculture and Fisheries was very helpful with data on the mussel culture. Mr. D. Gersie of the Delft Hydraulics Laboratory helped with the calculation of the percentage of water exchange of the estuary.

This study is communication nr. 132 of the Delta Institute for Hydrobiological Research.

PARTICULATE ORGANIC CARBON BUDGET FOR THE BENTHOS IN THE GREVELINGEN ESTUARY

The Grevelingen estuary lies in the southwestern part of The Netherlands (Fig. 1) and has an area of about 140 km^2. Prior to our study the slight fresh-water input from the rivers Rhine and Meuse was cut off and tributaries of these rivers were dammed. During our study salinity did not fall below 15.0 °/₀₀ Cl^- (Peelen 1974). The average tidal amplitude is about 2.6 m, and the tidal currents have a maximum speed of 1.5-2.0 $m.sec^{-1}$ locally. Of the 140 km^2 4 km^2 are covered by salt marshes and 55 km^2 are tidal flats without erect vegetation. The remaining 81 km^2 of water have an average depth at low tide of 6 m, 9% of this area is deeper than 20 m, and the maximum depth is about 50 m.

Wolff and De Wolf (in press) estimated secondary production by the macrobenthos to be 50.3-57.4 g ash-free dry weight$\cdot m^{-2}\cdot year^{-1}$ (weighted average for the whole estuary). In the following discussion I use a value of 57.4 g ash-free dry weight based on the most probable values of these earlier data. An ash-free dry weight/carbon ratio of 1.9 (Winberg 1971) results in an estimate of about 30.3 g $C\cdot m^{-2}.year^{-1}$ (Table 1).

Reported values of salt-marsh production are often very high. Keefe (1972) and Gabriel and De la Cruz (1974) recorded aboveground net production values for *Spartina alterniflora* marshes ranging from 445 to 3300 g dry weight.$m^{-2}.year^{-1}$. European values range from about 200-1000 g dry weight.$m^{-2}.year^{-1}$ (Joenje 1974;

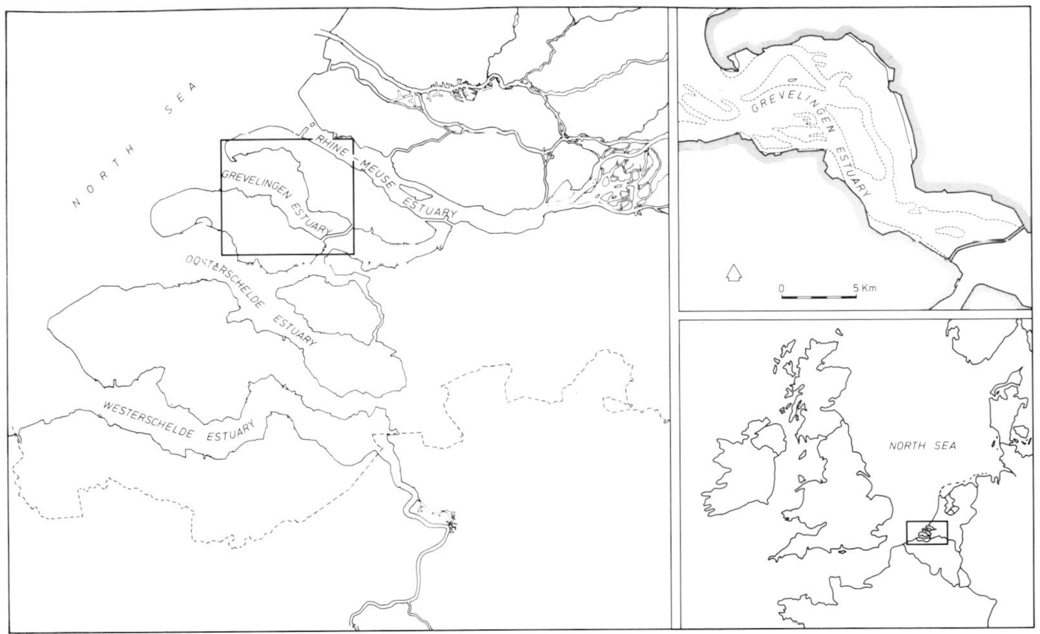

Fig. 1. Survey of the Grevelingen estuary.

Table 1. Weighted mean for the annual benthic secondary production in the Grevelingen estuary. Values from Wolff and De Wolf (in press) are divided by 1.9 to give carbon weight.

Species	Type of feeder	Amount
Hydrobia ulvae	(grazer)	2.4 g $C \cdot m^{-2} \cdot yr^{-1}$
Mytilus edulis	(filter-feeder)	8.5 " " " "
Cardium edule	(filter-feeder)	16.9 " " " "
Macoma balthica	(deposit-feeder)	0.5 " " " "
Arenicola marina	(deposit-feeder)	1.2 " " " "
All other macrobenthic species		0.8 " " " "

Ketner 1972; Wallentius 1973). For the 4 km^2 of salt marshes along the Grevelingen estuary this means a production of 100-500 g $C.m^{-2}.year^{-1}$. Teal (1962) reported that 45% of the net production of a Georgia salt marsh is exported as detritus to the open water system of the estuary, whereas the remainder is consumed in the marsh, while Nixon and Oviatt (1973) assumed that 23% is exported from a New England marsh. Along the Grevelingen estuary, however, part of the net production is transported by storm floods to levels above the normal spring high tide level. Part of this material is removed by the agencies maintaining the sea walls, and it is not known whether the remaining part ever returns to the estuary. Therefore it is assumed that 10-45% of the above-ground net production of the Grevelingen marshes is exported as detritus to the aquatic system and the salt marsh contribution to the aquatic part of the estuary is thought to be about 0.3-7 g $C.m^{-2}.year^{-1}$. Even if the complete production of the salt marsh went to the estuary, the yield would only be about 15 g $C.m^{-2}.year^{-1}$, an insignificant quantity.

Dense beds of *Zostera marina* in the Grevelingen estuary cover about 2 km^2 (unpublished observations Delta Institute) and less dense beds cover another 10 km^2 (Nienhuis 1970; unpublished observations). Mann's (1972, 1973) summary of what is known about the production of *Zostera marina* indicated that except for a high value of 1500 g $C.m^{-2}.year^{-1}$ based on extrapolation of short-term observations, all values range between 58 and 340 g $C.m^{-2}.year^{-1}$ and the *Zostera* primary production for the entire estuary is estimated at 696-4080 $ton.year^{-1}$. Grazing of the *Zostera* is negligible, except for feeding by wigeon (*Anas penelope*) and brent geese (*Branta bernicla*). Regular counts indicate that these species consumed maximally about 50 tons of *Zostera* expressed as carbon weight per year. The maximal amount available as detritus for the aquatic food web, then, is 5-30 g $C.m^{-2}.year^{-1}$. The actual figure is probably much closer to the former value than to the latter one.

For the tidal flats of the western Wadden Sea, Cadée and Hegeman (1974) determined the mean annual primary production of the benthic microalgae at 101 (± 38.5) g $C.m^{-2}.year^{-1}$. Since the tidal flats of the Grevelingen estuary are very similar in sediment composition and appearance to the flats of the Wadden Sea, and since the distance between the two areas is only 150 km, the benthic microflora in the Grevelingen estuary probably has a similar production. Since the area of tidal flats is 55 km^2, the total annual production is estimated at 5555 ± 2118 tons C. Averaged over the whole estuary, benthic microflora may contribute 41 ± 16 g $C.m^{-2}.year^{-1}$ to the benthic food web.

During our study primary production by phytoplankton was 179 g $C.m^{-2}. year^{-1}$ (Vegter personal communication): a value obtained in the main tidal channel where the depth of the channel was greater than the compensation depth. Since the compensation depth was similar to the tidal amplitude, corrections had to be made for the phytoplankton production over the submerged tidal flats. Assuming that all other conditions remain the same, we subsequently estimated the average phytoplankton production, the area of tidal flats included, to be about 130 g C.m^{-2}.year^{-1}.

The amount of organic matter supplied to the estuary by sewers may be estimated from the number of inhabitants contributing to untreated sewage. Klomp and Speksnijder (1973) estimated the number of inhabitants to be 11,625 and assuming that 52.5 g dry organic matter per capita is produced daily (Liebmann 1960), we arrive at a total supply of 223 ton dry matter to the Grevelingen area in 1972. This is equivalent to about 117 tons of carbon, i.e., a supply of about 1 g C.m^{-2}.year^{-1}. The supply by land drainage (5305 ha) is not known, but using the phosphorus budget proposed by Klomp and Speksnijder (1973), we arrive at a similar amount. Thus the total supply from land drainage and sewers is about 2 g C.m^{-2}.year^{-1}.

The total amount of particulate organic carbon from all sources is then 317-451 g C.m^{-2}.year^{-1} (Table 2).

Table 2. Benthic food budget, expressed as particulate organic carbon, for the aquatic part of the Grevelingen estuary.

Food Source		Amount
Contribution salt marshes		0.3- 7 g C·m^{-2}·yr^{-1}
Production seagrass beds		5 - 30 " " " "
Production microphytobenthos		25 - 57 " " " "
Production phytoplankton		130 " " " "
Land run-off		2 " " " "
Import from North Sea		155 - 225 " " " "
	Total	317 - 451 g C·m^{-2}·yr^{-1}

The net transport of living plankton and detritus between the estuary and the North Sea is the only source or sink which is difficult to quantify. Seaward net transport of floating parts of phanerogams and macroalgae does occur but is probably unimportant because most winds blow landward. Entrapment of detritus by salinity stratification does not occur since the estuary always is well mixed. The only mechanism which may cause a landward net transport of detritus and may counteract a seaward transport, is the tidal mechanism described by Postma (1954, 1961, 1967) for the Wadden Sea. Postma (1954) estimated that the western Wadden Sea received about 80 g C.m^{-2}.year^{-1} in 1950 by means of this mechanism, and De Jonge and Postma (1974) inferred that owing to the increasing pollution of the southern North Sea, this amount had increased to about 240 g C.m^{-2}.year^{-1} in 1970.

If the same mechanism is acting in the Grevelingen estuary, Postma's (1954) method may be used to quantify its effect. From monthly observations (May 1967-April 1971) it was determined that the average concentration of dissolved phosphorus at three sampling localities well within the Grevelingen estuary was 3.35 μgat P.liter^{-1}. During the same period, the average concentration of dissolved phosphorus in the two entrance channels of the estuary was 2.76 μgat P.liter^{-1}. Hence, a gradient of 0.59 μgat P.liter^{-1} exists between the inner part of the estuary and its entrances. Therefore at high tide the surplus of dissolved phosphorus in the estuary amounts to $0.59 \times 0.8 \times 10^{12} \simeq 0.47 \times 10^{12}$ μgat, or about 14.600 kg dissolved P. The high tide volume of the estuary is about 0.8×10^{12} liter.

This phosphorus surplus is exchanged during the tidal exchange with the North Sea, which is estimated at 7-10% per tidal cycle (Eysink 1974; D. Gersie personal communication). Thus 0.07-0.10 x 14.600 kg P = 1022-1460 kg of dissolved P is exchanged with the North Sea per tidal cycle. This flux of dissolved phosphorus towards the North Sea has to be balanced by the land runoff, estimated at 18.40 kg P.year^{-1} ≃ 26 kg P.tidal cycle^{-1} (Klomp and Speksnijder 1973), and a flux of particulate P from the North Sea towards the estuary as described by Postma (1961) of (1022-1460) - 26 = 996 - 1434 kg P.tidal cycle^{-1}, a value equivalent (De Jonge and Postma 1974; Manuels and Postma 1974) to about 31-45.000 kg C.tidal cycle^{-1}, or to 155-225 g C.m^{-2}.year^{-1}. Similarly the flux of particulate organic matter during the shorter period we studied the production of the macrobenthos, was computed from the P-values at 210-298 g C.m^{-2}.year^{-1}. Although these figures are subject to probable error, their substitution in Table 2 shows that the tidal transport of particulate organic matter is of paramount importance to the benthic community of the Grevelingen estuary. The value found may be compared to Terwindt's (1967) calculations that in the Oosterschelde estuary adjacent to the Grevelingen estuary some 0.2 - 0.3.10^{-6} tons of mud are deposited annually in an area of about 150 km^{2}. Assuming that on the average 5% of the mud consists of organic C (Manuels and Postma 1974), about 67 g C.m^{-2}.year^{-1} is deposited in this area. The difference from the Grevelingen estuary values may be due to the many uncertainties in the calculations and to the greater stretch of coastal water between the estuary and the mouth of the rivers Rhine and Meuse.

COMPARISON WITH OTHER ESTUARIES

Budgets of particulate organic carbon comparable to that for the Grevelingen estuary are not numerous. A similar budget for particulate organic phosphorus may be constructed for the Western Wadden Sea, The Netherlands, from data by De Jonge and Postma (1974) (Table 3). This budget is very similar to mine for the Grevelingen estuary.

Data from Day et al. (1973) may be used to construct a similar budget for the aquatic part of the estuarine system of Barataria Bay, Louisiana, USA (Table 4). Their data expressed as dry organic

Table 3. Benthic food budget, expressed as particulate organic phosphorus, for the western Wadden Sea, The Netherlands (from De Jonge and Postma 1974).

Food Source		Amount
Contribution salt marshes		insignificant
Contribution seagrass beds and macro algae		insignificant
Primary production *in situ* (phytoplankton and microphytobenthos)		$2\ g\ P \cdot m^{-2} \cdot yr^{-1}$
Land run-off and sewers		insignificant
Import from North Sea		$6\ g\ P \cdot m^{-2} \cdot yr^{-1}$
	Total	$8\ g\ P \cdot m^{-2} \cdot yr^{-1}$

Table 4. Annual budget of particulate organic carbon, for Barataria Bay, Louisiana (from Day et al. 1973).

Source and Sink		Amount
Contribution saltmarshes		$297\ g\ C \cdot m^{-2} \cdot yr^{-1}$
Production phytobenthos		244 " " " "
Production phytoplankton		209 " " " "
	Total	$750\ g\ C \cdot m^{-2} \cdot yr^{-1}$
Consumption in estuary		$432\ g\ C \cdot m^{-2} \cdot yr^{-1}$
Export to Gulf of Mexico		318 " " " "
	Total	$750\ g\ C \cdot m^{-2} \cdot yr^{-1}$

matter weights, have been divided by 2 to obtain carbon weights. A comparable budget probably could be established for the Georgia estuaries, where Teal (1962) and Odum and De la Cruz (1967) indicated an important contribution of detritus from the salt marshes and a net transport of particulate organic matter from the estuary to the shelf waters. Nixon and Oviatt (1973) proposed an annual energy budget for a marsh embayment in New England with a tidal range up to 3 ft (Table 5) and although their data are expressed as $kcal.m^{-2}.year^{-1}$, the behavior of the system they studied is similar to that of the estuarine systems in Louisiana and Georgia. Barsdate et al. (1974), who presented a carbon budget for Izembek Lagoon, Alaska, found a tremendous export to the Bering Sea of floating eelgrass, but did not mention possible import of suspended detritus. Odum and Heald (1975) described in qualitative terms the export of detritus from mangrove forests to nearby coastal and estuarine waters in Florida, USA. Their findings are similar to those of Golley et al. (1962) in a Puerto Rico mangrove forest.

Hence, a picture of two different types of estuaries arises, one deriving detritus from salt marshes, mangroves or eelgrass beds

Table 5. Annual energy budget for the Bissel Cove marsh embayment, New England (from Nixon and Oviatt 1973).

Source and Sink	Amount	
Contribution saltmarshes	240 - 470	$Kcal \cdot m^{-2} \cdot yr^{-1}$
Net immigration of fish and shrimp	3.5	" " "
Contribution from streams (dissolved organic matter)	15	" " "
Primary production phytoplankton and benthos	9,600	" " "
Total	9,858.5-10,088.5	$Kcal \cdot m^{-2} \cdot yr^{-1}$
Consumption within embayment	9,800	$Kcal \cdot m^{-2} \cdot yr^{-1}$
Storage and export to Narragansett Bay	58.5 - 288.5	" " "
Total	9,858.5-10,088.5	$Kcal \cdot m^{-2} \cdot yr^{-1}$

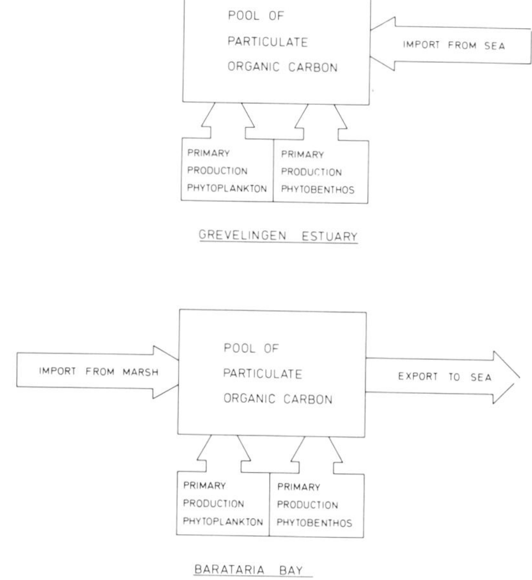

Fig. 2. The main characteristics of the benthic food budgets for the Grevelingen estuary, The Netherlands, and Barataria Bay, Louisiana, USA.

and fertilizing the adjacent sea with detritus, the other deriving detritus from the sea and not exporting detritus to any other system (Fig. 2).

These differences can be partly attributed to the following factors: (1) On the American coasts the marsh grass *Spartina alterniflora* occupies about two-thirds of the intertidal zone below the high water mark (Redfield 1972) while on European coasts, *Spartina maritima* and *S. townsendii* as well as other salt-marsh plants hardly descend below high tide level (Beeftink 1965). Thus, at relatively the same places where European estuaries show bare tidal flats American estuaries contain extremely productive *Spartina* marshes. (2) Detritus floating at the surface will move down a concentration gradient, unlike detritus kept in suspension by turbulent water movements which in tidal estuaries moves up the concentration gradient. Since in the European estuaries described here floating detritus is of little importance, inshore transport will predominate. In many American estuaries, however, the possible inshore transport of suspended detritus will be counteracted by the offshore transport of floating material, since its concentration in the estuary will be higher than in the coastal sea. (3) The European estuaries described here are characterized by onshore winds, whereas the American counterparts experience more offshore winds, which influence the transport direction of floating detritus. (4) The European estuaries possess tidal mechanisms that transport particulate organic matter in an inshore direction. The tidal range at Barataria Bay, Louisiana, and at Bissel Cove, New England (maximally about 0.9 m), may be too small to support this mechanism, but the tidal range in the Georgia marshes (about 2 m) should be sufficient for it. (5) The Atlantic Ocean along the American east coast is in general less rich in nutrients, and hence in phytoplankton, than the North Sea.

MECHANISMS MAINTAINING HIGH BENTHIC PRODUCTION

Schelske and Odum (1961) have already reviewed the mechanisms maintaining high productivity in estuaries in general, and pointed out that in the Georgia estuaries primary production is organized very efficiently in that production by *Spartina*, benthic algae and phytoplankton is largely complementary and is maintained on a high level year round. They considered rapid turnover of nutrients and release of dissolved nutrients by the sediment to be the mechanism maintaining this production. They also stated that the estuary acts as a nutrient trap through vertical mixing of waters of different salinities and biological removal of nutrients by the benthic fauna. They did not specify, however, the source of trapped nutrients. They excluded a fresh-water source of dissolved nutrients and an oceanic source of particulate organic matter and/or sediment, although Odum (1971) pointed to a marine origin of nutrients.

I propose that the following mechanisms support high secondary production in estuaries:

High Primary Production in situ

1. Supply of dissolved nutrients by river discharge (Ketchum 1967).--According to Riley (1967) and Pomeroy et al. (1972) this is a relatively rare phenomenon; clean rivers tend to flush the estuary and thus also decrease the amount of nutrients from other sources.

2. Supply of dissolved nutrients from deep offshore waters (Ketchum 1967; Riley 1967).

3. Supply of dissolved nutrients from sediments and interstitial waters.--This has been described by Schelske and Odum (1961) and by Pomeroy et al. (1965, 1972), who considered mainly chemical and microbiological processes. McRoy et al. (1972) described a mechanism by which submerged *Zostera* supplied dissolved phosphate from the sediment to the water. However, ultimately such a supply depends on an import of sediment or dissolved nutrients from some other source.

4. Rapid turnover of nutrients due to tidal action (Schelske and Odum 1961).

5. Supply of dissolved nutrients from sewage.

Import of Particulate Organic Matter

1. River discharge and land runoff containing fresh-water plankton and/or detritus (Copeland 1970; Meade 1972).--Windblown material may also be placed in this category (Darnell 1967).

2. Tidal mechanisms causing an inshore transport of marine plankton and detritus as described by Postma (1954, 1961, 1967) and Groen (1967).--This paper assumes that the mechanism also acts in the Dutch Grevelingen estuary. Although Pomeroy et al. (1972) attributed the high concentration of organic matter in the estuaries of Georgia to a supply from the marshes, the tidal import mechanism might also play a role in the Georgia estuaries.

3. Entrapment of particulate organic matter from various sources in a salt wedge system (Odum 1971; Meade 1972).

4. Tidal flushing from extensive salt marshes and mangrove forests (Teal 1962; Day et al. 1973; De la Cruz 1973; Golley et al. 1962).

5. Sewage.

None of these mechanisms excludes any of the others. Hence in some estuaries a very large food supply for the primary consumers may be created from various sources. However, no mechanism is common to all estuaries and coastal inlets, so that in arid regions there probably exist non-tidal coastal systems without any extra food source - like the open sea. In conclusion, estuaries and coastal inlets may be very rich in food for all primary consumers, but are not necessarily so.

Mechanisms providing a larger share of food to the benthos than to the zooplankton or the nekton seem to be related to either the shallow nature of estuaries or to the tidal currents.

It is generally accepted that the marine benthos feeds on that part of the surface production left behind by the pelagic consumers, i.e., bacteria, zooplankton and nekton (Sanders 1956; Steele 1973). Thus the amount of food available for the benthos should correlate negatively with the depth of the water column. Indeed, Rowe (1971) found a positive relationship between benthic biomass and surface productivity and a negative relationship between benthic biomass and depth in the deep sea; Spärck (1935) reached a similar conclusion for coastal waters. Hargrave (1973), however, established a significant positive relationship between surface primary production and amount of phytoplankton reaching the bottom, and a significant negative correlation between depth of the mixed layer and the amount of phytoplankton reaching the bottom. A correlation with total depth was not significant. Because Hargrave (1973) did not use data from very great depths in his regression analysis, and because in the other data his "remaining-depth" factor is relatively small in comparison to his "mixed-layer depth" factor, his conclusions are not contrary to the conclusion of Spärck (1935) and Rowe (1971). In shallow estuaries with average depths of only a few meters sinking phytoplankton therefore may form a large source of food for the benthos. However, living phytoplankton species usually have sinking rates under 1 $m.day^{-1}$ (Smayda 1970), so the zooplankton is left ample time to exploit the living phytoplankton. Tidal currents, on the other hand, make the phytoplankton production much more readily available to the benthos. In the Grevelingen estuary, for example, tidal currents in the range 0.1-1.0 $m.sec^{-1}$, would cause the vertical component of the turbulent diffusion coefficient to be approximately 50-500 $cm^2.sec^{-1}$, implying that surface production becomes available to benthic filter-feeders at a few meters depth within an hour or less. Furthermore, in conjunction with this vertical transport due to the tidal currents there is a continuous horizontal transport of plankton-loaded water. This places the benthos in a more favorable position than the zooplankton, because in such a situation the benthos is able to compete for food on an almost equal basis.

The possibility that the often high yield of benthic secondary production is partly caused by a larger share of r-selected species in estuaries than elsewhere, has not yet been investigated in detail. The unpredictable nature of the abiotic factors in many estuaries makes this a likely possibility.

Summarizing, the mechanisms causing high benthic secondary production in estuaries are: (1) supply of dissolved nutrients from various sources causing a high primary production; (2) supply of particulate organic matter from various sources and (3) the shallow nature of estuaries. The possible preponderance of r-selected species would convert this high production into a high yield.

REFERENCES

Barsdate, R. J., M. Nebert, and C. P. McRoy. 1974. Lagoon contributions to sediments and water of the Bering Sea, pp. 553-576. In: D. W. Hood and E. J. Kelley [eds.], Proc. Int. Symp. Bering Sea Study, Fairbanks.

Beeftink, W. G. 1965. De zoutvegetaties van ZW-Nederland beschouwd in Europees verband. Meded. Landbouwhogeschool, Wageningen 65-1: 1-167.

Cadée, G. C. and J. Hegeman. 1974. Primary production of the benthic microflora living on tidal flats in the Dutch Wadden Sea. Neth. J. Sea Res. 8: 260-291.

Copeland, B. J. 1970. Estuarine classification and responses to disturbances. Trans. Am. Fish. Soc. 99: 826-835.

Darnell, R. M. 1967. Organic detritus in relation to the estuarine ecosystem, pp. 376-382. In: G. H. Lauff [ed.], Estuaries. Am. Assoc. Adv. Sci. Publ., Washington, D. C.

Day, J. W., W. G. Smith, P. R. Wagner, and W. C. Stowe. 1973. Community structure and carbon budget of a saltmarsh and shallow bay estuarine system in Louisiana. Cent. Wetland, Louisiana State Univ. Publ. No. LSU-SG-72-04: 79 p.

de Jonge, V. N. and H. Postma. 1974. Phosphorus compounds in the Dutch Wadden Sea. Neth. J. Sea Res. 8: 139-153.

De la Cruz, A. A. 1973. The role of tidal marshes in the productivity of coastal waters. Bull. Assoc. Southeast. Biol. 20: 147-156.

Eysink, W. D. 1974. Diffusie in estuaria. Schaalonderzoek in prototype en hydraulische modellen van het estuarium Brouwershavense Gat-Grevelingen in samenwerking met Rijkswaterstaat--Fysische afdeling. Verslag Model-en Prototypeonderzoek. Rapport Waterloopkundig Lab. M 1010, 37 p.

Gabriel, B. C. and A. A. de la Cruz. 1974. Species composition, standing stock, and net primary production of a salt marsh community in Mississippi. Chesapeake Sci. 15: 72-77.

Golley, F., H. T. Odum, and R. F. Wilson. 1962. The structure and metabolism of a Puerto Rican red mangrove forest in May. Ecology 43: 9-19.

Groen, P. 1967. On the residual transport of suspended matter by an alternating tidal current. Neth. J. Sea Res. 3: 564-574.

Hargrave, B. T. 1973. Coupling carbon flow through some pelagic and benthic communities. J. Fish. Res. Board Can. 30: 1317-1326.

Joenje, W. 1974. Production and structure in the early stages of vegetation development in the Lauwerszee-polder. Vegetatio 29: 101-108.

Keefe, C. W. 1972. Marsh production: a summary of the literature. Contr. Mar. Sci. 16: 165-181.

Ketchum, B. M. 1967. Phytoplankton nutrients in estuaries, pp. 329-335. In: G. H. Lauff [ed.], Estuaries. Am. Assoc. Adv. Sci. Publ., Washington, D. C.

Ketner, P. 1972. Primary production of salt-marsh communities on the island of Terschelling in the Netherlands. Verh. Rijksinst. Natuurbeheer 5: 1-184.

Klomp, R. and J. C. Speksnijder. 1973. De waterkwaliteit van het Grevelingenmeer in 1972. Rijkswaterstaat Deltadienst afd. Milieu-onderzoek Nota 73-22. 56 p.

Liebmann, H. 1960. Handbuch der Frischwasser--un Abwasserbiologie, II. München. 1149 p.

McRoy, C. P., R. J. Barsdate, and M. Nebert. 1972. Phosphorus cycling in an eelgrass (*Zostera marina* L.) ecosystem. Limnol. Oceanogr. 17: 58-67.

Mann, K. H. 1972. Macrophyte production and detritus food chains in coastal waters. Me. Ist. Ital. Idrobiol. 29 Suppl.: 353-383.

_____. 1973. Seaweeds: their productivity and strategy for growth. Science 182: 975-981.

Manuels, M. W. and H. Postma. 1974. Measurements of ATP and organic carbon in suspended matter of the Dutch Wadden Sea. Neth. J. Sea Res. 8: 292-311.

Nienhuis, P. H. 1970. The benthic algal communities of flats and saltmarshes in the Grevelingen, a sea-arm in the S.W.-Netherlands. Neth. J. Sea Res. 5: 20-49.

Nixon, S. W. and C. A. Oviatt. 1973. Ecology of a New England salt marsh. Ecol. Monogr. 43: 463-498.

Odum, E. P. 1971. Fundamentals of ecology (3rd ed.) Saunders.

_____ and A. A. de la Cruze. 1967. Particulate organic detritus in a Georgia salt-marsh estuarine ecosystem, p. 383-388. In G. H. Lauff [ed.], Estuaries. Am. Assoc. Adv. Sci. Publ. Washington, D. C.

Odum, W. E. and E. J. Heald. 1975. Mangrove forests and aquatic productivity, p. 129-136. In A. D. Hasler [ed.], Coupling of land and water systems. Berlin.

Peelen, R. 1974. Data on temperature, oxygen, sediment and transparency of the water in the northern part of the Delta area of the Netherlands between 1961-1972. Hydrobiologia 45: 115-134.

Pomeroy, L. R., E. E. Smith, and C. M. Grant. 1965. The exchange of phosphate between estuarine water and sediments. Limnol. Oceanogr. 10: 167-172.

_____, R. J. Reimold, L. R. Shenton, and R. D. H. Jones. 1972. Nutrient flux in estuaries, p. 274-296. In G. E. Likens [ed.], Nutrients and eutrophication. Am. Soc. Limnol. Oceanogr. Spec. Symp. No. 1.

Postma, H. 1954. Hydrography of the Dutch Wadden Sea. Arch. néerl. Zool. 10: 405-511.

_____. 1961. Transport and accumulation of suspended matter in the Dutch Wadden Sea. Neth. J. Sea Res. 1: 148-190.

_____. 1967. Sediment transport and sedimentation in the estuarine environment, p. 158-179. In G. H. Lauff [ed.], Estuaries. Am. Assoc. Adv. Sci. Publ. Washington, D. C.

Redfield, A. C. 1972. Development of a New England salt marsh. Ecol. Mongr. 42: 201-237.

Riley, G. A. 1967. Mathematical model of nutrient conditions in coastal waters. Bull. Bingham Oceanogr. Coll. 19: 72-80.

Rowe, G. T. 1971. Benthic biomass and surface productivity, p. 441-454. In J. D. Costlow [ed.], Fertility of the sea. Gordon and Breach Sci. Publ. 2. New York.

Sanders, H. L. 1956. Oceanography of Long Island Sound. X. The biology of marine bottom communities. Bull. Bingham Oceanogr. Coll. 15: 345-414.

Schelske, C. L. and E. P. Odum. 1961. Mechanisms maintaining high productivity in Georgia estuaries. Proc. Gulf Carib. Fish. Inst. 14: 75-80.

Smayda, T. J. 1970. The suspension and sinking of phytoplankton in the sea. Oceanogr. Mar. Biol. Ann. Rev. 8: 353-414.

Spärck, T. 1935. On the importance of quantitative investigation of the bottom fauna in marine biology. J. Cons. int. Explor. Mer. 10: 3-19.

Steele, J. H. 1973. The structure of marine ecosystems. Blackwell Sci.

Teal, J. M. 1962. Energy flow in a salt marsh ecosystem of Georgia. Ecology 43: 614-624.

Terwindt, J. H. J. 1967. Mud transport in the Dutch Delta area and along the adjacent coastline. Neth. J. Sea Res. 3: 505-531.

Wallentius, H. G. 1973. Above-ground primary production of a *Juncetum gerardi* on a Baltic sea-shore meadow. Oikos 24: 200-219.

Winberg, G. G. 1971. Symbols, units and conversion factors in studies of fresh water productivity. IBP, London.

The Importance of Sediment Stability in Seagrass Communities

Robert J. Orth
Virginia Institute of Marine Science
Gloucester Point, VA 23062

ABSTRACT

Dense stands of seagrass are shown to stabilize sediments from studies of *Zostera* beds in the Chesapeake Bay and *Thalassia* beds in Bermuda. Particle size distribution, and degree of sorting decreased and organic content increased from bare sand to the center of a seagrass bed. Macrofaunal distribution in seagrass beds and experimental manipulation of *Zostera* beds in the Chesapeake Bay indicate that sediment stability results in high infaunal diversity and density. The dense rhizome mat also serves to decrease the effects of predation by preventing blue crabs from digging beneath the sediment surface layer.

INTRODUCTION

The diversity and abundance of many benthic faunal assemblages appear to be controlled by the physical properties of the sediment in which they live (see Gray 1974 for a review) or by biological interactions, i.e., competition and predation (Gray 1974; Woodin 1974). The importance of sediment stability as a limiting factor is little understood but it certainly plays an important role in the establishment and ultimate maintenance of the infaunal community.

In many exposed intertidal and shallow subtidal environments, sediments resuspended and transported by wave energy and tidal currents are the dominant forces preventing successful recruitment of many benthic forms. Associated with these habitats is a fauna characterized by low species diversity and density (Dexter 1969, 1972; Day et al. 1971). Survival in this environment requires a species to be either a rapid burrower, e.g., *Donax* spp. and haustoriid amphipods, or a tube builder with a tube penetrating deep into the sediment, e.g. *Callianassa* spp. and spionid polychaetes.

Biological activity can also produce unstable sediments. Intensive reworking of fine sediments by deposit feeders results in a highly granulated surface layer which is easily resuspended by tidal currents. Such instability inhibits suspension feeders by clogging filtering structures and resuspending and burying newly settled larvae (Rhoads and Young 1970; Young 1971; Rhoads 1974).

Conversely, increased stability of the sediment surface, either through a physical or biological agent, can increase the diversity of fauna. For example, tubes of polychaetes and crustaceans have been observed to stabilize sediment and cause a concomitant increase in species diversity (Buchanan 1963; Fager 1964; Mills 1967; Rhoads and Young 1971). Objects in the sediment such as wooden stakes and rocks, in addition to supporting an attached epifaunal community, appear to attract a rich infaunal community close to them (personal observation). The hydrodynamics of water flow around such objects creates some areas of reduced water flow which may allow larvae to settle and not be washed away. Also, accumulation of organic-rich suspended particles and fecal pellets allow development of deposit feeding benthos around such objects.

Seagrasses are well known for their ability to stabilize sediments by baffling currents and damping wave action (Ginsburg and Lowenstam 1958; Wood et al. 1969; Coull 1970; Hartog 1970; Taylor and Lewis 1970; Zieman 1972). Seagrass beds are common in shallow environments, but little work has been done to quantify the structure and organization of infaunal communities in seagrass beds. The infauna of seagrass communities is generally much more diverse than that of surrounding unvegetated areas (O'Gower and Wacasey 1967; Orth 1973; Santos and Simon 1974) but the mechanisms that allow for and maintain high infaunal diversity (e.g., productivity, spatial heterogeneity and sediment stability) are unclear.

The purpose of this paper is to examine the effect of sediment stability on seagrass infaunal communities on the basis of sediment and faunal distribution in seagrass beds and experimental manipulations.

I wish to thank D. Boesch, C. Rees and R. Virnstein for reading the manuscript and for their helpful comments during the study. I am indebted to R. Diaz for statistical aid and the Virginia Institute of Marine Science for the use of their facilities.

Contribution No. 710 of the Virginia Institute of Marine Science, Gloucester Point. This work is based on a dissertation submitted in partial fulfillment of the requirements for the Ph.D. in the Department of Zoology, University of Maryland, College Park. Research supported by NSF Grant GI-34869 to the Chesapeake Research Consortium, the Chesapeake Bay Fund of the Department of Zoology, University of Maryland, and a grant-in-aid from Sigma-XI.

STUDY AREA

Much of the work described here was carried out in eelgrass, *Zostera marina*, beds in the lower Chesapeake Bay near Sandy Point, at the mouth of the York River and off Browns Bay in the Mobjack Bay (Fig. 1A). Both sites have narrow unvegetated intertidal zones of well-sorted medium to coarse sand. The *Zostera* beds begin at the MLW mark, where sediments become finer and more poorly sorted than corresponding *Zostera*-free areas. The lower limits of *Zostera* beds occur at 1.5 to 2.0 m below MLW owing primarily to light attenuation in these somewhat turbid estuarine waters. Intertidal, unvegetated sand bars (Orth and Gordon 1975) are commonly interspersed through the *Zostera* beds at Sandy Point and other more exposed beds in the Bay (Fig. 2A). These sand bars are 5-7 m wide and may be 1-2 km long. There may be as many as 7 parallel bars in Chesapeake Bay, but at Sandy Point there are two parallel sand bars with a dense *Zostera* bed between them.

In some areas, *Zostera* is distributed in patches of various sizes and shapes. This patchiness may be attributed to disturbance of a dense bed by biological agents, e.g., cownose rays (Orth 1975), to patterns of vegetative growth, or the vagaries of seedling recruitment (personal observation).

Additional work was carried out in turtle grass, *Thalassia testudinum*, beds in Bermuda (Fig. 1B), which exhibit discontinuous patterns and patches similar to those found in eelgrass beds of Chesapeake Bay. These patterns may be related to biological disturbance (Randall 1965; Ogden et al. 1973), or to physical characteristics of the sedimentary environment (Zieman 1972).

METHODS

Habitat Studies

A transect line was constructed across a 43-m wide *Zostera* bed (Figs. 2A, B) between two sand bars at Sandy Point, and sampled at six stations (Figs. 2A, B) in July 1972. At each station, a 2-m line was positioned parallel to the edge of the bed, the original transect line being the center of each parallel line. Prior to sampling, the *Zostera* on each line was clipped at the base to prevent contamination with epifauna. Along each 2-m line seven cores were taken randomly to a depth of 20 cm with a plexiglas corer (0.007 m^2), 5 for biological and 2 for sediment characteristics. Biological cores were fixed in 5% formaldehyde and sieved through a 1.0-mm mesh screen. The retained fraction was preserved in 5% buffered formalin, stained with phyloxine B (Mason and Yevich 1967) and sorted under a dissecting microscope. *Zostera* biomass was estimated at each station by clipping all the leaves from a 0.1-m^2 quadrat, removing all epiphytic growth and drying for 48 hr at 60°C.

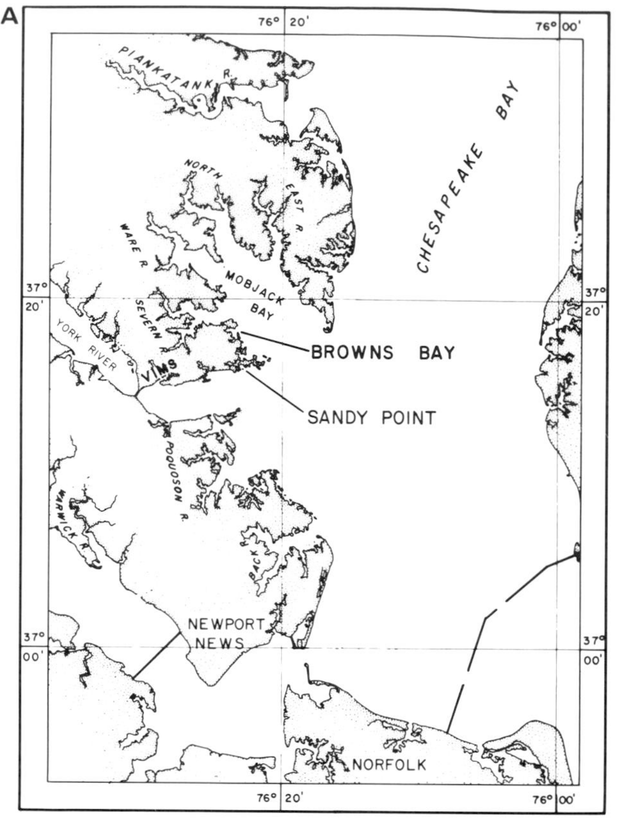

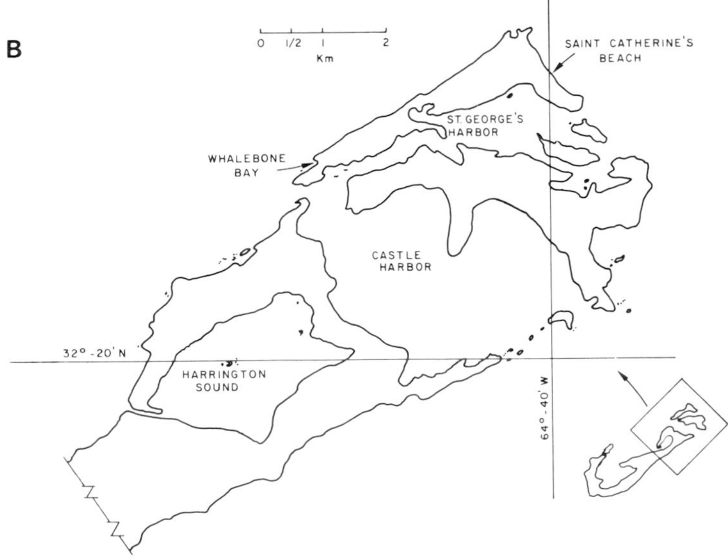

Fig. 1. A. Map of lower Chesapeake Bay showing location of sampling areas at Browns Bay and Sandy Point. B. Map of Bermuda showing location of sampling areas at Whalebone Bay and Saint Catherine's Beach (after Coull 1970).

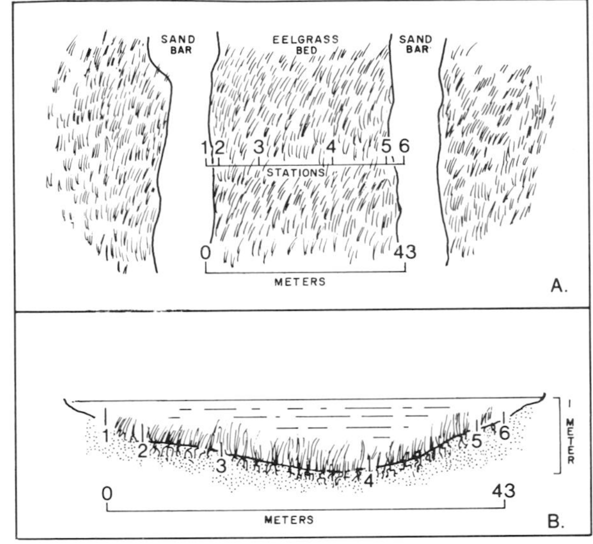

Fig. 2. Pictorial representation of study area at Sandy Point. A. Transect across *Zostera* bed situated between sand bars showing positions of sampling locations. B. Cross section of the transect.

Sediment grain size was determined through the standard dry sieve and pipette technique (Folk 1968). A portion of each sediment sample was retained and analyzed for total organic matter by ashing at 550°C.

In Bermuda, sediment samples were taken from *Thalassia* beds at two locations: Whatebone Bay (WB), and embayment, and Saint Catherine's Beach (SCB), a more wave-exposed area. Biological samples were taken at Whalebone Bay only. Three cores for sediment and 10 cores for fauna were taken randomly in the *Thalassia* beds approximately 2 m from the bare sand and in the bare sand adjacent to the grass bed. Faunal samples were sieved through a 1.0-mm mesh screen.

Manipulative Experiments

These experiments were designed to test the effects of various levels of disturbance on community organization within a given *Zostera* bed.

In August 1972, four sites were selected in a dense bed of *Zostera* at Sandy Point: two sites were treated by clipping the grass at the base, the other two sites serving as controls. Additional growth was clipped on a monthly basis. All sites were located with a wooden stake inserted into the sediment and defined as the center of a circle with a radius of 3 m. Eight radial transects were set up within each circle, each transect being divided at 0.3-m intervals which denoted postions from which samples could be taken randomly. A table of random numbers was used to determine the transect and position on the transect for each sample prior to the field collection. Sampling was initiated in August, the two clipped plots being sampled prior to manipulation, and continued in September and December 1972, and March, July and September 1973. Additional samples were taken at one of the control areas in April and August 1973. At every sampling five cores for faunal analysis and one sample for sediment analysis were taken. The faunal samples were subsequently washed through a 1.0-mm mesh screen.

Immediately after experimental manipulation began in August 1972, a large influx of cownose rays, *Rhinoptera bonasus*, completely disturbed one of the clipped sites. Nonetheless, sampling was continued to allow a comparison between a ray-disturbed and an undisturbed area. In August 1973, all four sites were completely disturbed by the cownose rays, leaving no possibility for further comparisons.

The second disturbance experiment, initiated in August 1974 at Browns Bay, consisted of six treatments: a control; a plot in which eelgrass was clipped; a plot in which the sediment surface was disturbed by vigorous hand movement through the sediment; two plots in which a board was moved across the sediment surface 10 and 20 times, respectively, to simulate wave activity; and a plot employing a predator exclusion cage. All plots except for the cage were 0.1 m^2. The cage was constructed of 3/8-inch steel reinforcing rods covered with galvanized wire mesh (1/2-inch openings). The dimensions of the cage were 50 cm x 50 cm x 20 cm high with the bottom sides of the cage penetrating 3 cm into the sediment. Thirty-six plots were established in August (six treatments with six replicates per treatment), of which twelve (six treatments with two replicates per treatment) were sampled in September, October, and November 1974. Each disturbance plot was disturbed approximately every other day until it was sampled. Plots sampled in September were disturbed 12 times, those in October 21 times and those in November 30 times. *Zostera* in the clipped plots was cut when the grass was more than one cm above the sediment surface. Cages were cleaned as deemed appropriate.

Five infauna cores and one sediment core were taken from each plot at the time of sampling. *Zostera* was clipped at each plot immediately before sampling to prevent contamination with the associated epifauna. Samples were washed through a 0.5-mm mesh screen.

Qualitative observations were made on sediment stability with the use of sediments painted with Krylon fluorescent paint. Sediment was collected from the surface of the *Zostera* bed at Browns Bay, dried for 48 hr at 80°C, and sprayed with colored Krylon. A small circular patch (5 cm in diameter) of dyed sediment was placed on the sediment surface in the different treatments. The dispersion of this dyed patch was used as a measure of sediment mobility.

RESULTS

Habitat Studies

The infaunal community associated with *Zostera* beds in Chesapeake Bay is dominated by tube-dwelling polychaetes, oligochaetes and peracarid crustaceans (Orth 1973, 1975). Bivalves and other groups such as echinoderms, gastropods and insects constitute a small fraction (less than 10%) of the total fauna.

The numerically important polychaete families in this study

include the Spionidae, Chaetopteridae, Capitellidae, Syllidae and Nereidae. The oligochaete family Tubificidae, amphipod family Ampeliscidae and isopod family Idoteidae were also well represented.

Data from the transect at Sandy Point indicate significant differences in both sedimentological (Fig. 3) and infaunal (Fig. 5) characteristics within a particular *Zostera* bed and within *Zostera* patches of varying sizes. Results for the sediment samples from the six stations along the transect (Fig. 3) show that particle size and degree of sorting (data presented in phi [ϕ] units = $-\log_2$mm) are greatest and organic carbon content least in bare sand (stations 1 and 6). Particle size and degree of sorting decreased and organic carbon increased from the edges of the *Zostera* bed (stations 2 and 5) to station 4 where *Zostera* was most dense. The shift in modal size class is seen in the percent ϕ fractions where the 3-4 ϕ class is dominant at stations 3 and 4 against the 2-3 ϕ class in bare sand.

The biomass of *Zostera* at the four stations was: station 2--25.1 g; station 3--29.0 g; station 4--31.1 g; station 5--26.1 g.

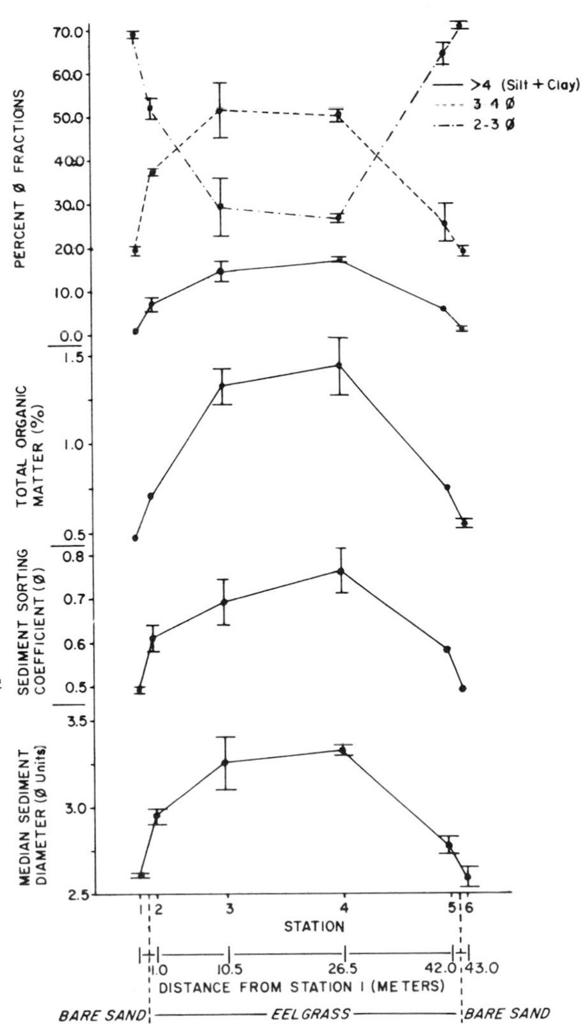

Fig. 3. Mean and range (two samples) for particle size distribution, total organic matter (%), sediment sorting coefficient (ϕ where ϕ [phi] = $-\log_2$mm), and median sediment diameter (ϕ) for the six stations on the transect across a *Zostera* bed at Sandy Point, July 1972. Those points without range bars have coincident values.

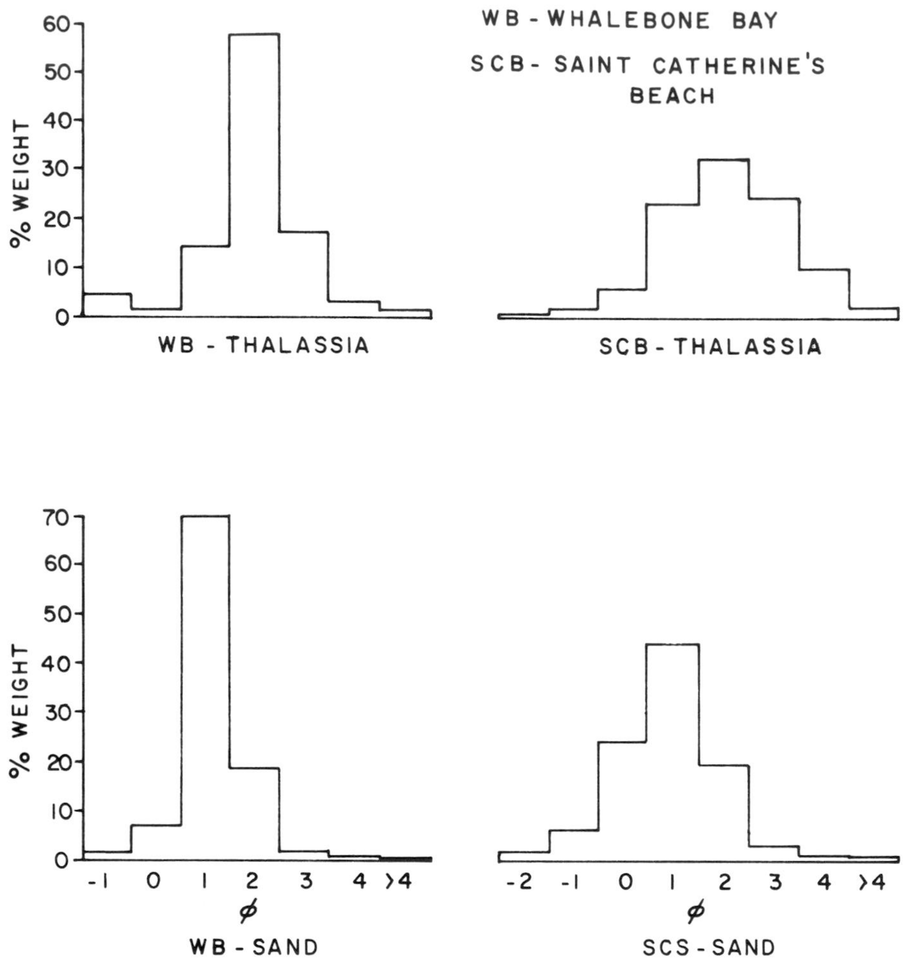

Fig. 4. Percentage frequency distribution for sediment fractions at Whalebone Bay and Saint Catherine's Beach.

Faunal results were analyzed for variance (ANOVA) (Fig. 5). Homogeneity of variances was tested by the F-max test (Sokal and Rohlf 1969). If evidence of heterogeneity was found ($p < 0.05$), the data were transformed (log [x+1]) and retested by F-max. In some cases where transformation was necessary, all statistical calculations were conducted in the transformed space and were back-transformed to the original scale for presentation in tables and graphs. For convenience, data that were transformed and then back-transformed are designated L-Tr. A-posteriori multiple comparisons were made between means by the Student-Newman-Keuls (SNK) procedure (Sokal and Rohlf 1969) when main effects were declared significant.

The number of species and individuals per core was minimal at both bare sand stations (stations 1 and 6), increased dramatically at the periphery of the *Zostera* bed (stations 2 and 5) and was most diverse and dense at station 4 (Fig. 5). Stations which did not

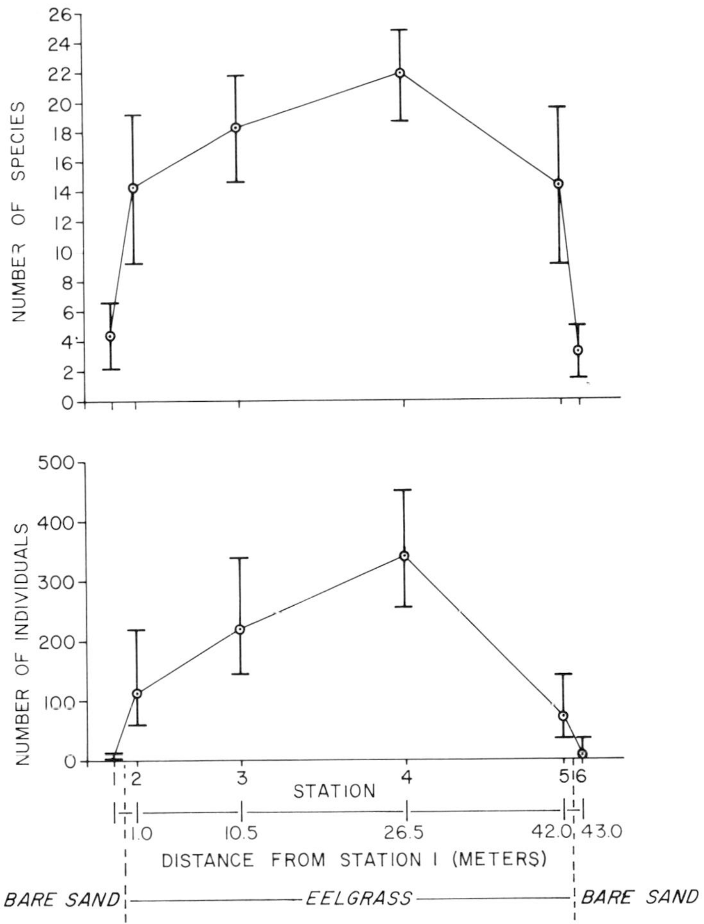

Fig. 5. Mean (⊙) and 95% confidence intervals ($\bar{X} \pm t_{.05}S_{\bar{x}}$, vertical line) for number of species per core and number of individuals (L-Tr) per core for the six stations along the transect across a *Zostera* bed at Sandy Point, July 1972. (L-Tr indicates data were log-transformed [log (x+1)] statistical calculations performed in the transformed space, and back-transformed to the original scale for presentation in figures.)

significantly differ ($p > 0.05$) in number of species were: 2, 3, and 5; 3 and 4; and 1 and 6. For number of individuals, the following stations were not significantly different: 2 and 3; 2 and 5; 3 and 4; and 1 and 6.

The polychaetes *Heteromastus filiformis* and *Streblospio benedicti* were the most abundant species at all stations and their distributional patterns were similar to that of mean number of species and individuals per core (Table 1). Other dominant species whose abundances also followed this pattern were *Peloscolex gabriellae* (oligochaete), *Nereis succinea* (polychaete), *Ampelisca vadorum* (amphipod) and *Edotea triloba* (isopod).

At the Bermuda sampling locations the grain size distribution

Table 1. Mean and 95% confidence intervals ($\bar{X} \pm t_{.05}S_{\bar{x}}$) for numbers of individuals (L-Tr) per core for the polychaetes *Heteromastus filiformis* and *Streblospio benedicti* found at each of the six stations sampled on the transect across the *Zostera* bed at Sandy Point. (L-Tr indicates data were log-transformed [log (x+1)], statistical calculations performed in the transformed space, and back-transformed to the original scale for presentation in tables.)

Station	*Heteromastus*	*Streblospio*
1	2.4 (0.2- 8.4)	0
2	20.8 (9.6-48.3)	45.9 (27.9- 75.0)
3	35.7 (28.8-44.4)	89.7 (61.0-131.7)
4	43.8 (24.3-78.4)	156.1 (120.0-203.1)
5	31.1 (17.4-58.1)	7.7 (1.5- 29.5)
6	5.3 (0.7-22.3)	0

shifted toward finer grain sizes in the *Thalassia* beds (Fig. 4). Median grain size decreased in *Thalassia* at both locations (WB--0.64 ϕ to 1.52 ϕ; SCB--0.36 ϕ to 1.49 ϕ) as did the degree of sorting (WB--0.50 ϕ to 0.74 ϕ; SCB--0.92 ϕ to 1.14 ϕ).

In Whalebone Bay, the infauna of *Thalassia* was much more diverse than in bare sand (Fig. 6).

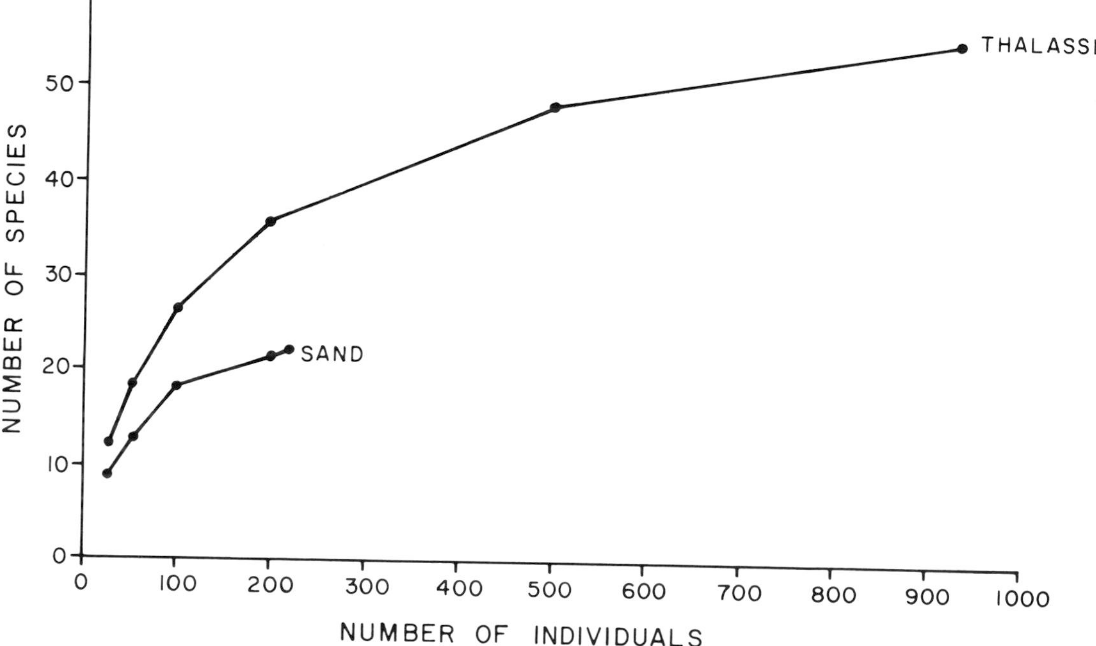

Fig. 6. Rarefaction curves (Sanders 1968) for *Thalassia* and sand stations in Whalebone Bay. The end point of each curve is the number of species and individuals found at each station.

Manipulative Studies and Response to Disturbances

At Sandy Point, where the first manipulation study was conducted, the data for number of species and individuals (L-Tr) per core were analyzed by a 4 x 4 factorial ANOVA (4 treatments--the two control sites, clipped site and the cownose ray sites; 4 months--September, December 1972, March and July 1973). Table 2 shows the mean number of species per core and number of individuals (L-Tr) per core with ranges of means which are not significantly different (p > 0.005) from each other (SNK procedure).

Table 2. Mean number of species per core and number of individuals (L-Tr) per core for the disturbance experiment conducted at Sandy Point, August 1972 to September 1973. Horizontal lines beneath means indicate groups of means which are not significantly different (p>0.05) from each other. Stations 1 and 2 are controls, station 3 is the cownose ray-disturbed station and station 4 is the clipped station (see Table 1 for explanation of L-Tr).

	SPECIES				INDIVIDUALS			
				SEPTEMBER				
Station	3	4	1	2	3	4	1	2
Mean	4.2	8.8	12.8	13.8	8.4	29.3	73.5	75.4
				DECEMBER				
Station	3	4	2	1	3	4	2	1
Mean	6.0	9.4	11.0	14.8	11.3	35.7	80.1	95.2
				MARCH				
Station	3	1	4	2	3	4	1	2
Mean	3.8	12.4	12.8	14.4	5.8	71.3	118.7	147.6
				JULY				
Station	3	4	1	2	3	4	2	1
Mean	5.8	7.4	9.6	9.8	10.2	19.1	28.6	42.2

The August 1972 and September 1973 data were excluded from this analysis and analyzed with a one-way ANOVA; the August data were taken prior to any disturbances (i.e., there were no treatment effects) while the September data, because of the ray disturbances at all sites, could not be compared with previous sampling periods. The four sites were not significantly different (p > 0.05) during these two periods in number of species or individuals (L-Tr) per core.

Clipping of *Zostera* reduced the number of species and individuals in relation to the controls, except in March when station 1 (control) was similar to station 4 (clipped site) (Fig. 7, Table 2).

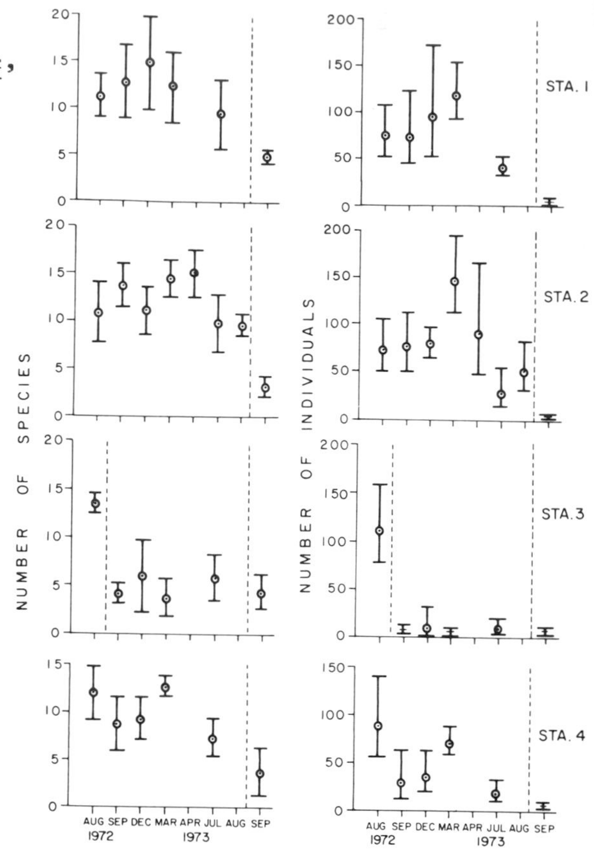

Fig. 7. Mean (⊙) and 95% confidence intervals ($\bar{X} \pm t_{.05}S_{\bar{x}}$, vertical line) for number of species per core and number of individuals (L-Tr) per core. Stations 1 and 2 are controls, station 3 was disturbed by cownose rays in August 1972, and station 4 was disturbed by clipping the leaves. Dashed vertical line indicates the date when cownose ray disturbance was observed at Sandy Point (see Fig. 5 for explanation of L-Tr).

Following the ray disturbance in August 1972, station 3 was significantly different ($p < 0.05$) from other stations at all sampling periods except for July 1973, when the number of species was not significantly different ($p > 0.05$). The densities of individuals and species at station 3 were similar to those in surrounding unvegetated sand areas. Sand ripples were observed at this station after the disturbance whereas before they were absent and were not seen in areas where *Zostera* was present.

All stations were sampled in September 1973, shortly after the rays disturbed all stations in August and virtually decimated the entire *Zostera* system (leaves, roots and rhizomes) in the area (Orth 1975). The densities of individuals and species at all stations were similar to surrounding unvegetated areas.

The recruitment of many dominant species occurred in late fall and early spring, as evidenced by the presence of many juveniles in December and March samples. At the clipped site (station 4), *Polydora ligni*, *Spiochaetopterus oculatus*, *Heteromastus filiformis*, *Nereis succinea* and *Peloscolex gabriellae*, the five numerically dominant species throughout the study period, were sampled in far fewer numbers than at either control station (1 and 2). The ray-disturbed station (station 3) had the lowest numbers of individuals for each species except for *Nereis* and *Polydora* in July 1973.

At the Browns Bay experimental area replicate plots (one-way ANOVA) did not differ significantly ($p > 0.05$) in number of species and number of individuals (L-Tr) per core. A 3 x 6 (months x treatments) factorial analysis of variance was run with a total of 10 cores for each treatment. The SNK procedure was used to test for differences among means.

In a subjective ranking of all treatments as to the degree of disturbance, the caged treatment represented the lowest level of disturbance, followed by the control, 10 board movements, 20 board movements and the hand treatment. The clipped treatment represented the highest level of disturbance.

In this three-month experiment, the effect of the board movements was to significantly reduce ($p < 0.05$) the number of species per core from that of the control (Fig. 8). The disturbance with 20 board movements generally had fewer species per core but this difference was never significant.

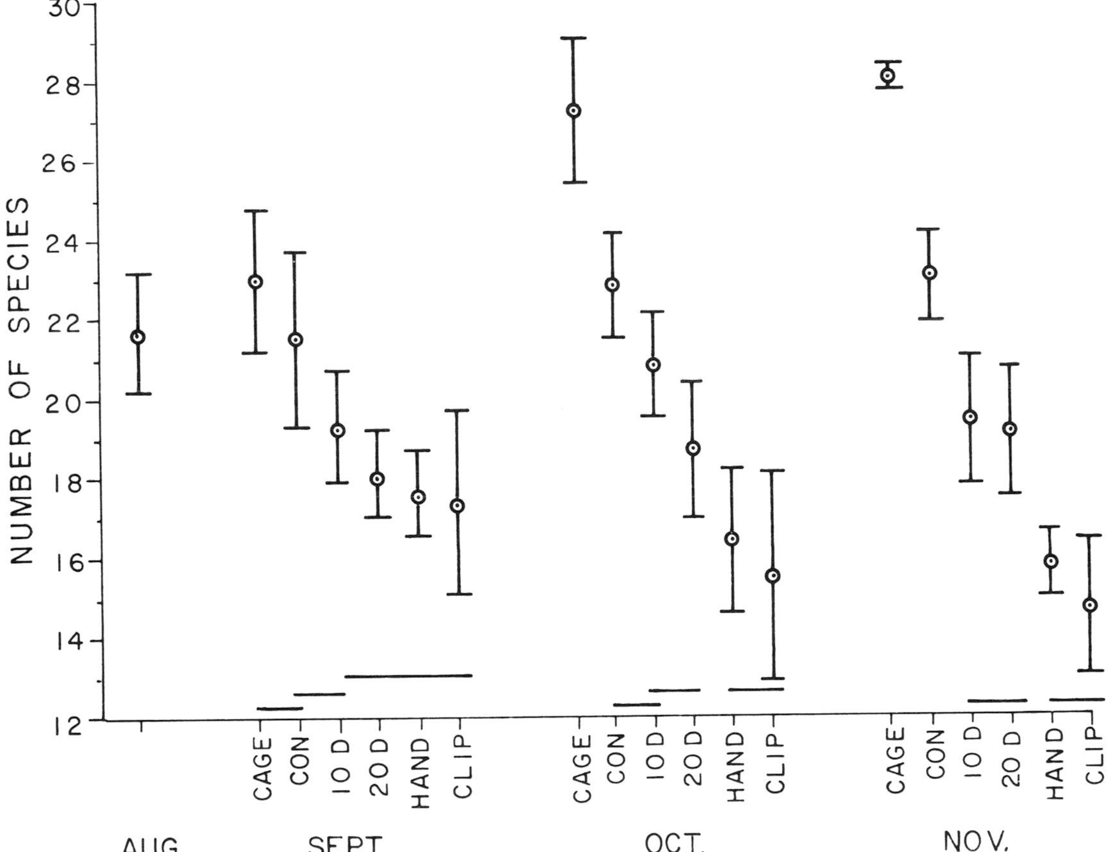

Fig. 8. Mean (⊙) and 95% confidence intervals ($\bar{X} \pm t_{.05}S_{\bar{x}}$, vertical line) for number of species per core for the disturbance experiment at Browns Bay, 1974 (see text for explanation of treatment). Horizontal lines above treatment designations (CON-control; 10D= board disturbance with 10 movements; 20 D=board disturbance with 20 movements; HAND=hand disturbance; CLIP=clipped disturbance; CAGE= caged treatment) indicate groups of means which are not significantly different ($p > 0.05$) from each other.

Within two months, the hand and clip disturbance (representing the highest levels of disturbance) significantly reduced ($p < 0.05$) the number of species per core more so than all other treatments. The cage treatment representing minimal disturbance increased significantly ($p < 0.05$) in number of species per core inside the cage and was significantly greater than all other treatments by October (Fig. 8).

The response of the total number of individuals per core followed a similar pattern as described above for the number of species per core with the exception of the board movement treatments. The cage had significantly more ($p < 0.05$) individuals per core than all other treatments by October (Fig. 9). The clipped treatment had the fewest number of individuals per core and was significantly lower ($p < 0.05$) than all other treatments including the hand disturbance by October (Fig. 9).

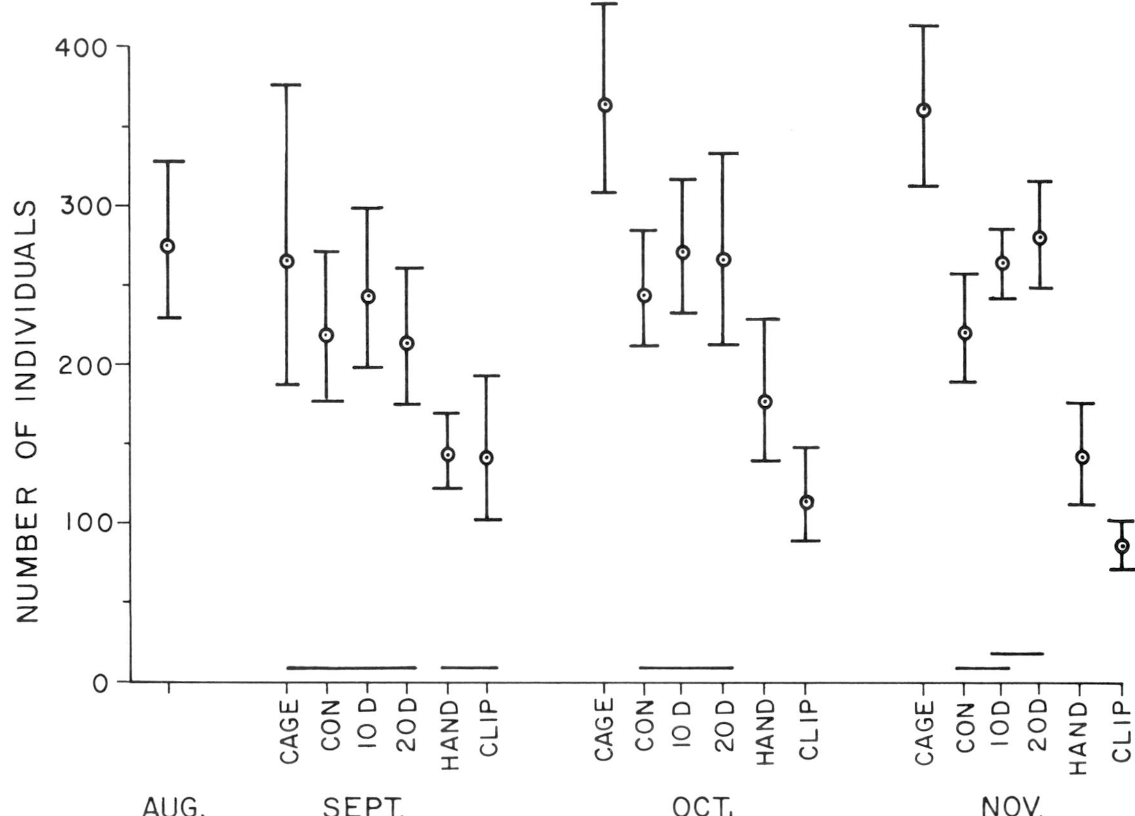

Fig. 9. Mean (⊙) and 95% confidence intervals ($\bar{X} \pm t_{.05}S_{\bar{x}}$, vertical line) for number of individuals (L-Tr) per core for the disturbance experiment at Browns Bay, 1974 (see text for explanation of treatments). Horizontal lines above treatment designations (see Fig. 8) indicate groups of means which are not significantly different from each other (see Fig. 5 for explanation of L-Tr).

Treatments with board movements were not significantly different ($p > 0.05$) from the control except in November where the 20 board treatment was significantly greater ($p < 0.05$) than the control (Fig. 9). There were more individuals in these two disturbances than in the control in October and November, but as mentioned above, this was significant in one case only.

Increased numbers in the board treatments were due primarily to an increase in the polychaete, *Polydora ligni*. The board disturbance removed the top sediment layer and exposed the rhizomes of *Zostera*, which increased the amount of space available for setting of *Polydora*. The mean density of *Polydora* per core for the control, 10 and 20 board treatments for October was 23.8, 56.5 and 59.8, and for November, 36.8, 77.7 and 87.3 individuals per core, respectively. *Polydora* also increased in abundance in relation to the control inside the cages (49.6 individuals in October, 60.2 individuals per core in November) where the rhizome layer remained unexposed. The increased stability of the sediments inside the cage along with the cage's effect of trapping larvae and protecting them from predators may have enhanced the settlement and survival of *Polydora*.

The ostracod, *Sarsiella zostericola*, which inhabits the sediment surface, was adversely affected by any disturbance of the surface. Very few individuals were found in the board, hand and clip disturbances (less than 0.1 individual per core), whereas in the cage, there was a significant increase over the control (14.4 vs 2.5 individuals in October; 12.3 vs 1.5 individuals per core in November). Ovigerous *Sarsiella* were found in September and October and the containment of the newly released young within the cages, because of increased sediment stability, resulted in greater numbers for this treatment.

Gemma gemma, small venerid bivalve, is found in many shifting sand environments. With the removal of *Zostera* in the clipped treatments, *Gemma* density increased in successive months (4.0, 10.2, 14.4 individuals per core for September, October and November) as opposed to the control (2.7, 6.6 and 3.7 individuals per core) and the cage (8.0, 5.8, 5.8 individuals per core) for the three-month sampling period. *Gemma* was absent from the board and hand treatments because these disturbances removed or disturbed their habitat (the sediment surface layer). Amphipods have been blamed for the absence of bivalves in some areas because they ingest juvenile bivalves (Segerstraale 1962, 1965, 1973; Vassallo, 1969) and the nearly complete absence of the amphipod *Ampelisca vadorum* from the clipped sites (it was abundant both in the control and cage sites--24 individuals per core in November) may partly explain this increase in *Gemma*.

Studies conducted with dyed sediments and visual observation during periods of heavy wave activity indicated that sediments were most stable in the cage, less stable in the control, and least stable in the clipped areas. The dispersion of dyed sediments in the clipped area was similar to that in the sandy, unvegetated areas. Sand ripples which are characteristic of wave- and current-exposed environments, were observed, in time, in the clipped area.

DISCUSSION

The instability of the shallow bare sand environment accounts for the lack of species and individuals in this habitat. On the other hand, how can so many species and individuals coexist in the grass beds? Numerous factors are involved. Many species are recruited as larval forms, whose behavioral responses to substrate, light, dissolved oxygen, salinity, and presence of conspecifics or other species, may all influence their settlement (Gray 1974). Although the reaction of larvae of soft-bottom species to water currents is not well known, it is reasonable to expect that if larvae behave passively, the baffling effect of seagrass beds would cause them to preferentially settle out in the bed. The grass bed may selectively trap those larvae with certain behavioral adaptations and prevent their further dispersal by currents.

Once larvae have settled in the grass bed, neither physical nor biological processes are likely to remove juveniles and adults from the habitat. Sediment stability, as evidenced by the movement of dyed sediments, is dependent upon density of grass and proximity to bare sand. This relationship was evident during periods of storm activity. *Zostera* beds and adjacent bare sand areas immediately after a storm indicated erosion of sediments in unvegetated areas of up to 10-20 cm. Sand ripples were obvious features of unvegetated bottoms, their height and wave length depending on the intensity of the storm. The edges of the *Zostera* bed commonly protruded above the adjacent sand areas with roots and rhizomes exposed along these edges. The tubes of some species (e.g., *Ampelisca vadorum* and *Sabella microphthalma*) were exposed among the rhizomes and many were still inhabited. Inside the bed, however, sand ripples were not obvious and the rhizome system was never exposed. Species found in the sediment surface layer (e.g., *Gemma*, *Sarsiella*, and non-tube building polychaetes) were absent from the exposed edges, apparently having been washed away by heavy wave action. At Sandy Point, there was a net loss of 15 to 30 cm of sediment in the study area after the entire *Zostera* bed was eliminated by cownose ray activity.

Leaf blades can increase the complexity of the substrate, and may therefore be important to sessile species requiring an attachment site for initial settlement. Adults of some dominant species (e.g., *Ampelisca vadorum* and *Sabella microphthalma*) were found in unattached tubes in the sediment, but tubes of juveniles were usually attached to the leaf bases or other solid objects. However, this is a limited resource since leaf blades are limited in number. Moreover, in the winter months eelgrass epifauna move into the sediment and remain attached to the blade, e.g., the gastropods *Crepidula convexa* and *Bittium varium* (Orth 1973).

Predation, primarily by motile predators, may significantly decrease both the number of species and their total abundance in soft sediment environments (Woodin 1974; Virnstein 1976). In Chesapeake Bay, blue crabs, *Callinectes sapidus*, seem to be important predators of infauna (personal observation; Virnstein 1976. They obtain their prey either by thrusting their chelae into the sediment to obtain shallow, surface dwelling animals or by using their chelae and walking legs to dig holes 6-12 cm deep to gather deeper dwelling animals.

In excavating the hole, the blue crab scoops up mud and sand with the chelae and walking legs, and carries the sediment in the crook of the chela. The crab thus forms an inclined excavation and moves up and down the incline as it digs deeper and deposits the sediment on the surface. Using the chelae and fifth walking leg, the crab loosens the sediment in the hole and thus facilitates further digging. During digging, the crab will pick at the sides of the hole with the chelae to feed upon infaunal animals.

Blue crabs do not appear to prey heavily on *Zostera* infauna because the thick rhizome mat 2 cm beneath the sediment surface prevents them from digging far beneath the surface. This impediment confines their foraging in *Zostera* to the top 1 or 2 cm of sediment. As most of the *Zostera* infauna dwell in tubes that extend beneath the rhizome layer, their ability to withdraw rapidly into their tubes prevent their being preyed upon.

When the protective rhizome layer was removed or thinned out, blue crabs could penetrate these areas. Blue crab holes were observed in the clipped plot at Sandy Point in July 1973, but were absent from the adjacent dense eelgrass bed. Clipping apparently reduced the density and biomass of the rhizome layer.

Blue crabs were frequently observed to feed on *Zostera* epibiota by grabbing the leaves at the base with their chelae and passing it through their mandibles, removing the epibiota in the process. Thus, because of the protective rhizome layer and the accessibility of the epibiota, the impact of blue crabs may be greater on epifaunal members of the *Zostera* community than on the infauna.

Experimental stabilization of sediments lacking seagrasses had the same effect on infauna as seagrasses. Caging in the York River undertaken simultaneously with this study resulted in an infaunal community similar to that found in *Zostera* (Virnstein 1976). The variety and abundance of dominant species were similar. Cages appeared to stabilize the sediment surface and exclude the same predators which are deterred by the rhizome mat. The increase in species richness and density of benthos in caged areas in the *Zostera* bed (Figs. 8, 9) is apparently a result of greater sediment stability.

Many of the numerically dominant species in Virnstein's studies (1976), e.g., *Heteromastus filiformis*, *Streblospio benedicti*, *Glycinde solitaria* and *Peloscolex gabriellae*, are widely distributed in Chesapeake Bay. However, they reach their greatest abundance on deeper bottoms in lower salinity regions (10-20 °/₀₀) and disturbed areas such as those affected by pollution (Boesch 1977). Their ability to colonize these habitats may be related to the absence of more stenotolerant species which might otherwise preclude these eurytolerant opportunists. Shallow water environments (e.g., less than 3 m) are physiologically stressful because of variable and extreme temperatures and can be exploited only by species tolerant of these conditions.

In this study diversity and density of infauna were reduced according to levels of disturbance, the most intense effect being total removal of the *Zostera* system by cownose rays. Natural wave activity is probably not as intense as simulated by the board movements in this study except along the edges of the grass bed. Board movements across the surface exposed the rhizomes, but they were never seen in a dense *Zostera* bed except at the edges, even after intense storm activity. There appeared to be little sediment movement in the eelgrass bed because roots exposed by the disturbance were not covered by sediments during the course of the study.

Seagrass systems have a major impact on shallow water sediments by baffling waves and currents and preventing erosion. This effect is most evident after the loss of a seagrass system from a particular area (Wilson 1949; Maggi 1973; Orth 1975; Rasmussen 1973). Seagrass systems stabilize sediments, allow for increased settlement of infaunal larvae and prevent juveniles and adults from being resuspended and transported away. Disturbances within the system which could reduce the diversity and density of species, e.g., waves and predation, are mitigated by the presence of seagrasses.

REFERENCES

Boesch, D. F. 1977. A new look at the distribution of benthos along the estuarine gradient, p.245-266. In B. C. Coull [ed.], Ecology of marine benthos. Belle W. Baruch Library in Marine Science, v. 6. Univ. South Carolina Press.

Buchanan, J. B. 1963. The bottom fauna communities and their sediment relationships off the coast of Northumberland. Oikos 14: 155-175.

Coull, B. C. 1970. Shallow water meiobenthos of the Bermuda platform. Oecologia 4: 325-357.

Day, J. H., J. G. Field, and M. Montgomery. 1971. The use of numerical methods to determine the distribution of the benthic fauna across the continental shelf of North Carolina. J. Anim. Ecol. 40: 93-126.

Dexter, D. M. 1969. Structure of an intertidal sandy-beach community in North Carolina. Chesapeake Sci. 10: 93-98.

_____. 1972. Comparison of the community structures in a Pacific and an Atlantic Panamanian sandy beach. Bull. Mar. Sci. 22: 419-462.

Fager, E. W. 1964. Marine sediments: Effects of tube-building polychaete. Science 143: 356-359.

Folk, R. L. 1968. Petrology of sedimentary rocks. Hemphill's, Austin, TX. 170 pp.

Ginsburg, R. M. and H. A. Lowenstam. 1958. The influence of marine bottom communities on the depositional environment of sediments. J. Geol. 66: 310-318.

Gray, J. S. 1974. Animal-sediment relationships. Oceanogr. Mar. Biol. Ann. Rev. 12: 223-261.
Hartog, G. den. 1970. The seagrasses of the world. North-Holland.
Maggi, P. 1973. Le problème de la disparition des berbiers à Posidonies dans le Golfe de Giens (var). Science et Pêche. Bull. Inst. Pêches Marit. 221: 7-20.
Mason, W. T. and P. P. Yevich. 1967. The use of Phloxine. B and Rose Bengal to facilitate sorting benthic samples. Trans. Amer. Micros. Soc. 86: 221-223.
Mills, E. L. 1967. The biology of an ampeliscid amphipod crustacean sibling species pair. J. Fish. Res. Bd. Can. 24: 305-355.
Ogden, J. C., R. A. Brown, and N. Salesky. 1973. Grazing by the echinoid *Diadema antillarum* Philippi: Formation of halos around West Indian patch reefs. Science 182: 715-717.
O'Gower, A. K. and J. W. Wacasey. 1967. Animal communities associated with *Thalassia, Diplanthera*, and sand beds in Biscayne Bay. I. Analysis of communities in relation to water movement. Bull. Mar. Sci. 17: 175-210.
Orth, R. J. 1973. Benthic infauna of eelgrass, *Zostera marina*, beds. Chesapeake Sci. 14: 258-269.
_____. 1975. Destruction of eelgrass, *Zostera marina,* by the cownose ray, *Rhinoptera bonasus*, in the Chesapeake Bay. Chesapeake Sci. 16: 205-208.
_____ and H. Gordon. 1975. Remote sensing of submerged aquatic vegetation in the lower Chesapeake Bay. Final Report to National Aeronautics and Space Administration. Contract No. NASI-10720.
Randall, J. E. 1965. Grazing effect on sea grasses by herbivorous reef fishes in the West Indies. Ecology 46: 255-260.
Rasmussen, E. 1973. Systematics and ecology of the Isefjord marine fauna (Denmark). Ophelia 11: 1-495.
Rhoads, D. C. 1974. Organism-sediment relations on the muddy sea floor. Oceanogr. Mar. Biol. Ann. Rev. 12: 263-300.
_____ and D. K. Young. 1970. The influence of deposit-feeding organisms on sediment stability and community trophic structure. J. Mar. Res. 28: 150-178.
_____ and _____. 1971. Animal-sediment relations in Cape Cod Bay, Massachusetts. II. Reworking by *Molpadia oolitica* (Holothuroidea). Mar. Biol. 11: 255-261.
Sanders, H. L. 1968. Marine benthic diversity: A comparative study. Amer. Nat. 102: 243-282.
Santos, S. L. and J. L. Simon. 1974. Distribution and abundance of the polychaetous annelids in a South Florida estuary. Bull. Mar. Sci. 24: 669-689.
Segerstraale, S. G. 1962. Investigations on Baltic populations of the bivalve *Macoma balthica* (L.). Part II. What are the reasons for the periodic failure of recruitment and the scarcity of *Macoma* in the deeper waters of the inner Baltic? Commentat. Biol. 24: 1-26.

_____. 1965. Biotic factors affecting the vertical distribution and abundance of the bivalve, *Macoma balthica* (L.) in the Blatic Sea. Bot. Gothoburg 3: 195-204.

_____. 1973. Results of bottom fauna sampling in certain localities in the Tvärminne area (inner Baltic), with special reference to the so-called *Macoma-Pontoporeia* theory. Commentat. Biol. 67: 1-12.

Sokal, R. R. and F. J. Rohlf. 1969. Biometry. W. H. Freeman and Co.

Taylor, J. D. and M. S. Lewis. 1970. The flora, fauna and sediments of the marine grass beds of Mabé, Seychelles. J. Mat. Hist. 4: 199-220.

Vassallo, M. T. 1969. The ecology of *Macoma inconspicua* (Broderip and Sowerby, 1829) in Central San Francisco Bay. Part. I. The vertical distribution of the *Macoma* community. Veliger 11: 223-234.

Virnstein, R. W. 1976. The effects of predation by epibenthic crabs and fishes on benthic infauna in Chesapeake Bay. Ph.D. thesis, College of William and Mary. 86 p.

Wilson, D. P. 1949. The decline of *Zostera marina* at Salcombe and its effects on the shore. J. Mar. Biol. Ass. U.K. 28: 395-412.

Wood, E. J. F., W. E. Odum, and J. C. Zieman. 1969. Influence of sea grasses on the productivity of coastal lagoons, p. 495-502. In. Lagunas Costeras, un Simposia. Mem. Simp. Intern. Lagunas Costeras. UNAM-UNESCO.

Woodin, S. A. 1974. Polychaete abundance patterns in a marine soft-sediment environment: the importance of biological interactions. Ecol. Monogr. 44: 171-187.

Young, D. K. 1971. Effects of infauna on the sediment and seston of a subtidal environment. Vie Milieu 22 (Suppl.): 557-571.

Zieman, J. C. 1972. Origin of circular beds of *Thalassia* (Spermatophyta: Hydrocharitaceae) in South Biscayne Bay, Florida, and their relationship to mangrove hammocks. Bull. Mar. Sci. 22: 559-574.

Effects of Pollution on Inshore Benthos

A. D. McIntyre
Department of Agriculture and Fisheries of Scotland
Marine Laboratory, P. O. Box 101, Victoria Road
Torry, Aberdeen AB9 8 DB
Scotland

ABSTRACT

The coastal region is particularly subject to pollutants, but their effects on inshore benthos are difficult to assess because of the complex nature of that environment and the problem of distinguishing between natural and pollution-induced events. This problem was approached by a program of long-term experiments, biological assays and field observations. Some experiments involving a three-stage food chain over periods of several months indicated that low levels of pollutants, sometimes two orders of magnitude less than the LC_{50} value, can have significant adverse effects at all trophic levels studied. Other experiments showed that sea water from an industralized region could be less favorable than clean coastal water for growth and development of organisms. These conclusions are discussed in the light of field observations on benthic communities, and an attempt is made to estimate the level of organic input which will produce changes in such communities.

INTRODUCTION

Pollution of the seas is a fashionable concern at present, and shelf and coastal regions are clearly most susceptible. Pollutants have significantly altered the characteristic benthic communities of numerous areas. In particular, the dumping grounds for sewage sludge and dredged materials, and the terminal sections of effluent pipes from factories and refineries have been extensively studied. But these "hot spots" are usually of limited extent, where the damage can be observed and at least partly controlled, so that up to a point the consequences are understood and are the accepted result of a planned activity.

Some workers consider that the consequences of lower levels of pollution over a wider area should be a greater cause for concern, and urge that a fuller appreciation of these consequences is clearly required. This view is opposed by others who point out the difficulty of documenting a significant example of serious detrimental effects on marine communities in the field which can be attributed unequivocably to chronic pollution. Recently, a group of scientists examined relevant data from the North Sea in detail but was unable to identify any such effects on major fish species (Goldberg 1973). The demonstration of these effects would seem to demand a dual approach. First, experimental evidence is needed to demonstrate that the levels found in the environment can influence the species exposed to them. Second, it should be shown that such effects do indeed take place in nature and lead to the consequences predicted from the experiments. This paper describes some examples of relevant work from the Marine Laboratory, Aberdeen, and considers how they might be brought together to present an attack on the problems of sublethal pollution effects. The Firth of Clyde on the southwest coast of Scotland, a region of increasing industralization, was selected as a suitable study site of a polluted area, and the outer west coast of Scotland, particularly the sea loch, Loch Ewe, was chosen as a locality likely to provide a clean control (Fig. 1).

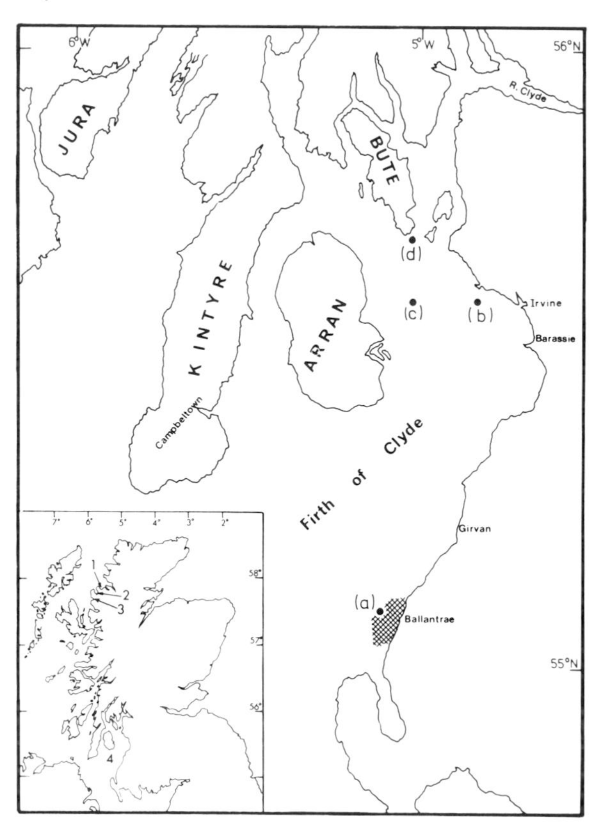

Fig. 1. Firth of Clyde, showing (a) the herring spawning ground (b) the inshore station for collecting "polluted" water (c) the offshore central Clyde station for "clean" water (d) the sewage sludge dumping ground. The inset shows locations referred to in the text, (1) Gruinard Bay (2) Loch Ewe (3) Gairloch, and indicates the relative position of the Firth of Clyde (4).

EXPERIMENTAL STUDIES ON FOOD CHAINS

The classical approach to the question of whether given levels of a contaminant affect an organism is to employ some form of LC_{50} experiment, in which one or more individuals of a species to be tested are subjected to a range of concentrations for a limited period (usually measured in hours) and the number of dead counted. While this can give values useful for some purposes, its disadvantages are well recognized, particularly that it deals only with the short-term acute problems, and that the experiment usually places individual organisms in a highly artificial situation. In order to study sub-lethal levels, workers are increasingly turning to more appropriate experiments. During the past seven years a more sophisticated arrangement has been in use at Aberdeen in which a simplified eco-system involving several trophic levels of a food web is subjected under experimental conditions to low concentrations of pollutants for several months.

The ecosystem which we have used most involves primary producers, herbivores and predators represented by phytoplankton, a benthic bivalve, and a species of juvenile flatfish. One great advantage of this food chain is that we have been studying it both in the field and experimentally in a general ecological context since 1963 and have acquired a good knowledge of its structure and dynamics. Therefore, we have had the advantage of working with a reasonably well understood system (Steele et al. 1970). The experimental format (Fig. 2), consists of a set of fiberglass tanks (measuring 3.7 x 1.8 x 1.2 m) each containing a layer of sterile dune sand 10-cm deep, stocked

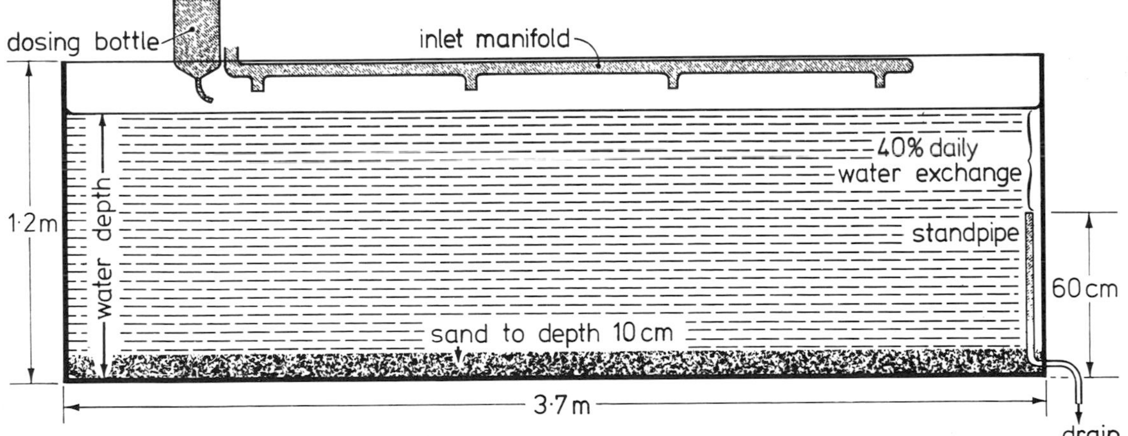

Fig. 2. A unit of the series of fiberglass tanks in food chain pollution experiments.

with 3,000 individuals of the bivalve, *Tellina tenuis*, and 40 specimens of the newly settled stage of the flatfish, *Pleuronectes platessa*. Clean water is pumped daily from the sea into a large settlement tank which feeds by gravity into the experimental tanks, giving a water exchange rate of 40% of the tank volume daily. This provides a simplified simulation of the food web in the nearby Sandy Bay, with sea water providing the natural phytoplanktonic food for the stocked bivalves. These in turn are preyed on by the fish cropping the bivalve siphons, which are thereafter regenerated. A new experiment can be set up each year in the spring when the young fish first appear on the bottom and is usually continued until at least the autumn so that data for several months are available.

Pollutants in amounts calculated to give predetermined concentrations in the water are added to the tanks daily when the water is exchanged, and three replicated pollutant levels plus a control are generally used. The highest pollutant level is selected to give a concentration about one-tenth of the 96 hr LC_{50}, the lowest at about two or three times that actually found in the sea and the remaining level approximately intermediate between the others. Experiments so far have used copper, mercury, cadmium and lead, and selected combinations of these as well as some organochlorines. Concentration levels in the water, the sand, the tank walls and the organisms are monitored regularly (Saward et al 1975).

An obvious objection to extrapolating experimental results to the sea, is that the field situation is much more complex. In an attempt to overcome this objection some of the contaminants were used in pairs and, further, selected tanks were treated with nutrients. Results from some of the copper and mercury experiments which are summarized in Table 1 indicate that copper, added as aqueous copper sulphate, has significant effects at all concentrations (10, 30 and 100 µg Cu/l) on all levels of the food chain: reduction in phytoplankton activity, decline in bivalve condition, and decrease in fish growth. Mercury concentrations of 0.1, 1.0 and 10 µg Hg/l, added as aqueous mercuric chloride, showed similar, but less marked effects, In the tanks enriched with nitrogen (3.0 µg at NO_3-N/l) and phosphorus (0.6 µg at PO_4-P/l) no significant modification was observed in the copper or mercury effects; an important result since earlier experiments (Trevallion et al 1973) had shown that such levels of enrichment were beneficial to both phytoplankton and *Tellina* When copper and mercury at the intermediate dose levels were applied together, no synergistic effects were observed.

A general feature of all these experiments is that food chain effects can be examined. Since the plaice did not eat whole *Tellina* but merely cropped the siphons, which contained little contamination, no trophic level build-up was observed. However, food chain interaction could be adduced to explain some of the effects; for example, the reduction in primary production resulting from copper treatment had deleterious effects at all higher trophic levels.

Tellina from an industrialized beach on the Clyde coast were analyzed as a check on how the experimental data compares with field conditions, and levels of 200-300 µg Cu/g dry flesh were measured. This result compares with 270 µg Cu/g in specimens from the 10 µg Cu/l tanks after 100 days exposure and contrasts with 50 µg Cu/g in control animals. We thus seem to be dealing with a realistic experiment in that levels of accumulation which produced decreased growth in tanks were similar to levels found in the field. It could still be argued that even with the addition of pairs of contaminants together with nutrients, the experimental medium was still far from a close simulation of Clyde water, which is contaminated by a vast range of material from domestic waste, industrial effluent, agricultural run-off and petroleum.

Table 1. Effects of copper and mercury on the three main components of the *Tellina*-plaice food chain.

	Treatment	Effects
Effects on Phytoplankton	COPPER Dose levels 10, 30 and 100 μg/l	STANDING CROP (Chlorophyll a and total pigment levels). Reduced at all dose levels. TOTAL CARBON FIXATION/CHLOROPHYLL a. Reduced at all dose levels.
	MERCURY Dose levels 0.1, 1.0 and 10 μg/l	STANDING CROP Reduced at all dose levels. TOTAL CARBON FIXATION/CHLOROPHYLL a. Reduced for dose levels for 1.0 and 10 μg/l, however significantly higher for dose level of 0.1 μg/l.
	COPPER (10 μg/l) plus NUTRIENT ENRICHMENT (3.0 μg atoms NO_3-N/L 0.6 μg atoms PO_4 P/L)	STANDING CROP. Algicidal effect of copper not significantly modified by nutrient addition. TOTAL CARBON FIXATION/CHLOROPHYLL a. Indications that photosynthetic inhibition slightly less in the presence of nutrients. Results insignificant.
	MERCURY (1.0 μg/l) plus NUTRIENT ENRICHMENT (3.0 μg atoms NO_3-N/L 0.6 μg atoms PO_4-P/L)	STANDING CROP. Algicidal effect not significantly modified. TOTAL CARBON FIXATION/CHLOROPHYLL a. Mean level lower than control, however on certain sampling occasions levels not significantly different from control levels.
	COPPER (10 μg/l) plus MERCURY (1.0 μg/l)	Effects of copper alone not significantly modified by the addition of mercury. Effects more marked than for mercury alone.
Effects on *Tellina*	COPPER Dose levels 10, 30 and 100 μg/l	CONDITION (Dry flesh weight/standard length). Lower at all dose levels. NITROGEN LEVELS. Lower at all dose levels. CARBOHYDRATE LEVELS. Lower at all dose levels. For 10 and 30 μg/l levels not particularly evident until later in the experiment as winter reserves were being deposited. SIPHON WEIGHT. Reduced at dose levels of 30 and 100 μg/l.
	MERCURY Dose levels 0.1, 1.0 and 10 μg/l	CONDITION. No effect. CARBOHYDRATE LEVELS. Lower at dose level μg/l during later stages of the experiment. Similar to control levels at dose concentration 1.0 μg/l. Markedly higher at dose level 0.1 μg/l. SIPHON REGENERATION. Reduced at dose levels 1.0 and 10 μg/l.
	COPPER (10 μg/l) plus NUTRIENT ENRICHMENT (3.0 μg atoms NO_3-N/L 0.6 μg atoms PO_4-P/L)	Effects of copper not significantly modified by the addition of nutrients.
	MERCURY (1.0 μg/l) plus NUTRIENT ENRICHMENT (3.0 μg atoms NO_3-N/L 0.6 μg atoms PO_4-P/L)	Reduction in carbohydrate reserves, no other significant effect. Reserves of carbohydrate did not differ markedly from those of control tank.
	COPPER (10 μg/l) plus MERCURY (1.0 μg/l)	Effects of copper alone not significantly modified by the addition of mercury. Effects more marked than for mercury alone.
Effects of Plaice	COPPER Dose levels 10, 30 and 100 μg/l	GROWTH. Reduced at all dose levels. Greater reduction for dose levels of 30 and 100 μg/l. CONDITION (Weight/length^3 x 100). Reduced in all ranks including controls. No significant effect of copper.
	MERCURY Dose levels 0.1, 1.0 and 10 μg/l	GROWTH. Reduced at all dose levels. Effects not so marked as those of copper and apparently not concentration dependent. CONDITION. Reduced in all tanks including controls. No significant effect of mercury.
	COPPER (10 μg/l) plus NUTRIENT ENRICHMENT (3.0 μg atoms NO_3-N/L 0.6 μg atoms PO_4-P/L)	Effects of copper alone not significantly modified by the addition of nutrients.
	MERCURY (1.0 μg/l) plus NUTRIENT ENRICHMENT (3.0 μg atoms NO_3-N/L 0.6 μg atoms PO_4-P/L)	Effects of mercury alone not significantly modified by the addition of nutrients.
	COPPER (10 μg/l) plus MERCURY (1.0 μg/l)	Effects of copper alone not significantly modified by the addition of mercury.

EXPERIMENTAL STUDIES WITH DIFFERENT TYPES OF NATURAL WATER

The obvious next step towards the natural situation was to conduct the experiments using water collected from polluted areas. The *Tellina*-plaice food chain simulation was not feasible because of the large volume of water required. Instead, herring eggs were used as the experimental material since Ballantrae Bank in the Clyde is an important spawning ground for this species (Baxter and Steele 1973). The eggs are deposited as a sheet on a coarse gravel bottom and even-

Fig. 3. Percentage hatch for herring eggs reared in different copper treatments.

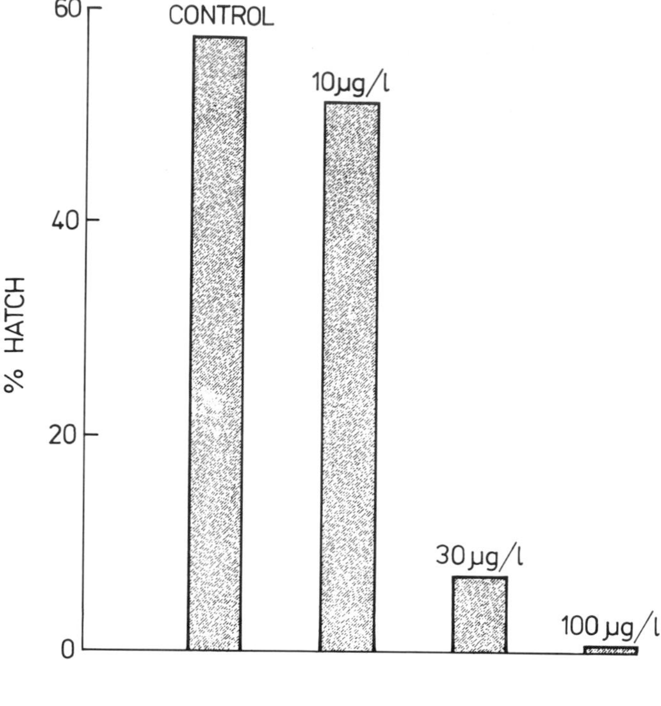

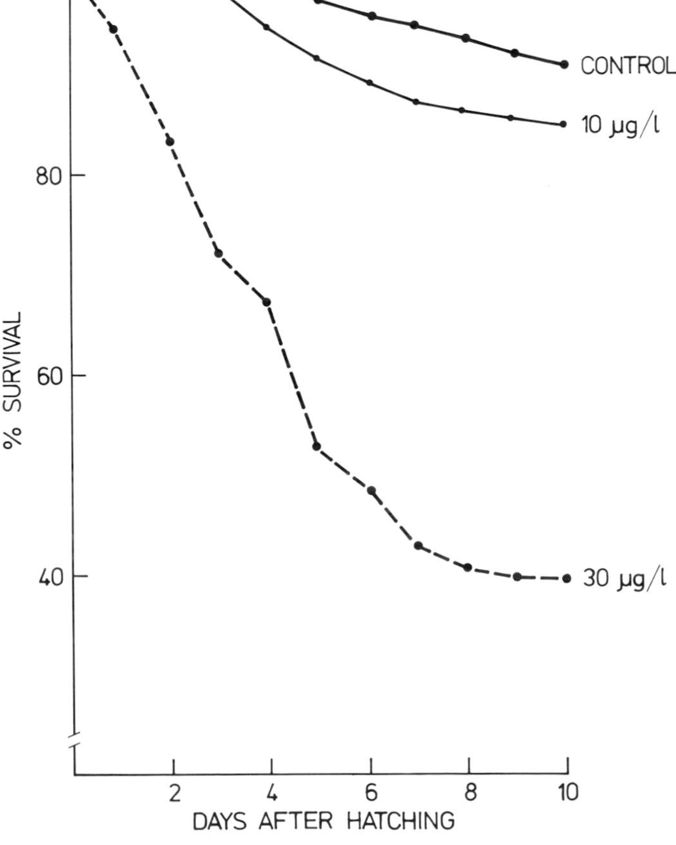

Fig. 4. Survival of newly hatched herring larvae in different copper treatments.

tually the larvae hatch and become pelagic. The copper experiment was repeated with herring eggs stripped from ripe females, fertilized artificially and deposited on glass slides which were then incubated at copper concentration of 10, 30 and 100 μg Cu/l. The results showed marked effects on the time to hatching of the eggs and on the percentage hatch (Fig. 3), as well as on the survival of the larvae (Fig. 4).

Using water from three sources in the Clyde with Loch Ewe water as a control, these experiments were continued in 1973. The first water source was the spawning bank area itself, the second a "clean" offshore area in the central Clyde, and the third a polluted coastal zone (Irvine Bay) through which larvae normally drift on passage to the nursery grounds (see Fig. 1). The results were conclusive, indicating that the coastal water in 1973 was least favorable for development of eggs as reflected in higher mortalities and shorter time to hatching (Fig. 5). Survival of larvae was also much lower in the coastal water (Fig. 6).

Attempts to detect the cause of differences were unsatisfactory. The four waters were analyzed for salinity, pH and various metals but no consistent and significant differences were detected. The one important difference was in BOD, which was substantially higher in the inshore water, an apparent symptom of the unfavorable quality, and an indicator of coastal influence.

In the following year, however, a similar set of experiments yielded results that were significally different from those of 1973. There were no clear differences in the time intervals to egg hatching, and larval mortality was negligible in all water types for the first 14 days after hatching (Baxter 1974). A comparison of nitrate and BOD levels in the various areas in 1973 and 1974 is perhaps significant. As shown in Table 2, the levels of both were much lower in 1974, and this can probably be correlated with important hydrographic differences in the two years. In 1972/73, winter rainfall was low, and the flushing of the Clyde sea area was reduced, causing a concentration of pollutants in inshore waters. In 1973/74, however, high rainfall led to a much greater rate of water exchange.

Table 2. Nitrate and BOD levels in different water types in the Clyde during 1973 and 1974. (from Baxter 1974)

Site	Nitrate μg at/l 1973	Nitrate μg at/l 1974	BOD mg/l 1973	BOD mg/l 1974
Ballantrae Bank	10.3	5.1	1.14	0.50
Irvine Bay	35.0	12.2	2.31	0.55

FIELD OBSERVATIONS

The approach described above took us nearer to field conditions, since we used natural water and demonstrated that areas subjected to

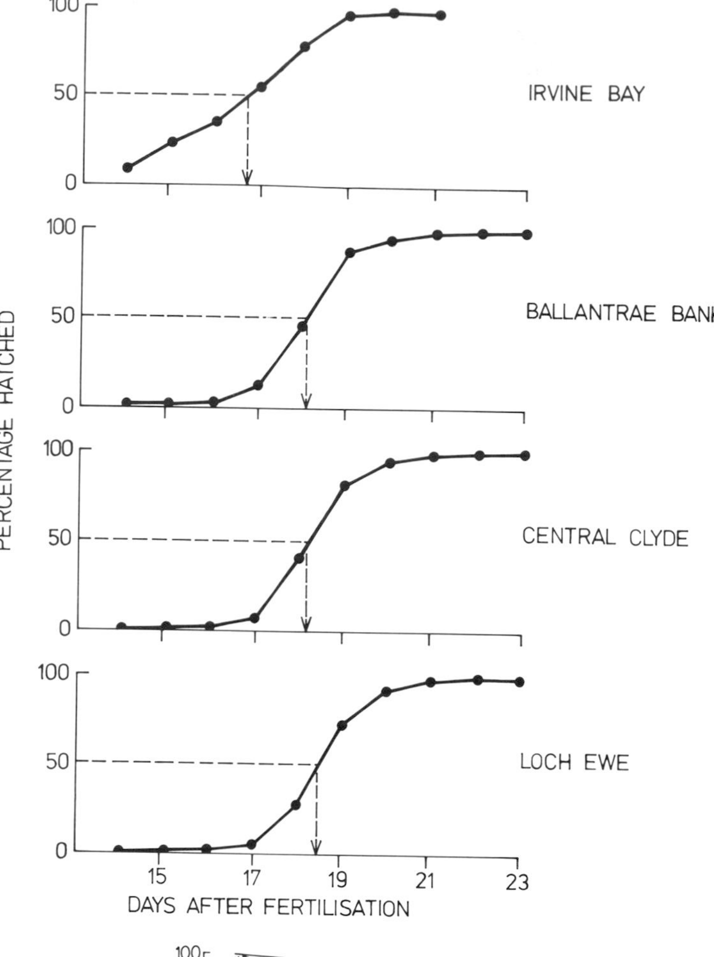

Fig. 5. Time to hatching of herring eggs reared in water from different localities. [From Baxter and Steele 1973.]

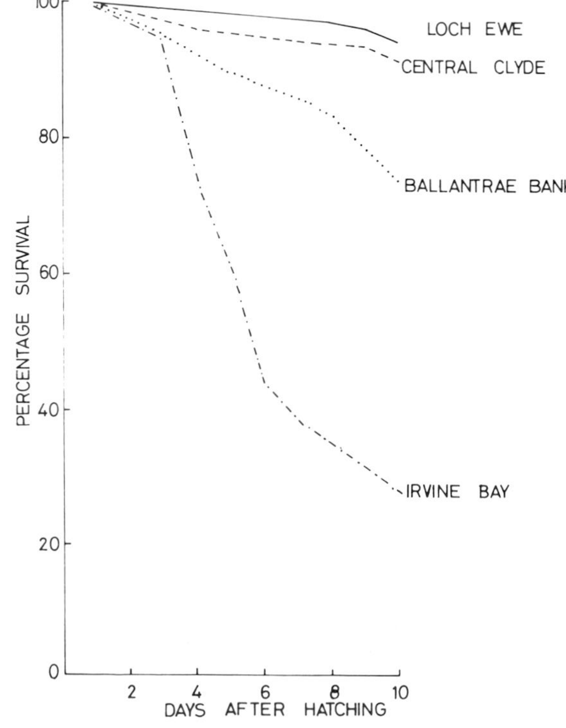

Fig. 6. Survival of newly hatched herring larvae reared in water from different localities. [From Baxter and Steele 1973.]

pollution were less favorable for species known or likely to live there. Further, the differences in experimental results from year to year could be explained by a hypothesis involving water circulation. The next move was clearly to examine actual communities in these areas, in order to discover possible stress symptoms. The obvious difficulty was the lack of a suitable control. However, sandy beaches off the Scottish west coast have been extensively examined (McIntyre 1970) and a good knowledge is available of the typical beach community and its variation so that this habitat seemed a suitable one for study. Table 3 compares some of the richest of these macrofauna communities in the clean water outside the Clyde area (see Fig. 1 for location) with that at Barassie Beach in Irvine Bay.

Sampling was similar on all these surveys, a series of quadrats being dug to a depth of 15 cm and sieved through a 1/2-mm sieve. (Further details are available in McIntyre 1970.). The Clyde beach clearly is very much richer in terms of individual numbers and biomass. Also, more species have been found on this beach, and while the data in Table 3 do not indicate a higher species diversity at Irvine in terms of number of species per unit number of individuals, more extensive surveys suggest that diversity has not been adversely affected. The impression of high density is confirmed by other components of the macrofauna in the immediate sub-tidal region at Irvine; the invertebrate epifauna is also substantially more numerous and juvenile flatfish are more than an order of magnitude denser than in Loch Ewe.

Yet this abundant benthos clearly inhabits a polluted beach. The nitrate levels are 5-10 times higher than normal; copper residues in the bivalves can rise to more than four times background; sewage affects the amenity values of the area; and the water has been shown to be unfavorable for the development of herring eggs and larvae. Can we conclude that a substantial amount of pollution has no adverse affect on the macrofauna, and is in fact beneficial in producing a higher density of benthos and a corresponding increase in the flatfish of this nursery ground? If so, one may suggest that any adverse effects of metals and other pollutants have been masked, and that the resultant effect might be attributed to enrichment by organic matter. In these circumstances, it is important to consider how much the system can stand. Would continued industrialization of the coast lead eventually to an over-input with adverse effects in terms of a significant decrease in species diversity, and if so at what level might such effects take place?

We have some relevant data from another part of the Clyde where sewage sludge from Glasgow has been dumped for the last 50 years or so and at present is being deposited in quantities of over 1 million tons per year (Topping and McIntyre 1972). This is one of the hot spots referred to earlier and the effect is clearly observable. A traverse to the center of the dumping area from clean muddy ground several miles away gives a clear indication of a decline in species diversity with an increase in biomass (Table 4). A preliminary

Table 3. Comparisons of the intertidal macrofauna at the low water mark in Irvine Bay in the Clyde, with that of the three richest beaches sampled on the Scottish west coast outside the Clyde. Showing number of individuals and dry weight per 1/16m^2, total number of species found, and the median diameter of the sediments.

Species	Irvine	Gruinard	Aultbea	Gairloch
Urothoe elegans	1			
Bathyporeia pilosa	35			13
B. elegans	73	24		19
B. pelagica		22		5
B. guilliamsoniana		3	5	
Pontocrates arenarius	36	1		2
Atylus swammerdami	4			
Iphinoe trispinosa	1			
Bodotria scorpoides	4			
Pseudocuma longicornis	48	7		
P. gilsoni				1
Spio filicornis	42	14		16
Spiophanes bombyx	1			
Nerine cirratulus			1	
Spionidae			2	
Paraonis fulgens				3
Chaetozone setosa	3			
Psammodrilus balanoglossoides			11	
Capitellidae	9	3	2	
Travisia forbesii			22	3
Euzonus flabellifera				1
Ophelia rathkei			1	
Owenia fusiformis			2	
Sigalion mathildae	1	2		
Phyllodoce sp.	4			
Eteone sp.		1		1
Nereis sp.	3			
Nephtys cirrosa		4	3	
N. hombergii	2			
Exogene hebes			4	
Syllidae			4	
Nemertea		1	4	
Tellina tenuis	218	45	55	14
T. fabula			1	
Montacuta ferruginosa			3	
Donax vittatus	17			
Cochlodesma praetenue			7	
Spisula elliptica	1			
S. subtruncata			1	
Venus striatula	1		2	1
Ensis ensis				1
Total individuals	504	172	134	80
Total species	20	12	18	13
Dry weight	4.36 g	0.89 g	0.74 g	0.24 g
Median diameter of sediment	140 μ	200 μ	160 μ	240 μ

Table 4. Numbers and wet weight per m^2 of macrofauna collected (1) on the dumping ground, (2) on the edge of the ground, and (3) off the ground to the south west.

Macrofauna	(1) ON	(2) EDGE	(3) OFF
Polychaeta			
Harmothoe sp		10(1.0g)	
Pholoe minuta		35(0.1g)	
Aphroditidae	45(0.8g)		5(+)
Phyllodoce sp		5(+)	5(+)
Eteone sp	125)		
Phyllodocidae	5) (2.3g)		
Leocrates sp	5(+)		
Ophiodromus flexuosus		10(0.2g)	
Syllidae	5(+)	15(+)	40(0.1g)
Nephtys hombergii		15(0.2g)	
Glycera sp	5(+)	50(4.7g)	20(5.4g)
Goniada maculata		45(0.6g)	5(+)
Lumbrineris hibernica		50(2.4g)	55(0.6g)
Oligognathus ? sp			10(+)
Eunicids (juv)	640(0.2g)	100(+)	
Scolelepis fuligenosa		245(0.4g)	
Prionospio sp			130(0.2g)
Spionidae			265(4.4g)
Paraonis gracilis	10(+)	145(0.1g)	25(+)
Tharyx marioni		65(0.2g)	130(0.7g)
Tharyx sp			
Audouinia sp	670)		
Heterocirrus sp	115) (23.0g)	5(0.3g)	
Cirratulus sp	695(6.1g)	5(+)	
Chaetozone setosa	20(0.1g)	345(0.6g)	40(0.1g)
Cirratulid sp	680(7.5g)		
Diplocirrus glaucus		190(2.3g)	5(+)
Scalibregma inflatum		65(0.7g)	
Lipobranchius jeffreysi	5(0.4g)	50(32.2g)	
Ammotrypane aulogaster	5(+)	10(0.6g)	
Capitellidae	12130(30.8g)	4360(6.4g)	230(0.5g)
Rhodine loveni		5(1.5g)	
Maldanidae			10(0.3g)
Pectinaria koreni		30(4.1g)	
Lanice conchelega		5(1.0g)	
Terebellides stroemi		5(+)	35(0.1g)
Terebellidae			5(0.1g)

Macrofauna	(1) ON	(2) EDGE	(3) OFF
Oligochaeta			
Peloscolex sp	32110(56.3g)	60(+)	
Mollusca			
Nucula turgida		20(2.8g)	5(0.1g)
Nucula tenuis		65(2.8g)	85(2.4g)
Nucula sulcata			5(5.0g)
Nuculana minuta			5(+)
Abra alba		70)	
Abra (juv)		10) (6.5g)	
Cylichana cylindracea		20(0.1g)	
Philine scabra		5(0.2g)	
Solenogastres			25(0.3g)
Crustacea			
Harpinia sp		10(+)	15)
Corophium affine			5)
Lysianassidae			5) (0.1g)
Amphipoda (unid)		5(+)	5)
Cumacea		25(+)	25)
Calocaris cacandreae			10(11.7g)
Echinodermata			
Amphiura chiajei			20)
Amphiura filiformis			5) (8.2g)
Ophiuroid (juv)	5(+)	5(+)	5)
Others			
Nemertea	5(+)	165(0.3g)	70(0.2g)
Cerianthus	5(2.4g)		
Foraminifera			5(+)
Sipunculoidea		5(1.1g)	
Priapuloidea		20(0.7g)	
Grand totals	47285(129.9g)	6350(74.1g)	1310(40.5g)

examination of the meiofauna also suggests that it is greatly reduced on the dump ground.

We might speculate on the level of input associated with these changes. Recent studies show that primary production on the Scottish west coast is around 90 gC/m^2/yr^{-1} and suggest that 30% of this can be taken as the input to the bottom, which is about 27 gC/m^2 (Steele and Baird 1972). On the dumping ground, the rate of carbon input to the bottom from the sludge at present can be calculated as about 1,500 gC/m^2/yr^{-1}, or about 55 times the natural rate. Since the surviving taxa (opportunistic species among the capitellids, spionids and oligochaetes) are clearly thriving one must assume they are not unduly affected by the contaminants in the sludge and that the change observed would be at least partly accounted for by the organic input at some 55 times the normal. For man, this change is adverse in that the reduction in species diversity has eliminated *Nephrops norvegicus* an important commercial species of the muds, and has produced a community not favored by fish as food (McIntyre and Johnston 1975).

In the Irvine Bay area the increased organic input is much less than on the sludge ground, and much more difficult to quantify, but some calculations can be made. Estimates of suspended solids from the main river system entering the bay indicate a value of 8.34 tons day^{-1} dry weight, of which the carbon content may be as low as 10%, i.e. 0.83 tons C day^{-1}. From knowledge of population numbers and information of sewage treatment processes from the local river board, the quantities of sewage solids entering the bay are calculated at 12.4 tons day^{-1} dry weight, of which 35% or 4.34 tons day^{-1} is carbon. Using the method of Johnston (1973) and assuming that these solids are uniformly distributed within a zone 1-km wide from the coast, we suggest that the input to the bottom from these sources to the 13-km stretch of Irvine Bay is 5.17 tons C per day, or 390 mg Cm^2 day^{-1}. To this must be added the input from primary production in the sea, which, due to eutrophication from sewage liquids and industrial and agricultural effluents, is here estimated to be as high as 400 mg. Allowance for a 30% fallout to the bottom yields an addition of 120 mg C from primary production, for a total of 510 mg Cm^2 day^{-1}, roughly six times the normal background level for Scottish waters. Such a level of input appears to be associated with a quantitative enhancement of the benthos without species diversity reduction, compared with the 55 times normal enrichment on the sludge ground which resulted in adverse effects. These data provide the beginnings of a quantification of the levels at which effects occur. In this connection a closer look at the meiofauna of Irvine Bay is instructive.

Figure 7 compares the total meiofauna at Irvine Bay with that of a typical sandy beach in one of the sea lochs further north. Even the lowest (spring) values from the Clyde are greater than the highest (autumn) values from the sea loch. At first sight the meiofauna seems to be similar to the macrofauna in showing a considerable enhancement in the Clyde. However, the composition of the Clyde meiofauna suggests differences (Fig. 8). The typical meiofauna of open sandy beaches of the Scottish west coast (McIntyre and Murison 1973) is taxonomically diverse, with copepods at least as abundant as nematodes, turbellarians and gastrotrichs moderately rich, and all

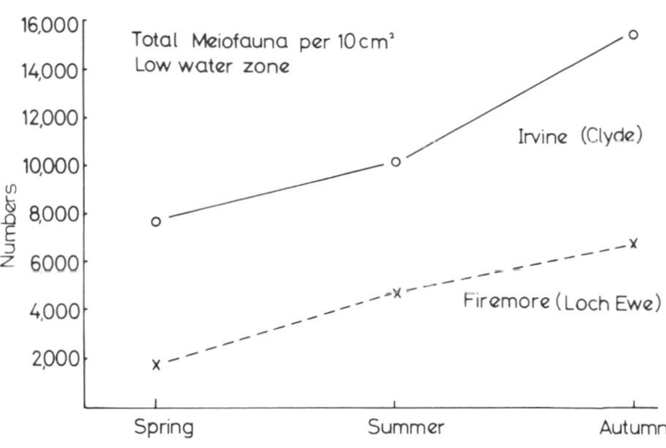

Fig. 7. Comparison of total population counts of meiofauna in a polluted beach in the Clyde and a clean beach of a Scottish sea loch. Samples were collected in core tubes of 2.2-cm internal diameter to a depth of 32 cm, and were elutriated using a 44 µ sieve to retain the organisms.

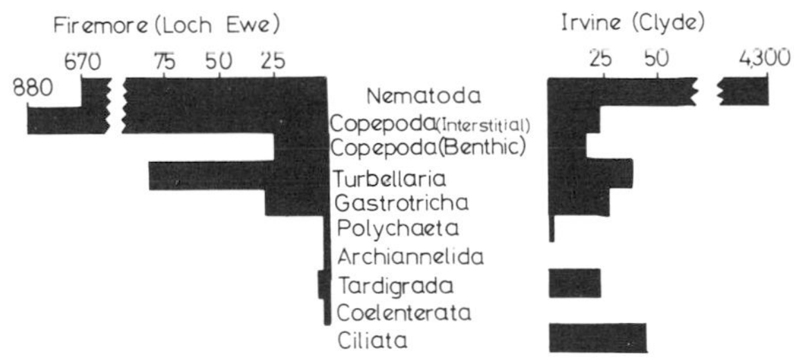

Fig. 8. Comparison of the composition of meiofauna population on a polluted beach in the Clyde and a clean beach of a Scottish sea loch, showing the mean numbers per core at low water mark from samples collected over a 12-month period.

the other main taxa represented. In Irvine Bay, however, although the total population is high in numbers, it is composed largely of nematodes. Copepods were insignificant at most stations sampled, and during the year archiannelids and coelenterates were not found (Fig. 8). Significantly, ciliates were present in most samples, and since Protozoa counted in this study are only those that can be recognized in the residue of a 40 µ sieve after fixing in formalin, it seems reasonable to assume that very much higher populations are present.

The striking feature of these data on meiofauna for Irvine beach is the marked reduction in copepods compared with other beaches examined on the Scottish west coast and indeed even down to the English Channel (Harris 1972). Usually copepods are present in considerable numbers and several species are well represented. Considering the distribution of copepods on Irvine beach in more detail, Figure 9 illustrates the transects and Table 5 shows numbers per core at various tidal levels in four of these transects throughout the year. Transects E and F cover the largest part of the beach south of the river, and there copepods were either absent, or almost so, at ten out of twelve stations sampled, and were present only in very low numbers at the remaining two stations which were in the low water zone. In the northern part of the bay, copepods were numerous, although counts tended to be sparse at high water in traverse A, and even more so at low water. An analysis of the species composition of these populations is of interest.

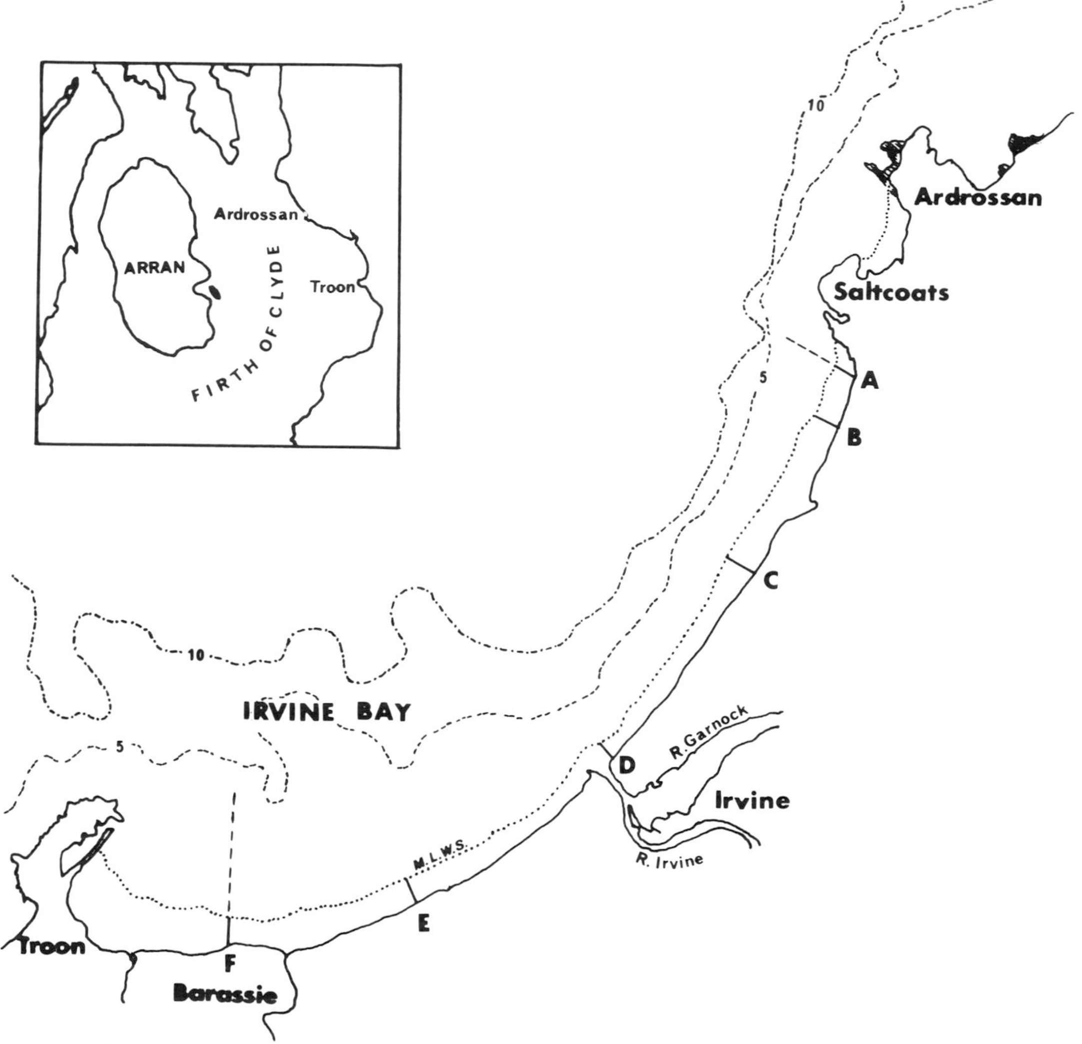

Fig. 9. Positions of sampling transects at Irvine Bay (see Table 5 for details).

Table 5. Number of copepods per 2.2 cm diameter core at each tidal level on 4 transects. Irvine Bay (Clyde) 1972.

Transect	Sampling Period	Tide Level H.W.	M.T.L.	L.W.
A	March	114	97	4
	July	15	114	1
	Sept	11	278	146
C	July	204	79	141
E	March	1	0	0
F	March	0	0	0
	July	0	2	23
	Sept	0	4	36

At the low water stations of transect F in July and September, the few copepods which occurred were primarily *Thompsonula hyaenae*, *Canuella perplexa* and *Harpacticus flexus* (Fig. 10). These are all large species, more than 600 μ in length, and are not truly interstitial. They occurred in Irvine Bay mainly below the low water mark and were found in the intertidal zone (except for an occasional individual carried up near the mid-tide level) only when extreme low water spring tides permitted sampling further down the beach than usual. Thus in the south part of the beach (the most extensive part) interstitial copepods are virtually non-existent.

In the northern part (transect A and C) where copepods are more numerous, a species analysis again helps in the interpretation. The high count at LW in September at transect A consisted almost entirely of *Thompsonula hyaenae*, a non-interstitial subtidal species. Sampling at that time was done at low water mark in the lowest spring tides of the year, so these individuals were collected virtually in the subtidal zone. We are left, then, with a picture of intertidal distribution of interstitial copepods in a lens-shaped area lying obliquely across the north corner of the beach. Of this population (Fig. 11) over 80% consists of the single species, *Paraleptastacus espinulatus*, a truly interstitial species, not exceeding 400 μ in length. The only other species worth noting were *P. spinicauda* and *Arenopontia subterranea*, also truly interstitial animals. These were found in very small numbers, and the latter was restricted to only a few stations. The remaining species occurred mostly as single individuals at one or two positions.

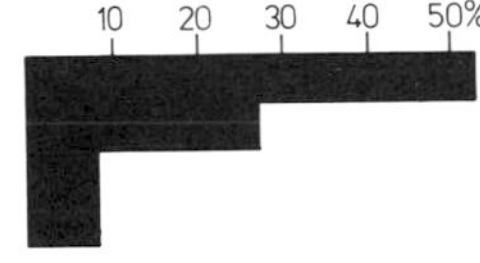

Fig. 10. Species analysis of the benthic copepod population on the south section of Irvine beach (transect F) in September 1972.

20 40 60 80%
Paraleptastacus espinulatus
P. spinicauda
Arenopontia subterranea
Arenosetella germanica
Stenocaris minuta
Nitocra typica <1%
Rhizothrix gracilis <1%
Canuella perplexa <1%

NORTH IRVINE - Percentage of each copepod species

Fig. 11. Species analysis of the benthic copepod population on the north section of Irvine beach in 1972.

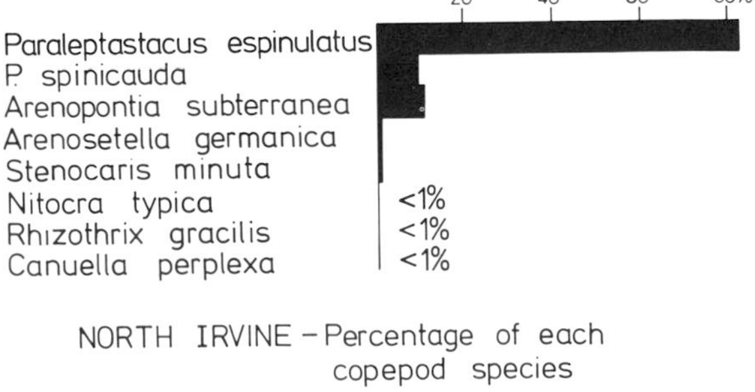

On other sandy bays studied in Britain the copepod population is normally much more dense and also much more diverse. At Firemore on Loch Ewe, for example, of 14 species normally collected, 8 are found at most tidal levels and in most samples (McIntyre and Murison 1973). The virtual elimination of the copepod population over most of the beach at Irvine and its reduction to almost a single species population over the rest of the area requires explanation.

There are two obvious differences between Irvine and the twenty or so other beaches we have looked at along this coast. First, while Irvine is clearly an exposed beach, it is rather more sheltered than some of the others; and second, as indicated at the beginning, it is more generally polluted. Perhaps due to the increased shelter, the particle size of the sediment may be smaller than that ideally required by truly interstitial forms but not yet fine enough for the benthos species which thrive on muds. Indeed, the median particle size in some parts of the beach is around 150 μ compared with over 200 μ on most of the other beaches. Yet, a more complete examination of the beach does not support this suggestion. Even in areas where the particle size at Irvine is 220-260 μ, the copepods are still sparse or absent.

If the structure of this meiofauna community cannot be fully explained in terms of sheltered conditions, a pollution effect should be considered. Although the macrofauna is not yet adversely influenced (and indeed is quantitatively enhanced), we may be observing at Irvine adverse effects on the benthos in terms of a reduction in numbers and diversity of interstitial copepods. It is interesting that the numerically dominant species, *P. espinulatus*, is not common on the other beaches examined. The second most common species at Irvine, *Arenopontia subterranea*, is the one species which flourished in experimental sand columns for over a year, even when the duration of the experiment was imposing stress conditions (McIntyre et al. 1970). Perhaps these two might be regarded as opportunistic species among the interstitial copepods, just as some spionids and capitellids are though of among the macrofauna polychaetes.

CONCLUSIONS AND SUMMARY

It may be generally accepted that the benthos of many estuarine and industrialized inshore locations inhabit water and sediments which are contaminated by a wide range of substances not present, or at least not present in the same high concentrations, in more open or less urbanized situations. However, because of the difficulty of identifying any effects of these contaminants in the field, and of separating such effects from the background noise of natural fluctuations, it is not easy to evaluate the long-term problem of chronic coastal pollution. The approach described in this paper, of combining long-term experimental work with extensive field observations, suggests a reasonable prospect of success, although the results presented here do not form a coherent picture.

The experimental work on food chains in tanks used calculated minimum concentrations which were only a little higher than those found in the field. Due to losses to the tank walls and to the substratum, water concentrations were probably close to those in the field. Significant adverse effects took place at all trophic levels examined.

The findings in this study demonstrated that water from areas of putative pollution was indeed less favorable to organisms. The specific contaminants have not as yet been isolated. However high BOD and nitrate levels are identified as indicators of unfavorable water.

Extension of these studies to benthic communities in the field showed a quantitatively enhanced macrofauna inhabiting a polluted coastal strip, but there were signs that the associated meiofauna was under stress. Attempts to quantify the pollution situation in terms of organic input to the bottom indicated that this input was probably about six times normal. These data could be interpreted as suggesting that this input level, producing depression of meiofauna diversity, may be at just beyond the optimum value for overall community health. Further increase of input could tip the community toward the unbalanced situation found in the sludge dumping ground where a 55 times normal organic input has almost eliminated the meiofauna and greatly reduced the species diversity of the macrofauna.

The mechanisms of adverse affect are of obvious interest. These range from direct influence resulting from the accumulation of fine particulate material, to toxic reactions of metals or other contaminants. In areas of extensive water mixing the impact on the organism will be from a complex mixture of many possible substances. As shown above, it is only when a single influence predominates that it is possible to attribute observed changes to an identified causal agent. As a result, undue weight is probably given to the organic component of pollution input. The experimental results show that associated contaminants such as various heavy metals must play a part, but means of specifically detecting these effects in the field have yet to be devised. One possible approach might be to study effects along a pollution gradient, assuming that an environment suitably uniform in other factors could be found.

In considering the dangers of benthic communities, even if adult organisms are resistant, planktonic larvae could be affected, leading to reduction of recruitment at least locally. On the other hand, even if local populations are eliminated, colonization from neighboring areas could replenish the stock if pollution abated. Further, the development of tolerance to certain contaminants (e.g., *Nereis diversicolor* to copper, Bryan and Hummerstone 1971) could afford protection to the species.

An adequate assessment and understanding of the threat to coastal benthos of chronic pollution requires continued substantial research effort.

REFERENCES

Baxter, I. E. 1974. Further experimental studies on Clyde herring eggs and larvae. International Council for the Exploration of the Sea: CM 1974/E:35.

_____, and J. H. Steele. 1973. Mortality of herring larvae in the Clyde Sea area. International Council for the Exploration of the Sea: CM 1973/E:29.

Bryan, G. W. and L. G. Hummerstone. 1971. Adaptation of the polychaete *Nereis diversicolor* to estuarine sediments containing high concentrations of heavy metals. 1. General obervations and adaptation to copper. J. Mar. Biol. Assoc. U.K. 51:845-863.

Goldberg, E. D. [Ed.] 1973. North Sea science. MIT Press.

Harris, R. P. 1972. Reproductive activity of the interstitial copepods of a sandy beach. J. Mar. Biol. Assoc. U.K. 52: 507-524.

Johnston, R. 1973. Nutrients and metals in the North Sea, p. 293-307. In E. D. Goldberg [ed.], North Sea science. MIT Press.

McIntyre, A. D. 1970. The range of biomass in intertidal sand, with special reference to the bivalve, *Tellina tenuis*. J. Mar. Biol. Assoc. U.K. 50: 561-575.

_____ and R. Johnston. 1975. Effects of nutrient enrichment from sewage in the sea, pap. 14. In Discharge of sewage from sea outfalls. Pergamon Press.

_____ and D. J. Murison. 1973. The meiofauna of a flatfish nursery ground. J. Mar. Biol. Assoc. U.K. 53: 93-118.

_____, A. L. S. Munro, and J. H. Steele. 1970. Energy flow in a sand ecosystem, p. 19-31. In J. H. Steele [ed.], Marine food chain. Oliver and Boyd.

Saward, D., A. Stirling, and G. Topping. 1975. Experimental studies on the effects of copper on a marine food chain. Mar. Biol. 29: 351-361.

Steele, J. H. and I. E. Baird. 1972. Sedimentation of organic matter in a Scottish sea loch. Memorie 1st ital. Idrobiol. 29 (Suppl.) 3.

_____, A. D. McIntyre, R. R. C. Edwards, and A. Trevallion. 1970. Inter-relations of a young plaice population with its invertebrat food supply, p. 175-388. In. A. Watson [ed.], Animal populations in relation to their food resources. Brit. Ecol. Soc. Symp. No. 10. Blackwell.

Topping, G. and A. D. McIntyre. 1972. Benthic observations on a sewage sludge dumping ground. International Council for the Exploration of the Sea: CM 1972/E:30.

Trevallion, A., R. Johnston, D. M. Finlayson, and N. T. Nicoll. 1973 Studies in the bivalve, *Tellina tenuis* da Costa. IV. Further experiments in enriched sea water. J. Exp. Mar. Biol. Ecol. 11: 189-206.

Studies on the Dispersion Patterns of Scottish Sea Loch Benthos from Contiguous Core Transects

J. D. Gage and **G. G. Coghill**
Dunstaffnage Marine Research Laboratory
P. O. Box 3
Oban, Argyll, PA34 4AD
Scotland

ABSTRACT

Motile benthic species contributed a disproportionate share of overall community clustering in contiguous core samples taken along a line transect from two positions, muddy sand and soft mud in Loch Creran and, one position, soft mud in Loch Etive on the west coast of Scotland. Dispersion of motile species chiefly accounted for clustering peaks occurring at block sizes corresponding to linear scales from about 1 to 3.5 m in Creran muddy sand and Etive soft mud. Core samples of the benthos were taken by means of SCUBA and abundant species therein were analyzed by Greig-Smith's method of block-size analysis of spatial dispersion. Confidence limits indicative of the random expectation were generated by methods including a Monte Carlo procedure employing Poisson variates derived from pseudorandom numbers. Intensity and predominating scale of overall community clustering at different sampling positions were compared on the basis of mean deviation from the upper Poisson bound.

INTRODUCTION

Spatial dispersion[1] remains one of the least studied aspects of the marine benthos. Yet it would be useful in estimating population parameters such as density and might provide, as it has in

[1]In this report "dispersion" signifies a one-dimensional attribute of a pattern in relation to a particular area or shape at a given density (Rogers 1974). The term "dispersion" is preferred to "distribution," which has a statistical meaning (Pielou 1969), and to "pattern," which denotes a zero-dimensional spatial property describing the arrangment of objects with respect to one another.

terrestrial studies, information about dispersion controls--e.g., whether different levels of species diversity on different sediment are controlled by habitat partitioning caused by environmental inhomogeneity originating either from a biologically generated mosaic or from gradients of abunance reflecting changes in physical conditions.

Unfortunately, sample statistics of community structure, such as species diversity, embody assumptions of randomness in dispersion that are rarely tested. (The model of randomness adopted here is that spatial-point process where any point has an equal and independent probability of occurring at any position on a plane.) Indeed, the effect of nonrandom dispersion on such sample statistics is for the most part unknown. Furthermore, studies of community structure generally assume some degree of temporal stability, i.e., that we are sampling a community of animals that has reached some type of successional climax and if the fauna is motile, their dispersions are persistent enough to be worth studying. Changes in a dispersion pattern may result from a successional system where the rates vary in space for some reason. When the birth, death and immigration (or emigration) rates of populations are density dependent, then unless the organisms are evenly spaced, the density effect must also vary and result in a changing dispersion. Particular dispersions may result from direct environmental effects such as the moving crest of a sand wave or a patch of decaying seaweed on an otherwise level bottom; or by interspecific or intraspecific behavioral interaction among individuals of the benthic community.

Dispersion patterns may also be influenced by inhomogenous factors which differ in time, scale, and effect during the life history of an organism. For example, in the coastal benthic situation hydrographic inhomogeneity, such as near-bottom eddies over an undulating seabed, might result in a patchy settlement of larvae that is reinforced by their natural tendency to finally settle near each other. Small-scale inhomogeneity caused by predation might be occurring. For example, the tentacle spread of a burrowed terebellid worm over the sediment surface may cause 'holes' in the small-scale dispersion pattern of a small surface-living species. Complexity and variability in distribution of the populations of the many species that make up the benthic community obviously precludes formulation of simple mathematic models of spatial dispersion. The benthic ecologist therefore falls back on some essentially simple empirical approaches. These usually involve easily calculated statistics such as the variance/mean ratio testing the null hypothesis of Poissoness (where variance = mean), the dispersion pattern being assessed in terms of the Poisson expectation. Deviations in one direction indicate a tendency towards regular (even) spacing of individuals, or a clustered (aggregated) dispersion in the other. Because of its convenience the Poisson has been commonly used when it may be mathematically preferable to employ statistics based on either the binomial (for even dispersion) or the various contagious distributions that include the negative binomial. It is worth noting that such distributions may describe either natural dispersions caused by purely stochastic processes (as when birth, death and immigration rates of a population are constant) or those caused when the presence of one individual or event (e.g. prey) increases, or decreases, the chance that another individual will occur nearby.

Because the benthic ecologist is usually interested in the dispersion patterns of an extended continuum rather than a small discrete space, dispersion patterns need to be defined in terms of arbitrarily chosen sample units, whose size and/or shape will affect the different indices in different ways, and with a variable effect depending on the underlying disperson. Rogers (1974) discussed some of the problems of inference associated with the fitting of nonrandom distribution to sample-unit data. Boswell and Patil (1970) and Patil and Stiteler (1974) illustrated different models of dispersion patterns which have the same probability distribution for sample counts. In the case of the Poisson distribution, Patil and Stiteler (1974) pointed out that because sample-unit counts from populations other than those randomly dispersed may result in a Poisson distribution, Poissoness cannot be equated with randomness. Consequently, it is incorrect to equate the null hypothesis of the Poisson distribution with a random dispersion in tests for pattern. A knowledge of the statistical distribution of the number of individuals in a randomly located sample unit is therefore insufficient to describe its dispersion.

An alternative approach, to adopt distance measures in sampling (where distance to other individuals from either randomly selected individuals or points is measured), is usually impossible because the populations are usually burrowed out of sight of the investigator. Although invalidated in testing for randomness, pattern statistics based on the Poisson nevertheless provide an indication of the form and intensity of dispersion pattern; but any conformity of sample counts to the Poisson expectation merely shows that the hypothesis of randomness in dispersion is not disproved.

Another objection to the Poisson is its limitation in size and shape of sample units (Greig-Smith 1964). Unless a density-independent statistic such as Morisita's (1959) $\underline{I}_{\delta}$, or a suitable transformation is adopted, the results will be strongly influenced by the sample area and the mean density in the samples which when small will suggest conformity to the Poisson expectation. This occurs because for a clustered dispersion pattern, tests of fit to the Poisson indicate an apparent fit to the Poisson before beginning to show aggregation when either the sample area or the population density is increased. The sample area may show further evenness, randomness, or aggregation, depending on the dispersion of the patches themselves. The most marked aggregation would be indicated at the sample size approximating the dimension of the patches. Consequently, aggregation in the dispersion patterns of the benthic community need not be suspected unless several sizes of sample are taken from a population (Greig-Smith 1964). Although Morisita's

I_δ overcomes this difficulty, it does so on the restrictive assumption that any given population is divided into sub-areas of randomly dispersed individuals. The desire of the benthos investigator to vary the size of his sample area is usually restricted by his sampling gear, which is capable only of taking a fixed area of the sea-bed; and because he usually samples from a ship, he may not even know the approximate scale of the bottom area sampled. Assuming that previous studies (e.g., Reys 1971) have adequately established the existence of aggregated dispersions in marine benthos, one needs to know at what scale (or "grain" sensu Pielou 1969) the clustering is most pronounced. Is it of such fine grain that it is likely generated by the activity of other (small) individuals (see Jumars 1975)? Or is it so large as to be caused, by large motile epifauna; or so coarse grained as to be caused by local differences in the sediment or by local perturbation from the investigator's bottom trawl?

In Gage and Geekie's (1973) study of spatial dispersions in sea-loch benthos, grab samples were taken systematically at equidistant points, about 10-20 m apart, arranged in a circle roughly 50-100 m in diameter at each station. Dispersion only detectable at a larger scale of sampling, it was thought, would be associated with local differences in sediment and hydrography, and thus part of that pattern considered in the mapping of faunal distributions in coastal areas. Because of the spacing between each sample, their sampling design was most sensitive to clumps of width slightly less than the sample spacing. Detection of smaller clumps down to the size of the sample (0.1 m^2), and smaller, was increasingly unsatisfactory. It was also increasingly affected by the dispersion of the clumps themselves. Clumps considerably smaller than 0.1 m^2, of course, remained undetected.

This paper discusses the problem of measuring, at the same stations, benthic dispersion patterns at spatial scales ranging from about 100 m^2 to less than 0.01 m^2. We have examined the way a measure of dispersion varies with sample size and on this basis present a dimensional description, within the range of scales of the analysis, of the dispersion shown by different species. Gage and Geekie (1973) showed that, at the scale of their sampling, the dispersion of the benthic fauna was overall more aggregated on the sandy, current-swept bottoms than on the soft muds in quieter waters. Whether the observed patterns result from a biologically generated mosaic or a collective response to spatial inhomogeneity in physical conditions are not considered here; rather, the emphasis in the present report is on introducing our contiguous sampling method and on comparing our values with the values of the dispersion statistic obtained in order to compare with the earlier results at larger scales. This paper also discusses trends in dispersion based on the motility of the species of the benthic community analyzed. We hope that the results will be empirically useful in studies of overall community, and community subgroup, dispersion for comparison of different stations at various scales of analysis, rather than as individual test criteria for randomness in the dispersion of a species.

METHODS

The method of employing counts from a large grid of contiguous small quadrats was originally proposed by Greig-Smith (1952). By means of a nested hierarchical analysis of variance, the variance of the counts for each species is partitioned into components and data from basic sampling units are entered into blocks of increasingly larger size. This results in a nested hierarchical apportionment of variances between block sizes where, assuming a random distribution of individuals, each mean square is an estimate of the variance of the Poisson distribution for the counts in the basic sampling units. In the modified form of Kershaw (1957) that was adopted for the present investigation, basic samples are taken along a line transect rather than over a grid. Variances are then blocked in pairs and are plotted versus block size (see Grieg-Smith 1964, Kershaw 1973). Peaks in the plot correspond to patches at the linear dimension given by the block size.

This, now classical, method of the block size analysis of spatial dispersion thus employs the mean square (variance) between component blocks so that dispersion is measured as the sum of squares generated by the departure of the observed counts from a state of perfect homogeneity characterized by identical counts in the sampling units. The reliability of the method of dispersion pattern analysis by this nested analysis of variance has been tested empirically by Kershaw (1957). The results were consistent with each other as long as the basic unit was smaller than the smallest scale of dispersion to be selected, and the abundance of the species was not too low.

A possible disadvantage of the transect approach is that the dispersion investigated is linear rather than three-dimensional and as such may be much influenced by the direction of the line. On the other hand a greater range of dispersion scales can be investigated, and any linear bias may be checked by working replicate transects running at different directions.

Assuming a random dispersion of individuals, each mean square of the analysis is an estimate of the variance of the Poisson distribution for the counts in the basic sampling units. However, as many authors have pointed out, because each block is formed by successive recombination of the basic sample counts, the mean squares thus calculated are not independent, except in the case of random dispersion; effective tests of significance, such as the Index of Dispersion and _F_ ratio tests (see Greig-Smith 1964) are thus precluded. Pielou (1969) and Goodall (1971) also pointed out that the mean squares apply to a restricted range of scales, since block size is doubled at each step. Information on possible dispersions evident only at intermediate scales between blocks is thus lost. Goodall (1971) has also stressed the unequal division of degrees of freedom to the detriment of comparisons at the largest scales. Another possible source of error concerns the increasingly rectangular shape of the samples when they are combined in increasing block sizes. Stiteler and Patil (1971) demonstrated from simulation studies that sample values of the variance-to-mean ratio from a regular (but not random) dispersion can be made arbitrarily large, implying an aggregated dispersion pattern, if the sample is rectangular. However, populations having regular dispersions are exceedingly rare on land, and there are no reasons for believing that this is not also true for the marine benthos. It is also worth bearing in mind that the use of the variance of sample counts as the basis for estimating dispersion is not without error. Greig-Smith (1964, p. 69) cited a clearly nonrandom case consisting of a generally regular dispersion, with occasional groups of individuals, that yielded a variance exactly equal to the mean.

Despite these drawbacks, ecologists have chosen to use the method because it provides at least an approximate, description of dispersion pattern and emphasizes plurality of scales which renders it more ecologically meaningful than other approaches.

The method has obvious application to the marine benthos. Because of its apparent sensitivity, it is particularly useful where, as on a level sea bottom, highly clumped dispersions are rare, and physical conditions seem homogeneous; and where, consequently, even if the fauna were visible to the investigator, he would probably not detect any visually obvious nonrandom dispersion. Nonetheless, practical difficulties in its application may be experienced by any systematic sampling from a ship, from which it is difficult to precisely control the location of the samples units. Even if, as in this study, diving methods are adopted in order to allow a line transect of contiguous sampling to be worked, counts of the fauna cannot be made directly; whole samples of the sediment need to be taken and the contained fauna extracted. Therefore the validation of dispersion from plots of the dispersion pattern statistic versus block size, by replication of the transects, is much less easy. Consequently, the benthic ecologist tries to circumvent problems caused by lack of independence that are inherent in the nested hierarchical design. Mead (1974) has developed alternative tests of dispersion from contiguous sample data using randomization arguments. He measured dispersion in terms of the probabilities on the randominzation distribution of obtaining counts less than, or equal to, and greater than, or equal to, the observed values. However, because of its agglomerative nature this test provides no values for the smallest scale of pattern at different block sizes. The only previous analysis of dispersion of marine benthos by a line transect of contiguous samples (Angel and Angel 1967) indicated from application of the _t_ test that at least three of the species were aggregated at all the smaller block sizes. This result suggested that their sample (core) size was too large to detect the minimum scale of dispersion. Indeed if the rule of thumb of Curtis and McIntosh (1950) were adopted, the appropriate size of sample unit should be approximately twice the size of the mean area of the animal. Jumars (1975) suggested that dispersion at a scale reflecting environmental grain generated by the organisms themselves (tentacle spread, limited mobility, tubes and other biogenic structures) is most important in controlling community structure, such as species richness, of bathyal benthos. The lack of values at the scale of the basic sampling unit may then be a limitation in the application of Mead's randomization method to the marine benthos.

We adopted a Monte Carlo approach to providing limits for the random expectation for each species. This method predicts 95 percent confidence limits for Poisson variates which generate values of mean square tending to equal the mean. The Poisson variates with a given mean were derived by a procedure given in Davies (1971) from strings of pseudorandom numbers. For 500 replicate sets a frequency polygon was constructed for each block size and the 2.5 percent tails measured. In order to provide as smooth a set of bounds for the Poisson expectation as possible from the Monte Carlo data, the mean of the total of 71 sets of limits, expressed as variance/mean ratios, was calculated. In this way the Monte Carlo limits for the 95 percent Poisson envelope are thus derived from $500 \times 71 = 3.5 \times 10^3$ runs of Poisson variates. This use of Poisson variates is obviously subject to the criticism of the non-equivalence of the Poisson to the random expectation for sample counts. Nonetheless, since previous studies fail to show that the majority of samples of natural random dispersions do not conform to the Poisson, the mean squares when expressed as deviation from the 95 percent limits of Poisson variates remain strongly indicative of population or (when collectivized as a summary statistic) of overall community dispersion. The values were collectivized as the mean deviation from the upper bound of the Poisson expectation at each block size in order to provide an estimate of 'overall clustering' of the populations making up the benthic community. This concept of overall clustering is obviously a composite of individual (population) dispersions and ignores dispersion generated or intensified (or weakened) by the relative spatial positions of other populations. For example, the collectivized value is hopefully sensitive to the clusters formed by individuals of a commensal bivalve around its heart urchin host, but not to clusters that depend solely on the concurrence of the two or more species. Such a community pattern may be identified as between-species dispersion, in contrast to within-species dispersion measured in separate species. The latter is therefore not analogous to the "total pattern" concept of Noy-Meir and Anderson (1971) which employs a principal component analysis of the total data and includes between-species effects in its integrated description of overall dispersion.

The study of Angel and Angel (1967) consisted of a simple transect 32 m long in the Fanafjord in Norway along which 256 contiguous core samples were taken. For comparative purposes, we sited one transect on a sediment bottom similar to that sampled by Angel and Angel. Because we also desired to investigate possible differences in dispersion patterns of the fauna of different inshore soft bottom environments, a program of contiguous core sampling was undertaken in 1972 at three stations, at (or near in the case of C-3) which benthic dispersion pattern had been studied previously (Gage and Geekie 1973) by replicated sampling from ship. Two stations were in Loch Creran (stations C-3 and C-12) and one in Loch Etive (E-24); two were on soft mud (C-12 and E-24 both at 20 m depth), while the other (C-3, 13 m depth), like that of Angel and Angel (1967) was on muddy sand. Two transects were worked at station C-12. The second (C-12B) was worked in August, seven months after the first (C-12A, January). Transect C-3 was worked in April and E-24 in July 1972. Although their relative positions were not precisely located, they were within 100 m of each other, and it was unlikely that their positions overlapped. Station positions and data on sediment granulometry, faunal abundances, and hydrography are given in Gage (1972*a*, *b*).

The transects were marked by a line 18 m long stretched between two heavy sinkers on the bottom. It was found necessary to orientate the transect perpendicular to the local tidal currents so that sediment clouds thrown up by the diver were carried away behind him at the working area. Sampling at the Etive station had to await a dry spell of weather because the amount of light available at the bottom was markedly affected by recent heavy rainfall owing to light absorption by dissolved humic pigments and suspended detritus. Because of the desirability of including as wide a spectrum of species as possible with a concomitant wide spread in densities, the size of sample unit was designed to pick up the smallest possible scales of dispersion present, while collecting sufficient numbers of individuals. Core tubes measured 5 cm internal diameter by 25 cm in length. Their external diameter was 5.5 cm so that allowing for a slight gap between them, the total length of the transect of 256 contiguous cores was approximately 14.5 m. At the muddy sand station, our sampling technique, which approximated that of Angel and Angel (1967), was to twist into the sediment a steel core tube sharpened at one end, and fitted with handles at the other. After the core tube was gently lowered and twisted into the sediment, hammering was necessary in order to fill the entire tube. The core sampler was positioned by means of a grid divided into sixteen sections. The sample was extruded by pulling out the core tube after sealing the upper end with a bung. The lower end was similarly sealed on its removal from the sediment. The sample was then immediately removed from the tube and transferred into a plastic bag by the diver, who carefully removed the lower bung while pushing the core tube into the bag and pushing out the contents with a piston. The bags were sealed by tying them, consecutively, to a length of line. To ensure a standard technique, all samples were taken by one diver. The transect was completed during five diving hours over a period of five days.

The two soft mud stations were sampled more quickly because a set of sixteen core tubes strapped together permitted sixteen contiguous core samples to be taken simultaneously. The core tubes were made of rigid ABS plastic and each fitted with a threaded lid with one-way valve. The block of sixteen could easily be pushed into the soft muddy sediment and then carefully pulled out to obtain the sample. The lower ends of the core tubes were immediately sealed with bungs, and the sealed blocks of cores then hauled back to the surface. A rod pushed into the mud was used to mark the starting position for each subsequent block. Such a transect 16 m long could be completed within two diving hours. Great care was taken to avoid disturbing the sediment surface prior to sampling on both types of sediment. Nonetheless, because sampling was not completed at one time, possible changes in the dispersion patterns of motile species during our sampling period should be taken into account which might affect the validity of the results as being descriptive of real pattern.

Another possible source of error may have resulted from the assumption that the circular cores used in the present investigation properly constitute a contiguous transect in the sense of Kershaw (1957). One problem would arise when possible periodicity in the depth approximates a harmonic of the core radius, because the actual width of the transect is varying (P. A. Jumars personal communication). However, such a regular dispersion seems extremely unlikely to occur in nature, but, of course, cannot be excluded.

All samples were washed through a 420 μM-aperture sieve and fixed immediately in 5 percent formaldehyde. All fauna were later picked from the washed samples. Because of the labor involved, no attempt was made to measure any of the standard sediment parameters (e.g., granulometry) along the transect, although it is possible that certain inhomogeneity at the sediment/water interface, such as clumps of decaying vegetation or local changes in reducing conditions may have influenced the dispersion of the fauna.

RESULTS AND DISCUSSION

Only species occurring with a total abundance of >25 per transect (mean >0.01 per core) were analyzed. This yielded 28 species for transect C-3, 13 for transect C-12A, 15 for transect C-12B, and 15 for transect E-24. These species and their mean square values calculated for block size analysis of variance are listed in Table 1. A regression coefficient was applied (Greig-Smith 1964) to the mean squares in order to correct for any "trend" (gradient) in the abundance along the length of the transects, which may mask dispersion at the larger block sizes. The greater number of species available from transect C-3 reflects the greater species diversity as well as the higher numerical abundances of the benthos on muddy sand as opposed to soft mud (Gage 1972b).

Table 1. Limits of the Poisson expectation, variance/mean ratios, and the total number of individuals for the species analysed in each transect. Values exceeding the Poisson expectation calculated from $1 \pm 2\sqrt{\frac{2n}{(n-1)^2}}$ are underlined with a straight line while those falling below it are underlined with a wavy line. Values exceeding the Monte Carlo limits as well are underlined with two straight lines while those falling below are underlined with two wavy lines. Species judged to be motile are indicated by 'M'.

			Ratio Variance/Mean									
			Block Size									
			1	2	4	8	16	32	64		128	
Station C-3												
95% Limits of the Poisson expectation calculated a) from $1 \pm 2\sqrt{\frac{2n}{(n-1)^2}}$		Upper	1.18	1.25	1.36	1.51	1.75	2.14	2.89		5.00	
		Lower	0.82	0.75	0.64	0.49	0.25	0.00	0.00		0.00	
b) from the Monte Carlo method		Upper	1.32	1.45	1.60	1.78	2.28	3.09	3.57		5.03	
		Lower	0.67	0.60	0.47	0.34	0.19	0.03	0.00		0.00	
Species	Total Abundance	Motility										
Abra alba	34		1.18	0.88	1.00	1.00	0.52	1.32	1.11	(1.17)	0.25	(0.12)
Ampelisca sp.	50	M	0.84	1.20	0.80	0.71	0.45	2.02	0.30	(0.90)	0.56	(2.88)
Ampharete acutifrons	32		1.00	1.25	0.69	1.11	1.83	1.44	0.77	(1.25)	0.33	(8.00)
Chone filicaudata	95		0.87	1.00	0.62	1.23	1.46	2.49	2.33	(2.32)	0.09	(0.09)
Cirratulidae sp.	35	M	1.06	1.00	1.17	1.46	1.17	2.84	6.37	(6.31)	0.59	(0.71)
Crenella decussata	33		1.06	0.82	0.89	0.88	2.21	1.02	0.65	(0.76)	0.46	(0.27)
Diastylis laevis	26	M	1.20	1.08	1.00	1.46	1.15	2.70	3.42	(3.45)	0.00	(0.00)
Glycera alba	85	M	1.18	1.28	1.07	0.98	2.54	1.38	0.39	(0.76)	0.58	(2.65)
Isopoda sp.	65	M	1.12	1.31	0.94	1.04	2.09	1.86	1.14	(1.49)	1.60	(8.14)
Loricata sp.	26		1.31	0.92	1.15	1.39	1.22	1.73	2.00	(2.23)	0.65	(2.46)
Lumbrinereis hibernica	70	M	0.97	1.08	0.60	1.12	1.67	1.87	1.65	(2.71)	0.92	(16.51)
Mya arenaria	196		1.46	1.87	1.50	2.27	1.37	8.57	4.00	(3.75)	-0.01	(0.02)
Mysella bidentata	67		1.42	1.74	1.33	1.15	1.69	2.64	0.91	(0.91)	0.01	(0.01)
Nephtys hystricis	108	M	1.04	1.04	2.02	0.79	0.81	7.91	15.62	(21.92)	-3.00	(17.92)
Nucula sulcata	31	M	1.26	1.19	0.80	1.26	2.53	2.63	2.56	(3.64)	-0.15	(3.90)
Ostracoda sp.	392	M	2.51	3.27	4.84	8.10	6.67	25.40	2.02	(2.17)	2.58	(9.81)
Owenia fusiformis	137		0.79	0.94	1.23	0.82	2.33	1.58	0.20	(0.53)	-0.49	(0.36)
Paraonis lyra	946		1.30	1.60	2.60	2.94	3.43	10.83	14.27	(14.25)	1.00	(0.71)
Parvicardium ovale	96		1.14	0.83	1.02	1.08	0.32	8.57	11.02	(11.44)	0.04	(0.37)
Pholöe minuta	153	M	1.78	1.67	2.20	1.88	3.83	2.65	2.02	(1.50)	5.14	(9.94)
Phyllodoce sp.	33	M	1.36	1.18	1.60	1.90	2.54	0.75	2.53	(2.57)	0.98	(2.45)

Table 1 continued

Species	Total Abundance	Motility	Ratio Variance/Mean, Block Size 1	2	4	8	16	32	64		128	
Station C-3												
Pilargidae sp.	113	M	1.26	2.04	2.93	3.41	1.47	7.89	0.74	(1.11)	-0.63	(1.49)
Prionospio malmgreni	39		0.85	1.00	1.92	0.75	0.94	8.19	3.30	(3.92)	-0.74	(0.64)
Scalibregma inflatum	36		0.89	0.94	1.17	1.50	1.11	3.60	1.31	(1.38)	1.18	(1.00)
Terebellides stroemi	26		1.23	0.85	0.77	2.03	2.89	1.58	1.47	(2.46)	0.60	(7.54)
Thyasira flexuosa	36		0.89	1.00	0.94	0.62	0.34	1.15	3.14	(2.94)	0.80	(2.78)
Trichobranchus glacialis	25		1.08	0.84	0.76	1.00	0.92	0.46	4.49	(4.52)	0.41	(1.00)
Urothoë elegans	313	M	0.99	1.61	1.04	2.53	0.65	4.87	4.32	(4.28)	0.12	(0.26)
Station C-12, Transect A												
Abra alba	100		1.30	1.50	1.50	1.60	0.68	3.42	7.08	(7.24)	2.99	(16.00)
Amphiura filiformis	38		0.84	0.79	0.84	0.74	2.31	0.16	0.73	(0.68)	0.30	(0.42)
Capitomastus minimus	36		1.44	1.06	2.28	1.33	1.60	0.69	4.47	(4.05)	1.59	(5.49)
Corbula gibba	26		1.08	1.23	1.61	1.61	0.93	0.86	1.81	(1.92)	0.00	(0.00)
Diplocirrus glaucus	32		1.06	1.50	1.37	0.62	0.50	5.87	4.20	(4.25)	0.00	(0.00)
Lumbrinereis hibernica	39	M	1.05	1.05	0.85	0.64	1.56	0.80	0.74	(0.74)	0.00	(0.02)
Melinna palmata	75		0.95	0.76	0.89	1.09	1.78	1.00	1.31	(0.87)	1.71	(5.88)
Mysella bidentata	184	M	3.52	4.59	5.68	4.30	3.06	0.16	3.26	(3.97)	0.46	(0.45)
Nephtys hystricis	73	M	1.16	1.11	0.86	1.13	0.45	0.35	1.52	(1.60)	0.18	(0.12)
Paraonis gracilis	86		1.05	1.12	0.88	1.88	3.19	0.77	1.19	(1.23)	0.00	(0.00)
Pholöe minuta	159	M	1.63	1.50	1.43	1.96	2.24	2.05	1.60	(2.29)	0.54	(5.29)
Prionospio malmgreni	232		1.12	1.03	2.00	2.48	1.57	3.23	1.46	(1.77)	2.51	(14.50)
Rhodine loveni	30		1.07	0.60	0.93	1.52	3.66	1.24	4.19	(4.33)	0.82	(0.53)
Station C-12, Transect B												
Abra alba	191		0.86	1.08	1.09	1.74	1.60	1.72	3.91	(4.11)	0.37	(3.27)
Ampelisca sp.	30	M	1.60	1.06	1.79	1.46	1.44	1.45	0.84	(1.67)	-0.13	(4.80)
Amphiura filiformis	43		1.05	0.95	1.42	0.72	0.93	0.76	0.27	(0.30)	-0.03	(0.58)
Capitomastus minimus	69		1.03	1.55	0.80	2.19	3.49	3.53	7.80	(8.48)	0.09	(6.39)
Cirratulus cirratus	29	M	1.07	0.65	1.13	1.62	1.49	0.54	2.04	(2.10)	0.40	(2.29)
Diplocirrus glaucus	38		1.10	0.89	0.89	1.00	2.10	2.58	0.69	(0.68)	0.00	(0.00)
Lumbrinereis hibernica	44	M	1.18	1.36	0.95	1.54	0.82	0.38	1.14	(1.14)	0.16	(0.82)
Melinna palmata	33		0.94	1.00	0.81	1.06	0.33	0.15	3.84	(3.78)	0.15	(0.27)
Mysella bidentata	248	M	2.52	3.15	4.57	2.01	4.96	2.26	6.00	(6.08)	0.21	(0.58)
Nephtys hystricis	55	M	0.96	1.07	0.74	0.42	0.39	0.52	0.56	(0.52)	0.25	(0.45)

Table 1 continued

Species	Total Abundance	Motility	Ratio Variance/Mean — Block Size 1	2	4	8	16	32	64		128	
Station C-12, Transect B												
Paraonis gracilus	40		0.95	0.90	1.40	0.99	1.65	1.21	1.45	(1.30)	1.57	(6.40)
Pholöe minuta	89	M	0.89	1.09	0.78	1.15	1.91	1.02	1.86	(1.40)	1.75	(4.05)
Prionospio malmgreni	137		1.14	1.92	0.88	1.13	1.08	2.06	0.94	(1.05	-0.02	(0.06)
Rhodine loveni	34		0.94	0.88	1.06	0.35	1.28	0.93	2.84	(3.06)	0.34	(0.12)
Scalibregma inflatum	26		1.00	0.61	0.84	0.99	1.84	0.38	1.32	(1.54)	0.37	(0.15)
Station E-24												
Amphiura filiformis	62	M	0.74	1.00	0.84	1.20	1.17	0.81	1.97	(2.35)	0.03	(4.13)
Aricidia catherinae	237		2.31	4.12	6.90	4.70	5.84	9.20	3.99	(11.16)	-1.39	(38.08)
Capitomastus minimus	636		1.87	2.32	1.44	1.39	2.82	2.19	1.66	(4.88)	-2.55	(20.45)
Corbula gibba	32		1.37	1.12	1.62	2.25	0.70	1.33	1.31	(1.06)	1.87	(3.12)
Diastylis laevis	59	M	1.27	1.37	1.54	0.86	1.85	1.25	2.94	(2.32)	2.96	(6.12)
Dorvillea sp.	124	M	1.02	0.81	1.40	2.01	2.63	4.64	0.45	(0.08)	7.78	(31.00)
Fabriciola baltica	109		1.99	1.86	3.70	3.64	2.12	1.25	0.63	(0.60)	0.60	(0.74)
Hydrobia ulvae	157	M	1.67	1.60	2.07	2.66	1.96	1.82	3.00	(2.83)	1.19	(3.37)
Nematoda	170	M	2.43	3.14	3.86	2.49	10.19	9.95	4.84	(9.94)	-2.39	(15.90)
Nereimyra punctata	113	M	1.76	1.31	3.05	1.54	2.35	10.56	-0.25	(0.75)	3.15	(16.36)
Paraonis lyra	71		1.53	1.62	3.42	0.86	3.90	1.11	10.23	(9.31)	7.05	(10.27)
Pholöe minuta	349	M	2.64	1.98	4.14	2.00	7.25	28.92	10.26	(8.98)	3.52	(13.64)
Prionospio malmgreni	139		1.36	1.43	1.17	3.62	2.95	0.54	2.65	(2.54)	0.54	(1.21)
Scoloplos armiger	55		1.14	1.11	1.66	2.18	1.12	0.98	-0.05	(0.24)	0.18	(3.07)
Terebellides stroemi	33		0.94	0.94	1.85	0.18	0.88	2.99	3.47	(3.30)	0.27	(0.76)

The validity of the plots at the range of scales of this analysis may be assessed by comparing the results obtained for transects C-12A and C-12B. Although only 12 of the 15 species analyzed were common to both sets of data, the plots (Fig. 1), expressed as variance/mean ratios (because of their frequently differing density in the transects) versus block size, showed a variable though generally close agreement. There appeared to be no correlation between the relative degree of consistency of the two plots and differences in the means of the species in the two transects, or between the different degree of motility of the species. This agreement is surprising in view of the time gap between the two sets of samples, and indicates a persistence in spatial dispersion apparently unaffected by either possible change in position of the fauna on the bottom or any change in density.

Although the 95% limits of the Poisson are given in Figure 1, the significance of the peaks or troughs exceeding the Poisson

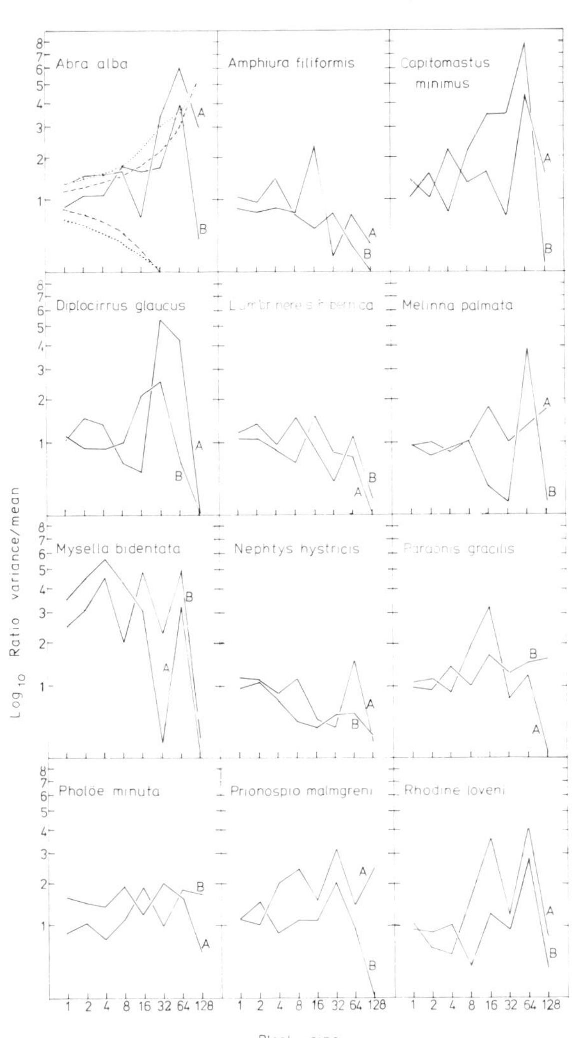

Fig. 1. Plots of ratio variance/mean (heavy lines) versus block size for 12 species common to Transects C-12A and C-12B. 95% confidence bounds for the Poisson are shown calculated (a) from $1 \pm 2\sqrt{2n/(n-1)^2}$ (pecked lines) and (b) from the Monte Carlo method (dotted lines).

limits as indicative of nonrandom dispersion may be taken as considerably improved owing to the consistency of the peaks in the replicates in further distinguishing inherent trends in the dispersion of the population from chance effects (Thompson 1958; Kershaw 1957).

Our results may be illustrated by the small erycinacean bivalve, *Mysella bidentata* in the C-12 transects. The values of the dispersion statistic plotted in Figure 1 indicate nonrandom clustering at all block sizes (BS) from 1 to 16 for Transect C-12A and from BS 1-64 for Transect C-12B. The greatest degree of similarity between the two plots is shown at the smallest block sizes where the numbers of degrees of freedom (df) available are highest. The apparent similarity in the values at the largest block sizes (where the df are lowest) may be of little real importance. Clustering at scales from approximately 0.05-1.0 m (BS1-16) is, however, well demonstrated; the sample values exceed the Poisson limits calculated both from

$$1 \pm 2\sqrt{\frac{2n}{(n-1)^2}}$$

and from the Monte Carlo method. It will be noted that the trough in the C-12A plot for *Mysella* at BS 32 (4 df) lies within the Poisson limits, so that no regularity (evenness) in dispersion is indicated at any scale.

The Monte Carlo bounds are somewhat wider than those calculated on the assumption of independent data. Presumably, the discrepancy may be connected with the non-independence of the successively recombined data blocks.

C-12 plots in Figure 1 show that many other species yield even better consistency in the transect replicates than *Mysella*, while a few are slightly worse. The plots for the tellinid bivalve, *Abra alba*, for example, show good consistency and, in contrast to *Mysella*, indicate a large-scale clustering at a scale of approximately 3.5 m. A similar conclusion might be drawn from the plots for the flabelligerid polychaete, *Diplocirrus glaucus*, which also shows some consistency in the replicates, which despite not individually exceeding the limits for the Poisson expectation, may, nevertheless, indicate an inherent trend to clustering at scales corresponding to BS 32 and 64 (approximately 2-3.5 m) on the basis of the consistency in peaks. On the other hand, the plot for the nephtyd polychaete, *Nephtys hystricis*, may, on the basis of plot consistency, indicate a tendency towards increasing regularity in dispersion with increasing scale, despite the variance/mean values falling within the Poisson expectation for every block size. *Nephtys hystricis* also showed slightly regular dispersion at the relatively large scale of sampling by Gage and Geekie (1973). Both *Mysella bidentata* and *Abra alba* were shown to have a significant aggregation on the basis of Gage and Geekie's study and the studies of Franz (1973) and Rosenberg (1974) also demonstrated a clustered dispersion of *Mysella*.

The only species occurring at sufficient abundance at all three transect locations was the small sigalionid polychaete *Pholoë minuta*. It is therefore of interest to compare the results obtained. In Figure 2 the plots show good resemblance, perhaps suggesting that the dispersion is biologically controlled rather than the result of environmental inhomogeneity, which would probably not be the same in the wide range of benthic environments purposely represented by the three transect locations. The degree of similarity between the plots is increased considerably by using (Fig. 2) a variable scale so that the vertical dimension of the largest peaks were similar, and by using values uncorrected for "trend." This suggests that assessment of dispersion purely in terms of the relation of dispersion statistics to significance bands of the random expectation may ignore some of the potential of the block size analysis of variance method in describing natural dispersion.

Although it was hoped that comparisons of the muddy-sand Transect C-3 could be made with the data of Angel and Angel (1967) dominating species did not coincide in the two data sets.

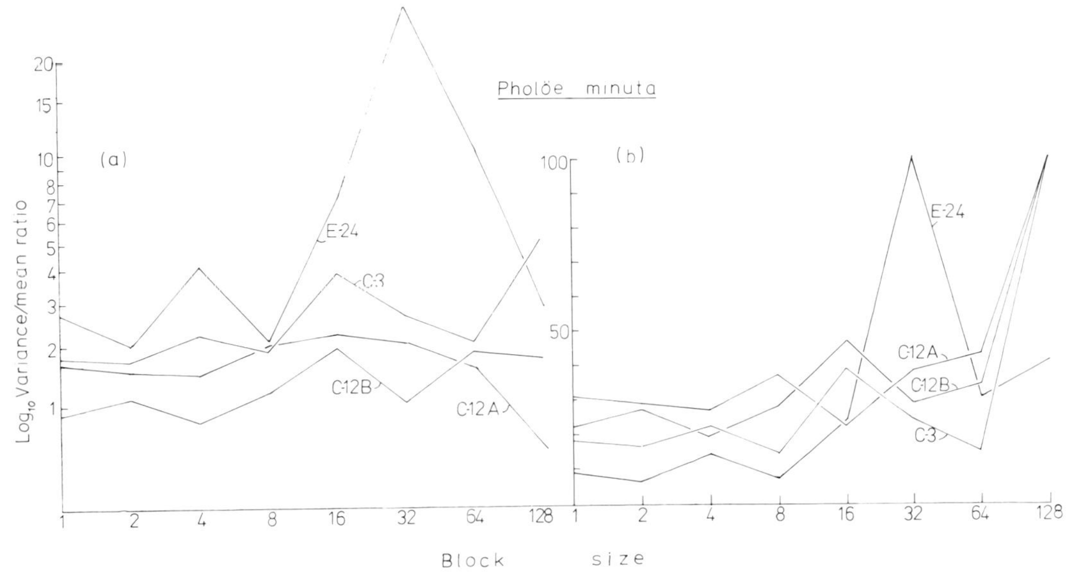

Fig. 2. Plots of ratio variance/mean versus block size for *Pholoë minuta* in different transects (a) common scale on vertical axis, (b) variable scale on vertical axis (values uncorrected for position); the variance/mean ratios plotted as percentages of the maximal value for each transect.

Comparison of Total Community Dispersion

The limited number of species dispersions analyzed at each transect location might be criticized as being unrepresentative of the range in community dispersions. However, on the basis of the community evaluation of Gage (1972b), their combined numerical abundance appears to represent an overwhelming numerical dominance in the total community, so that they may be taken to adequately describe total community dispersion.

Total community dispersion is here expressed as the mean of the sum of the individual species dispersions, as distinct from the dispersion of the sum of the individuals not separated into the component species. The sum of individual species dispersions may be expressed as the sum of the values of the dispersion statistic expressed as a percentage of the total possible in conditions of maximum clustering. Such a definition focuses on clustered dispersion rather than regularity because values falling below the Poisson expectation are rare (Table 1). Since the "trend" correction has its greatest affect on the values for the largest block sizes, the uncorrected values for BS 64 and 128 are given in parentheses. The correction clearly appeared to impose an artificial regularity to these dispersion values.

Because a value of natural maximum clustering may be quite difficult to measure, a simple alternative is to express,as is done here, the dispersions as the mean of the values related to the Poisson expectation. This circumvents the difficulties inherent in comparisons of statistics with highly different degrees of freedom. The result of comparison of the transects with the individual variance/mean ratios expressed as the mean of their deviations from the upper Poisson bound is given in Figure 3. The general range of the mean of these deviations for the two C-12 transects is rather similar and decreases only slightly with increasing block size. However, those for C-3 and E-24 show peaks of deviation at BS 16-64, and represent a peak in clustering at scales roughly from 1 to 3.5 m.

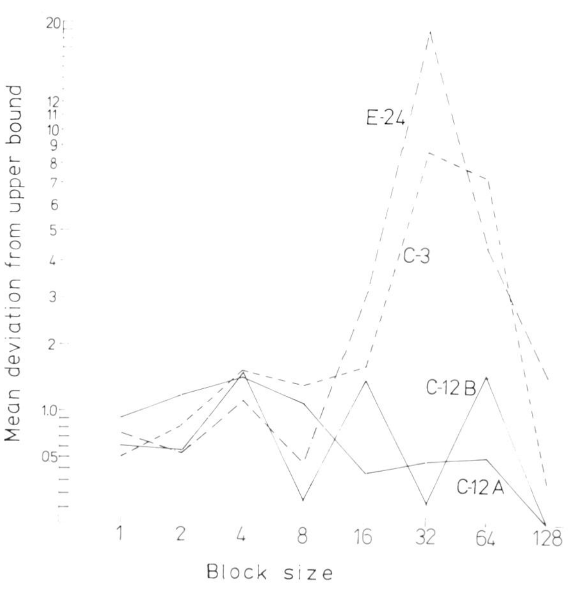

Fig. 3. Overall clustered dispersion of fauna versus block size expressed as the mean deviation from the upper Poisson bound.

The variance/mean ratios listed in Table 1 suggest that for each transect relatively few species contributed a disproportionate share of the total sum of values for a given block size. It is not the authors' intention to pursue this topic, or to discuss the degree of correlation in dispersion between species. However, as a start to estimating the relative influence of environmental and biological elements on clustered dispersion in the benthos, species in the transects were divided into motile and sedentary categories and their total deviation from the upper Poisson bound summed separately. The result (Table 2) suggests first, that the motile species were more clustered at all block sizes up to and including BS 32. The differences at the larger block sizes may be disregarded because of the small df available. It is also evident that the peak in deviation at BS 32 shown in the data for transects C-3 and E-24 is contributed chiefly by motile species. Table 1 makes clear that the species chiefly responsible are *Pholöe minuta* for E-24 and the ostracod species for C-3, while the taxon chiefly responsible for the less elevated mean deviation for BS 16 was the Nematoda (which were considered collectively and not separated into species.

Table 2. Overall clustered dispersion of the "motile" and "sedentary" elements of the total fauna analyzed in the transects, expressed as the total deviation from the upper Poisson bound.

	Block Size							
	1	2	4	8	16	32	64	128
Motile species	8.18	10.05	20.02	13.89	23.40	68.85	18.03	2.75
Sedentary species	2.87	5.65	14.06	10.60	11.73	34.11	37.08	2.02

It seems reasonable to conclude that motile species that can move around actively on the bottom are capable of assuming and maintaining a particular spatial dispersions, based on their behavioral capabilities, which sedentary animals would not be capable of. Although a clustered dispersion of sedentary species may have a biological basis (such as gregarious larval settlement) it would, presumably, also reflect a lasting response to temporary environmental inhomogeneity (such as smothering by a patch of seaweed debris), which the dispersion of a motile species would only reflect while that inhomogeneity existed. But perhaps more important would be the incapability of a sedentary species to adjust to stochastic effects, such as random thinning, which the actively maintained dispersion of a motile species could accommodate.

CONCLUSION

With the exception of anomalous sediment at E-24, the present results support the earlier conclusion based on grab sampling at or near transects, that fauna of the muddy sand sediments show greater overall clustering in their dispersions than those of soft mud. This agreement reinforces similar conclusions reached by other investigators (e.g., Reys 1971). The present dimensional study of dispersion indicates that clustering of motile species at scales corresponding to BS 16-64 (approximately 1-3.5 m) contributes most to the differences in the present comparison. This conclusion is partially corroborated by the results of Angel and Angel's (1967) block size analysis of their contiguous core transect on muddy sand, from which it is possible to calculate that the greatest intensity of pattern is also shown at the largest block sizes. But it is not possible to ascertain whether the clustering peaks of the present study correspond to that dispersion resulting in the overall differences in clustering shown at different localities by Gage and Geekie on the basis of their relatively large-scale sampling.

REFERENCES

Angel, H. H. and M. V. Angel. 1967. Distribution pattern analysis of a benthic community. Helgolander wiss. Meeresunters 15: 445-454.

Boswell, M. T. and G. P. Patil. 1970. Chance mechanisms generating the negative binomial distribution. In Random counts in scientific work, v 1. Pennsylvania State University Press.

Curtis, J. T. and R. P. McIntosh. 1950. The interrelations of certain analytic and synthetic phytosociological characters. Ecology 31: 434-455.

Davies, R. G. 1971. Computer programming in quantitative biology. Academic Press.

Franz, D. R. 1973. The ecology and reproduction of a marine bivalve, *Mysella planulata* (Erycinacea). Biol. Bull. 144: 93-106.

Gage, J. 1972a. A preliminary survey of the benthic macrofauna and sediments in lochs Etive and Creran, sea-lochs along the west coast of Scotland. J. Mar. Biol. Assoc. U. K. 52: 237-276.

_____. 1972b. Community structure of the benthos in Scottish sea lochs. I. Introduction and species diversity. Mar. Biol. 19: 281-297.

_____ and A. D. Geekie. 1973. Community structure of the benthos in Scottish sea lochs. II. Spatial pattern. Mar. Biol. 19: 41-53.

Goodall, D. W. 1971. Comment to paper by Noy-Meir and Anderson, p. 225-227. In G. P. Patil, E. C. Pielou, and W. E. Waters [eds.], Statistical ecology,v 3, Many species populations, ecosystems, and systems analysis. Pennsylvania State University Press.

Greig-Smith, P. 1952. The use of random and contiguous quadrats in the study of the structure of plant communities. Ann. Bot. 16: 293-316.

______. 1964. Quantitative plant ecology, 2nd ed. Butterworths.

Jumars, P. A. 1975. Environmental grain and polychaete species diversity in a bathyal benthic community. Mar. Biol. 30: 253-266.

Kershaw, K. A. 1957. The use of cover and frequency in the detection of pattern in plant communities. Ecology 38: 291-299.

______. 1973. Quantitative and dynamic plant ecology, 2nd ed. Arnold.

Noy-Meir, I. and D. J. Anderson. 1971. Multiple pattern analysis, or miltiscale ordination: towards a vegetation hologram?, p. 207-225. In G. P. Patil, E. C. Pielou, and W. E. Waters [eds.], Statistical ecology, v. 3, Many species populations, ecosystems, and systems analysis. Pennsylvania State University Press.

Mead, R. 1974. A test for spatial pattern at several scales using data from a grid of contiguous quadrats. Biometrics 30: 295-307.

Morisita, M. 1959. Measuring of the dispersion of individuals and analysis of the distributional patterns. Mem. Fac. Sci. Kyushu Univ. (Ser. E) 2: 215-235.

Patil, G. P. and W. M. Stiteler. 1974. Concepts of aggregation and their quantification: a critical review with some new results and applications. Res. Popul. Ecol. 15: 238-254.

Pielou, E. C. 1969. An introduction to mathematical ecology. Wiley.

Reys, J. -P. 1971. Analyses statistique de la microdistribution des espèces benthiques de la région de Marseille. Tethys 3: 381-403.

Rogers, A. 1974. Statistical analysis of spatial dispersion. Pion.

Rosenberg, R. 1974. Spatial dispersion of an estuarine benthic faunal community. J. Exp. Mar. Biol. Ecol. 15: 69-80.

Stiteler, W. M. and G. P. Patil. 1971. Variance-to-mean ratio and Morisita's index as measured of spatial patterns in ecological populations, p. 423-452. In G. P. Patil, E. C. Pielou, and W. E. Waters [eds.], Statistical ecology, v. 1, Spatial patterns and statistical distributions. Pensylvania State University Press.

Thompson, H. R. 1955. Spatial point processes, with applications to ecology. Biometrika 42: 102-115.

______. 1958. The statistical study of plant distribution patterns using a grid of quadrats. Aust. J. Bot. 6: 322-343.

Community Dynamics

Infaunal Biomass and Production on a Mudflat, San Francisco Bay, California

Frederic H. Nichols
U. S. Geological Survey
345 Middlefield Road
Menlo Park, CA 94025

ABSTRACT

Broad intertidal mudflats adjacent to *Spartina/Salicornia* salt marshes are a prominent feature of the San Francisco Bay estuary. As an initial step in an intensive study of the cycling of organic matter on a mudflat in south San Francisco Bay, California, the biomass distribution of all common macroinfaunal (> 0.5 mm) invertebrate species was determined for four seasons and annual productivity estimated. Total specimen numbers (mean of four seasons) varied between 53,000 and 155,000 m^{-2} at three stations along a 154-m intertidal transect normal to the marsh edge, but there were large seasonal variations. Infaunal biomass (mean of four seasons) varied from 13 to 24 g ash-free dry weight m^{-2} without large seasonal variations. The bivalves, *Gemma gemma* and *Macoma balthica*, together accounted for most (72 to 85%) of this biomass. Minimum rates of annual productivity, estimated using a factor relating production to biomass (4.5 x mean annual biomass) as well as size frequency data, varied from 53 to 100 g $m^{-2}yr^{-1}$, or at least 25 g C $m^{-2}yr^{-1}$. This high secondary productivity, supporting a large shorebird community, is probably maintained by several mechanisms: (1) tidal transport of detritus from the salt marsh, especially following winter die-off of the higher marsh plants, (2) continuous resuspension of surface sediment, benthic diatoms, and detritus through tide and wind wave action, (3) the presence of a diatom layer on the mud surface throughout much of the year, and (4) the presence of plankton, treated sewage, and riverborne particulate matter in the water column.

INTRODUCTION

The high rate of production in salt-marsh ecosystems is well documented. Keefe, in a review of marsh-production literature (1972), suggested that high productivity in marshes, commonly several kg m^{-2} yr^{-1}, is a function of high nutrient availability, long plant-growing season, and rapid decomposition of plant material with concomitant recycling of necessary metal ions. Because a substantial proportion (up to 49%) of the plant material produced has been shown to be exported from the marsh to the adjacent estuary (Teal 1962, Cameron 1972), the potential for high secondary production should be great in areas where the exported organic matter from salt marshes accumulates. A number of investigators working in mudflat environments (e.g., Boyden and Little 1973) have proposed high productivity for this habitat despite the normally limited number of species. But only recently (e.g., Burke and Mann 1974, Warwick and Price 1975) have appropriate data been gathered. In estuaries where the mudflat is areally important, secondary production could represent a sizeable percentage of the organic matter exported from the salt marsh.

San Francisco Bay is characteristic of some estuaries of the western United States in having a broad shallow bottom with narrow deep channels formed by the submergence of subaerial features (alluvial fans and stream channels) by transgressing seas. The topography shows a transformation from rugged upland regions to the broad, gently sloping nearshore region where marsh gradually gives way to mudflat at about mean tide level (Cooper 1926). At places the intertidal mudflats of south San Francisco Bay extend a kilometer or more between the salt marshes and the channels. The salt marshes have been greatly reduced through man's development of the nearshore region, but the mudflats remain an imposing feature of the bay. These flats exhibit little relief, except for an occasional shell bank, and little slope.

In contrast to the intensive studies of salt-marsh systems of the eastern United States, detailed studies of San Francisco Bay salt marshes and adjacent mudflats are few. Hinde (1954) observed the vertical distribution of plants in relation to tide levels of a south San Francisco Bay marsh, Recher (1966) studied the seasonal distribution and behavior of migratory birds that feed on the mudflats adjacent to the same marsh, and Cameron (1972) investigated insect diversity in a north San Francisco Bay marsh. Recher and Cameron estimated seasonal patterns in standing crop of the respective faunal groups, but made no estimates of the productivity of the populations under investigation. The only published quantitative data concerning the invertebrates of a mudflat seem to be those of Vassallo (1969, 1971), who collected data during one summer period on the eastern shore of south San Francisco Bay (see Nichols 1973).

A systematic field sampling and laboratory analytical program was developed during a study of the San Francisco Bay estuary (McCulloch et al. 1970; Peterson et al. 1975) to assess the physical, chemical, and biological properties of the water flowing into and the water mass within the bay, and to develop an organic matter budget for the estuary. A further objective of the study was to assess the role of the mudflat in the budget. This paper is an initial report of seasonal patterns in standing crop of the common infaunal species of a mudflat in this estuary. The data are used to make tentative estimates of total infaunal production, defined here as growth or the increase in total tissue weight of species populations within a specified time interval (see Nichols 1975).

Special thanks are due L. C. White, Director of Nature and Science for the City of Palo Alto, for his cooperation in allowing use of the wildlife preserve, and J. K. Thompson for her invaluable assistance in the field and laboratory work throughout the study. Other colleagues too numerous to cite participated in lesser but equally important ways.

MATERIALS AND METHODS

This study was carried out at three stations located on a 154-m transect across the mudflat adjacent to the City of Palo Alto salt marsh (Fig. 1). The study site is at Sand Point, where shell material and firm clay lie beneath the soft surface mud layer (at least 15 cm in thickness).

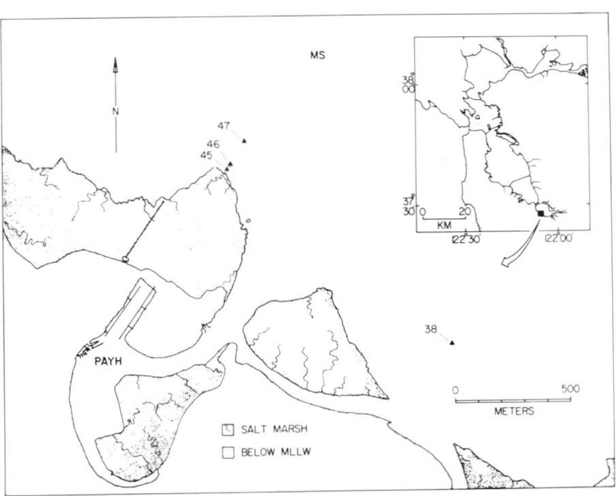

Fig. 1. Palo Alto salt marsh and mudflat, with inset map of San Francisco Bay. Mayfield Slough (MS), which passes through the Palo Alto Yacht Harbor (PAYH), joins the main channel of south San Francisco Bay to the north off the map.

The tide range (mean higher high water to mean lower low water) is 2.5 m. The elevations of the mudflat surface at the three stations were determined, with reference to a nearby bench mark, by standard surveying techniques. The first station, 45, is located 110 cm above mean lower low water (MLLW) and 12 m from the edge of the marsh where the mudflat ceases to be interrupted by patches of *Spartina* and shell debris. The second station, 46, at 90 cm above MLLW, is 28 m from station 45 below a slight drop in the mudflat elevation and adjacent to a small exposed shell bank. Station 47, at 80 cm above MLLW and 142 m from station 45, is located on the broad expanse of mudflat having little relief or gradient in elevation. Stakes marked location and height of the mud surface with reference to permanent elevation markers.

During December 1974, sediment samples were collected at each station, and particle size determined by standard dry sieving technique for coarse material and a hydrophotometer technique (Jordan et al. 1971) for fine material.

Temperature and salinity measurements have been made in the channel almost monthly since 1969 (McCulloch et al. 1970) and all data gathered during each of the 12 months since 1969 were averaged to depict long-term seasonal patterns in these parameters.

Beginning in February 1974 macrofauna were collected monthly at each station in three 57-cm^2 core samples, 20 cm in length taken randomly within a 1.0-m^2 quadrat positioned arbitrarily within several meters of the station markers. The samples were washed on a 0.5-mm screen and preserved in formalin, then transferred after several days to 70% alcohol. For this study, all species from quarterly samples (February, May, August, and November 1974) were identified, counted and weighed wet. As part of a survey of the benthos throughout the bay, additional samples were collected in January and August 1973 from shipboard with a 0.1-m^2 van Veen grab sampler at station 38 (Fig. 1), a faunistically and sedimentologically similar location. These samples, washed on a 1-mm screen and preserved as above, provide data on the larger, less abundant species.

Biomass was determined from the mean wet weight (after blotting for 10 min) of all specimens of each of the common species. The wet weight of the molluscs included shell weight. The few, usually very small individual specimens of the remaining species were not weighed. Mean wet weights were converted to ash-free dry weight (AFDW) using Lie's (1968) factors: 0.133 for polychaetes and oligochaetes, 0.150 for crustaceans, and 0.055 for bivalves. Seasonal differences in count and biomass data were tested with a one-way analysis of variance. Where no differences existed, the annual mean count and biomass values were used. Where seasonal differences did exist, seasonal means were computed separately.

Several workers (e.g., Dickie 1972) have shown that estimates of biomass can be used to compute crude measures of production. Therefore, production was initially computed by multiplying the mean of the four seasonal estimates of biomass for each species by a common production/mean biomass factor that Waters (1969) suggested might be "more universally applicable": 4.5, hereafter referred to as the turnover ratio (TR). Total production for each station is the sum of that for each of the common species. A more precise measure of the production-biomass ratio for the dominant species, *Gemma gemma* and *Macoma balthica*, was possible with these data in only two situations: at station 45, where growth and mortality of an essentially unimodal population of *Gemma* could be estimated, and at station 38 for *Macoma*. At stations 46 and 47, the populations of

Gemma consisted of several overlapping cohorts, and *Macoma* was represented by too few specimens. Where the calculations were possible, production was computed as the summation of growth of mean-sized animals between sampling dates, determined through integration of the curve depicting the relation between numbers of specimens and mean specimen size at different times of year (Allen 1951). For these populations it was assumed that age structure in a given month was the same from one year to the next: the data for *Gemma* in November 1974 at station 45 were used as November 1973 data (and likewise for the August *Macoma* samples at station 38) in order to characterize the population age structure closer to the time of recruitment.

RESULTS

Size analysis of surface sediments showed the predominance of mud (mean grain size less than 0.062 mm): 76, 81 and 96% at stations 45, 46 and 47, respectively. Sand made up the bulk of the remaining material, although ongoing studies indicate that the relative percentage of this size fraction changes seasonally. The sediment at station 47 contained very little coarse material and a ratio of silt to clay of about 2:1. Monthly measurements of mudflat elevation showed that during later summer (August to October) greater erosion resulted in a lowering of mudflat elevation about 7-9 cm. This change coincided with the summer period of strong afternoon winds and concomitant wind waves.

Because south San Francisco Bay is geographically removed from the main part of the estuary (Sacramento River to the Golden Gate), the dilution of south bay water is not substantial except during late winter (Fig. 2), although the small freshwater streams and domestic sewage outfalls in the south bay region may have localized, nearshore effects. Salinity rarely drops below 8 to 9 $^{o}/oo$ in the channels of south San Francisco Bay. Because of the short duration of exposure to low salinities and the fact that interstitial salinity in fine sediments usually remains high (Alexander et al. 1932, Sanders et al. 1965), salinity does not appear to limit the distribution of the estuarine organisms found on the mudflat.

Temperature of the water (Fig. 2) or that of the surface mud at low tide may become sufficiently high in summer to be lethal, especially in view of the paucity of numbers of several of the smaller species at that time of year. This possibility has not yet been examined.

Numerical abundance of the species on this mudflat reflected to some degree the sampling techniques used: the common species were in most cases those that are small, but with an adult size larger than 0.5 mm (Table 1). As a result, the count data given for at least some of these species (Table 2) are underestimates, in particular, for *Gemma gemma, Streblospio benedicti, Ampelisca milleri* and

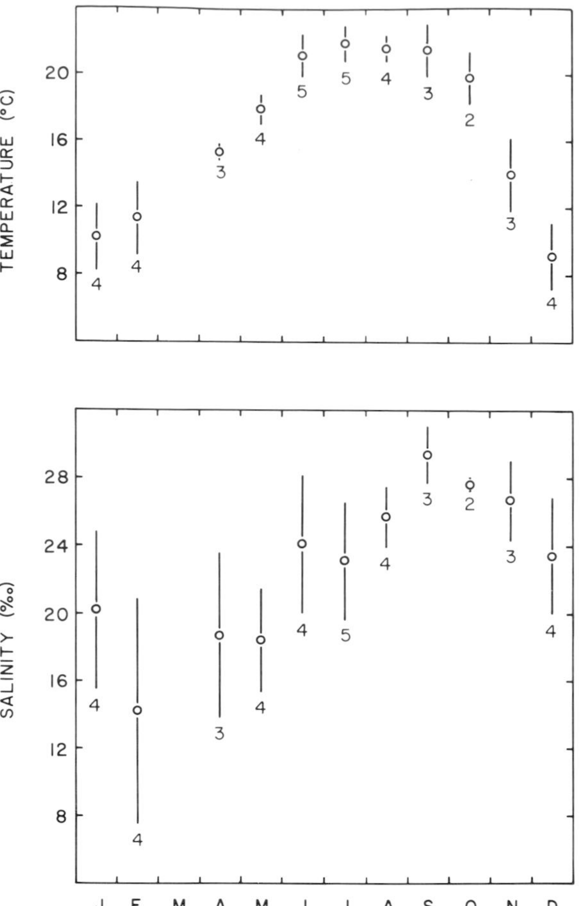

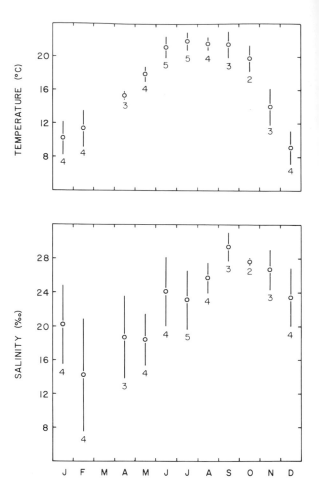

Fig. 2. Average monthly temperature and salinity at 1-2 m depth in the main channel of south San Francisco Bay off Palo Alto. The number of observations and limits of one standard deviation on either side of the mean are shown.

the ostracods, as their populations are known to have juveniles smaller than 0.5 mm. However, since we sampled that part of the species populations making up the largest portion of the biomass, the data are considered valid for useful production estimates.

Highest numbers of specimens and biomass recorded from these samples occurred in late autumn and winter at all stations, lowest in summer. Annual mean numbers of specimens greater than 0.5 mm varied from 53,000 to 155,00 m^{-2} depending on the station, but seasonal extremes were marked: 11,000 to 79,000 m^{-2}, 138,000 to 168,000 m^{-2}, and 56,000 to 137,000 m^{-2} at stations 45, 46, and 47

The clam, *Gemma gemma*, and the polychaete, *Streblospio benedicti*, were the overwhelming numerical dominants (Table 2). *Gemma gemma* alone accounted for most of the numbers, and with the exception of station 45, much of the biomass. At station 46 there was no seasonal difference in numbers of *Gemma* specimens. Except for one sample in November in which 1726 specimens were recovered, the range of specimens collected throughout the year was 344 to 751 per sample. A detailed study of the dynamics of this population is now underway, and preliminary data suggest that we are losing somewhat more than one-half of the *Gemma* specimens during the summer recruitment period through our 0.5 mm screen (J. K. Thompson personal

Table 1. Mudflat species with relative abundances in 57-cm^2 core samples at stations 45, 46, and 47 (C = common; CS = seasonally common; U = uncommon, seen frequently but in small numbers and not consistently; R = rare, seen occasionally).

Species	Abundance	Species	Abundance
Gemma gemma	C	*Pseudopolydora kempi*	R[a]
Macoma balthica	C	*Streblospio benedicti*	C
Musculus senhousia	R[b]	Syllidae sp.	R[a]
Mya arenaria	CS	Oligochaeta	C
Nassarius obsoletus	U	*Ampelisca milleri*	CS
Odostomia spp.	U	*Corophium* spp.	U
Urosalpinx cinerea	R[b]	*Grandidierella japonica*	C
Capitellidae spp.	R[a]	Ostracoda spp.	C
Cirratulidae spp.	R[a]	*Synidotea laticauda*	R[b]
Eteone californica	C	Bryozoa	U
Heteromastus filiformis	C	Cirripedia	U
Marphysa sanguinea	R[b]	*Diadumene* sp.	U
Neanthes succinea	R[b]	Nematoda	R[a]
Polydora ligni	C	Turbellaria	R

[a]generally too small to be retained on a 0.5-mm screen.
[b]large, but too widely spaced in nature to be collected regularly in a 57-cm^2 core sample.

communication). Therefore, our abundance estimates for this species in May and August should be doubled, although this correction is not incorporated in the production computations described below.

Macoma balthica, though represented by relatively few specimens in the core samples, was consistently an important contributor of biomass. *Mya arenaria* was important only in summer. Together, *Gemma gemma* and *Macoma balthica* accounted for 85, 77, and 72% of total biomass (mean of four seasons) in the core samples at the three stations respectively. An analysis of variance in biomass measurements revealed no significant difference in biomass of *Gemma gemma* and *Macoma balthica* among seasons. The weight of individual *Gemma* specimens was greatest in summer when numbers in our samples were least.

Data from the core samples concerning *Macoma* were too limited for interpretation of population age structure, but the 0.1 m^2 grab samples from nearby station 38 helped in this regard. The large samples revealed an abundance of smaller sized specimens in August and few large specimens in February (Table 3), suggesting recruitment in spring. Nonetheless, samples showed that the *Macoma* numbers and biomass data from the core samples are reasonable. As in the core samples, the grab samples showed no difference in *Macoma* biomass between seasons, and the annual means are comparable (3.1 g AFDW m^{-2}

Table 2. Species numbers (N/m^2) and biomass (AFDW g/m^2) at four times of year. Total biomass given with and without the *Macoma* and *Mya* data.

Species	February		May		August		November	
	N	AFDW	N	AFDW	N	AFDW	N	AFDW
Station 45								
G. gemma	18000	0.947	15000	0.947	3300	0.947	25000	0.947
M. balthica	1100	10.348	2200	10.348	3900	10.348	3000	10.348
M. arenaria	0	0.0	470	0.093	350	1.775	0	0.0
S. benedicti	47000	2.637	21000	0.585	1300	0.064	23000	0.948
H. filiformis	120	0.126	120	0.126	120	0.126	120	0.126
E. californica	530	0.077	8600	0.721	760	0.023	1400	0.022
P. ligni	1300	0.028	0	0.0	58	<0.001	1200	0.024
Oligochaeta	9700	0.213	4700	0.077	530	0.004	7500	0.132
A. milleri	120	0.002	180	0.003	58	<0.001	2900	0.120
G. japonica	410	0.008	120	0.003	640	0.013	3000	0.132
Ostracoda	290	0.004	350	0.002	180	0.002	2500	0.016
Total	78570	14.390	52740	12.905	11196	13.310	69620	12.900
less *Macoma* and *Mya*		4.042		2.464		1.187		2.552
Station 46								
G. gemma	110000	10.275	110000	10.275	110000	10.275	110000	10.275
M. balthica	1000	8.652	1000	8.652	1000	8.652	1000	8.652
M. arenaria	180	1.168	530	0.077	1300	9.987	530	2.171
S. benedicti	43000	2.116	24000	0.565	2200	0.083	28000	1.326
H. filiformis	340	0.565	340	0.565	340	0.565	340	0.565
E. californica	700	0.078	6700	0.667	1500	0.105	1200	0.014
P. ligni	510	0.011	510	0.011	510	0.011	510	0.011
Oligochaeta	9100	0.111	5200	0.095	2800	0.025	12000	0.240

Table 2. Continued

Species	February		May		August		November	
	N	AFDW	N	AFDW	N	AFDW	N	AFDW
A. milleri	0	0.0	120	0.001	18000	0.695	7800	0.692
G. japonica	58	0.065	58	0.065	410	0.065	3900	0.065
Ostracoda	180	0.001	230	0.002	350	0.006	3100	0.035
Total	165068	23.042	148688	20.975	138410	30.469	163380	24.046
less *Macoma* and *Mya*		13.222		12.246		11.830		13.223
Station 47								
G. gemma	34000	7.375	74000	7.375	45000	7.375	94000	7.375
M. balthica	380	1.188	380	1.188	380	1.188	380	1.188
M. arenaria	0	0.0	700	0.196	350	0.736	580	5.722
S. benedicti	25000	1.031	27000	0.726	580	0.011	16000	0.912
H. filiformis	640	0.492	640	0.492	640	0.492	640	0.492
E. californica	350	0.086	2900	0.086	1200	0.086	350	0.086
P. ligni	120	0.001	410	0.011	0	0.0	700	0.020
Oligochaeta	1500	0.007	940	0.003	0	0.0	700	0.003
A. milleri	1700	0.039	760	0.016	4100	0.120	8400	0.779
G. japonica	470	0.012	230	0.008	2600	0.079	11000	0.568
Ostracoda	1600	0.014	2500	0.017	1100	0.017	4100	0.050
Total	65760	10.238	110460	10.118	55950	10.104	136850	17.195
less *Macoma* and *Mya*		9.050		8.734		8.180		10.285

Table 3. Species numbers (N/m^2) and biomass (AFDW, g/m^2) at two times during 1973 at station 38.

Species	February		August	
	N	AFDW	N	AFDW
Macoma balthica	180	3.173	1600	3.091
Mya arenaria	--[a]	---	70	0.710
Nassarius obsoletus	60	2.809	20	0.920
Neanthes succinea	7	0.307	60	0.554

[a]only one 11.7 mg (AFDW) specimen collected

Table 4. Biomass (B, g AFDW/m^2, mean of four seasons) and production (P, g AFDW/m^2yr^{-1}) for common mudflat infaunal species.

Species	Station 45		Station 46		Station 47	
	B	P	B	P	B	P
G. gemma	0.947	4.3	10.275	46.2	7.375	33.2
M. balthica	10.348	46.6	8.652	38.9	1.188	5.4
M. arenaria	0.467	2.1	3.351	15.1	1.664	7.5
S. benedicti	1.081	4.9	1.023	4.6	0.670	3.0
H. filiformis	0.126	0.6	0.565	2.5	0.492	2.2
E. californica	0.211	1.0	0.216	1.0	0.086	0.4
P. ligni	0.013	0.1	0.011	<0.1	0.008	<0.1
Oligochaeta	0.107	0.5	0.118	0.5	0.003	<0.1
A. milleri	0.032	0.1	0.347	1.6	0.239	1.1
G. japonica	0.039	0.2	0.065	0.3	0.167	0.8
Ostracoda	0.006	<0.1	0.011	<0.1	0.025	0.1
Total	13.377	60.4	24.634	110.7	11.917	53.7

at station 38, and 10.3, 8.7 and 1.2 g AFDW m^{-2} at stations 45, 46, and 47.

Of the non-bivalve species, only *Streblospio benedicti*, and perhaps *Heteromastus filiformis* and *Ampelisca milleri* contributed importantly to overall biomass. *Streblospio* and *Ampelisca* were seasonally important with regard to abundance, while *Heteromastus* was found in low numbers throughout the year. The oligochaetes were numerically abundant, especially in autumn and winter, at the two nearshore stations but mean size was too small for the numbers to be reflected in biomass totals.

Several of the large invertebrates inhabiting the mud flat, the polychaetes, *Marphysa sanguinea*, and *Neanthes succinea*, and the molluscs, *Musculus senhousia* and *Nassarius obsoletus*, were taken only rarely in the corer. Because we have, as yet, too few quantitative estimates of the seasonal abundances of these species, they have not been included in the count and biomass summary (Table 2). The importance of two of these, *Neanthes* and *Nassarius*, is suggested in the samples from station 38 (Table 3). To the casual observer, *Nassarius obsoletus* is the only invertebrate of the mudflat. In fact, this species forms, in some areas, a pavement of shells on the mud surface. Further study may reveal that they are at least as important as *Macoma* or *Gemma* with regard to biomass.

Total biomass data show only slight seasonal variations, even after exclusion of the *Macoma* and *Mya* data, which tend to overemphasize the weight of single large specimens.

The computation of mean annual biomass and, subsequently, annual production (Table 4) provides a summary of the importance of the individual species in the mudflat organic matter budget. *Macoma*, dominant at the marsh edge of the mudflat, was replaced by *Gemma* as the dominant at stations 46 and 47. *Mya* was also important at stations 46 and 47. *Mya* was also important at stations 46 and 47, while *Streblospio* was moderately important at all stations. The other common species apparently contributed much less to secondary productivity of the mudflat.

Growth production for *Gemma gemma*, determined during the nine-month period between November and August from mean body weight increase and specimen number decrease at station 45 was 1.5 g m^{-2}, or about 2.0 g $m^{-2}yr^{-1}$; an annual TR of 2.1. Because a great number of specimens in small size classes were lost during sampling, these values probably are underestimates and indicate mean body size (in the months following recruitment) larger than is actually the case and a lower apparent growth rate during the year. This error is compounded by the presence in all samples of some specimens of other cohorts which tends to lessen the difference between mean specimen weight at the beginning and end of the period examined. Moreover, although the very small specimens not sampled do not greatly affect the mean biomass value, they are very productive (Nichols 1975); their inclusion would greatly increase the value of the Y intercept of the "Allen" production curve and thereby the area under the curve.

A mean-sized specimen of *Macoma balthica* at station 38 grew nine-fold (1.9 to 17.6 mg AFDW) between August and February, or 14.0 g AFDW m^{-2}. This represents a TR of 4.5 for the six-month period, assuming that biomass remained constant at about 3 g (Table 3) and that growth and mortality were linear. Because ongoing growth studies reveal that growth for this species shows great seasonal variations, and because the decline in numbers of specimens is certain to be non-linear with highest mortalities suffered by recent recruits, this six-month TR of 4.5 is probably an overestimate. It may be closer to an annual value.

DISCUSSION

Biomass and Production

The usefulness of the ratio of production to biomass (turnover ratio) for making approximate estimates of annual production from biomass measurements is the object of some discussion (e.g., Mann 1969, Waters 1969, Dickie 1972). Waters (1969) demonstrated that the turnover ratio (TR) of freshwater benthic invertebrates, when calculated on the basis of the cohort lifetime, is relatively constant, falling between 2.5 to 5.0, with a mode of about 3.5. Dealing primarily with univoltine species populations, he theoretically calculated the TR for varying initial and final population sizes (with regard to both weight and numbers). Because insect larvae have unusally large terminal populations, Waters suggested that a TR value of 4.5 is more universal. I have shown elsewhere (Nichols 1975) that populations of a marine benthic polychaete had a mean TR of 4.3, while the newly settled young specimens of the same species had TR's between 4.6 and 5.7, suggesting that populations dominated by young, fast-growing specimens may have higher TR's. Waters (1969) pointed out that smaller, short-lived species can also be expected to have higher turnover rates, especially if there are many cohorts per year. Our preliminary study of size frequency distributions of the common mudflat species suggests, tentatively, that they have only one to several recruitment periods per year, but that the recruitment periods may last for several months. Consequently, a factor of 4.5 may be sufficiently reliable for a first estimate of the productivity of the common species populations except perhaps for *Macoma* and *Mya*.

Burke and Mann (1974) and Warwick and Price (1975) reported, respectively, TR's for *Macoma balthica* of 1.53 and 0.9, and TR's for *Mya arenaria* of 2.54 and 0.5. However, our populations of these two species seem to be composed primarily of first-year individuals, and as such would have higher production to biomass ratios. This conclusion is tentatively borne out in the case of *Macoma* at station 38, where the rough calculation from two seasons gave a TR of 4.5 for a six-month period. The similarly computed TR for *Gemma* of 2.1 is a minimum annual turnover rate. True turnover is probably much greater. Actual measurement of production for the *Macoma* and *Gemma* populations is now underway. In the meantime, the present estimates are sufficient to demonstrate that annual growth production for these species is somewhat greater than the value of mean biomass and that use of the constant factor for a turnover ratio does not alter the conclusion that benthic secondary production on the mudflat is very high (perhaps up to 50 to 100 g organic matter $m^{-2}yr^{-1}$). Assuming that about half of the dry organic matter is carbon, secondary production can be at least 25 g C $m^{-2}yr^{-1}$.

The dominant species, *Gemma gemma*, is much more productive on this mudflat than the most productive species in other areas where *Gemma* does not occur. Hughes (1970) determined average production (growth and recruitment) for the bivalve, *Scrobicularia plana*, to be 7.2 g AFDW $m^{-2}yr^{-1}$. Kay and Brafield (1973) estimated production for the polychaete, *Neanthes virens*, to be 8.4 g dry weight $m^{-2}yr^{-1}$. Milne and Dunnet (1972), in a summary of productivity of the Ythan Estuary, provided some data (their Fig. 8) from which I calculate production for the gastropod, *Hydrobia ulvae*, and the amphipod, *Corophium volutator*, to be about 5 g AFDW $m^{-2}yr^{-1}$ each, assuming their data to be wet weights. Burke and Mann (1974) determined production for *Mya arenaria* and *Macoma balthica* on a sand flat to be 11.6 and 1.93 g dry flesh weight $m^{-2}yr^{-1}$. Warwick and Price (1975) determined that the polychaetes, *Nephtys hombergi* and *Ampherete acutifrons*, were the most productive macrofaunal invertebrates on an estuarine mudflat, with production rates of 7.3 and 2.3 g AFDW $m^{-2}yr^{-1}$, respectively. Also in their study area *Mya arenaria* and *Macoma balthica* produced 2.7 and 0.3 g AFDW $m^{-2}yr^{-1}$.

The data from Sanders et al. (1962) and Green and Hobson (1970) confirm that *Gemma gemma* can overshadow all other species. They have shown, as we have, that densities of *Gemma gemma* can be greater than 10^5 m^{-2}, with the largest numbers attributable to recent recruits. I have shown (Nichols 1975) that newly settled polychaetes, though numerous, initially do not contribute greatly to overall biomass and production because of their very small size. But because of the dominance of small *Gemma gemma* specimens, the relation between size and productivity must be investigated before we can be sure that our estimates of production for this species are not unreasonably low.

Spatial and Temporal Variations in Biomass Distributions

The major faunal difference among our stations was the presence of *Gemma* and *Macoma* in large numbers (with a total annual mean biomass of 19 g AFDW m^{-2}) at station 46, relative to the abundance of *Gemma* at the nearshore station and the abundance of *Macoma* at the seaward station. The dominance of one species does not appear to depend on a reduced role of the other. But the high combined biomass at station 46 remains unexplained. The apparent lack in some instances of seasonal differences in numbers or biomass within stations (Table 2) resulted in part from the contagious distributions of several of the species, especially that of *Gemma gemma*. The ratio of variance to mean for counts from replicate core samples taken at the two stations showing significant seasonal differences varied from 0.9 to 86.5, with a mean of 21.5. Although this high ratio is affected by the small number of samples and large number of specimens within each sample, it does reflect patchy distribution. Whether this represents true contagious distribution of the entire *Gemma* population, or simply that of the large (>0.5 mm) specimens, remains to be seen. But the relative consistency with which *Gemma* appears in our samples at each station permits us to have confidence in our estimates of mean biomass.

We have noted that small specimens of *Gemma* and *Streblospio benedicti* are constantly moved from place to place by wave and tidal action. Thus their distributions may be more by chance than substrate selection. On the other hand, the varying surface characteristics of the mudflat may influence distribution. Visual observation of the density of cells suggests that the region of highest primary productivity in the diatom layer on the mudflat surface occurs between the marsh edge and station 46 on the upper exposed surfaces of the low wave-formed ridges that make up the surface relief of the upper mudflat. In the level region beyond station 46, the mudflat is almost always covered with a surface film of water that apparently retards the development of a thick diatom mat, a ready food source for the invertebrates but possibly also a deterrent to colonization and tube building.

Seasonal patterns in the biomass distribution of the mudflat infauna are not highly significant even after data for the large species are deleted (Table 2). This lack of clear seasonal pattern, though partly due to our sampling techniques, probably results from a combination of factors: varying recruitment patterns, lack of cold winter temperatures, more or less continuous predation by shorebirds and large invertebrates, and a continuous supply of food. The lack of cold winter temperatures permits reproduction and growth of invertebrates throughout the year. In fact, greatest numbers were found on the mudflat between autumn and spring despite heavy bird feeding during this period (Recher 1966). We must assume, therefore, that there is an abundant supply of food throughout the year for the maintenance of the mudflat invertebrate community.

Such high productivity in estuaries is commonly attributed to a large supply of detritus transported from the salt marsh (de la Cruz 1973). Bacterial breakdown of the marsh plant material following die-off between November and March (Cameron 1972) may require a period of months before the organic matter is fully available to the mudflat animals (Odum and de la Cruz 1967). The slow decomposition process begun in winter may provide a continuing input of organic matter throughout the year. The decomposition process is no doubt aided by the physical processes in all shoal areas of San Francisco Bay. These areas, including the mudflat studied, are subject to wave action, especially during summer, and thus to resuspension of surface sediments (Anderson 1972) which causes measurable seasonal lowering of the mud surface noted. This phenomenon is particularly noticeable from an aircraft on a windy day: shoal areas can be distinguished from the channels by the turbidity of the water. Continual resuspension of surface sediments may help prevent the burial of detritus before decay is complete. Thus the attached microorganism populations would be allowed to develop and to break down the otherwise refractory marsh grass material, thereby making organic matter available to the consumers on the mudflat.

On the other hand, Wolff (1977) pointed out that in some estuarine systems, the importance of the export of detritus from salt marshes may be less than assumed when compared with other sources of organic matter. He determined the particulate organic matter within the Grevelingen Estuary in The Netherlands to be mainly material transported from the open sea through tidal exchange, and primary production within the estuary. In San Francisco Bay the major external source of particulate matter is river runoff. The total suspended sediment load carried into the bay is large (about 11,800 metric tons day^{-1} of which 1800 is contributed directly to South San Francisco Bay; Porterfield et al. 1961). This sediment, with the associated organic detritus and attached bacteria represents a potential food supply throughout the year, but especially in winter when runoff is high. Included with the suspended particles are living plants and animals. Through wind and tidal mixing in this shallow estuary, suspended sediment, detritus, bacteria, and plankton are always in contact with the bottom and thus are directly available to the benthos as food (Wolff 1977). In the southern part of San Francisco Bay, river input is low and must be considered only a secondary source of organic matter for the mudflat system. Here the resuspension and tidal transport of surface sediments play the important role in supplying a continuous and perhaps evenly distributed food supply (in addition to that material already in the water column) over the entire region, as well as aiding in the regeneration of dissolved nutrients from the sediment surface. Locally, domestic sewage may provide a large supply of nutritive material: one such discharge lies just west of the study area, where the treated effluent flows across the mudflat. A study of the composition, quantity and rate of supply of organic material, as well as of the rates of breakdown and utilization on the mudflat, is necessary before the relative importance to the benthos of the various sources of organic material can be determined.

Importance of the Mudflat Fauna

As a group, the small secondary producers of the mudflat convert the microflora and fauna of the sediment and water column, as well as the marsh-derived detritus and associated bacteria, into organic matter useable by higher organisms. In turn, the larger, less abundant invertebrates of the mudflat, *Marphysa sanguinea*, *Neanthes succinea*, and *Nassarius obsoletus*, may prey upon the many smaller species, thereby regulating population size and distribution of the smaller. As omnivores and potential carnivores they can affect the structure and complexity of this community (Paine 1966).

The most noticeable consumers of the mudflat infauna were the shore birds that rest and feed there on their seasonal migrations. Wolff (1976) has shown that shorebirds can consume annually a very significant proportion of estuarine benthic productivity, possibly up to 20 g AFDW m^{-2}yr^{-1} in some tidal flat areas. Stomach contents of selected birds species in our study area (Recher 1966) showed that nearly all of the invertebrate species listed in Table 2 were food for many of the bird species. Overall, *Neanthes succinea* was numerically important but *Gemma gemma* the most common food for three species. This observation might merely reflect Recher's ability to identify more readily specimens of *Neanthes* and the clams from hard parts, since the smaller soft-bodied worms may leave little trace in stomach contents. But perhaps the birds actively seek out the large *Neanthes* specimens, taking a disproportionate number relative to abundance. Recher showed how stomach contents reflected both the morphology and feeding behavior of individual bird species: the long-billed species were able to collect the deep-living *Macoma* specimens, whereas the surface feeders such as sandpipers collected amphipods and ostracods.

The finding that total biomass is comprised mostly of two or three bivalve species, together with our nonquantified observations of the abundance of *Nassarius obsoletus*, is in agreement with Burke and Mann's (1974) suggestion that molluscs are the chief primary consumers on some estuarine mudflats. We can only speculate that the reason for the dominance of *Gemma* and *Macoma* here is that food is not limiting for the invertebrates, but that the habitat is continually disturbed by the resuspension of surface sediments and heavy predation by shorebirds. Thus, the habitat might be underexploited by invertebrates. The very small (seldom longer than 3 mm) *Gemma*, living just below the sediment surface, broods its young, thereby reducing early mortality. The young are released in vast numbers and are scattered by wave action, perhaps settling and thriving in areas not already colonized by members of the same species or by the equally small *Streblospio* or *Ampelisca*. Mortality of the newly settled animals is probably attributable to bird predation, although at any location lateral transport out of the area may result in apparent mortality. *Macoma*, on the other hand, depends on successful settlement of planktonic larvae. But as a deep-living species (10 to 15 cm in this muddy habitat), it avoids predation by most of the bird species as well as erosion or burial by tide and wind wave action. With its long siphon, *Macoma* can selectively feed upon the plentiful food on or above the sediment surface. With a flexible feeding behavior and without competition for space in the mud, the small animals grow quickly. It is not clear, however, why the population contains few specimens over one or two years of age. This situation may result from lethal summer temperatures or increased chances, as they grow larger, of discovery by long-billed bird species. *Mya* is only seasonally important (numerous small specimens each summer), perhaps because it lives near the sediment surface and is subject to heavy predation pressure. This would account for the lack of large-sized specimens.

Our observations of a large standing crop of infaunal invertebrates throughout the year indicate that the mudflat acts as a sink for much of the organic matter produced in the marsh, in the water column, and on the mudflat itself; it also provides abundant food for resident and migratory birds. As such, the mudflat invertebrate community is an important link in the cycling of organic matter of the San Francisco Bay estuary.

REFERENCES

Alexander, W. B., B. A. Southgate, and R. Bassindale. 1932. The salinity of the water retained in the muddy foreshore of an estuary. J. Mar. Biol. Assoc. U. K. 18: 297-298.

Allen, K. R. 1951. The Horokiwi Stream. Bull. Mar. Dept. New Zealand Fish. 10: 1-231.

Anderson, F. E. 1972. Resuspension of estuarine sediments by small amplitude waves. J. Sediment. Petrol. 42: 602-607.

Boyden, C. R. and C. Little. 1973. Faunal distributions in soft sediments of the Severn Estuary. Estuar. and Coast. Mar. Sci. 1: 203-223.

Burke, M. V. and K. H. Mann. 1974. Productivity and production: biomass ratios of bivalve and gastropod populations in an eastern Canadian estuary. J. Fish. Res. Bd. Can. 31: 167-177.

Cameron, G. N. 1972. Analysis of insect trophic diversity in two salt marsh communities. Ecology 53: 58-73.

Cooper, W. S. 1926. Vegetational development upon alluvial fans in the vicinity of Palo Alto, California. Ecology 7: 1-30.

de la Cruz, A. A. 1973. The role of tidal marshes in the productivity of coastal waters. Bull. Assoc. Southeast. Biol. 20: 147-156.

Dickie, L. M. 1972. Food chains and fish production, pp. 201-221. In Symposium on environmental conditions in the northwest Atlantic, 1960-1969. Int. Comm. Northwest Atlantic Fish. Spec. Pub. 8.

Green, R. H. and K. D. Hobson. 1970. Spatial and temporal structure in a temperate intertidal community, with special emphasis on *Gemma gemma* (Pelecypoda: Mollusca). Ecology 51: 999-1011.

Hinde, H. P. 1954. Vertical distribution of salt marsh phanerograms in relation to tide levels. Ecol. Monogr. 24: 209-225.

Hughes, R. N. 1970. An energy budget for a tidal-flat population of the bivalve *Scrobicularia plana* (Da Costa). J. Anim. Ecol. 39: 357-381.

Jordan, C. F., Jr., G. E. Fryer, and E. H. Hemmen. 1971. Size analysis of silt and clay by hydrophotometer. J. Sediment. Petrol. 41: 489-496.

Kay, D. G. and A. E. Brafield. 1973. The energy relations of the polychaete *Neanthes (=Nereis) virens* (Sars). J. Anim. Ecol. 42: 673-692.

Keefe, C. W. 1972. Marsh production: a summary of the literature. Contrib. Mar. Sci. Univ. Texas 16: 163-181.

Lie, U. 1968. A quantitative study of benthic infauna in Puget Sound, Washington, USA, in 1963-64. FiskDir. Skr. Ser. HavUnders 14: 229-556.

Mann, K. H. 1969. The dynamics of aquatic ecosystems. Adv. Ecol. Res. 6: 1-81.

McCulloch, D. S., D. H. Peterson, P. R. Carlson, and T. J. Conomos. 1970. A preliminary study of the effects of water circulation in the San Francisco Bay estuary--some effects of fresh-water inflow on the flushing of south San Francisco Bay. U.S. Geol. Surv. Circ. 637A: 1-27.

Milne, H. and G. M. Dunnet. 1972. Standing crop, productivity and trophic relations of the fauna of the Ythan Estuary, pp. 86-106. In R. S. K. Barnes and J. Green [eds.], The estuarine environment. Applied Sci. Pub. Ltd.

Nichols, F. H. 1973. A review of benthic faunal surveys in San Francisco Bay. U.S. Geol. Surv. Circ. 677: 1-20.

_____. 1975. Dynamics and energetics of three deposit-feeding benthic invertebrate populations in Puget Sound, Washington. Ecol. Monogr. 45: 57-82.

Odum, E. P. and A. A. de la Cruz. 1967. Particulate organic detritus in a Georgia salt-marsh-estuarine ecosystem, pp. 383-388. In G. H. Lauff [ed.], Estuaries. Amer. Assoc. Advance. Sci. Pub. 83.

Paine, R. T. 1966. Food web complexity and species diversity. Amer. Natur. 100: 65-75.

Peterson, D. H., T. J. Conomos, W. W. Broenkow, and E. P. Scrivani. 1975. Processes controlling the dissolved silica distribution in San Francisco Bay, pp. 153-187. In L. E. Cronin [ed.], Estuarine research. I. Chemistry and biology. Academic Press.

Porterfield, George, N. L. Hawley, and C. A. Dunnam. 1961. Fluvial sediments transported by streams tributary to the San Francisco Bay area. Open-File rep. U.S. Geol. Surv. 70 p.

Recher, H. F. 1966. Some aspects of the ecology of migrant shorebirds. Ecology 47: 393-407.

Sanders, H. L., P. C. Mangelsdorf, Jr., and G. R. Hampson. 1965. Salinity and faunal distribution in the Pocasset River, Massachusetts. Limnol. Oceanogr. Supp. 10: R216-R229.

_____, E. M. Goudsmit, E. L. Mills, and G. E. Hampson. 1962. A study of the intertidal fauna of Barnstable Harbor, Massachusetts. Limnol. Oceanogr. 7: 63-79.

Teal, J. M. 1962. Energy flow in the salt marsh ecosystem of Georgia. Ecology 43: 614-624.

Vassallo, M. T. 1969. The ecology of *Macoma inconspicua* (Broderip & Sowerby, 1829) in central San Francisco Bay. I. The vertical distribution of the *Macoma* community. Veliger 11: 223-234.

_____. 1971. The ecology of *Macoma inconspicua* (Broderip & Sowerby, 1829) in central San Francisco Bay. II. Stratification of the *Macoma* community within the substrate. Veliger 13: 279-284.

Warwick, R. M. and R. Price. 1975. Macrofauna production in an estuarine mudflat. J. Mar. Biol. Assoc. U. K. 55: 1-18.

Waters, T. F. 1969. The turnover ratio in production ecology of fresh-water invertebrates. Am. Nat. 103: 173-185.

Wolff, W. J. 1976. The trophic role of birds in the Grevelingen Estuary, The Netherlands, compared to their role in the saline Lake Grevelingen. Proc. 10th Europ. Symp. Mar. Biol., Ostend, Belgium 2: 673-689.

______. 1977. A benthic food budget for the Grevelingen estuary, The Netherlands, and a consideration of the mechanisms causing high benthic secondary production in estuaries, pp. 267-280. In B. C. Coull [ed.], Ecology of marine benthos, Belle W. Baruch Library in Marine Science, v. 6, Univ. South Carolina.

Community Structure of the Macrobenthos Associated with Seagrass of the Indian River Estuary, Florida

D. K. Young and **M. W. Young**
Smithsonian Institution
Fort Pierce Bureau
Fort Pierce, FL 33450

Abstract

Effects of predation on community structure of the macrobenthos associated with dense stands of *Halodule wrightii* in the Indian River estuary of east central Florida were studied using cages. The three study sites represented a stress gradient of temperature, salinity and tide. Major changes, as affected by caging, were measured by species diversity, species evenness and species richness, showing opposite effects at the sites representing two extremes of the environmental stress gradient. At the site characterized by a physically unstable and unpredictable environment, the increases of several species within the cage were in accord with predator-prey theory. At the other extreme, where the environment was more physically stable and predictable, increases in diversity of caged macrofauna were inconsistent with current hypotheses of biological interactions affecting community structure.

INTRODUCTION

The central ecological concept considered in this study is that changes in faunal diversity within a given habitat type along an environmental stress gradient can be related to physical environmental predictability and biological interactions in the establishment, organization and maintenance of marine benthic communities. One assumption commonly underlying this concept has been that species diversity is directly and perhaps causally related to community stability (Odum 1971). However, as Hurlbert (1971) and others have warned, species diversity should be regarded only as a "function of species richness and the evenness with which the individuals are distributed among these species". Therefore, in this study species diversity, species richness and species evenness were measured to gain initial insight into the structure of macrobenthic communities associated with one species of seagrass of the Indian River estuary of east central Florida. Interpretations regarding densities of organisms are beyond the scope of this paper and will be reported elsewhere.

Effects of predation on the structure of macrobenthos associated with the seagrass *Halodule* (=*Diplanthera*) *wrightii* were studied by field experimentation with cages at three study sites representing a stress gradient of temperature, salinity and tide. Currently proposed hypotheses of effects of predator-prey interactions, within-community interactions and environmental factors were considered in an attempt to explain differences in community structure as affected by the cages.

As Sanders (1968, 1969), Dayton (1972), Dayton et al. (1974) and others (see reviews by Buzas 1972; Pianka 1966) have suggested, biological interactions become increasingly important as environmental predictability increases. Biological interactions of the benthos from temperate to tropical marine shallow waters to the deep sea may include such factors as trophic diversification, e.g., specializations of feeding (Kohn 1968); niche diversification, e.g., biochemical and microhabitat specializations (Grassle and Sanders 1973); biological disturbances (Dayton and Hessler 1972); and predation effects (Paine 1966). Other factors affecting community structure of the soft-bottom benthos include substratum selection by settling larvae (Gray 1974), competition for space (Woodin 1974) and sediment stability (Rhoads and Young 1970). Combinations of all these factors are likely to occur within a diverse, soft-bottom, benthic community and the relative importance of each would be expected to vary depending upon the particular community and the environment.

We are indebted to our research staff comprised of B. Brown, S. Dudley, K. Krapf (part-time), M. Middleton and J. Miller for assistance in the field, processing, sorting and identifications of specimens. Help in specimen identification was provided by M. Pettibone, J. Simon, D. Dauer and K. Eckelbarger (polychaetes), D. Pawson and L. Thomas (echinoderms), E. Estevez (isopods), J. Dudley and F. Maturo (bryzoans) and R. Gore (decapods). G. Kerr helped with programming and D. Mook assisted in field work. This work benefited from theoretical discussions with M. Buzas, R. Jones and R. Virnstein. M. Laffey prepared Figures 1 and 2. K. Wright prepared and typed the manuscript.

Contribution 55, Harbor Branch Foundation, Inc. This study was funded by the Harbor Branch Foundation, Inc. and by a grant from the Atlantic Foundation to the Smithsonian Institution.

STUDY AREA

The Indian River

The long, narrow body of water bounded on the east by a continuous chain of offshore barrier islands along 190 km of the east central coast of Florida is locally known as the "Indian River" (Fig.

1). The Indian River is a bar-built estuary typical of the Southeastern United States and Gulf of Mexico coastlines. The barrier island is bisected by three inlets (St. Lucie, Fort Pierce and Sebastian) along the southern half of the estuary, all of which have been dredged within the last 40 years and are maintained artificially (Walton 1974a, b). At the northern terminus of the estuary a narrow dredged channel (Haulover Canal) connects the Indian River with Mosquito Lagoon, which opens to the Atlantic Ocean at Ponce de Leon Inlet 40 km to the north. With recorded history, as is typical for bar-built estuaries, natural breaching of the barrier island has occurred during storm events.

The Indian River has an average depth of 1.5 m. The relative effect of tides, surface runoff, wind mixing and evapotranspiration varies locally within the estuary and is highly variable. The majority of rainfall occurs during the months from May through October, and November through April are normally dry (Thomas 1970). In the "blind" northern end of the Indian River, the flushing time of the water is in excess of 150 days (Carter and Okubo 1965) and astronomical tidal effects are dampened by the shallowness and constrictions (natural and artificial) of the estuary. Wind-induced currents and wind tides become increasingly influential in movement and mixing of water in that part of the estuary north of Sebastian Inlet (80 km south of Haulover Canal). In general, there is a trend toward wider ranges of physical environmental variables and greater unpredictability of tides as one progresses from the influences of the Atlantic Ocean through the inlets to those regions where flushing times are slowest.

Six species of seagrass (*Halodule wrightii*, *Syringodium filiforme*, *Thallasia testudinum*, *Ruppia maritima*, *Halophila engelmannii* and *Halophila* sp.) are found in the Indian River estuary (N. Eiseman, personal communication). *Halodule wrightii* was selected as the species characteristic of the study habitat because this species is widely distributed throughout the estuary and occurs in the shallowest water where the greatest environmental stresses are to be expected. In the United States this species has been reported along the Atlantic coast nearly continuously from North Carolina south to Florida and along the Gulf of Mexico coastline (Phillips 1960). Of the seagrasses, *Halodule wrightii* has been found to be the most tolerant of high salinities, both in the laboratory and in the field conditions of hypersaline Texas lagoons (McMillan and Mosely 1967).

Three study sites in *H. wrightii* seagrass areas within the Indian River estuary at St. Lucie Inlet, Link Port and Haulover Canal illustrate spatial extremes and extremes in ranges of physical environmental variables. Only the macrobenthos co-occurring with *H. wrightii* were studied. Sampling is biased toward 100% cover of seagrass and similar water depth. The sediments of the *H. wrightii* study sites can be broadly classified as well-sorted fine sand containing substantial amounts of clay-silt-sized sediment intermixed with shell hash. Anaerobic conditions characterized by dark, sulfur-rich sediments prevail below 1 cm.

St. Lucie Study Site

The southernmost study site is in an area of extensive *H. wrighti* cover on the barrier island side (east) of the estuary, immediately north of St. Lucie Inlet (Fig. 1). A small amount of *S. filiforme* is present and isolated patches of *T. testudinum* are seen occasionally. There is extensive and periodic flushing of the area by tidal currents that follow the north side of the inlet during flood and ebb tides (Walton 1974a).

Link Port Study Site

This study site is located on the mainland (west) side of the estuary immediately north of a dredge-spoil finger of Link Port channel, and approximately 9.5 km north of Fort Pierce Inlet (Fig. 1). A typical transect perpendicular to the natural shoreline of red mangrove at this site shows *H. wrightii* extending 4 to 70 m or more from shore into *T. testudinum* and *S. filiforme* seagrass stands. Currents and semi-diurnal tides are influenced by wind to a greater extent at this site than at St. Lucie. Current velocities usually range up to 10 cm/sec on the channel (east) side of the seagrass areas (Wilcox, unpublished manuscript).

Haulover Study Site

The northernmost site studied is within a cove immediately north of the spoil bank formed from the dredging of the Haulover Canal at

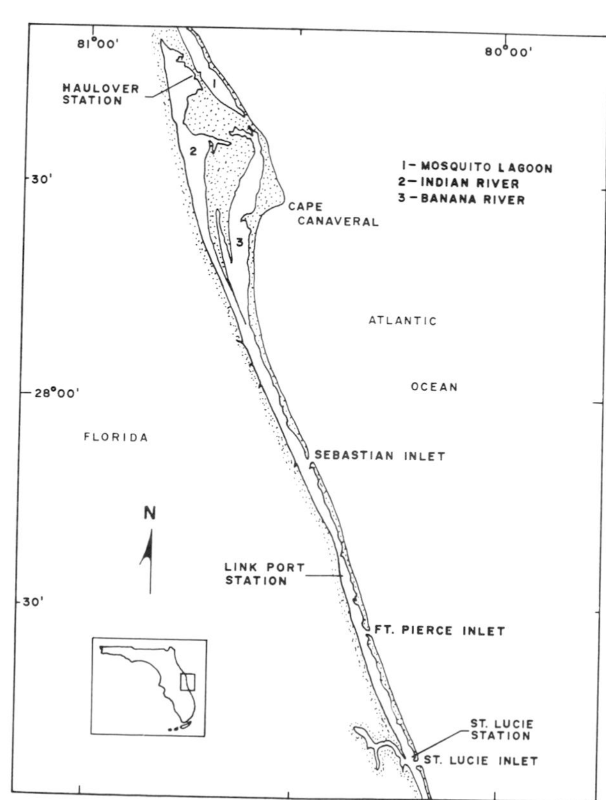

Fig. 1. Map of the Indian River Estuary, Florida, showing locations of the Haulover, Link Port and St. Lucie sampling sites.

the northern terminus of the Indian River estuary (Fig. 1). The inner part of the cove supports a dense stand of *H. wrightii* intermixed with sparse *R. maritima*. Patchy stands of *S. filiforme* and *H. engelmannii* occur in deeper water, starting 100 m or more from shore. The tide, currents and water mixing at this site are dominated by winds. The water height is free of any astronomical tidal influences to an accuracy of 0.30 cm (Browne 1970).

METHODS

Benthic samples were collected with a coring device operated on the principle of a post-hole digger (Baird et al. 1971), which obtains an undisturbed plug of seagrass (including roots and rhizomes) and sediment (15 cm x 15 cm x 20 cm deep = 4500 cm^3). Samples were washed through a 1.0 mm mesh screen, transferred to a solution of rose bengal and 0.15% propylene phenoxytol in sea water (McKay and Hartzband 1970) for 20-30 minutes, and finally into a 5-10% solution of formalin in sea water. After 24-72 hr, epifauna was separated from seagrass blades and infauna was sorted from debris. All specimens were stored in 70% ethyl alcohol. There was no attempt to analyze epifauna separately from infauna because many macrobenthic species associated with *H. wrightii* clearly overlap these categories.

Cages of 1/2-inch mesh (12 mm x 12 mm) hardware cloth, 2 m on a side (4 m^2), and 2 m high were constructed at each sampling site. The cage penetrated the sediment by approximately 5 cm and extended above highest stages of flood tide. The mesh was cleaned as required.

No previous cage experiments in subtropical seagrass habitats have been reported. Our supposition was that caging off areas of intensive cover of *H. wrightii* found in a range of environmental extremes would provide a means of assessing the relative importance of predation on community structure of the macrobenthos. Several factors were taken into consideration to account for potential disruptive influences due to the presence of the cage structures.

First, we predicted that there might be changes in current velocities and directions. These changes in turn, might affect (1) rate of sedimentation and (2) changes of physical and chemical characteristics of the sediment within the cages. Both factors were indirectly measured and observed during the course of the study (see Methods) and were deemed more meaningful ecologically than direct short-term measurements of current velocities and directions.

Second, we predicted that there might be changes in species occurrences and numbers of individuals in each species owing to the following factors: (1) preclusion of transient and resident predators such as finfishes, rays, large decapod crustaceans and horseshoe crabs, (2) preclusion or selection of passively drifting larva, and (3) post-larval biological interactions such as within-community predation and competition for requisites such as space and food. It was originally postulated that changes in community structure as affected by the cages would be influenced primarily by the preclusion of transient and resident predators (defined here as being too large to pass through 1/2-inch mesh).

A set of 5 pilot replicates was taken from each sampling site at the time of construction of the cages on 29 August 1974 at Haulover Station, on 12 September 1974 at St. Lucie Station and on 16 September 1974 at Link Port Station. Analyses of these data indicated that 4 replicates per sample were sufficient for the purposes of this study (see Results). Thereafter, 4 replicates from inside and outside of the cage at each site were taken at 4 sampling periods during 8-17 October 1974, 14-22 November 1974, 13-19 December 1974 and 24-27 February 1975.

During sampling, measurements were made of surface water salinity surface water temperature, water depth and range of sediment-water interface temperatures (with a maximum-minimum thermometer). Flux of seston (living and dead components of suspended matter in mg dry wt/cm^2/day) was measured by gravimetrically analyzing seston collected in 0.5-l jars with 22 cm^2 openings at 16 cm above the sediment surface inside and outside the cages at each site.

Data were analyzed using Shannon's information function,

$$[H' = - \sum_{i-1}^{s} p_i \ln p_i] \quad \text{(Pielou 1966)},$$

where p_i is the proportion of the ith species and s is the total number of species. Species evenness was measured by E', where E' = eH'/s (Buzas and Gibson 1969). Species richness was measured by S-1/lnN (Margalef 1968) in order to relate the number of species to the number of individuals. Use of parametric statistical tests of differences for these indices is questionable here (see Hutcheson 1970; Lloyd et al. 1968) and numbers of samples that would justify nonparametric tests are impractical. All three indices have inherent mathematical weaknesses (Peet 1975; Heip and Engels 1974), but are used here for comparison with the literature and to provide a convenient means of determining major trends of change in community structure as affected by this field experimental approach.

RESULTS

Means and ranges of selected measurements at the three sites during the period of study are summarized in Table 1. As expected, the ranges of water temperature, water salinity, sediment-water

Table 1. Tidal characteristics, ranges of surface water temperature, sediment-water interface temperature, surface water salinity and water depth at Haulover, Link Port and St. Lucie sites.

Condition	Haulover	Link Port	St. Lucie
Surface water temperature, °C (at time of sampling)	11 - 32.5	18.5 - 31.5	19.5 - 30
Sediment-water interface temperature, °C (max.-min.)	8 - 34	14 - 32	14 - 33
Surface water salinity, $^{o}/oo$ (at time of sampling)	22 - 42	25 - 35	32 - 34
Water depth, cm (at time of sampling)	22 - 100	30 - 60	34 - 65
Tide	Mixed-wind dominated	Semidiurnal-wind influenced	Semidiurnal

interface temperature and water depth increase progressively from the St. Lucie to the Haulover site. Data are not available on predictability of tidal stages at the three sites, but predictability is probably less at Haulover relative to the other two sites because the tides there are wind-dominated (Table 1).

Measurements of water temperature and salinity over a 2 1/2 year period (June 1972 - November 1974) near the Link Port site (Wilcox, unpublished manuscript) demonstrate a wider range of salinity (17-37$^{o}/oo$) and temperature (11.5-32°C) than measured during the relatively short period of this study. Greater ranges of these variables probably occur over the long-term at the Haulover site also.

Tides are known to vary greatly within the Indian River estuary during periods of spring tides, high winds and high precipitation (Walton 1974a). It is unlikely, in any case, that the seagrass sites studied ever become dry or remain so over long periods of time because of the sensitivity of *H. wrightii* to dessication (Phillips 1960).

No obvious changes in the sediments were observed within the cages during the experiment. Drift grasses, algae and debris were trapped against the mesh of the cages only at the level of high water stages at each site, so that blockage of water currents through the mesh was minimal. No significant differences (Student's t, 99% confidence) of seston flux (mg/cm^2/day) were measured inside and outside of cages at all three sites.

Polychaetes (53.5%) and molluscs (16.9%) comprised over 70% of the total number of 24,288 specimens representing 230 taxa (listed in Appendix 1). Species identification and trophic information were also most complete for these dominant groups. For these reasons, analyses based on polychaetes and molluscs from the sites studied were assumed to be representative of responses at the community level of organization. Analyses of the 5 pilot replicates taken prior to the field experiment at each of the three study sites indicated that 90% or more (Gaufin et al. 1956) of the expected species of molluscs and polychaetes would be found in four of the replicates of each sample representing an area of 900 cm^2. The greater amount of time and effort necessary to sample and process additional replicates was deemed unprofitable in terms of the probable increase in new (unsampled) species; therefore the number of replicates per sample for the experiment was reduced to four.

Table 2 summarizes indices of species diversity, species evenness and species richness for polychaetes and molluscs from all monthly samples at the three sites and shows the trend of changes (Fig. 2) of these three indices by month and treatment (inside and outside cages). The relative dependence of species diversity, H', on species evenness, E', and species richness, S-1/lnN, is readily apparent between sites and treatments.

Table 2. Species diversity (H'), species evenness (E') and species richness (S-1/lnN) of polychaetes and molluscs at Haulover, Link Port and St. Lucie sites during August-September (A) for pilot replicates, and October (B), November (C), December (D), and February (E) for outside and inside cage samples. N is number of replicates for each sample.

Sampling Site, Times and Treatments	H'	E'	S-1/lnN
1. Haulover			
A. Pilot replicates (N=5)	2.32	0.24	5.66
B. Outside cage (N=4)	2.84	0.50	5.83
Inside cage (N=4)	2.21	0.41	3.82
C. Outside cage (N=4)	2.51	0.28	6.09
Inside cage (N=4)	1.56	0.11	5.46
D. Outside cage (N=4)	2.49	0.25	7.29
Inside cage (N=4)	2.16	0.18	6.36
E. Outside cage (N=4)	2.68	0.32	6.31
Inside cage (N=4)	2.68	0.25	7.82
2. Link Port			
A. Pilot replicates (N=5)	2.26	0.25	5.50
B. Outside cage (N=4)	2.58	0.36	5.97
Inside cage (N=4)	2.28	0.29	5.17
C. Outside cage (N=4)	2.21	0.31	4.58
Inside cage (N=4)	2.45	0.32	5.56
D. Outside cage (N=4)	2.64	0.40	5.30
Inside cage (N=4)	2.67	0.40	6.09
E. Outside cage (N=4)	2.27	0.27	5.88
Inside cage (N=4)	2.36	0.31	5.81
3. St. Lucie			
A. Pilot replicates (N=5)	2.08	0.28	4.45
B. Outside cage (N=4)	2.82	0.51	6.05
Inside cage (N=4)	3.03	0.61	6.69
C. Outside cage (N=4)	2.73	0.43	6.46
Inside cage (N=4)	2.90	0.68	6.25
D. Outside cage (N=4)	2.44	0.35	5.24
Inside cage (N=4)	3.27	0.58	8.32
E. Outside cage (N=4)	2.42	0.51	4.70
Inside cage (N=4)	3.17	0.74	6.33

Fig. 2. Species diversity (H'), species evenness (E') and species richness (S-1/lnN) of polychaetes and molluscs at Haulover, Link Port and St. Lucie sites during August-September for pilot replicates, and October, November, December and February for outside and inside cage samples. Dashed line indicates inside cage samples and solid line indicates outside cage samples.

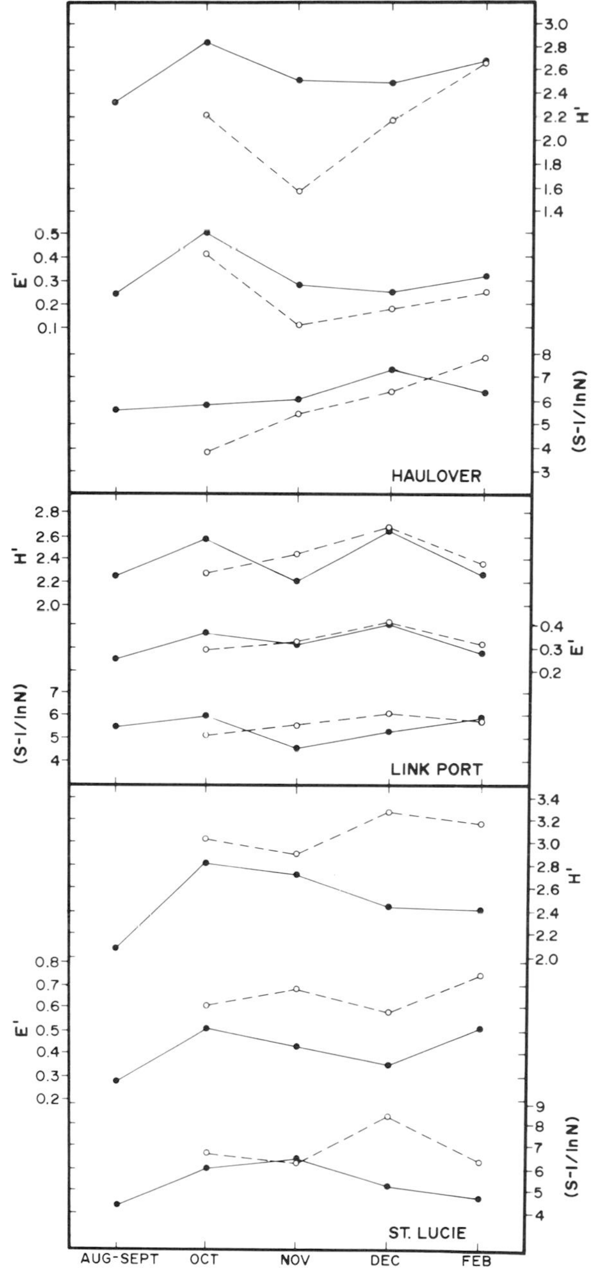

At the Haulover site there is a good relationship between the curves describing diversity and evenness. The indices of diversity and evenness are consistently lower for inside versus outside cage samples, except during February when the diversity indices are the same value (H'=2.68) and reflect an increase in richness of the cage sample.

The trends are similar and the differences are small between all three indices at the Link Port site. There appears to be little effect of the cage on community structure of the macrobenthos as measured by these indices.

All values of diversity, evenness and richness are higher for samples inside versus outside the cage at the St. Lucie site, with the exception of a lower value for richness in November. An inverse relationship exists between the curves of diversity and evenness for within-cage samples. The richness values show a similar pattern as shown by diversity indicating that the richness component has a relatively greater effect on diversity than evenness.

The curves describing diversity, evenness and richness components show a progressive trend from the Haulover to Link Port to St.

Lucie sites. The indices for caged versus uncaged samples are lower at Haulover, higher at St. Lucie and similar at Link Port. Diversity and evenness values are highest for the cage samples at the St. Lucie site (Table 2).

Percentages of numbers of polychaetes and molluscs representing various feeding types from inside and outside of cages at the three sites are given in Table 3. Percent composition of feeding types was more similar at St. Lucie and Haulover than at Link Port. Deposit feeders which were dominant at all stations outside cages increased greatly inside cages at St. Lucie and Haulover, with no percentage change at Link Port. Similarly, carnivores decreased within cages at St. Lucie and Haulover, but increased at Link Port. Suspension feeders increased slightly at St. Lucie while decreasing at Link Port and Haulover. The feeding type termed "others" (herbivores, scavengers, parasites, etc.) represents the lowest percentage of polychaetes and molluscs from all sites, a bias resulting from the inclusion of species from those feeding types assumed to have greatest ecological importance in the community. This bias was intentional because most benthic invertebrates encompass several of these "types" and would certainly be classified as omnivores. The ranking of feeding types outside cages at all sites (deposit feeders > carnivores > suspension feeders > others) is changed within cages only at the St. Lucie and Haulover sites, where suspension feeders > carnivores.

Table 4 ranks the ten most numerous species from inside and outside cages at all three sites. No species represents more than 21% of the total numbers of individuals at any site outside the cages. Percent dominance of the top-ranked species within cages drops to 10% at St. Lucie and 15% at Link Port, but increases to 45% at Haulover. The top-ranked species outside cages at both St. Lucie and Link Port, a polychaete (*Clymenella mucosa*), is displaced in dominance inside cages at those sites by an amphipod (*Grandidierella* sp. A). The large increase in percent dominance of a top-ranked species at Haulover (from 17% outside the cage to 45% inside the cage) is due to the same species of polychaete (*Polydora ligni*) in both instances. Some changes in the rank of species undoubtedly results from differences in total numbers of individuals relative to the distribution of species abundances inside and outside cages at the same site. However, large increases of particular species within cages are

Table 3. Percentage abundances of major feeding types of polychaetes and molluscs at Haulover, Link Port and St. Lucie sites (DF=deposit feeders; SF=suspension feeders; C=carnivores; O=other).

Feeding Types	Haulover Outside Cage	Haulover Inside Cage	Link Port Outside Cage	Link Port Inside Cage	St. Lucie Outside Cage	St. Lucie Inside Cage
DF %	51	74	73	73	53	68
SF %	18	14	10	6	12	16
C %	28	9	16	20	29	11
O %	3	3	<1	<1	6	4

are obvious, as in the case of the amphipod, isopod and tanaid crustaceans. Percentage dominance of the top 10 species ranges from 60 to 75% inside cages to 51 to 83% outside cages.

Table 4. Top-10 ranked species, number of individuals and percentage of total number of individuals at Haulover, Link Port and St. Lucie experimental stations (P=polychaet ; G=gastropod; Pel.=pelecypod; A=amphipod; I= isopod; T=tanaid; E=echinoderm; S=sipunculid).

Rank	Species Name	# individuals	% of total # individuals	
Haulover (outside cage)				
1	*Polydora ligni* (P)	896	17.48	
2	*Exogone dispar* (P)	606	11.82	
3	*Phascolion* sp. (S)	563	10.99	
4	Paratanaidae A (T)	280	5.46	
5	*Clymenella mucosa* (P)	279	5.44	
6	*Fabriciola* sp. A (P)	206	4.02	
7	*Cymadusa* sp. A (A)	177	3.45	
8	*Prionospio heterobranchia* (P)	128	2.50	
9	*Erichsonella filiformis isabelensis* (I)	125	2.44	
10	Nemertinea	116	2.26	
		Total Number of Individuals		5125
Haulover (inside cage)				
1	*Polydora ligni* (P)	3076	44.59	
2	*Phascolion* sp. (S)	420	6.09	
3	Paratanaidae A (T)	419	6.07	
4	*Capitella capitata capitata* (P)	416	6.03	
5	*Cymadusa* sp. A (A)	255	3.70	
6	*Fabriciola* sp. A (P)	237	3.44	
7	*Synaptula hydriformis* (E)	229	3.32	
8	*Brachidontes exustus* (Pel.)	224	3.25	
9	*Exogone dispar* (P)	222	3.22	
10	*Terebella rubra* (P)	221	3.20	
		Total Number of Individuals		6899
Link Port (outside cage)				
1	*Clymenella mucosa* (P)	484	20.23	
2	*Cerithium muscarum* (G)	273	11.41	
3	*Streblospio benedicti* (P)	235	9.82	
4	*Phascolion* sp. (S)	215	8.99	
5	*Laeonereis culveri* (P)	173	7.23	
6	*Crepidula fornicata* (G)	89	3.72	
7	Nemertinea	71	2.97	
8	*Capitella capitata capitata* (P)	69	2.88	
9	*Polydora ligni* (P)	63	2.63	
10	*Erichsonella filiformis isabelensis* (I)	58	2.42	
	Cymadusa sp. A (A)	58	2.42	
		Total Number of Individuals		2392
Link Port (inside cage)				
1	*Grandidierella* sp. A (A)	476	15.30	
2	*Cerithium muscarum* (G)	412	13.24	
3	*Melita nitida* (A)	293	9.42	
4	*Tharyx annulosus* (P)	281	9.03	
5	*Cymadusa* sp. A (A)	210	6.75	
6	*Clymenella mucosa* (P)	133	4.27	
	Erichsonella filiformis isabelensis (I)	133	4.27	

Table 4. (cont.)

Rank	Species Name	# individuals	% of total # individuals
7	*Laeonereis culveri* (P)	131	4.21
8	*Phascolion* sp. (S)	100	3.21
9	*Cymodoce faxoni* (I)	94	3.02
10	*Crepidula fornicata* (G)	68	2.19
		Total Number of Individuals	3112
St. Lucie (outside cage)			
1	*Clymenella mucosa* (P)	254	17.66
2	Nemertinea	92	6.40
3	*Diastoma varium* (G)	88	6.12
4	*Phascolion* sp. (S)	81	5.63
5	*Fabricia sabella* (P)	75	5.22
6	*Cymadusa* sp. A (A)	68	4.73
7	Paratanaidae A (T)	62	4.31
8	*Streblospio benedicti* (P)	59	4.10
9	*Polydora socialis* (P)	53	3.69
10	*Aricidea* sp. A (P)	47	3.27
		Total Number of Individuals	1438
St. Lucie (inside cage)			
1	*Grandidierella* sp. A (A)	112	9.77
2	Nemertinea	111	9.69
3	*Cymadusa* sp. A (A)	86	7.50
4	*Phascolion* sp. (S)	56	4.89
5	*Fabricia sabella* (P)	44	3.84
6	*Erichsonella filiformis isabelensis* (I)	43	3.75
7	*Streblospio benedicti* (P)	39	3.40
8	*Clymenella mucosa* (P)	35	3.05
9	*Cymodoce faxoni* (O)	33	2.88
10	*Tharyx annulosus* (P)	27	2.36
		Total Number of Individuals	1146

DISCUSSION AND CONCLUSIONS

When the selected environmental variables measured at the three study sites are ranked in order of increasing ranges, an environmental stress gradient is clearly evident: Haulover > Link Port > St. Lucie. The ranges of temperature, salinity and tidal height reported in this study are greater than those measured by Jackson (1972) in his study of *Thalassia* communities in Jamaica. Jackson (1973) later defined environmental stress in relation to distribution and occurrence of selected molluscs according to their physiological tolerances. While no direct correlations of stress and tolerance *per se* were examined in this study, it was assumed that dominant macrobenthic species associated with *H. wrightii* would respond differently to caging in relation to varying degrees of environmental stress, and that the effects of their responses would be seen at the community level of organization.

Contrary to temperate marine and estuarine environments, where diversity of benthos is higher in stenohaline than euryhaline zones

(Boesch 1972), the seagrass-associated macrobenthos of the subtropical Indian River estuary is equally diverse in areas of narrow and wide ranges of salinity. This study also presents an apparent paradox to the stability-time hypothesis of Sanders (1968), in that species diversity of the seagrass-associated macrobenthos does not decrease along a gradient of environmental stress in the Indian River estuary, as Sanders' hypothesis would predict. High diversity of macrofauna occurs at both extremes of the gradient at the Haulover and St. Lucie sites.

The stability-time hypothesis (Sanders 1968) states that physical instability and unpredictability of an environment prevents the establishment of diverse benthic communities, but rather communities which he defined as "physically controlled" and characterized by low diversity. Conversely, in a physically stable and predictable environment, benthic communities, given sufficient time, will become more diverse through biological interactions or "biological accommodation." To explain occurrences of diverse benthic communities in habitats characterized by environmental stress, Slobodkin and Sanders (1969) refined the original hypothesis of Sanders by contrasting "short-term, non-equilibrium or transient high diversity" with "long-term or evolutionary high diversity". Grassle and Sanders (1973) have emphasized that, "...the two contrasting types of diversity cannot be set forth as simple alternatives". They further stated that short-term high diversity can be expected to be progressively less important along a gradient from physically controlled to biologically accommodated conditions influencing community structure. If one speculates that the diverse macrobenthic community at the Haulover site results from short-term high diversity, this apparent paradox of the stability-time hypothesis can be clarified by the caging experiment.

Interactions of predation and community structure have been elucidated by caging experiments in the field for rocky intertidal communities (Dayton 1971), subtidal sponge communities (Dayton et al. 1974), subtidal fouling communities (Sutherland 1974) and intertidal soft-bottom communities (Woodin 1974). These experimental studies were prompted, in part, by the classical predator-prey study by Paine (1966) which hypothesized that, "Local species diversity is directly related to the efficiency with which predators prevent the monopolization of the major requisites by one species". As predicted by Paine's hypothesis, species diversity decreased inside the cage at the Haulover site. Species evenness also decreased inside the cage, due primarily to an explosive increase of the polychaetes *Polydora ligni* (17-45% increase) and *Capitella capitata capitata* (<1-6% increase) (Table 4). These polychaete species have been described as "opportunistic species" by Grassle and Grassle (1974) or r-strategists, "adapted for life in a short-lived unpredictable habitat" (Wilson and Bossert 1971). The question, therefore, remains: What factors are responsible for the increases of these opportunistic species within the cage at Haulover?

A contributing condition which may help to explain these increases is the "year-class" phenomenon noted by Sanders (1968), by which extreme environmental variations at Haulover may have facilitated rapid population growth of these particular species. *Polydora ligni* and *Capitella capitata capitata* show no such increases in numbers within the cages at St. Lucie and Link Port, so that potentially disruptive influences of the cage structure can be discounted in explaining the population increases of these same species at Haulover. These species apparently were able to increase in numbers inside the cage at Haulover in the relative absence of fish and other transient predators as though the macrobenthic community at this site were responding to a reduction of predation pressure. Grassle and Sanders (1973) suggested that in physically unpredictable and unstable environments, the removal or exclusion of a predator results in increased numbers of prey species with high reproductive rates.

Subtidal, benthic field experiments in Chesapeake Bay (Virnstein, personal communication) have shown large increases inside cages of the pelecypod *Mulinea lateralis*, an opportunistic species. A high susceptibility to predation might explain the rapid decrease of opportunistic species with environmental stabilization following a disruptive influence (e.g., oil spill--Sanders et al. 1972; dredging--Reish 1963; pollution--Rosenberg 1972, Dean and Haskin 1964). Such fluctuations in numbers of opportunistic species have been suggested as features of genetic variability (Grassle 1972; Levinton 1973) or poor competitive ability (Grassle and Grassle 1974).

This caging study suggests that susceptibility to predation may be an important factor in regulating population sizes of opportunistic species, as indicated by results from pollution abatement studies. In this regard, pollution or other such environmental disturbances may exclude predators in the same way that some cages allowed opportunistic species to increase population sizes rapidly. According to the stability-time hypothesis, these increases would be expected to be greatest in physically controlled communities.

In order to meet the requisites of the short-term diversity hypothesis of Slobodkin and Sanders (1969), a community must be studied over a period of years rather than months. Over the longer term the macrobenthos at Haulover might experience far greater fluctuations in species and numbers of individuals than observed in the relatively short time span of this study. As presently planned, future sampling at the Haulover site should provide necessary information about frequencies of occurrence of selected species from the macrobenthic community over the longer term in order to determine if a temporary non-equilibrium situation exists. The December 1974 and February 1975 samples suggest that this may be the case since the rapid influx of species resulted in increasing richness and diversity.

Similar trends and small differences between diversity, evenness and richness of macrobenthos at the Link Port site are shown in Figure 2. The fact that environmental stress at this site is between the extremes measured at the Haulover and St. Lucie sites implies that physical and biotic factors are in some way "balanced" at this location, and preclusion of predators does not markedly affect community structure as measured by diversity, evenness and richness.

Similarly, at Link Port there are small differences of percentage of feeding types as affected by the cage (Table 3). In contrast, the percentage dominance of individual taxa has been greatly altered by the cage (Table 4). Internal or within-community regulation apparently maintains a "structural stability" (Boesch 1972) of the macrobenthos at this site. This effect by a caging experiment upon a macrobenthic community has not previously been reported in the literature.

The increases in diversity, evenness and richness of the macrobenthos within the cage at the St. Lucie site (Fig. 2) might not be predicted by the predator-prey hypothesis of Paine (1966). Predators intensively cropping prey populations would be expected to reduce competition among prey species by allowing more prey species to coexist. As Grassle and Sanders (1973) state, the effects of predators on community structure have been well demonstrated in environments that are primarily physically controlled. In contrast, predation effects in more physically predictable and stable environments require further study.

Whether or not the within-habitat macrobenthic communities studied here conform exactly to definitions of physically controlled or biologically accommodated communities in the sense of Sanders (1968) is not important. According to trends of diversity, evenness and richness, these communities responded in three clearly different ways to preclusion of predators: (1) decrease (Haulover site), (2) little or no effect (Link Port site), and (3) increase (St. Lucie site). Opposite effects of caging are seen at the sites representing the two extremes of the environmental stress gradient. More caging studies of the macrobenthos are required in environments characterized by stability and predictability of environmental variables. Internal (within-community) regulation may play a greater role than predation by transient predators in the structuring of macrobenthic communities. These subtle regulation mechanisms cannot be adequately defined by caging experiments such as those used in this study.

REFERENCES

Abbott, R. T. 1974. American seashells. The marine Mollusca of the Atlantic and Pacific Coasts of North America. Van Nostrand Reinhold Co.

Baird, R. C., K. L. Carder, T. L. Hopkins, T. E. Pyle, and H. J. Humm. 1971. Anclote Environmental Project Report 1971. Mar. Sci. Inst., Univ. of So. Fla., St. Petersburg. 251 p.

Bloom, S. A., J. L. Simon, and V. D. Hunter. 1972. Animal-sediment relations and community analysis of a Florida estuary. Mar. Biol. 13: 43-56.

Boesch, D. F. 1972. Species diversity of marine macrobenthos in the Virginia area. Chesapeake Sci. 13: 206-211.

Browne, D. R. 1970. A study of the transport of water through the Haulover Canal. MS thesis. Fla. Inst. Technol. 82 p.

Buzas, M. A. 1972. Patterns of species diversity and their explanation. Taxon 21: 275-286.

_____, and T. G. Gibson. 1969. Species diversity: benthonic Foraminifera in Western North Atlantic. Science 163: 72-75.

Carter, H. H. and A. Okubo. 1965. A study of the physical processes of movement and dispersion in the Cape Kennedy area. Rep. NYO-2973-1, Chesapeake Bay Inst. 150 p.

Dales, R. P. 1963. Annelids. Hutchinson Univ. Libr., London.

Day, J. H. 1967. A monograph on the Polychaeta of Southern Africa. Brit. Mus. Nat. Hist.

Dayton, P. K. 1971. Competition, disturbance, and community organization: the provision and subsequent utilization of space in a rocky intertidal community. Ecol. Monogr. 41: 351-389.

_____. 1972. Toward an understanding of community resilience and the potential effects of enrichment to the benthos at McMurdo Sound, Antarctica, p. 81-95. In B. C. Parker [ed.], Proceedings of the colloquium on conservation problems in Antarctica. Allen Press.

_____ and R. R. Hessler. 1972. Role of biological disturbance in maintaining diversity in the deep sea. Deep-Sea Res. 19: 199-208.

_____, G. A. Robilliard, R. T. Paine, and L. B. Dayton. 1974. Biological accommodation in the benthic community at McMurdo Sound, Antarctica. Ecol. Monogr. 44: 105-128.

Dean, D. and H. H. Haskin. 1964. Benthic repopulation of the Raritan River estuary following pollution abatement. Limnol. Oceanogr. 9: 551-563.

Gaufin, A. R., E. K. Harris, and H. J. Walter. 1956. A statistical evaluation of stream bottom sampling data obtained from three standard samplers. Ecology 37: 643-648.

Grassle, J. F. 1972. Species diversity, genetic variability and environmental uncertainty, p. 19-26. In Fifth European Mar. Biol. Symp., Piccin Editore, Padua. 348 p.

_____ and H. L. Sanders. 1973. Life histories and the role of disturbance. Deep-Sea Res. 20: 643-659.

_____ and J. P. Grassle. 1974. Opportunistic life histories and genetic systems in marine benthic polychaetes. J. Mar. Res. 32: 253-284.

Gray, J. S. 1974. Animal-sediment relationships. Oceanogr. Mar. Biol. Ann. Rev. 12: 223-261.

Heip, C. and P. Engels. 1974. Comparing species diversity and evenness indices. J. Mar. Biol. Assoc. U. K. 54: 559-563.

Hurlbert, S. H. 1971. The nonconcept of species diversity: a critique and alternative parameters. Ecology 52: 577-586.

Hutcheson, K. 1970. A test for comparing diversities based on the Shannon formula. J. Theor. Biol. 29: 151-154.

Hyman, L. H. 1967. The invertebrates. v. VI. Mollusca I. McGraw-Hill.

Jackson, J. B. C. 1972. The ecology of molluscs of *Thalassia* communities, Jamaica, West Indies. II. Molluscan population variability along an environmental stress gradient. Mar. Biol. 14: 304-337.

_____. 1973. The ecology of mulluscs of *Thalassia* communities, Jamaica, West Indies. I. Distribution, environmental physiology and ecology of common shallow-water species. Bull. Mar. Sci. 23: 313-350.

Kohn, A. J. 1968. Microhabitats, abundance and food of *Conus* on atoll reefs in the Maldive and Chagos Islands. Ecology 49: 1046-1061.

Levinton, J. 1973. Genetic variation in a gradient of environmental variability: marine bivalvia (Mollusca). Science 180: 75-76.

Lloyd, M., J. H. Zar, and J. R. Karr. 1968. On the calculation of information-theoretical measures of diversity. Am. Midland Nat. 79: 257-272.

Margalef, R. 1968. Perspectives in ecological theory. Univ. Chicago Press.

McKay, C. R., and D. J. Hartzband. 1970. Use of propylene phenoxetol in narcotizing unsorted benthic invertebrate samples. Trans. Am. Micros. Soc. 89: 53-54.

McMillan, C. and F. N. Moseley. 1967. Salinity tolerances of five marine spermatophytes of Redfish Bay, Texas. Ecology 48: 503-506.

Morton, J. E. 1963. Molluscs (2nd. edition). Hutchinson Univ. Libr.

Odum, E. P. 1971. Fundamentals of ecology (3rd. edition). Saunders.

Paine, R. T. 1966. Food web complexity and species diversity. Am. Nat. 100: 65-75.

Peet, R. K. 1975. Relative diversity indices. Ecology 56: 496-498.

Perry, L. M. and J. S. Schwengel. 1955. Marine shells of the Western Coast of Florida. Bull. Am. Paleontol. 26: 1-318.

Phillips, R. C. 1960. Ecology and distribution of the Florida seagrasses. Fla. St. Bd. Conserv. Mar. Lab., Prof. Pap. Ser. No. 2. 72 p.

Pianka, E. R. 1966. Latitudinal gradients in species diversity. Am. Nat. 100: 33-46.

Pielou, E. C. 1966. The measurement of diversity in different types of biological collections. J. Theoret. Biol. 13: 131-144.

Reish, D. J. 1963. Further studies on the benthic fauna in a recently constructed boat harbor in southern California. Bull. So. Cal. Acad. Sci. 62: 23-32.

Rhoads, D. C. and D. K. Young. 1970. The influence of deposit-feeding organisms on sediment stability and community trophic structure. J. Mar. Res. 28: 150-178.

Rosenberg, R. 1972. Benthic faunal recovery in a Swedish fjord following the closure of a sulphite pulp mill. Oikos 23: 92-108.

Sanders, H. L. 1968. Marine benthic diversity: a comparative study. Am. Nat. 102: 243-282.

_____. 1969. Benthic marine diversity and the stability-time hypothesis. Brookhaven Symp. Biol. 22: 71-80.

_____, J. F. Grassle, and G. R. Hampson. 1972. The West Flamouth oil spill. I. Biology. Woods Hole Oceanogr. Inst. Ref. 72-20. (Unpublished Manuscript).

Santos, S. L. and J. L. Simon. 1974. Distribution and abundance of the polychaetous annelids in a South Florida estuary. Bull. Mar. Sci. 24: 669-689.

Slobodkin, L. B. and H. L. Sanders. 1969. On the contribution of environmental predictability to species diversity. Brookhaven Symp. Biol. 22: 82-92.

Sutherland, J. P. 1974. Multiple stable points in natural communities. Am. Nat. 108: 859-873.

Thomas, T. M. 1970. A detailed analysis of climatological and hydrological records of south Florida with reference to man's influence upon ecosystem evolution. Tech. Rept. 70-2, Univ. Miami Rosenstiel School Mar. Atmos. Sci. 89 p.

Walton, T. L. 1974a. St. Lucie Inlet. Glossary of Inlets Report 1. Fla. Sea Grant Prog. Rept. No. 2. 48 p.

_____. 1974b. Fort Pierce Inlet. Glossary of Inlets Report 2. Fla. Sea Grant Prog. Rept. No. 3. 39 p.

Wilson, E. O. and W. H. Bossert. 1971. A primer of population biology. Sinauer Assoc.

Woodin, S. A. 1974. Polychaete abundance patterns in a marine soft-sediment environment: The importance of biological interactions. Ecol. Monogr. 44: 171-187.

Young, D. K. and D. C. Rhoads. 1971. Animal-sediment relations in Cape Cod Bay, Massachusetts. I. A transect study. Mar. Biol. 11: 242-254.

APPENDIX I

List of presence (+) or absence (0) of macrobenthic invertebrates collected inside (in) and outside (out) cages at the Haulover, Link Port and St. Lucie sampling sites, 29 August 1974 to 27 February 1975; (DF)-deposit feeder; (SF)-suspension feeder; (C)-carnivore; (0)-other (herbivore, scavenger, parasite, etc.). Feeding types for molluscs and polychaetes primarily from Abbott (1974), Santos and Simon (1974), Bloom et al. (1972), Young and Rhoads (1971), Day (1967), Hyman (1967), Dales (1963), Morton (1963), and Perry and Schwengel (1955). Taxa are listed in order of abundance under each major taxonomic heading.

	Haulover		Link Port		St. Lucie	
	In	Out	In	Out	In	Out
Mollusca						
Gastropoda						
1. *Cerithium muscarum* (DF,0)	+	+	+	+	+	+
2. *Crepidula fornicata* (SF)	+	+	+	+	+	+
3. *Diastoma varium* (DF,0)	+	+	+	+	+	+
4. *Marginella apicina* (C,0)	+	+	+	+	0	+
5. *Turbonilla incisa* (0)	+	+	+	+	0	0
6. *Marginella* sp. A (C,0)	+	+	+	+	0	0
7. *Mitrella lunata* (C,0)	+	+	+	+	+	+
8. *Neritina virginea* (0)	0	0	0	+	+	+
9. *Vitrinella* sp. A (0)	+	+	+	0	0	0
10. *Melongena corona* (C)	+	+	+	+	0	0
11. *Pyrgocythara plicosa* (C)	+	0	+	+	0	0
12. *Circulus suppressus* (0)	+	+	0	+	0	0
13. *Haminoea elegans* (?C)	+	+	0	+	+	+
14. *Kurtziella atrostyla* (C)	0	+	0	0	0	0
15. *Nassarius vibex* (DF,0)	0	+	+	+	+	+
16. *Cerithiopsis greeni* (?DF)	+	0	0	0	0	0
17. *Bulla striata* (C)	+	0	0	0	+	+
18. *Odostomia* sp. A (0)	+	+	0	0	0	0
19. *Acteocina candei* (?C)	+	0	+	+	+	+
20. *Acteocina canaliculata* (?C)	0	0	0	+	+	+
21. *Anachis avara* (C)	0	0	+	+	0	0
22. *Caecum pulchellum* (0)	0	+	0	0	0	0
23. *Bursatella leachii pleii* (0)	0	0	0	0	0	+
24. *Crepidula plana* (SF)	0	0	0	0	+	+
25. *Aeolidacea* sp. A (C)	0	0	+	0	+	0
26. *Rissoina bryerea* (0)	0	0	0	+	+	0
27. *Haminoea succinea* (?C)	0	+	0	0	0	0
28. *Acteon punctostriatus* (DF)	0	+	0	0	0	0
29. *Alaba incerta* (?DF)	0	0	0	0	0	+
30. *Tricolia affinis* (0)	0	0	0	0	0	+
31. *Melampus bidentatus* (0)	0	0	0	0	+	0
32. *Epitonium rupicola* (C)	0	0	0	+	0	0
33. *Cephalaspidea* sp. A (C)	0	+	0	0	0	0
34. *Elysia* sp. A (0)	0	+	0	0	0	0
35. *Granulina ovuliformis* (0)	0	+	0	0	0	0
36. *Sayella fusca* (0)	+	0	0	0	0	0
Pelecypoda						
37. *Brachidontes exustus* (SF)	+	+	0	+	0	0
38. *Amygdalum papyrium* (SF)	+	+	+	+	+	+
39. *Parastarte triquetra* (SF)	0	0	+	+	0	0
40. *Tellina tampaensis* (DF)	+	+	+	+	0	0
41. *Chione cancellata* (SF)	+	+	0	+	+	+
42. *Lyonsia hyalina floridana* (SF)	+	+	+	+	+	+
43. *Lucina pectinata* (SF)	0	0	+	+	+	+

	Haulover		Link Port		St. Lucie	
	In	Out	In	Out	In	Out
Pelecypoda (cont.)						
44. *Tagelus plebeius* (DF)	0	+	+	+	+	+
45. *Anomalocardia auberiana* (SF)	+	+	0	+	+	+
46. *Macoma constricta* (DF)	0	0	+	+	+	+
47. *Macoma* sp. A (DF)	+	+	+	0	+	+
48. *Parvilucina multilineata* (SF)	0	0	0	0	+	+
49. *Laevicardium* sp. A (SF)	+	+	0	0	0	0
50. *Corbula contracta* (SF)	0	0	0	0	+	0
51. *Tellina versicolor* (DF)	+	0	0	0	+	0
52. *Codakia orbicularis* (SF)	0	0	0	0	+	+
53. *Pteria colymbus* (SF)	0	0	0	0	+	+
54. *Anomia simplex* (SF)	0	0	+	0	0	+
55. *Mulinea lateralis* (SF)	0	0	0	+	+	0
56. *Tellina paramera* (DF)	0	0	0	0	0	+
57. *Crassostrea virginica* (SF)	0	0	+	0	0	0
Annelida						
Polychaeta						
58. *Polydora ligni* (DF)	+	+	+	+	+	+
59. *Clymenella mucosa* (DF)	+	+	+	+	+	+
60. *Exogone dispar* (?C)	+	+	0	+	+	+
61. *Capitella capitata capitata* (DF)	+	+	+	+	+	+
62. *Tharyx annulosus* (DF)	+	+	+	+	+	+
63. *Fabriciola* sp. A (SF)	+	+	0	0	0	0
64. *Prionospio heterobranchia* (DF)	+	+	+	+	+	+
65. *Fabricia sabella* (SF)	+	+	0	+	+	+
66. *Laeonereis culveri* (O,?C)	+	+	+	+	+	0
67. *Streblospio benedicti* (DF)	+	+	+	+	+	+
68. *Terebella rubra* (DF)	+	+	0	0	0	0
69. *Aricidea* sp. A (DF)	+	+	+	+	+	+
70. *Melinna maculata* (DF)	+	+	+	+	+	+
71. *Branchioasychis americana* (DF)	+	+	+	0	0	0
72. *Dorvillea rudolphi* (?C)	+	+	+	+	0	0
73. *Podarke obscura* (?C)	+	+	+	0	0	0
74. *Capitella capitata ovincola* (DF)	+	+	+	+	+	+
75. *Haploscoloplos foliosus*	+	+	+	+	+	+
76. *Potamilla* sp. A (SF)	+	+	+	+	0	0
77. *Microphthalmus aberrans* (?C)	+	+	0	0	0	0
78. *Parahesione luteola* (?C)	+	+	+	+	+	0
79. *Capitomastus* sp. A (DF)	+	+	0	+	+	+
80. *Platynereis dumerilii* (O)	+	+	0	0	0	0
81. *Polydora socialis* (DF)	0	0	0	+	+	+
82. *Ctenodrilus serratus* (?DF)	+	+	0	0	0	+
83. *Capitellidae* sp. A (DF)	+	+	+	+	+	+
84. *Nereis (Neanthes) succinea* (O,?C)	+	+	+	+	+	+
85. *Thelepus setosus* (DF)	0	0	0	0	+	+
86. *Sepiochaetopterus costarum oculatus* (SF)	0	0	+	+	0	+
87. *Glycinde solitaria* (C)	+	+	+	+	+	+
88. *Gyptis vittata* (?C)	+	+	+	+	+	0
89. *Onuphis microcephala* (?C)	0	0	0	0	+	+
90. *Eusyllis lamelligera* (?C)	+	+	+	+	0	0
91. *Branchiomma nigromaculata* (SF)	+	+	0	0	0	0
92. *Diopatra cuprea* (C,SF)	+	+	+	+	0	0
93. *Mediomastus ambiseta* (DF)	0	0	+	+	+	+
94. *Cirriformia* sp. A (DF)	0	0	0	+	+	+
95. *Scolelepis texana* (DF)	+	+	+	+	+	0
96. *Arenicola cristata* (DF)	+	+	+	+	0	0
97. *Capitella capitata tripartita* (DF)	+	+	0	0	0	+

	Haulover		Link Port		St. Lucie	
	In	Out	In	Out	In	Out
Polychaeta (cont.)						
98. *Marphysa sanguinea* (DF)	+	+	+	+	0	+
99. *Parapionosyllis longicirrata* (?C)	+	+	+	0	0	+
100. *Minuspio cirrobranchiata* (DF)	0	0	+	0	+	+
101. *Heterocirrus alatus* (DF)	0	0	0	0	+	+
102. *Pectinaria gouldii* (DF)	+	+	0	0	+	0
103. *Glycera tesselata* (?C)	0	0	0	0	+	+
104. *Polydora attenata* (DF)	0	0	0	0	0	+
105. *Cirratulus* sp. A (DF)	0	0	0	+	+	0
106. *Brania clavata* (?C)	0	+	0	0	0	0
107. *Pista* sp. A (DF)	+	0	+	0	+	0
108. *Chone duneri* (SF)	0	0	+	+	0	0
109. *Heteromastus* sp. A (DF)	0	0	0	0	0	+
110. *Armandia agilis* (?)(DF)	0	0	0	0	+	0
111. Spionidae sp. ? (DF)	0	0	0	0	+	0
112. *Terebellides stromeii* (DF)	0	0	0	0	+	0
113. *Armandia maculata* (?)(DF)	0	0	0	0	+	+
114. *Aricidea fragilis* (DF)	0	+	0	0	0	+
115. Sabellidae sp. ? (SF)	0	0	0	+	0	0
116. *Trypanosyllis zebra* (?C)	+	+	0	0	0	0
117. *Lysidice ninetta ninetta* (O)	+	0	0	0	0	0
118. *Stenoninereis martini* (O,?C)	+	0	0	0	0	0
119. *Malacoceros vanderhorsti* (DF)	0	0	0	0	0	+
120. *Websterinereis* sp. A (O,?C)	0	0	0	0	0	+
121. *Cabira incerta* (?C)	0	0	0	0	+	0
122. *Eteone heteropoda* (?C)	0	0	0	0	+	0
123. *Lumbrineris tetraura* (?C)	0	0	0	0	+	0
124. *Paraprionospio pinnata* (DF)	0	0	0	0	+	0
125. *Isolda pulchella* (DF)	0	0	0	+	0	0
126. *Amphicteis gunneri floridus* (DF)	0	0	+	0	0	0
127. *Potamilla* sp. C (SF)	0	+	0	0	0	0
128. *Glycera americana* (?C)	0	+	0	0	0	0
129. *Polycirrus* sp. A (DF)	0	+	0	0	0	0
130. *Sphaerosyllis pirifera* (?C)	0	+	0	0	0	0
131. *Amphitrite ornata* (DF)	+	0	0	0	0	0
132. *Eteone longa* (?C)	+	0	0	0	0	0
133. *Eteone trilineata* (?C)	+	0	0	0	0	0
134. *Dasybranchus lunulatus* (DF)	+	0	0	0	0	0
135. *Harmothoe aculeata* (?C)	+	0	0	0	0	0
136. *Ophryotrocha puerilis* (O)	+	0	0	0	0	0
137. Serpulidae (SF)	+	+	+	+	+	+
138. *Hydroides dianthus* (SF)	+	+	0	0	0	0
139. *Spirorbis (Janua) corrugatus* (SF)	+	+	0	0	0	0
140. *Serpula vermicularis* (SF)	+	0	0	0	0	0
141. Oligochaeta	+	+	+	+	+	+
Sipuncula						
142. *Phascolion* sp.	+	+	+	+	+	+
143. Nemertinea	+	+	+	+	+	+
144. Phoronida	0	+	0	0	+	0
145. Nematoda	+	+	0	0	0	0
Arthropoda						
Crustacea						
Decapoda						
146. *Pagurus* sp.	0	0	+	+	+	+
147. *Alpheus normanni*	0	0	0	0	+	+

		Haulover		Link Port		St. Lucie	
		In	Out	In	Out	In	Out
	Decapoda (cont.)						
148.	*Alpheus heterochaelis*	+	+	+	+	+	+
149.	Xanthidae	0	0	0	0	+	+
150.	Hippolytidae	0	0	+	+	+	+
151.	*Palaemonetes intermedius*	+	+	0	0	0	+
152.	Decapoda larva	+	+	0	+	+	+
153.	*Palaemonetes pugio*	+	+	+	+	+	+
154.	*Panopeus* sp. (?)	0	0	+	0	+	+
155.	*Alpheus* sp.	+	0	+	0	+	+
156.	*Libinia dubia*	0	0	+	+	0	0
157.	*Panopeus occidentalis*	0	0	+	0	+	+
158.	*Alpheus armillatus*	0	0	0	0	+	+
159.	*Pinnixa* sp.	0	0	0	+	+	+
160.	Decapoda juvenile	0	0	0	0	+	+
161.	*Penaeus* sp.	0	0	0	+	0	+
162.	*Pinnixa retinens*	0	+	0	0	+	0
163.	*Palaemonetes* juvenile	0	0	0	+	+	+
164.	Caridea larva	0	0	0	0	+	+
165.	Palaemonidae juvenile	+	+	0	0	0	0
166.	*Eurypanopeus depressus*	+	0	0	0	0	0
167.	*Callinectes ornatus* (?)	0	0	0	+	0	+
168.	*Micropanope* sp.	0	0	+	0	0	+
169.	*Pinnixa chaetopterana*	0	0	0	0	+	0
170.	*Portunus* sp.	0	0	0	0	+	0
171.	*Latreutes fucorum*	+	0	0	0	+	0
172.	*Palaemonetes* sp.	0	0	+	0	+	0
173.	*Callinectes sapidus*	0	0	0	+	0	0
174.	*Callinectes similis* (?)	0	0	0	+	0	0
175.	*Hexopanopeus* sp.	0	0	+	0	0	0
176.	*Panopeus herbstii*	0	0	+	0	0	0
177.	Palaemonidae	0	0	0	0	0	+
178.	Sergestidae	0	0	0	0	0	+
179.	Majidae juvenile	0	0	0	0	0	+
180.	*Pinnixa floridana*	0	0	0	0	0	+
181.	Caridea juvenile	0	0	0	0	+	0
182.	*Palaemonetes vulgaris*	0	0	0	0	+	0
183.	Portunidae juvenile	0	0	0	0	0	+
184.	*Upogebia* sp.	0	0	0	0	+	0
185.	*Neopanope sayi*	+	0	0	0	0	0
	Amphipoda						
186.	*Cymadusa* sp. A	+	+	+	+	+	+
187.	*Grandidierella* sp. A	+	+	+	+	+	+
188.	*Melita nitida*	+	+	+	+	+	+
189.	*Corophium* sp. A	0	+	+	+	+	0
190.	*Ampelisca* sp. A	0	+	+	+	0	+
191.	*Gammarus mucronatus*	0	0	+	0	0	0
	Isopoda						
192.	*Erichsonella filiformis isabelensis*	+	+	+	+	+	+
193.	*Cymodoce faxoni*	+	+	+	+	+	+
194.	*Apanthura magnifica*	0	0	0	0	+	+
195.	*Edotea montosa*	0	0	+	+	0	0
196.	Bopyridae	0	+	0	0	0	0
	Tanaidacea						
197.	Paratanaidae A	+	+	+	+	+	+
198.	Paratanaidae B	+	+	0	0	+	+

	Haulover		Link Port		St. Lucie	
	In	Out	In	Out	In	Out
199. Cumacea	+	+	+	+	+	0
200. Mysidacea	+	+	+	0	0	0
Copepoda						
201. Copepoda	+	+	0	+	+	0
202. Copepoda larva	+	0	0	0	0	0
203. Harpacticoida	+	+	0	0	0	0
204. Calanoida	0	0	0	0	+	0
Ostracoda						
205. *Sarsiella disparalis*	0	+	0	0	0	0
206. Pycnogonida	+	0	+	+	+	0
Arachnida						
207. Halacaridae	0	+	0	0	0	0
Merostomata						
208. *Limulus polyphemus*	0	+	0	0	0	0
Echinodermata						
Ophiuroidea						
209. *Amphioplus thrombodes*	+	+	+	+	+	+
210. *Ophiophragmus filograneus*	+	+	+	+	+	0
211. Amphiuridae juvenile	+	+	+	+	+	0
Holothuroidea						
212. *Synaptula hydriformis*	+	+	0	0	0	0
213. *Thyone* sp.	+	+	+	+	0	0
214. Cucumariidae	+	0	0	0	0	0
215. *Holothuria* sp.	0	0	0	0	+	0
Ectoprocta						
216. *Conopeum tenuissimum*	+	+	+	+	+	+
217. *Bowerbankia gracilis*	0	0	0	+	+	+
218. *Bowerbankia* sp.	+	+	+	+	0	0
219. *Electra bellula*	0	0	+	+	+	+
220. *Bugula neritina*	0	+	0	0	+	+
221. *Bugula stolonifera*	0	0	0	0	+	0
222. *Nolella* sp.	0	0	+	0	0	0
223. *Bugula* sp.	0	0	0	0	+	0
224. *Zoobotryon verticillatum*	0	0	0	0	+	0
225. Ascidiacea	+	+	+	+	+	+
226. Cnidaria	0	0	0	0	+	0
227. Hydrozoa	+	+	+	+	+	+
228. Anthozoa	0	0	0	+	0	0
229. Porifera	+	+	+	+	0	0
Protozoa						
230. *Folliculina* sp.	0	0	+	+	0	+

Seasonal Cycles in Benthic Communities of the Georgia Continental Shelf

Dirk Frankenberg
Marine Sciences Program
University of North Carolina
Chapel Hill, NC 27514

and

A. Scott Leiper
Design Engineering Department
Duke Power Company
422 South Church Street
Charlotte, NC 28202

ABSTRACT

A comparison of benthic faunal assemblages on the continental shelf off Georgia in 1964 and 1970 shows that density of benthic populations may fluctuate greatly from season to season, year to year, and place to place. The density of animals studied often varied by 1 or more orders of magnitude within short ranges of space and/or time; the density of a numerically dominant member of the nearshore fine sand assemblage, *Spiophanes bombyx*, varied by more than 4 orders of magnitude within the collections reported. The implications of this variability to the community concept, the concept of community stability and the utilization of quantitative benthic information in pollution impact studies are discussed.

INTRODUCTION

Marine benthic animal communities have been studied both in the laboratory and field throughout this century (e.g., Petersen and Boysen-Jensen 1911; Jones 1950; Thorson 1957; Sanders and Hessler 1969), but our knowledge of shallow water benthos has largely been derived from studies in boreal latitudes (Petersen 1914; Thorson 1957; Sanders 1969). Less work has been devoted to tropical and subtropical habitats (Longhurst 1964; McNulty et al. 1962). Faunal affinities in boreal and deep sea benthic communities have also been statistically analyzed (Petersen 1914; Thorson 1957; Sanders 1960), but these analyses have been less successful in lower latitudes partly because of the short life cycles and meroplanktonic larval stages of many dominant low latitude species (Thorson 1957, 1966; Mileikovsky 1971).

The relative lack of knowledge of subtropical shallow water benthos led the senior investigator to initiate a study of the benthic fauna on the continental shelf off Georgia in 1963. The results of his studies (Frankenberg 1965, 1968, 1971) stimulated additional work in this area (Smith 1971, 1973; Leiper 1973), while independent work was conducted by Dörjes (1972). The present paper describes seasonality in the Georgia assemblages on the basis of information obtained in 1964 and 1970. The comparison illustrates the characteristic variability of the fauna and faunal assemblages of this region, and raises theoretical questions concerning the existence of "communities" in subtropical benthos. The data are also discussed in terms of the recent use of structural analyses of benthic communities to assess the man's impact on nature.

This research was supported in part by the National Science Foundation through grants GB-873, GA-24588X and DES-7502265, the Sapelo Island Research Foundation, and the Duke Power Company.

MATERIALS AND METHODS

During one survey conducted by Frankenburg from December 1963 through November 1964, ten replicate grab samples were taken each month at two stations, designated F-1 and F-2 (Fig. 1). In a second study from December 1969 through November 1970. Leiper collected twelve replicate grab samples at each of three stations, designated A, B and C (Fig. 1). Data are presented for January, February, April, June, August, September and November. In both studies samples were collected with an o.1-m^2 Aberdeen grab (Smith and McIntyre 1954) from an anchored vessel (R/V KIT JONES). All samples were washed through a seive with 1-mm^2 mesh (1 mm by 1 mm) and preserved in 10% buffered sea water formalin.

SAMPLING AREA AND STATION DESCRIPTION

The Georgia coast is characterized by large rivers, extensive salt marshes dominated by the marsh grass, *Spartina alterniflora*, 2- to 3-meter tides, barrier islands, turbid estuarine and inshore water, and a broad (ca 165 km) gently sloping continental shelf bordered by the Gulf Stream at the shelf-slope break. The Georgia continental shelf has two major sedimentary regions: an inshore area containing fine sand and silty sediment (grain size usually less than 0.25 mm), and an offshore band stretching to the shelf-slope break characterized by coarse sediments (grain size more than 0.5 mm; Table 1). Gorsline (1963) considered the fine-grained sediments to be recent and the coarser, offshore sands to be Pleistocene. The boundary between them is an area of interfingering coarse and fine sands. The sea water overlying these two sediment types differs; the inshore water is generally brackish (salinity 12-33°/₀₀), turbid

Fig. 1. Map of the Georgia coastal region with the sampling sites noted.

Table 1. Sampling area descriptions

Station	Longitude N	Latitude W	Depth (m) Low Tide	Salinity Range °/°°	Sediment Description	Median Grain Size (mm)	Distance from Shore (km)
F-1	31°24.5'	81°13.1'	3.5	25-33	fine sand	0.16	3.9
A	31°23.3'	81°12.5'	8.5	27-34.2	very fine sand	0.13	4.6
B	31°24.2'	81°09.7'	9.1	27.7-34	fine sand	0.19	8.4
C	31°25.1'	81°06.9'	10.4	28.2-33.6	medium sand	0.46	10.3
F-2	31°21.5'	81°48.0'	21	33-36	coarse sand	0.74	38.55

(Secchi depth less than 1 m), and high in nutrients but low in primary production owing to limited light. In contrast, the offshore water is more saline (salinity, 33-36°/°°, clear, (Secchi depth 9-10 m), low in nutrients but higher in primary productivity.

The sampling stations (Fig. 1) span both these regions. One station (C) is very near the modern relict boundary. The location designated S is the site sampled by K. L. Smith (1971, 1973). The locations and physical characteristics of the stations are summarized in Table 1.

RESULTS

The results of the two surveys are presented in Tables 2 through 6 and compared in Figures 2 and 3. These 5 tables [2 through 6] list density (average number of individuals/m^2) by month for the species that were once or more included among the monthly "numerical dominants", i.e. those most abundant species that together made up 50% of the total number collected in that month (Fager 1963; p. 425). Figures 2 and 3 illustrate seasonal changes in density of 8 numerically abundant species in 1964 and 1970.

Faunal densities in inshore fine sand (Stations F-1, A and B) were generally high in the early part of the year (January through April) and somewhat lower during summer and early fall. The assemblage is characterized by the polychaete, *Spiophanes bombyx*, pelecypods of the genus *Tellina*, and the cumacean, *Oxyurostylis smithi*, but otherwise varies markedly at different times. For example, at Station F-1 in 1964 *Spiophanes*, tellinids and *Oxyurostylis* were abundant from January through May, while another group of species, the polychaete *Magelona*, the pelecypod *Solen viridis*, the decapods *Pinnixa chaetopterana* and *Callianassa atlantica*, and the opiuroid *Hemipholis elongata*, were numerically dominant from June through November. Stations A and B were similarly dominated by *Spiophanes bombyx* and *Oxyurostylis smithi* early in the year but differed from Station F-1 in the latter part of the year. At Station A, *Spiophanes bombyx* remained the dominant organism through the summer, although

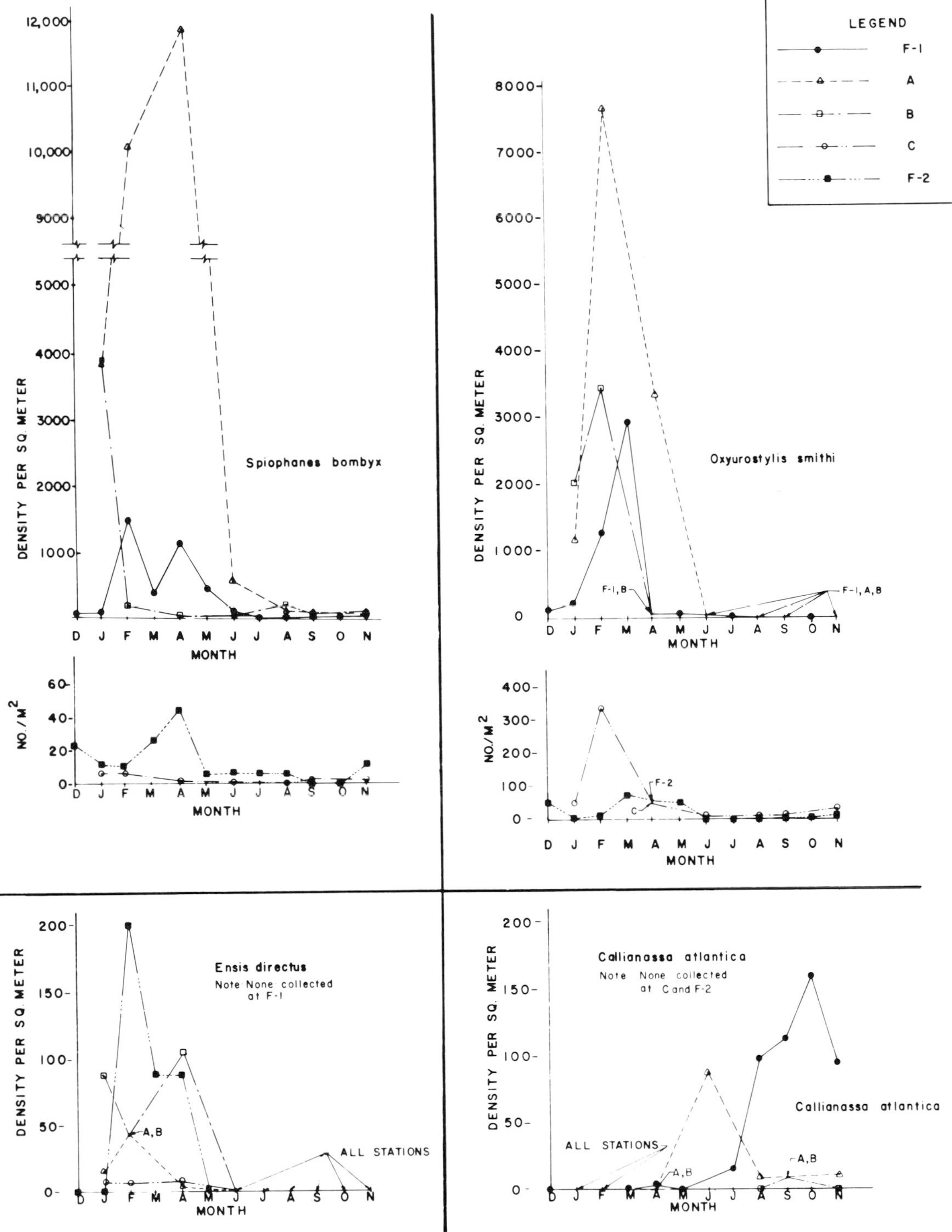

Fig. 2. Variations in seasonal abundance of the taxa noted. F-1 and F-2 are 1963 - 1964 stations; A, B and C are 1969 - 1970 stations.

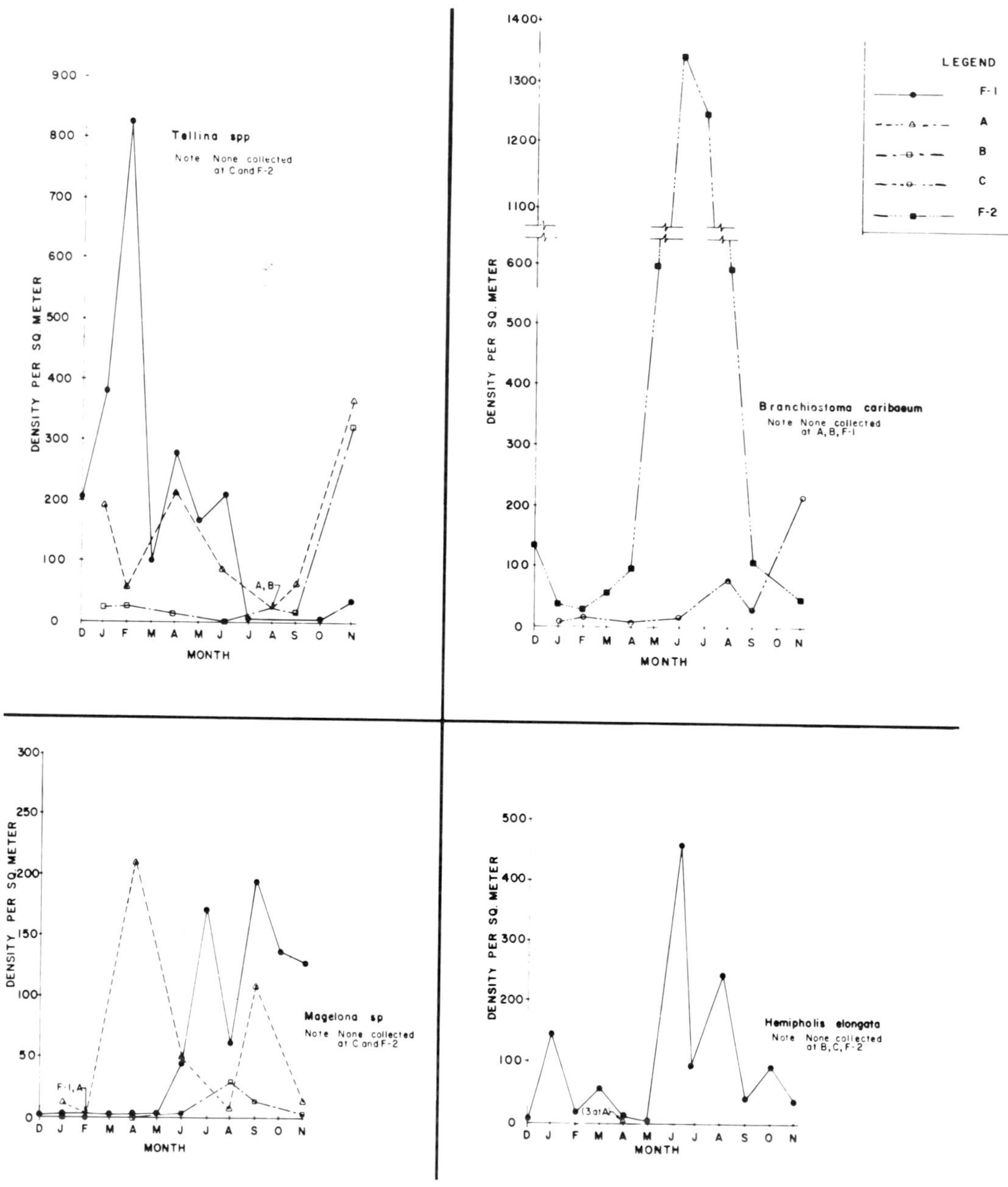

Fig. 3. Variations in seasonal abundance of the taxa noted. F-1 and F-2 are 1963 - 1964 stations; A, B and C are 1969 - 1970 stations.

Table 2. Station F-1--Seasonal faunal variation (avg. no. ind/m^2)

Species	1963 Dec	1964 Jan	Feb	Mar	April	May	June	July	Aug	Sept	Oct	Nov
Spiophanes bombyx	42	48	1464	365	1116	437	91	1	6	17	18	19
Tellina texana	62	377	743	98	246	144	193	6	5	7	7	34
Tellina iris	147	4	85	2	35	24	19	0	0	0	1	2
Abra aequalis	253	8	232	1	32	7	565	38	0	6	5	11
Terebra dislocata	8	95	14	5	13	1	21	0	0	22	35	53
Oxyurostylis smithi	75	200	1276	2914	60	33	12	7	0	1	2	14
Paraphoxus epistomus	134	52	149	25	99	31	21	2	13	25	59	306
Pinnixa chaetopterana	43	3	67	2	134	95	32	42	120	372	274	674
Magelona sp.	1	2	2	1	1	2	46	172	62	195	138	129
Solen viridis	1	3	1	1	0	0	122	47	40	6	4	3
Callianassa atlantica	0	0	0	0	2	0	6	15	97	112	159	95
Hemipholis elongata	1	147	13	59	9	1	460	93	243	39	91	35
Nemertea (unidentified)	0	0	4	1	23	13	59	45	1	0	0	0
Other species	360	700	465	604	267	223	580	245	375	467	330	459
Total no./m^2	1126	1637	4515	4078	2037	1011	2247	713	962	1269	1123	1834
Total no. species	51	74	58	59	59	47	70	59	61	57	57	59

its density dropped from a high of 11,844/m^2 in April to 35.0/m^2 in November, when the pelecypods *Tellina iris* and *Abra lioca* and the polychaetes *Armandia agilis* and *Capitita* sp. "A" made up 50% of the fauna. Station B, on the other hand, changed from being dominated by *Spiophanes bombyx* in January (3871.7/m^2, 77%) to a density and species composition quite distinct from that of A and F-1 later in the year. In April two nemerteans, *Tubulanus pellucidus* and *Carinomella lactea*, the pelecypod *Ensis directus*, and the amphipod *Paraphoxus floridanus* dominated the fauna. In the summer the barnacle *Balanus venustus niveus* became common, encrusting empty shells of *Ensis directus*. In August the sedentary polychaete *Sabellaria vulgaris* occurred with the barnacle. Both these animals were patchily distributed, being very abundant in some samples and completely absent from others. An assortment of amphipods and polychaetes made up the rest of the dominants.

Faunal density at Station C showed no clear pattern of seasonal change. The cyclostomate ectoproct *Cupuladria doma* characterized the assemblage in all months except April. *Oxyurostylis smithi* was also present throughout the year, and was a dominant during the winter

Table 3. Station A--Seasonal faunal variation (avg. no. ind/m^2)

Species	1969 Dec	1970 Jan	Feb	Mar	Apr	May	June	July	Aug	Sept	Oct	Nov
Spiophanes bombyx	-	3842	10073	-	11849	-	538	-	108	109	-	35
Nephtys picta	-	23	28	-	145	-	90	-	15	39	-	19
Callianassa atlantica	-	0	1	-	1	-	88	-	8	7	-	10
Tellina iris	-	194	27	-	24	-	85	-	11	56	-	417
Natica pusilla	-	23	23	-	14	-	16	-	38	39	-	65
Owenia fusiformis	-	37	73	-	108	-	20	-	37	83	-	65
Ogyrides limicola	-	0	0	-	1	-	73	-	33	0	-	3
Glycera dibranchiata	-	8	9	-	105	-	58	-	33	30	-	12
Magelona sp. A	-	11	0	-	210	-	48	-	6	109	-	13
Armandia agilis	-	18	5	-	4	-	1	-	6	0	-	146
Abra lioica	-	114	55	-	52	-	23	-	3	16	-	120
Capitita sp. A	-	212	332	-	1646	-	35	-	0	3	-	101
Oxyurostylis smithi	-	1131	7653	-	3368	-	10	-	1	0	-	28
Tubulanus pellucidus	-	10	3	-	3	-	23	-	1	3	-	5
Ensis directus	-	15	45	-	3	-	0	-	0	0	-	0
Carinomella lectea	-	18	119	-	168	-	0	-	0	0	-	0
Paraphoxus floridanus	-	23	3	-	17	-	0	-	0	1	-	0
Pectinaria gouldii	-	85	104	-	421	-	2	-	0	0	-	8
Notomastus sp. A	-	1	3	-	579	-	3	-	0	0	-	0
Phyllodoce arenae	-	8	56	-	478	-	3	-	1	0	-	3
Prionospio caspersi	-	53	13	-	13	-	14	-	9	0	-	23
Onuphis eremita	-	17	28	-	14	-	18	-	5	12	-	9
Sabellides occulata	-	93	249	-	82	-	0	-	0	0	-	2
Tellina versicolor	-	88	39	-	191	-	8	-	12	6	-	50
Edotea montosa	-	9	54	-	255	-	0	-	0	0	-	0
Cerapus tubularis	-	7	59	-	186	-	0	-	0	0	-	1
Phoronis psammophila	-	41	13	-	29	-	21	-	3	0	-	2
Other species (no.m^2)	-	331	113	-	619	-	289	-	143	182	-	309
Total no./m^2	-	6411	19180	-	20584	-	1466	-	473	695	-	1446
Total no. species (in 1.2 m^2)	-	77	84	-	107	-	76	-	58	51	-	73

months. Other dominants included the ascidean *Molgula arenata*, the nematode *Synonchus* sp. A, the cephalochordate *Branchiostoma caribaeum*, and the sipunculian *Aspidosiphon spinalis*. The sipunculian was found in the empty tests of large mollusks and sand dollars.

The offshore coarse sand assemblage (Station F-2) was characterized by the cephalochordate *Branchiostoma caribaeum*, the amphipods *Paraphoxus floridanus* and *Acanthohaustorius grayi*, and the polychaete *Glycera capitata*. The overwhelming seasonal aspect of this assemblage is the summer aggregation of *Branchiostoma caribaeum*, which accounts for the only significant density change in the assemblage (Frankenberg 1968). The abundant inshore species *Spiophanes bombyx* and *Oxyurostylis smithi* occur early in the year (January through June), along with the amphipod *Ampelisca compressa*. The mysid *Gastrosaccus johnsoni* becomes abundant from May through December, and two other species increase and decrease between February and May (the amphipod *Lembos* sp. and the pelecypod *Ensis directus*).

Table 4. Station B--Seasonal faunal variation (avg. no. ind/m^2)

Species	1969 Dec	1970 Jan	Feb	Mar	Apr	May	June	July	Aug	Sept	Oct	Nov
Spiophanes bombyx	-	3872	195	-	15	-	6	-	178	70	-	94
Nephtys picta	-	20	4	-	52	-	31	-	107	53	-	13
Tellina iris	-	24	27	-	8	-	0	-	17	11	-	14
Natica pusilla	-	38	6	-	12	-	0	-	4	8	-	11
Owenia fusiformis	-	508	6	-	53	-	0	-	16	58	-	218
Magelona sp. A	-	0	0	-	1	-	1	-	29	13	-	2
Armandia agilis	-	41	10	-	0	-	0	-	2	7	-	83
Oxyurostylis smithi	-	2022	3444	-	48	-	11	-	1	3	-	25
Tubulanus pellucidus	-	1	34	-	278	-	26	-	8	4	-	2
Ensis directus	-	90	43	-	105	-	0	-	1	0	-	1
Carinomella lactea	-	38	29	-	94	-	1	-	1	2	-	0
Paraphoxus floridanus	-	72	77	-	77	-	26	-	4	2	-	3
Phyllodoce arenae	-	55	4	-	3	-	0	-	3	3	-	1
Glycera dibranchiata	-	0	17	-	1	-	35	-	3	0	-	0
Platyishnopus capuciatus	-	13	98	-	31	-	30	-	21	7	-	2
Sabellaria vulgaris	-	1	1	-	0	-	0	-	58	45	-	0
Prionospio caspersi	-	88	1	-	3	-	0	-	22	88	-	38
Acanthohaustorius intermedius	-	0	83	-	0	-	80	-	3	0	-	0
Balanus venustus niveus	-	0	0	-	0	-	38	-	120	263	-	10
Onuphis eremita	-	37	9	-	23	-	11	-	5	3	-	18
Sabellides occulata	-	53	18	-	1	-	0	-	0	0	-	7
Strigilla mirabilis	-	0	34	-	2	-	20	-	8	1	-	1
Spio setosa	-	131	16	-	1	-	0	-	0	0	-	12
Phoronis psammophila	-	108	0	-	0	-	0	-	3	0	-	0
Other species (no. m^2)	-	417	311	-	295	-	101	-	199	256	-	175
Total no./m^2	-	7629	4467	-	1103	-	417	-	813	898	-	730
Total no. species (in 1.2 m^2)	-	83	83	-	63	-	55	-	74	83	-	66

Table 5. Station C--Seasonal faunal variation (avg. no. ind/m^2)

Species	1969 Dec	1970 Jan	Feb	Mar	Apr	May	June	July	Aug	Sept	Oct	Nov
Oxyurostylis smithi	-	49	335	-	43	-	7	-	4	8	-	28
Paraphoxus floridanus	-	6	8	-	6	-	10	-	2	51	-	28
Glycera dibranchiata	-	17	17	-	37	-	53	-	17	40	-	38
Mogula arenata	-	52	83	-	1	-	0	-	3	6	-	81
Synonchus sp. A	-	17	0	-	28	-	0	-	0	0	-	0
Balanus venustus niveus	-	8	1	-	3	-	18	-	76	1	-	1
Onuphis eremita	-	6	17	-	6	-	30	-	8	11	-	2
Discoporella umbellata	-	1	21	-	0	-	21	-	30	22	-	12
Aspidosiphon spinalis	-	0	37	-	0	-	2	-	158	7	-	132
Branchiostoma caribaeum	-	7	13	-	8	-	13	-	77	28	-	213
Tharyx cf. *acutus*	-	3	0	-	1	-	17	-	3	98	-	0
Megaluropus longimerus	-	0	0	-	0	-	0	-	4	35	-	0
Cupuladria doma	-	17	378	-	0	-	90	-	196	194	-	278
Scolelepis bousfieldi	-	0	105	-	33	-	0	-	0	0	-	0
Nephtys bucera	-	4	8	-	13	-	18	-	8	15	-	14
Strigilla mirabilis	-	1	6	-	9	-	3	-	1	4	-	0
Other species (no./m^2)	-	70	209	-	124	-	140	-	159	248	-	280
Total no./m^2	-	258	1238	-	312	-	422	-	746	768	-	1107
Total no. species (in 1.2 m^2)	-	50	75	-	68	-	70	-	73	96	-	79

Table 6. Station F-2--Seasonal faunal variation (avg. no. ind/m^2)

Species	1963 Dec	1964 Jan	Feb	Mar	Apr	May	June	July	Aug	Sept	Oct	Nov
Branchiostoma caribaeum	134	35	28	55	95	596	1345	1248	590	108	78	44
Paraphoxus floridanus	9	34	46	54	23	11	2	12	31	46	24	22
Acanthohaustorius grayi	49	27	29	29	55	76	60	27	29	22	13	27
Ampelisca compressa	21	16	8	8	19	14	1	5	4	3	0	0
Lembos sp.	1	0	9	38	51	7	2	9	5	0	0	0
Oxyurostylis smithi	47	4	17	77	55	49	0	1	0	0	5	18
Gastrosaccus johnsoni	12	1	3	2	6	18	33	58	20	29	21	62
Ensis directus?	0	0	201	88	89	2	0	0	0	0	0	0
Spiophanes bombyx	24	11	11	26	44	6	7	6	6	1	0	12
Syllis cornuta	47	0	2	6	16	1	2	3	0	1	0	0
Glycera capitata	18	9	12	16	13	10	7	17	17	19	5	22
Armandia sp.	4	9	36	9	2	2	6	10	8	0	1	0
Amphipholis squamata	33	11	0	3	10	10	6	21	8	2	3	0
Scolelepis squamata?	15	0	2	1	0	5	28	7	4	0	1	0
Phascolion sp.	7	11	9	9	34	6	7	6	6	1	0	4
Echinoid juveniles	6	18	24	5	0	10	2	4	11	27	4	5
Other species (no./m^2)	336	80	121	182	225	79	128	275	116	106	81	116
Total no./m^2	763	266	558	608	737	902	1638	1709	855	365	236	332
Total no. species (in 1.2 m^2)	83	55	57	83	67	49	51	71	57	45	39	62

DISCUSSION

Benthic faunal assemblages off Georgia are characterized by temporal and spatial changes in their component populations. For example, the dominant polychaete species of the inshore fine sand assemblages, *Spiophanes bombyx*, shows a density range of more than 4 orders of magnitude (1 to 11,847/m^2), with variations of 3 orders of magnitude at a single location (Station A) and at locations only 5.5 k apart during the same month (Stations A and B, 1970). Thus it is not surprising to find order-of-magnitude differences in the maximum densities in 1964 and 1970. Data presented in Table 2-6 show that density variation, rather than constancy, is typical of numerically dominant species in this region. In some cases there is a recurring seasonal density pattern: e.g., *Spiophanes bombyx*, *Oxyurostylis smithi*, and *Ensis directus* are abundant early in the year and rare late in the year (Fig. 2). In most cases, however, the population peaks vary greatly in both time and space: e.g., *Callianassa atlantica* (Fig. 2) is abundant August through November 1964, abundant only in June and at only one of 3 stations sampled in 1970; the ophiuroid *Hemipholis elongata* (Fig. 3) occurs in densities up to 460/m^2 in 1964, but only 3 specimens were collected from 25 square meters during 1970. Figures 2 and 3 present average densities calculated from 10 (1963-64) to 12 (1969-70) replicate samples, and therefore do not represent variability between replicates. Replicate samples usually differed from one another. Sometimes the differences were substantial (as with *Balanus venustus niveus* and *Sabellaria vulgaris* densities in August 1970 at Station B), but usually replicates varied less from one another than from samples taken at other times or other sampling stations. Variation between replicates and its significance to benthic sampling problems will be the subject of another paper.

A great deal of additional research will be necessary to fully elucidate causes of the faunal variability described above, but in a few cases causal relationships can be suggested. The 1964 mid-summer density peak of *Branchiostoma caribaeum* at Station F-2 is closely correlated with gonadal maturity, and may therefore represent a breeding aggregation (Frankenberg 1968). Reproductive swarming has been described in the pinnotherid crabs *Pinnotheres muculatus* and *Fabia subquadrata* (Pearce 1964, 1966) and may also be involved in the fall density peak of *Pinnixa chaetopterana* at Station F-1. Some density variation may indicate patchy settling of the meroplanktonic larvae characteristic of subtropical and tropical benthos (Thorson 1966). The density peak of *Ensis directus* appears to be an example of this phenomenon since small individuals comprised the population early in the peak and progressively larger ones appeared later. Larval settling may also underlie the density peaks of *Spiophanes bombyx* and *Callianassa atlantica*, although the supporting data are not as convincing as for *Ensis directus*. Predation may play an important role in the decline of density peaks. Casual observations during the collecting program suggest that predation by fish may remove large numbers of small crustacea (*Oxyurostylis smithi* and amphipods) from the assemblages. Simple longevity may be involved in the decline of some population peaks, although we have no direct evidence to support this hypothesis. Seasonal migrations may account for temporal variations in density at single sampling locations; the most convincing example of this possibility is for the cephalochordate *Branchiostoma caribaeum* described earlier (Frankenberg 1968), but it may be equally applicable to other species. Part of the reason for sampling 3 closely spaced stations in the 1970 study was to identify migrations, but the data showed little evidence of such migrations. Finally, some of the variability may be accounted for by the inaccurate relocation of sampling stations due to navigational error. Such failure, particularly in patchy sediment (Stations B and C), would naturally increase the apparent month-to-month faunal variation.

Faunal variations described here have both theoretical and practical implications. Density peaks may be interpreted as perturbations of community structure. Grant (1965) explored this concept in a temperate intertidal sandflat community (Barnstable Harbor, Massachusetts) recurringly perturbed by the influx of large numbers of the mud snail *Nassarius obsoletus*. He interpreted this influx as a disturbance that upsets the stability of the mudflat community by pushing the community back down the successional scale. He suggested that "too high a degree of community stability may . . . be detrimental, particularly in a temperate marine environment." Population peaks, whether random or regular, force the community to reorganize its structure. This mechanism may have adaptive value, particularly in an area where large percentages of the species have meroplanktonic larvae.

Spatial and temporal variability should also be included with other data in testing the community concept. This concept is a continuing subject of debate among terrestrial plant ecolgists, although most marine ecologists appear to share the belief of Fager (1963, p. 415) that "there are such things as communities in the sense of recurrent organized systems of organisms with similar structure in terms of species presence and abundances, and that it is possible and meaningful to study them, always keeping mind that they are open systems." Evidence of the existence of such entities in shallow water benthos is provided among others by Thorson (1957), Sanders (1960), and Day et al. (1971). Our data certainly emphasize the "openness" of such systems rather than their similarly of structure. Obviously any analysis of community structure based upon static numerical ratios between species would be totally inapplicable to the dramatically changing ratios characteristic of our study areas. Thus the single trellis diagram utilized by Sanders (1960) is not appropriate for our results. A set of temporally progressing trellis diagrams might be appropriate, but we feel that even this approach would be an artificially static characterization of what is essentially a dynamic situation. It would be interesting to apply the techniques of gradient analysis (Whittaker 1967) to data from shallow water benthos, for much of the variation inherent in our data suggests the need for an interpretation based on the individualistic concept of species distribution (Gleason 1926) rather than the community concept. Our sampling stations are separated by too much time and space to make such an analysis feasible, but our data suggest that gradient analysis might be a useful tool in interpreting distribution data for low latitude shallow water benthos.

The major practical implication of our results concerns use of benthic community structure as a baseline for evaluating environmental changes. Fresh-water ecologists are well aware of seasonality in benthic communities due to the importance of insect emergence (Wilhm 1967; Ranson and Dorris 1972); however, seasonality in marine benthic communities is less well recognized. It is interesting to speculate about the interpretation that might have been placed on our data had a significant pollution event taken place between 1964 and 1970. Our data would suggest that the event decimated the *Hemipholis elongata* population and caused a bloom of *Spiophanes bombyx*. Thus it is useful to note that the variations we observed occurred in the absence of any perceptable interference from man.

Although seasonality in both reproduction and larval settling is known to occur in many marine benthic species (Thorson 1966; Schoener 1969) seasonal change in the structure of entire benthic communities has seldom been described. It is possible that seasonal variation is a rare feature of benthic community structure. Seasonal variation has not been found in the soft bottom community of Buzzards Bay, Massachusetts (Sanders 1960) on the continental shelf of North Carolina (Day et al. 1971), or in the maritime coastal regions on the western edges of continents (Thorson 1966; Sanders 1969; Golikov and Scarlato 1968). Logistic constraints, however, may have limited many marine benthic investigations to a single season, usually summer, (Wigley and McIntyre 1964; Johnson 1970) so that sampling has been inadequate to delineate seasonal variations. Field (1969) sampled quarterly along a transect in False Bay, South Africa. Although his data indicated the occurrence of some seasonality, he stated that "sampling was not frequent enough or accurate enough to be certain that the differences observed are due to seasonal fluctuations in populations." Thus the lack of comment on seasonality in benthic community structure may not always indicate the absence of such seasonality. Our data demonstrate that seasonality is an important aspect of the benthic communities off Georgia; it will be interesting to see its role in other low latitude continental shelf areas.

REFERENCES

Day, J. H., J. G. Field, and M. P. Montgomery. 1971. The use of numerical methods to determine the distribution of the benthic fauna across the continental shelf of North Carolina. J. Animal Ecol. 40: 93-125.

Dörjes, J. 1972. Georgia coastal region, Sapelo Island, U.S.A. sedimentology and biology. VII. Distribution and zonation of macrobenthic animals. Senckenbergiana Marit. 4: 183-216.

Fager, E. W. 1963. Communities of organisms, p. 415-437. In M. N. Hill [ed.], The Sea, v. 2. Interscience.

Field, J. G. 1969. A numerical analysis of changes in the soft bottom fauna along a transect across False Bay, South Africa. J. Exp. Mar. Biol. Ecol. 7: 215-253.

Frankenberg, D. 1965. Variability in marine benthic communities off Georgia. Trans. Joint Conference Ocean Science and Ocean Engineering 2: 1111.

______. 1968. Seasonal aggregation in *Amphioxus*. Bio. Sci. 18: 877-878.

______. 1971. The dynamics of benthic communities off Georgia, U.S.A. Thalassia Jugoslavica 7: 49-55.

Gleason, H. A. 1926. The individualistic concept of the plant association. Bull. Torrey Bot. Club 53: 7-26.

Golikov, A. N. and O. A. Scarlato. 1968. Vertical and horizontal distribution of biocoenoses in the upper zones of the Japan and Okhotsk Seas and their dependence on the hydrological system. Sarsia 34: 109-116.

Gorsline, D. S. 1963. Bottom sediments of the U.S. South Atlantic continental shelf and slope. Geol. Soc. Am. Bull. 74: 422-440.

Grant, D. C. 1965. Specific diversity in the infauna of an intertidal sand community. Ph.D. thesis, Yale Univ., New Haven. 53p.

Jones, N. S. 1950. Marine bottom communities. Biol. Rev. 25: 283-313.

Johnson, R. G. 1970. Variations in diversity within benthic marine communities Am. Nat. 104: 285-300.

Leiper, A. S. 1973. Seasonal change in the structure of three sublittoral marine benthic communities off Sapelo Island, Georgia. Ph.D. thesis, Univ. Georgia. 296p.

Longhurst, A. R. 1964. A review of the present situation in benthic synecology. Bull. Inst. Oceanogr. Monaco 63: 1-54.

McNulty, J. K., R. C. Work, and H. B. Moore. 1962. Some relationships between the infauna of the level bottom and the sediment in South Florida. Bull. Mar. Sci. Gulf Carib. 12: 322-332.

Mileikovsky, S. A. 1971. Types of larval development in marine bottom invertebrates, their distribution and ecological significance: a re-evaluation. Mar. Biol. 10: 193-213.

Pearce, J. B. 1964. On reproduction in *Pinnotheres maculatus* (Decapoda: Pinotheridae). Biol. Bull. 127: 384.

_____. 1966. The biology of the mussel crab, *Fabia subquadrata*, from the waters of the San Juan Archipelago, Washington. Pacific Sci. 20: 3-35.

Peterson, C. G. 1914. The animal associations of the sea bottom in the North Atlantic. Kovenhavn Ber. Biol. Sta. 22: 89-98.

_____ and P. Boysen-Jensen. 1911. Valuation of the sea. I. Animal life on the sea bottom, its food and quantity. Rep. Danish Biol. Stat. 20: 1-81.

Ransom, J. D. and T. C. Dorris. 1972. Analysis of benthic community structure in a reservoir by use of diversity indices. Am. Midland Nat. 87: 434-447.

Sanders, H. L. 1960. Benthic studies in Buzzards Bay. III. The structure of the soft bottom community. Limnol. Oceanogr. 5: 138-153.

_____. 1969. Benthic marine diversity and the stability-time hypothesis, pp. 71-81. In Brookhaven Symposia in Biology, Number 22: Diversity and stability in ecological systems. Brookhaven National Laboratory, New York. 264p.

_____ and R. R. Hessler. 1969. Ecology of the deep-sea benthos. Science 163: 1419-1424.

Schoener, A. 1969. Ecological studies on some Atlantic ophiuroids. Ph.D. thesis, Harvard Univ. 115p.

Smith, K. L. 1971. Structural and functional aspects of a sublittoral community. Ph.D. thesis, Univ. Georgia, Athens. 160p.

_____. 1973. Respiration of a sublittoral community. Ecology 54: 1065-1075.

Smith, W. and A. D. McIntyre. 1954. A spring-loaded bottom sampler. J. Mar. Biol. Assoc. U. K. 33: 257-264.

Thorson, G. 1957. Bottom communities (Sublittoral and shallow shelf), p. 461-534. In J. W. Hedgpeth [ed.], Treatise on marine ecology and paleoecology, v. 1. Ecology. Geol. Soc. Amer. Mem. 67.

_____. 1966. Some factors influencing the recruitment and establishment of marine benthic communities. Netherlands J. Sea Res. 3: 267-293.

Whittaker, R. H. 1967. Gradient analysis of vegetation. Biol. Rev. 42: 207-264.

Wigley, R. L. and A. D. McIntyre. 1964. Some quantitative comparisons of offshore meiobenthos and macrobenthos south of Martha's Vineyard. Limnol. Oceanogr. 9: 485-493.

Wilhm, J. L. 1967. Comparison of some diveristy indices applied to population of benthic macroinvertebrates in a stream receiving organic wastes. J. Water Pollu. Control Fed. 39: 1673-1683.

Marine Macrobenthic Communities of the Sapelo Island, Georgia Region

Jürgen Dörges
Institut für Meeresgeologie und
Meeresbiologie "Senckenberg",
D-29400 Wilhelmshaven
Germany

ABSTRACT

The present study deals with the occurrence, distribution, zonation, diversity, and abundance of macrobenthic organisms of different marine communities around Sapelo Island, Georgia. The paper summarizes and compares data collected since 1969 on salt marshes, beaches, shelf areas, estuaries, shoals, tidal flats, and point bars.

INTRODUCTION

Shallow coastal waters are characterized by a variety of environments having great diurnal, seasonal, and annual fluctuations in their chemical, physical, hydrographical, and sedimentological properties. These coastal conditions support a large number of animal communities; an observation made as early as 1913 by Petersen and subsequently by many marine ecologists (e.g., Thorson 1957; Perkins 1974).

During 1969 and 1972 the macrobenthos near Sapelo Island, Georgia was sampled in several marine areas for biological and environmental data on specific environments and their characteristic benthic communities. At each location an attempt was made to discover the most important parameters influencing and limiting the individual composition of the resident community.

The approach we took, i.e., to examine interaction of biological and geological factors, turned out to be very useful, because physical and biogenetic structures within recent sediments can yield information about the strength and persistence of hydrographic processes which are important parameters controlling animal life, directly or indirectly. Certainly this approach is of value to both disciplines: biologists (Allen 1899; Petersen 1911, 1913, 1918; Ford 1923; Davis 1925; Hagmeier 1925) have pointed out the importance of animal-sediment relationships and paleontologists and geologists since Gressly (1838) have recognized biofacies in the marine environment. Most of the peleontological results have been summarized by Teichert (1958), Schäfer (1972), Reineck and Singh (1973), and Frey (1975). The sedimentological and paleontological results of studies in nearshore environments of Sapelo Island were summarized by Howard, et al. (1973).

The author expresses his sincere appreciation to Dr. James D. Howard for his assistance and support. Drs. Robert W. Frey, Donald C. Rhoads, and Bruce C. Coull kindly reviewed the manuscript and provided many suggestions and critical comments. Investigations were assisted by several students and the hard-working crew members of the R/V KIT JONES. Mrs. Renate Flügel prepared the text figures. Research was supported by National Science Foundation grants GA-719, GA-10888, GA-30565, GA 39999 x, and Deutsche Forschungsgemeinschaft.

REGIONAL SETTING

Along coastal Georgia many Sea Islands and large salt marshes form an estuarine area of rivers, tidal channels, flats, shoals, and bars (Howard, et al. 1973). Sapelo is one of the Sea Islands. The continental shelf here extends offshore more than 100 km (Fig. 9). It occupies the center of a broad reentrant between Cape Hatteras and Cape Canaveral (Henry and Hoyt 1968). Due to the broad expanse of the shelf the bottom slope is gentle. Sapelo Island itself is bordered by deep sounds having shoals near their inlets, and by several kilometers of salt marshes with an intricately branched tidal creek system (Hoyt, et al. 1966).

The tidal range along the coast averages 2.1 m, although net wave energy is generally low (Kuroda 1969). Longshore and tidal currents interact near inlets and river entrances to form shoals and spits (Oertel 1973) which are unstable in shape and position. Strong currents run in sounds and river estuaries, transporting much inorganic and organic material from the salt marshes to the front of the islands. Consequently, the nearshore and estuarine waters are very turbid, having a medium visibility of 0.5 m or less (Odum and de la Cruz 1967; Oertel 1971; Howard, et al. 1972).

METHODS

The collection of bottom samples at different depths was necessarily carried out with different kinds of equipment. Above the low water line, on beaches and tidal flats, an iron cylinder covering an area of 0.2 m^2 was pushed into the bottom, and the enclosed sediments were subsequently passed through a screen with 0.8 mm openings. After the sieved residue was fixed with formalin, the animals were identified and counted in the laboratory. Between the low water line and a water depth of 3 to 5 m, samples were taken with the Brett-sampler (Brett 1964) from the same iron cylinder, which was pushed into the bottom. Below the 3 or 5-m depth line, all samples were taken from research vessels by a heavy box corer modified after Reineck (1963). Physical and biogenic structures were analyzed from x-radiographs and epoxy casts of samples, and textural analyses were made from subsamples. Temperature, currents, salinity, suspended solids, oxygen content, and pH were measured in areas of highly fluctuating physical and chemical parameters, such as estuaries and point bars.

FAUNAL ANALYSES

Salt Marshes

Georgia salt marshes are located between the mainland and a chain of barrier islands. This environment has been investigated by many scientists of different disciplines (e.g., Ragotzkie, et al. 1959; Maney, et al. 1968).

The Georgia salt marshes contain mainly soft muddy sediments, an intricate tidal creek system which is relatively stable in position, and a dense vegetation of higher plants belonging to the genera *Spartina*, *Distichilis*, *Salicornia*, and *Juncus* (Basan and Frey 1972; Howard, et al. 1973). This characteristic flora is completely different from that of European tidal flats or waddenzee (Van Straaten 1954, 1964; Reineck 1970) although other environmental parameters, such as salinity and time of exposure, are comparable. In both areas there are low numbers of macrobenthic species, but a large number of individuals. The following generalities, then, seem appropriate: the time of exposure and the fluctuating salinity which is a physiological stress, limits the number of species; local differences in topography, sedimentology and vegetation type influence the occurrence of a single species.

On this basis it is possible to establish several subenvironments within the intertidal areas (Frey and Howard 1969; Dörjes 1970). An excellent summary of the sequence of subenvironments of Georgia salt marshes has been given by Howard, et al. (1973), who mentioned five zones differing in ecological conditions as well as in animal communities. The creek banks and the barrens are not typical salt marsh environments. The creek bank organisms, i.e., *Crassostrea virginica*, *Nassarius obsoletus*, *Diopatra cuprea*, *Upogebia affinis*, and *Heteromastus filiformis* also occur in other unvegetated intertidal or subtidal environments (Dörjes 1972; Howard and Dörjes 1972; Dörjes and Howard (1976). The barrens are almost uninhabited. Only fiddler crabs (*Uca*) feed there. Beside the natural stream side levees, which are inhabited by the marsh crab *Sesarma reticulatum*, the mud crab *Panopeus herbstii*, and the fiddler crab *Uca pugnax*, the low marsh and high marsh subenvironments are of particular interest. Dominant species in the low marsh area are the mollusks *Modiolus demissus*, *Littorina irrorata*, and some clumps of *Crassostrea virginica*, the decapod crustaceans *Uca pugnax*, *Sesarma reticulatum*, *Panopeus hebstii*, and *Eurytium limosum* (Teal 1958; Wolf and Fanning 1970), and the polychaete *Nereis succinea* (Frey, et al. 1973). Beside the plant roots the numerous fiddler crabs contribute significantly to an almost complete sediment bioturbation by digging and feeding. The high marsh which can be divided into several smaller zones or patches on the basis of plant distribution (Teal 1958, 1962) is inhabited mainly by *Uca pugilator*, and some local places by *U. pugnax* and *U. minax*.

Point Bars

Tidal creek point bars have been less intensively studied in the past than salt marshes although these environments correspond in some ecological conditions, such as time of exposure and fluctuating salinity. They are formed of sediments transported by tidal currents and usually they lack higher plants. In response to different energy levels in different areas of the bars, two or three subenvironments have developed which are characterized by different sediment textures and sediment structures (Land and Hoyt 1966: Howard, et al. 1973) The two bars investigated are located in Blackbeard Creek (Fig. 1) 3 km from the ocean and in Duplin River (Fig. 2) on the landward side of Sapelo Island, 11 km from Doboy Sound inlet. Their unvegetated sandy sediments contrast with the vegetated muddy sediments of the salt marsh environment. Both bars also show strong influence of hydrolic energy which causes clean sandy sediments at the ebb current exposed ends, muddy sediments at the marsh sides, and sands mixed with some quantities of clay and organic debris at the channel sides.

The benthic organisms occurring in or on these bars show the following adaptations and distribution trends:

1. The number of invertebrate species represented by high numbers of individuals (Figs. 1 and 2) is very limited. This finding corresponds with the conditions prevalent in salt marsh environments and other intertidal habitats such as beaches and shoals.
2. Owing to the unvegetated sediments, the tremendous energy fluctuations, and the more sandy sediments, the investigated species differ from those occurring in salt marsh environments. Nevertheless, none of the point bar species are really endemic, but all occur in other environments such as beaches, shoals, or unvegetated tidal flats having somewhat similar conditions.
3. The number of point bar species decreases with decreasing salinity, a phenomenon well known from other estuarine studies. Blackbeard Creek Point Bar, located close to the ocean, is inhabitated by 31 species, while Duplin River Point Bar, situated up-estuary, is inhabited by only 13 species. Salinity in Blackbeard Creek seldom reaches concentrations less than 28°/₀₀ (Land and Hoyt 1966) while salinity in Duplin River fluctuates more widely (Heard personal communication).

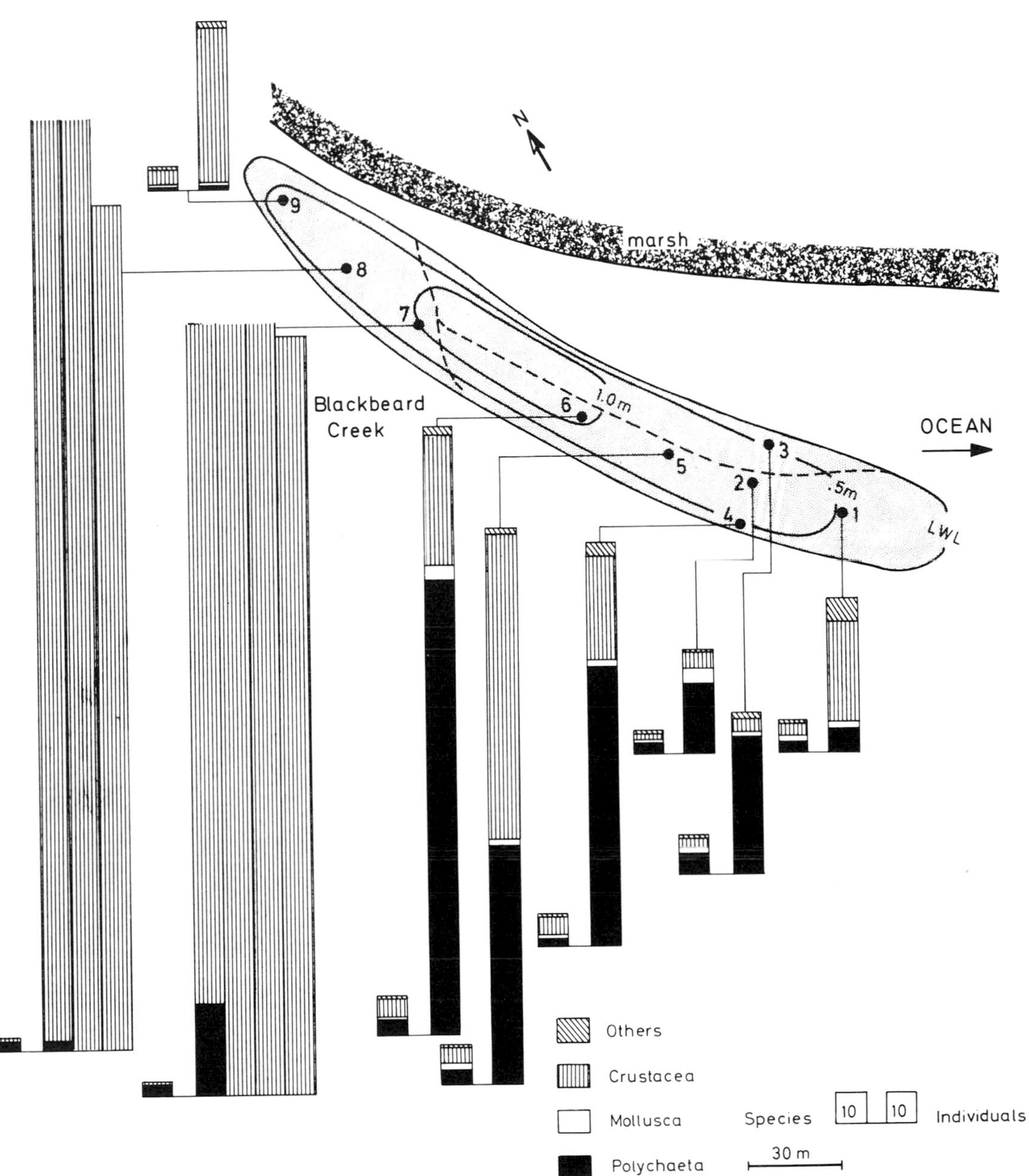

Fig. 1. Distribution and abundance of macrobenthic species and specimens on Blackbeard Creek Point Bar. Numbers of species and specimens per 0.2 m^2; dotted lines mark boundaries between different subcommunities.

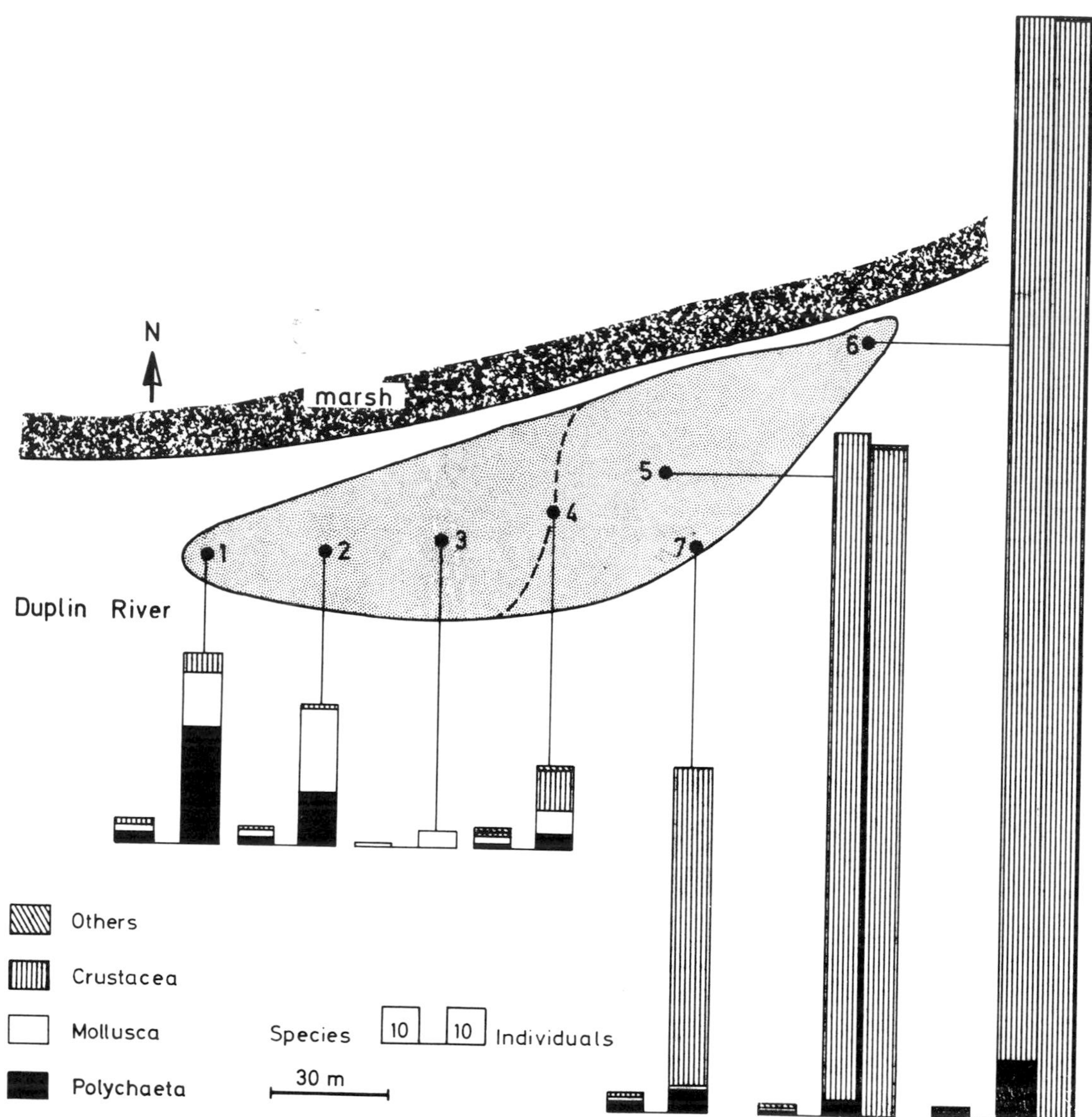

Fig. 2. Distribution and abundance of macrobenthic species and specimens on Duplin River Point Bar. Numbers of species and specimens per 0.2 m^2; dotted line marks boundary between two different subcommunitites.

4. The number and distribution of subenvironments is primarily related to the prevalent hydrographic and sedimentologic conditions. Generally, homogeneity increases with increased horizontal changes in current velocities. All subenvironments are characterized by different animal subcommunities. Usually the clean sands exposed to the currents are inhabited predominantly by haustoriid amphipods of the genera *Acanthohaustorius, Lepidactylus,* and *Bathyporeia*, as well as the ghost shrimp *Callianassa major*, which is also common in shoal and beach environments. The great number of individuals (Figs. 1 and 2) is obvious. With increasing clay minerals and organic debris the animal subcommunities change very rapidly, while the number of animal species increases and the number of individuals decreased (Fig. 1 and 2). Typical species of the channel side of the bars are *Laeonereis culveri, Heteromastus filiformis, Onuphis microcephala, Tellina* cf. *texana,* and several amphipods. The muddy sediments of the marsh sides are predominantly inhabitated by *Diopatra cuprea, Tagelus plebeius, Sthenelais boa, Upogebia affinis, Glycera dibranchiata,* and *Drilonereis longa*. Sometimes species of the marsh margins, i.e., *Nassarius vibex, N. obsoletus*, and *Uca* spp., enter the channel sides. Several of the species occurring on the channel sides must be considered "guests" from adjacent subtidal environments introduced by water currents or their own movements.

5. Previous investigations on Blackbeard Creek Point Bar (Land and Hoyt 1966; Mayou and Howard 1969 unpublished data) have shown that the number of characteristic species fluctuates insignificantly over long periods of time. Distinct differences in biogenic sediment structures (worm tubes, burrows, etc.) are also consequences of the existence of several past subcommunities.

Ogeechee Estuary

Freshwater, brackish, and salt water parts of an estuary in the Ogeechee River were investigated over a distance of 52 km (Dörjes and Howard (1976). In addition to 63 samples taken for biological and geological analyses, several physical and chemical properties were made.

The biological investigation in the Ogeechee (Fig. 3) showed 5 distinct macrobenthic communities, probably caused by changes in the sedimentological, chemical, and physical conditions. No doubt salinity is the main parameter controlling animal life in the brackish water; sediment texture and other parameters appear to be less important.

General trends in the distribution of the benthos are shown in Figure 3. The number of species occurring in the freshwater part of the river is low but the average number of specimens is relatively high. Where salinity reaches approximately 5°/∘∘ (mixo-oligohaline and mixo-mesohaline junction), the number of individuals decreases drastically whereas the number of species increases slightly. This trend continues throughout the mixo-mesohaline zone and ends abruptly at the mesohaline/polyhaline border, where salinity decreases to 18-20°/∘∘. From this transition area the number of species and

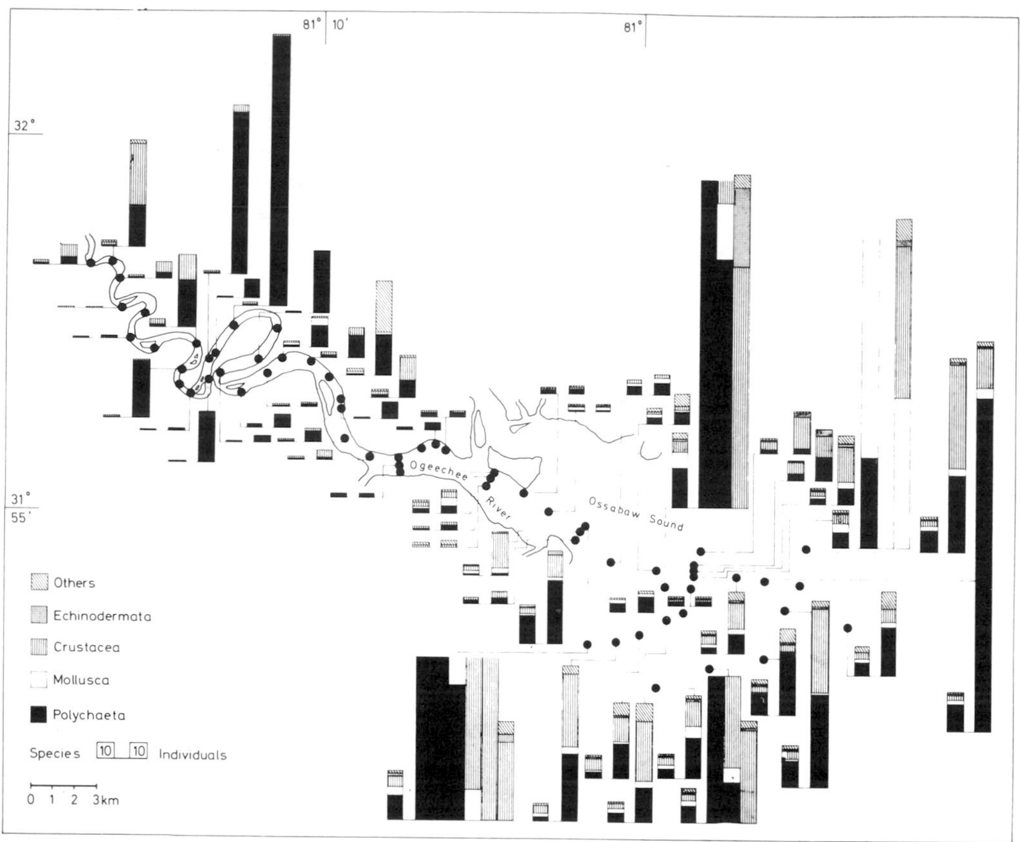

Fig. 3. Distribution and abundance of macrobenthic species and specimens in the Ogeechee River-Ossabaw Sound estuary. Numbers of species and specimens per 0.2 m^2 (from Dörjes and Howard 1976).

specimens increases markedly toward the ocean, reaching a maximum in the muddy sediments of the upper offshore. The number of epifaunal and fish species approximates that of the infauna. The number of species in the freshwater part is extremely low and diversity increases slightly in the mixo-mesohaline and abruptly in the mixo-polyhaline parts.

Biological breaks observed near points where salinity reaches a minimum of 5°/₀₀ or maximum of 18°/₀₀, respectively, correspond with other observations of estuarine environments. The salinities are in the "Venice-System" borders between the mixo-oligohaline/mixo-mesohaline and mixo-mesohaline/mixo-polyhaline zones (Segerstråle 1959; Caspers 1959a, b).

The most important members of the different communities are summarized below:

1. The freshwater area and the beginning of the mixo-oligohaline zone is dominated by the burrowing amphipod *Lepidactylus dytiscus* and the tube dwelling polychaete *Scolecolepides viridis* (Howard, et al. in press).

2. The mixo-mesohaline area is characterized by the bivalve *Macoma constricta*, the burrowing polychaete *Heteromastus filiformis*, and the tunicate *Bostrichobranchus pilularis*. The intense bioturbation recognized in the geological record probably is the result of long term activity of infauna because the numbers of species and specimens in this part of the estuary are conspicuously low (Fig. 3). The observed lebensspuren (Dörjes and Howard 1976) also indicate long-term changes in the community of this area.

3. Muddier parts of the mixo-polyhaline area are characterized by burrowing or tube-dwelling species. Areas of fine sand in the shallows near inlet shoals are usually less densely populated, and dominant species here are haustoriid amphipods of the genera *Acanthohaustorius*, *Haustorius*, and *Bathyporeia*. The polychaetes *Onuphis eremita*, *O. microcephala*, *Magelona* sp., and *Spiophanes bombyx* are also common. Other typical species are the bivalves *Solen viridis* and *Tellina* cf.*texana*, the sanddollar *Mellita quinquiesperforata*, and the shrimp *Ogyrides alphaerostris*. This community is in many respects identical with those found on sandy sediments of point bars (Howard, et al. 1976), beach-related tidal flats (Howard and Dörjes 1972), beaches (Croker 1967; Dörjes 1972), and inlet shoals. The main controlling environmental parameters seem to be currents and wave activity causing high rates of sediment reworking, as indicated by degree of bioturbation and kind of sedimentary physical structures (Greer 1976; Dörjes and Howard 1976). press).

4. The benthos of the muddy area seaward of the Ogeechee entrance and below normal wave base (Howard and Reineck 1972) is identical with the upper offshore of the shallow shelf (Smith 1971; Dörjes 1972). The lower rate of reworking of bottom sediments, the more constant temperatures, salinities, and food supplies make it possible for many species to exist. The most important species are the polychaetes *Capitomastus* cf. *aciculatus*, *Diopatra cuprea*, *Glycera americana*, *Magelona* sp., *Mesochaetopterus taylori*, *Notomastus latericeus*, *Owenia fusiformis*, *Pectinaria gouldi*, *Spiophanes bombyx*, and *Spiochaetopterus oculatus*, the bivalves *Abra aequalis* and *Tellina* cf. *texana*, the crustaceans *Callianassa biformis* and *Oxyurostylis smithi*, and the echinoderm *Hemipholis elongata*. The numerous burrowing and tube-dwelling polychaetes, bivalves, crustaceans, and echinoderms are responsible for the high degree of biogenic reworking visible in the geological record (Hertweck 1972; Dörjes and Howard (1976).

5. The muddy sediments below normal wave base are followed seaward by relict shelf sediments (Pilkey and Frankenberg 1964; Howard, et al. 1972) of the lower offshore (Howard and Reineck 1972). Many tube-dwelling polychaetes, the heart urchin *Moira atropos* and the lancelet *Branchiostoma virginiae* are the characteristic species. Because of the stability of the sediments over long intervals of time, bioturbation is extensive. Dörjes (1972) suggested that abundance and diversity of animal species per square unit are reduced because of smaller food supplies in this area.

Beach-Related Tidal Flats

Beach-related tidal flats like Nannygoat Flat and Cabretta Flat on Sapelo Island (Howard and Dörjes 1972) occur locally along the coast of Georgia. The composition of their resident animal community depends primarily on the hydrographic regime, which, of course, determines sediment texture (Howard, et al. 1973). Cabretta Flat merges landward with the beach, but seaward it is protected by an intertidal shoal shielding it from the open sea. Channel-like openings to the north and south allow water of the tidal creek to cross its surface during ebb and late flood tidal stages and result in clean sandy sediments. Nannygoat Flat lies in a protected bight. Two subtle beach bulges and a complex system of inlet shoals protect the flat from high wave energy. A lense of water laden with organic-rich sediment which stalls in this area of the beach during high tide provides abundant food for deposit and suspension feeding organisms.

The number of macrobenthic species is almost the same on both flats, but composition of the resident communities differs (Figs. 4 and 5). Slightly more than one-third of the total number of species was found in both areas, one-third was observed only on Cabretta Flat, and the other third only on Nannygoat Flat. The only major difference in the total number of individuals between the two areas is the overwhelming abundance of amphipod crustaceans on Cabretta Flat, which indicate conditions similar to those of beaches, shoals, shoreface areas, and sandy point bar deposits. Taxa differences of the investigated communities were more significant. At Cabretta Flat 40% of the species are crustaceans and 28% polychaetes. On Nannygoat Flat 38% are polychaetes and 36% crustaceans. Thus, polychaete individuals and species appear to increase with increasing clay mineral content (Figs. 4 and 5). Furthermore some species are characteristic of either one flat or the other. On Cabretta Flat the snail *Oliva sayana*, the ghost shrimp *Callianassa major*, the shrimp *Ogyrides alphaerostris*, and several haustoriid amphipods are characteristic occupants, whereas the sediments of Nannygoat Flat are preferred by the polychaetes *Heteromastus filiformis* and *Diopatra cuprea*, the bivalve *Mulinia lateralis*, the snail *Nassarius obsoletus*, and the small ghost shrimp *Callianassa biformis*. Consequently this

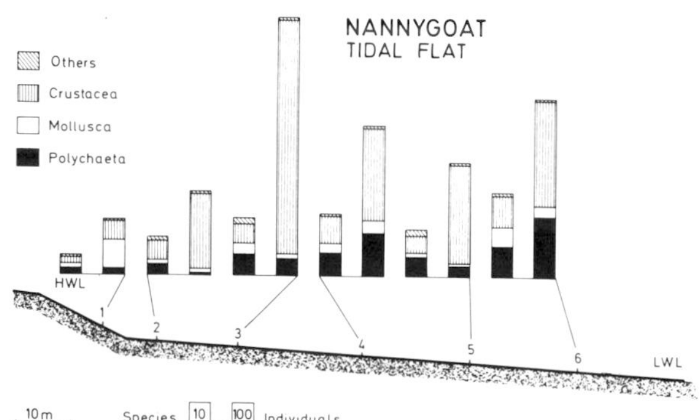

Fig. 4. Distribution and abundance of macrobenthic species and specimens per 0.2 m^2 on Nannygoat Flat.

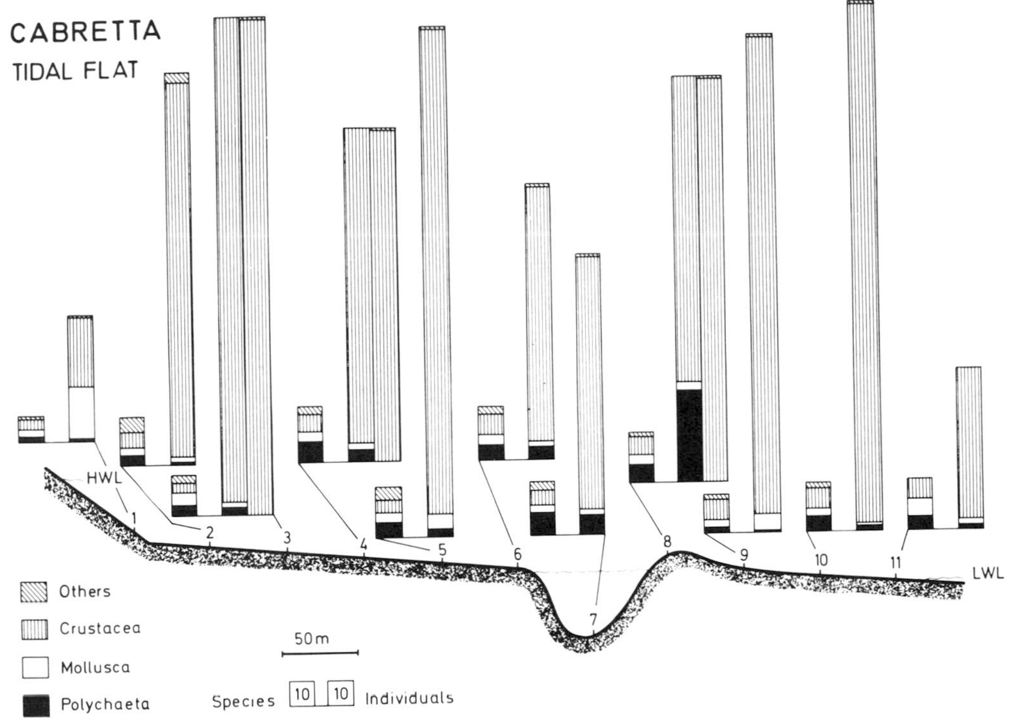

Fig. 5. Distribution and abundance of macrobenthic species and specimens per 0.2 m^2 on Cabretta Flat.

community is similar to that of creek banks (Howard, et al. 1973) or marsh-side point bar deposits. None of the species is restricted exclusively to either tidal flat (Dörjes 1972; Dörjes and Howard (1976).

Shoals

Shoals in front of the entrance to Doboy Sound south of Sapelo Island were also investigated. In this area, surf and currents cause an accumulation of clean sandy sediments and encourage high rates of sediment reworking. The resident community (Fig. 6) is almost identical to that of beach environments owing to similar hydrodynamic regimes. It consists of a few characteristic species, some having high numbers of individuals (Fig. 6). The most abundant species are the surf clam *Donax variabilis* and the amphipod *Haustorius* sp., which also have the highest numbers of individuals (>80%). On the lee side of the shoals surf energy decreased as indicated by few shell fragments in the sediment and increased number of individuals. The fewest individuals occur at the south end of shoal 1 and on the northern margins of shoals 2, 3, and 4 (Fig. 6).

The occurrence of the ghost shrimp *Callianassa major* and here and there the surf clam *Donax variabilis* seem to indicate high energy, whereas *Nerenides (Scolelepis) agilis*, *Bathyporeia* sp., and *Chiridotea caeca* prefer areas of lower energy. *Balanoglossus* sp. was found predominantly in the quiet areas.

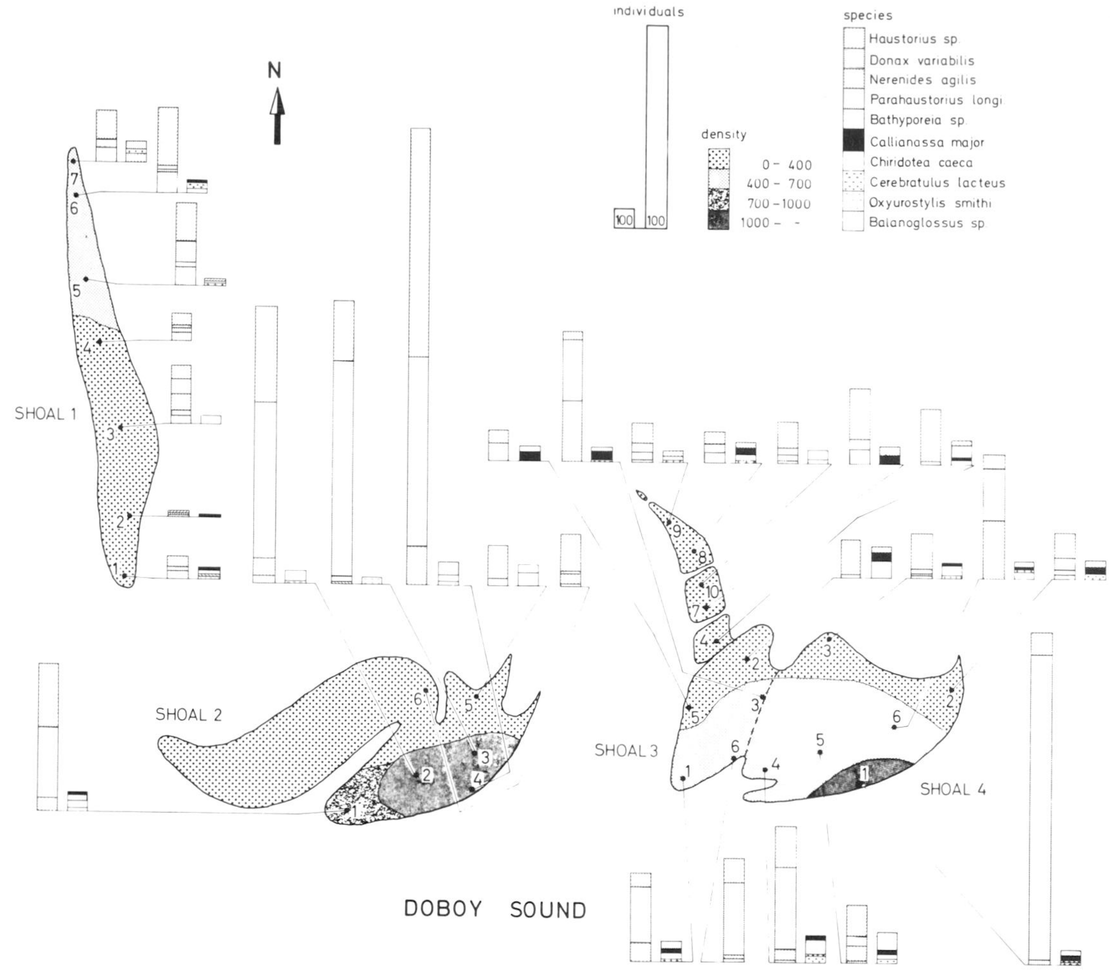

Fig. 6. Distribution and abundance of macrobenthic species and specimens on a series of shoals. Numbers of species and specimens per 0.2 m^2.

Beach and Shallow Shelf Environments

Two transects, referred to as the northern transect and the southern transect were sampled in 1969. At 51 stations distributed along the northern transect (Fig. 7) 48175 individuals representing 179 species and 12 different major taxa were collected. Most were polychaetes, followed in importance by molluscs and crustaceans (Dörjes 1972). The distribution of species and individuals along the northern transect (Fig. 7) is as follows:

1. Only a few marine and terrestrial migrants occur in the backshore and small parts of the upper foreshore. Characteristic species are the ghost crab *Ocypode quadrata* and insect larvae which are seldomly touched by salt water.
2. The foreshore, located between high and low water lines, is covered by clean fine sand. The daily changes of morphological and

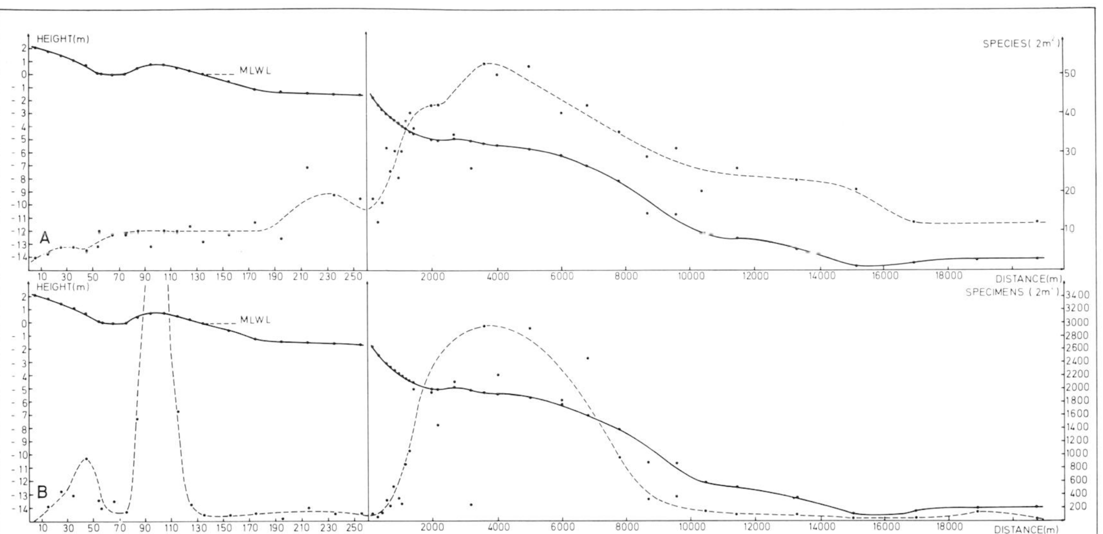

Fig. 7. Northern beach/offshore transect. (A) Number of species. (B) Number of individuals.

physical sediment structures (Wunderlich 1972; Howard, et al. 1973) as well as tidal processes indicate the foreshore as a rough environment. Only very few species having high numbers of individuals are adapted to the unstable conditions. Characteristic species are *Nerenides (Scolelepis) agilis*, *Donax variabilis*, *Callianassa major*, and several haustoriid amphipods which were also found on shoals, sandy beach-related tidal flats, and current-exposed point bar deposits.

3. The shoreface between low water line and normal wave base is covered by sandy sediments, and the physical energy is sufficiently strong to rework the sediment constantly (Howard and Reineck 1972; Howard, et al. 1973). A few foreshore species and additional species occur. Characteristic are haustoriid amphipods of the genera *Parahaustorius*, *Acanthohaustorius*, and *Bathyporeia*.

4. In the upper offshore below normal wave base, the numbers of species and specimens increase sharply with increasing mud content of the sediments, which are the result of complex variations in physical energy (Howard and Reineck 1972; Howard, et al. 1973). Common species are *Hemipholis elongata*, *Pectinaria gouldi*, *Oxyurostylis smithi*, *Tellina* cf. *texana*, *Abra aequalis*, *Callianassa biformis*, *Glycera americana*, *Notomastus latericeus*, *Owenia fusiformis* and *Spiochaetopterus oculatus* (see also Smith 1971).

5. The lower offshore, which is covered by coarse relict sediments (Pilkey and Frankenberg 1964), starts along the 10-m depth contour seaward (Howard and Reineck 1972; Howard, et al. 1973). The number of species and individuals decreases again, presumably in response to a corresponding decrease in availability of food. Typical species include *Moira atropos* and *Branchiostoma virginiae*.

The southern transect parallels the northern one, and covers the beach, a series of shoals and troughs, and parts of the shelf plain. At 36 stations 20261 individuals, representing 144 species and 10 major taxa were collected (Fig. 8). Again, most of the

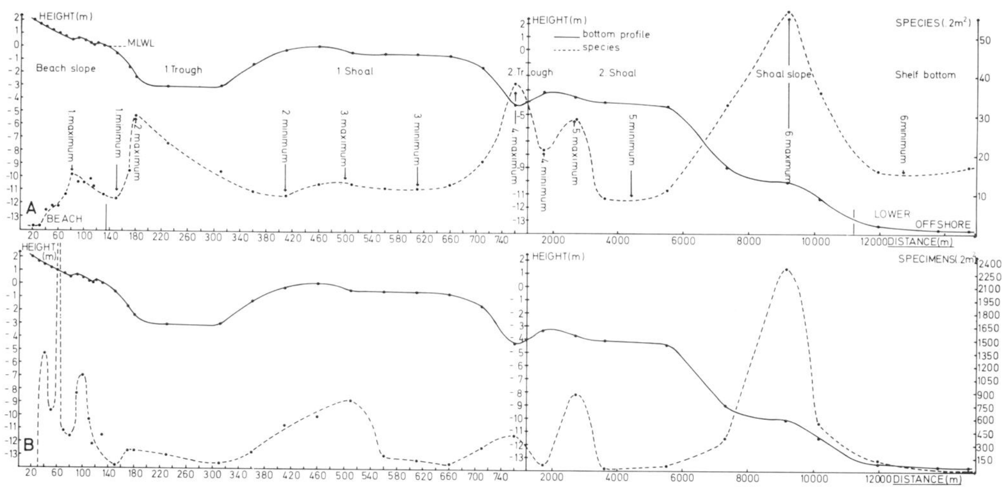

Fig. 8. Southern beach/offshore transect. (A) Number of species. (B) Number of individuals.

organisms are polychaetes, followed in abundance by crustaceans and molluscs. As in the northern transect the ten most common species include 86% of the total number of individuals.

In spite of the similar distribution of macrobenthic animals along the southern and northern transects, other differences exist owing to variable geomorphology (Fig. 8). Specific parallels are evident in the occurrence of species and specimens in the backshore, foreshore, and offshore environments along the two transects, but the normal zonation of animal communities is interrupted in the southern transect by shoals and troughs. No species living in the foreshore environment occurs in the first trough. Instead other species are present. Owing to the environmental conditions of the first shoal, which are similar to those of the beach, the shoal community of the southern transect approximates that of the lower foreshore of the northern transect. The community living in the muddy sediments of the second trough is similar to that of the first one, whereas the community of the second shoal does not include foreshore species, whose absence may be related to the location of the second shoal at 3 m during low water. On the seaward slope of the shoal the composition of the community changes again. The community in this area of muddy sediments is similar to that living in troughs and is identical to that of the upper offshore, below normal wave base.

Shelf

The shelf off coastal Georgia is blanketed across most of its broad expanse by medium to coarse, relict sediments (Howard, et al. 1973). The 100 stations investigated indicate that the composition of the benthos is rather similar but that it differs conspicuously from that of nearshore waters. Only 119 species, including 565 specimens, were found within an area of approximately 10000 km^2 (Fig. 9). These numbers contrast strikingly with those found in the nearshore waters of Sapelo Island; here, 179 species and 48175 specimens have been found at 51 stations along one transect 15 km long (Dörjes 1972). The most characteristic offshore species are the

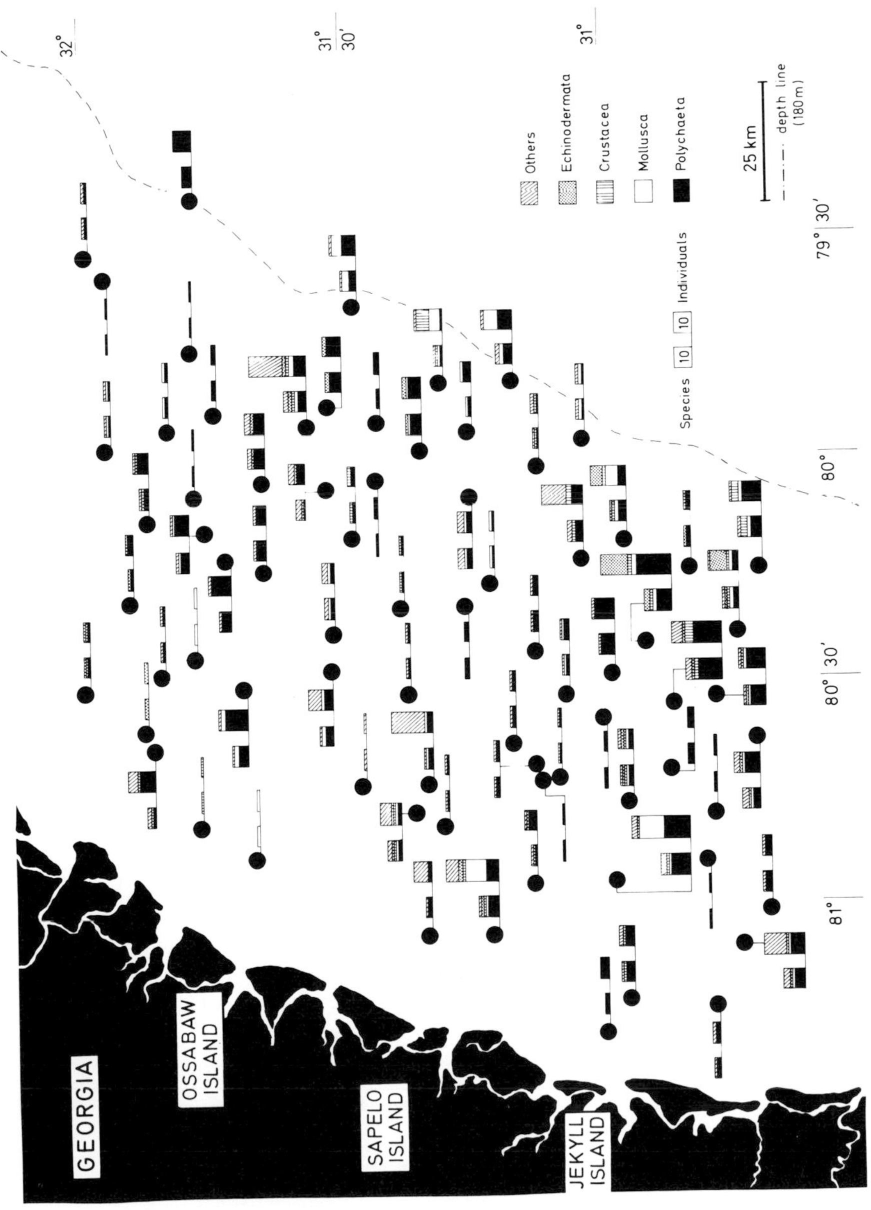

Fig. 9. Distribution and abundance of macrobenthic species and specimens on the Georgia shelf. Numbers of species and specimens per 0.2 m^2.

tube-dwelling polychaetes *Mesochaetopterus taylori*, *Onuphis eremita*, *Owenia fusiformis*, *Polyodontes lupina*, *Potamilla* sp. and *Petaloproctus socialis*, the bivalves *Macrocallista maculata*, *Laevicardium laevigatum*, *Chione cancellata*, *C. grus*, *C. intapurpurea*, *Glycimeris americana*, and *Aequipecten gibbus*, the bryozoan *Discoporella umbellata*, the lancelet *Branchiostoma virginiae*, and the echinoderms *Moira atropos* and *Amphiura fibulata*.

CONCLUSIONS

Faunistic investigations around Sapelo Island have documented a variety of marine environments, as expected. Almost everyone of these environments supports a specific macrobenthic community. The characteristic and most important macrobenthic species are summarized in Table 1.

1. The salt marsh community includes several endemic species. Only a few species are also common on unvegetated creek banks.
2. The community on creek banks contains species also present in other environments. The majority of these species were recorded from protected muddy flats and point bar deposits having similar environmental conditions. Only a few species are known from vegetated salt marshes.
3. The communities of protected muddy flats and point bar deposits are rather similar although the number of species recorded from muddy flats seems to be higher. Few of these species also occur on sandy deposits of unprotected flats, beaches, shoals, high salinity estuarine areas and in the shoreface.
4. Species assemblages on current exposed point bars, unprotected sand flats, beaches, shoals and shorefaces are almost identical. All of these environments have high rates of hydrolic energy which cause very mobile sediments.
5. The community inhabiting the upper offshore contains numerous species and individuals and several species seem to be endemic. Others are able to live in such protected environments as shelf, muddy flats, and high salinity estuarine areas. Only a few seem to be adapted to higher energy.
6. The lower offshore is identical with the shelf. The community shows almost no similarities with the other environments.
7. Animal communities vary among these estuarine environments according to salinity levels. One of the two species found in the freshwater zone seems to be endemic; the other one was also recorded from current exposed point bars. The community in the low salinity environment consists of several species which could not be found in any other investigated environment. Some species were also recorded from protected intertidal areas. The species assemblage in the high salinity part of the estuary is typical of other soft bottom deposits.

Table 1. The most important and characteristic species of the different environments around Sapelo Island.

Characteristic and most important species	salt marsh	creek banks	marsh sides of point bars close to ocean	protected muddy flats	current exposed point bars close to ocean	unprotected sandflats	beaches foreshore	shoals	shoreface	upper offshore	lower offshore	shelf	estuary freshwater	estuary low salinity	estuary high salinity	point bars low salinity
Sesarma reticulatum	+															
Uca pugnax	+															
Modiolus demissus	+															
Uca pugilator	+	+														
Uca minax	+															
Littorina irrorata	+															
Nereis succinea	+	+		+										+		+
Panopeus herbstii	+	+														
Polymesoda caroliniana	+															+
Crassostrea virginica	+	+														
Diopatra cuprea		+	+	+												+
Alpheus heterochaelis		+														
Heteromastus filiformis		+	+	+										+		+
Upogebia affinis		+	+													
Nassarius obsoletus		+	+	+												+
Onuphis microcephala		+	+	+		+			+						+	
Tagelus plebeius			+													+
Sthenelais boa			+													
Glycera dibranchiata			+	+					+							
Drilonereis longa			+	+					+		+					
Mulinia lateralis				+					+							
Callianassa biformis				+						+					+	
Bathyporeia sp.				+	+	+	+	+	+						+	
Acanthohaustorius sp.				+		+		+	+						+	
Lepidactylus dytiscus					+								+			+
Scoloplos fragilis					+	+		+	+	+	+					+
Callianassa major					+		+	+	+							
Haustorius sp.						+	+	+							+	
Donax variabilis						+	+	+								

Table 1 continued

Characteristic and most important species	salt marsh	creek banks	marsh sides of point bars close to ocean	protected muddy flats	current exposed point bars close to ocean	unprotected sandflats	beaches foreshore	shoals	shoreface	upper offshore	lower offshore	shelf	estuary freshwater	estuary low salinity	estuary high salinity	point bars low salinity
Nephthys picta				+		+		+								
Parahaustorius longimerus						+		+	+							
Spiophanes bombyx				+		+				+					+	
Nerenides agilis						+	+	+								
Saccoglossus kowalevski						+				+						
Oliva sayana						+										
Solen viridis						+			+						+	
Balanoglossus sp.						+		+								
Tellina cf. *texana*						+				+					+	
Neohaustorius schmitzi							+								+	
Emerita talpoidea							+									
Albunea paretii						+	+				+					
Chiridotea caeca							+	+								
Pagurus longicarpus									+							
Hemipholis elongata										+						
Pectinaria gouldii										+						
Oxyurostylis smithi										+					+	
Abra aequalis										+						
Glycera americana										+						
Notomastus latericeus										+						
Owenia fusiformis										+	+	+				
Spiochaetopterus oculatus										+	+	+				
Edotea montosa										+						
Capitomastus cf. *aciculatus*										+						
Magelona sp.										+	+				+	
Arabella iricolor										+						
Prionospio cf. *cirrifera*										+						

Table 1 continued

Characteristic and most important species	salt marsh	creek banks	marsh sides of point bars close to ocean	protected muddy flats	current exposed point bars close to ocean	unprotected sandflats	beaches foreshore	shoals	shoreface	upper offshore	lower offshore	shelf	estuary freshwater	estuary low salinity	estuary high salinity	point bars low salinity
Nucula proxima										+						
Moira atropos											+	+				
Branchiostoma virginiae											+	+				
Discoporella umbellata											+	+				
Venericardia tridentata											+					
Petaloproctus socialis											+	+				
Tellina iris											+					
Onuphis nebulosa											+					
Glottidia audebarti											+					
Onuphis eremita											+	+			+	
Polyodontes lupina												+				
Potamilla cf. *reniformis*												+				
Mesochaetopterus taylori											+	+				
Macrocallista maculata												+				
Laevicardium laevigatum												+				
Chione cancellata												+				
Amphiura fibulata												+				
Chione intapurpurea												+				
Dentalium sp.												+				
Scolecolepidis viridis													+			
Macoma constricta														+		
Bostrichobranchus pilularis														+		
Cyathura polita														+		

REFERENCES

Allen, E. J. 1899. On the fauna and bottom-deposits near the thirty-fathom line from the Eddy Stone Grounds to Start Point. J. Mar. Biol. Assoc. U. K. 5: 356-550.

Basan, P. B. and R. W. Frey. 1972. Paleontologic aspects of a salt marsh. (Abstr.) Geol. Soc. Am. 4: 445.

Brett, C. E. 1964. A portable hydraulic diver-operated dredge-sieve for sampling subtidal macrofauna. J. Mar. Res. 5: 1-7.

Caspers, H. 1959a. Die Einteilung der Brackwasser-Regionen in einem Aestuar. Estratto dall'Arch. Oceanogr. Limnol. Suppl. 11: 153-169.

_____. 1959b. Vorschläge einer Brackwassernomenklatur ("The Venice System"). Int. Rev. ges. Hydrobiol. 44: 313-316.

Croker, R. A. 1967. Niche diversity in five sympatric species of intertidal amphipods (Crustacea: Haustoriidae). Ecol. Monogr. 37: 173-200.

Davis, F. M. 1925. Quantitative studies on the fauna of the sea bottom. 2. Southern North Sea. Gt. Brit. Fish. Invest. 8: 34-350.

Dörjes, J. 1970. Das Watt als Lebensraum, p. 1-142. In H.-E. Reineck [ed.], Das Watt, Ablagerungs-und Lebensraum. W. Kramer, Frankfurt.

_____. 1972. Georgia coastal region, Sapelo Island, U.S.A.: sedimentology and biology. VII. Distribution and zonation of macrobenthic animals. Senckenbergiana Marit. 4: 183-216.

_____ and J. D. Howard. 1976. Estuaries of the Georgia coast, U.S.A. sedimentology and biology. IV. Fluvial-marine transition indicators in an estuarine environment, Ogeechee River-Ossabaw Sound. Senckenbergiana Marit. 7: 137-179.

Ford, E. 1923. Animal communities of the level sea bottom in the waters adjacent to Plymouth. J. Mar. Biol. Assoc. U. K. 13: 164-224.

Frey, R. W. [ed.]. 1975. The study of trace fossils. Springer-Verlag, Inc.

_____ and J. D. Howard. 1969. A profile of biogenic sedimentary structures in a Holocene barrier island-salt marsh complex, Georgia. Gulf Coast Assoc. Geol. Soc. 19: 427-444.

_____, P. B. Basan, and R. M. Scott. 1973. Techniques for sampling salt marsh benthos and burrows. Am. Midland Nat. 29: 228-234.

Greer, S. A. 1976. Estuaries of the Georgia coast, U.S.A.: sedimentology and biology. III. Sandbody geometry and sedimentary facies at the estuary-marine transition zone, Ossabaw Sound, Georgia: A stratigraphic model. Senckenbergiana Marit. 7: 105-135.

Gressly, A. 1838. Observations géologiques sur le Jura soleurois. Soc. Helvetiae Sci. Nat. N. Mém. 2: 7-26.

Hagmeier, A. 1925. Vorläufiger Bericht über die vorbereitenden Untersuchungen der Bodenfauna der Deutschen Bucht mit dem Petersen-Bodengreifer. Ber. Dtsch. Wiss. Kommiss. Meeresforsch. 1: 247-272.

Henry, V. J., Jr. and J. H. Hoyt. 1968. Quaternary paralic and shelf sediments of Georgia. Southeast. Geol. 9: 195-214.

Hertweck, G. 1972. Georgia coastal region, Sapelo Island, U.S.A.: sedimentology and biology. V. Distribution and environmental significance of lebensspuren and in-situ skeletal remains. Senckenbergiana Marit. 4: 125-167.

Howard, J. D. and J. Dörjes. 1972. Animal-sediment relationship in two beach-related tidal flats; Sapelo Island, Georgia. J. Sediment. Petrol. 42: 608-623.

_____ and H.-E. Reineck. 1972. Georgia coastal region, Sapelo Island, U.S.A.: sedimentology and biology. IV. Physical and biogenic sedimentary structures of the nearshore shelf. Senckenbergiana Marit. 4: 81-123.

_____, R. W. Frey, and H.-E. Reineck. 1972. Georgia coastal region, Sapelo Island, U.S.A.: sedimentology and biology. I. Introduction. Senckenbergiana Marit. 4: 3-14.

_____, _____, and, _____. 1973. Holocene sediments of the Georgia region, p. 1-58. In R. W. Frey [ed.], The Neogene of the Georgia coast. Georgia Geol. Soc., Athens.

_____, C. A. Elders, and J. F. Heinbokel. 1976. Estuaries of the Georgia coast, U.S.A.: sedimentology and biology. V. Animal-sediment relationships in estuarine point bar deposits; Ogeechee River-Ossabaw Sound, Georgia. Senckenbergiana Marit. 7: 181-203.

Hoyt, J. H., V. J. Henry, Jr., and J. D. Howard. 1966. Pleistocene and Holocene sediments, Sapelo Island, Georgia and vicinity. Geol. Soc. Am. Southeast. Sect. Guidebook Field Trip No. 1: 1-27.

Kuroda, R. 1969. Physical and chemical properties of the coastal waters off the middle of Georgia. Univ. Georgia Mar. Inst. Techn. Rep. OWRR (8-035-GA), 63 p.

Land, L. S. and J. H. Hoyt. 1966. Sedimentation in a meandering estuary. Sedimentol. 6: 191-207.

Maney, D. S., F. C. Marland, and C. B. West [eds.]. 1968. The future of the marshlands and Sea Islands of Georgia. Univ. Georgia Mar. Inst. and Coast. Area Plan. Develop. Comm., 128 p.

Mayou, T. V. and J. D. Howard. 1969. Recognizing estuarine and tidal creek sandbars by biogenic sedimentary structures (Abstr.). Bull. Am. Assoc. Petroleum Geol. 53: 731.

Odum, E. P. and A. A. de la Cruz. 1967. Particulate organic detritus in a Georgia salt marsh-estuarine ecosystem, p. 383-388. In G. H. Lauff [ed.], Estuaries. Am. Assoc. Adv. Sci. Spec. Publ. 88.

Oertel, G. F. 1971. Sediment-hydrodynamic interrelationships at the entrance of the Doboy Sound estuary, Sapelo Island, Georgia. Ph.D. thesis, Univ. Iowa, 172 p.

_____. 1973. Examination of textures and structures of mud in layered sediments at the entrance of a Georgia tidal inlet. J. Sediment. Petrol. 43: 33-41.

Perkins, E. J. 1974. The biology of estuarine and coastal waters. Academic Press, 678 p.

Petersen, C. G. J. 1911. Valuation of the sea. I. Animal life of the sea-bottom, its food and quantity. Rep. Dan. Biol. Stat. 20: 1-81.

_____. 1913. Valuation of the sea. II. The animal communities of the sea-bottom and their importance for marine zoogeography. Rep. Dan. Biol. Stat. 21:1-44.

_____. 1918. The sea bottom and its production of fishfood. A survey of the work done in connection with the valuation of the Danish waters from 1883-1917. Rep. Dan. Biol. Stat. 25: 1-62.

Pilkey, O. H. and D. Frankenberg. 1964. The relict-recent sediment boundary on the Georgia continental shelf. Georgia Acad. Sci. Bull. 22: 37-40.

Ragotzkie, R. A., L. R. Pomeroy, J. M. Teal, and D. C. Scott [eds.]. 1959. Proceedings of the salt marsh conference, Sapelo Island, Georgia. March 1958. Univ. Georgia Mar. Inst. 133p.

Reineck, H. E. 1963. Der Kastengreifer. Natur Mus. 93: 102-108.

_____ [ed.]. 1970. Das Watt. Ablagerungs- und Lebensraum. W. Kramer Verlag. 142 p.

_____ and I. B. Singh. 1973. Depositional sedimentary environments. Springer-Verlag. 439 p.

Schäfer, W. 1972. Ecology and paleontology of marine sediments. Oliver and Boyd. 568 p.

Segerstråle, S. G. 1959. Brackishwater classification. A historical survey. Arch. Oceanogr. Limnol. Suppl. 11: 7-33.

Smith, K. L. 1971. Structural and functional aspects of a sublittoral community. Ph.D. thesis, Univ. Georgia, Athens. 170 p.

Teal, J. M. 1958. Distribution of fiddler crabs in Georgia salt marshes. Ecology 39: 185-193.

_____. 1962. Energy flow in the salt marsh ecosystem of Georgia. Ecology 43: 614-624.

Teichert, C. 1958. Concept of facies. Bull. Am. Assoc. Petroleum Geol. 42: 2718-2799.

Thorson, G. 1957. Bottom communities (sublittoral or shallow shelf), p. 461-534. In J. W. Hedgpeth [ed.], Treatise on Marine Ecology and Paleoecology, Vol. 1, Ecology of Geol. Soc. Amer. Mem. 67.

Van Straaten, L. M. J. U. 1954. Composition and structure of recent marine sediments in the Netherlands. Leidse Geol. Mededel. 19: 1-110.

_____. 1964. Het Waddenboek. Nederl. Geol. Ver., J. Thieme & Cie, Zutphen, 223 p.

Wolf, P. L. and S. A. Fanning. 1970. Preliminary report on the distribution of fiddler crabs, *Uca*, in an undisturbed salt marsh. In L. R. Pomeroy, et al. [eds.], Field Experiments on the Flux of Radionuclides Through a Salt Marsh Ecosystem. Prog. Rept. U.S. Atomic Energy Comm., ORO-3238-8.

Wunderlich, F. 1972. Georgia coastal region, Sapelo Island, U.S.A.: sedimentology and biology. III. Beach dynamics and beach development. Senckenbergiana Marit. 4: 47-49.

The Community Biology of Intertidal Macrofauna Inhabiting Sandbars in the North Inlet Area of South Carolina, U.S.A.

A. F. Holland
Martin Marietta Laboratories
1450 South Rolling Rd.
Baltimore, MD 21227

and

John Mark Dean
Belle W. Baruch Institute for Marine Biology and Coastal Research
and the Department of Biology
University of South Carolina
Columbia, SC 29208

Abstract

Thirty-two (0.25 m^2) samples were taken from intertidal sandy and muddy-sandy substrates ranging in elevation from 0-80 cm above MLW in the North Inlet estuary near Georgetown, S. C. Four discrete faunal assemblages were identified. Each assemblage was numerically dominated by at least one species of haustoriid amphipod. Changes in fauna assemblages that occurred along environmental gradients were a function of the steepness of the gradient. Species diversity decreased with increasing elevation above MLW. Suspension feeders dominated sandy habitats and deposit feeders dominated muddy-sandy habitats. The structure of the faunal assemblages of these sandbars was similar to that reported for open beach and other rigorous environments.

INTRODUCTION

Intertidal sandbars are among the most rigorous of environments. Not only are organisms inhabiting these areas exposed to a wide range of physical stresses (e.g., dessication, temperature variation, unusual weather phenomena, sediment transport, tidal currents), but they also experience a full range of biological interactions (e.g., competition and predation). Intuitively, it can be hypothesized that since these habitats have both sharp elevational and sedimentary gradients, they are inhabitated by more than one faunal assemblage. Since the environmental gradients common to these habitats are relatively steep it could further be hypothesized that they result in relatively discrete communities. This study set out to obtain preliminary data to test these two hypotheses. Other objectives of this study were: (1) to define macrofaunal invertebrate assemblages inhabiting sandbars in the North Inlet area of the South Carolina coast;

(2) to determine relative numerical rankings of individual species; (3) to delineate habitat types on the basis of faunal composition and environmental conditions; and (4) to determine the governing environmental factors associated with various community types.

The community biology of sandy intertidal habitats has not been investigated as well as the community biology of subtidal or rocky intertidal habitats (e.g., Sanders 1958, 1960; Connell 1961; McNulty et al. 1962; Sanders et al. 1962; Paine 1966; Dexter 1969; Hughes and Thomas 1971a, b; Dörjes 1972; Boesch 1973). Little information is available on the environmental factors controlling community structure and function in these habitats. This is especially true for the haustoriid amphipod communities so characteristic of intertidal sandy environments of the eastern U.S. (Croker 1967; Dexter 1967, 1969; Bousfield 1973).

Studies conducted in soft bottom intertidal habitats (e.g., Green et al. 1967; Green 1968; Dexter 1969; Johnson 1970; Dörjes 1972; Woodin 1974) have not applied the more rigorous quantitative methodologies often used in investigations of subtidal habitats (e.g., Stephenson et al. 1970; Boesch 1973; Polgar 1975). Yet, these mathematical techniques have been effective in simplifying organism-habitat relationships. These analytical methods are clearly useful in synthesizing major community attributes (e.g., faunal associations, distributional patterns in space and time, and organism-sediment interactions) on the basis of which *a priori* classification and grouping assumptions hypothesized on an intuitive basis can be tested statistically.

This work was supported by the Belle W. Baruch Institute for Marine Biology and Coastal Research and the Environmental Technology Center of Marin Marietta Corporation. Contribution No. 88 of the Belle W. Baruch Institute for Marine Biology and Coastal Research.

METHODS

The Study Area

All samples were taken in the North Inlet *Spartina* marsh-tidal creek complex (33°22.0'N, 79°10.0'W) during mid-summer, 1972. This ecosystem is a high salinity, unpolluted marsh complex located approximately 20 km from Georgetown, S. C. (Fig. 1), within which three sandbars were selected for extensive sampling.

Sampling, Sieving and Sorting Techniques

Thirty-two quantitative ($0.25m^2$) samples were taken along transverse and longitudinal transects to a depth of 25 cm using a shovel and 0.25 m^2 marking frame. Samples were sieved using the technique described by Sanders et al. (1965). All organisms retained on a 1.0-mm sieve were identified to species and counted.

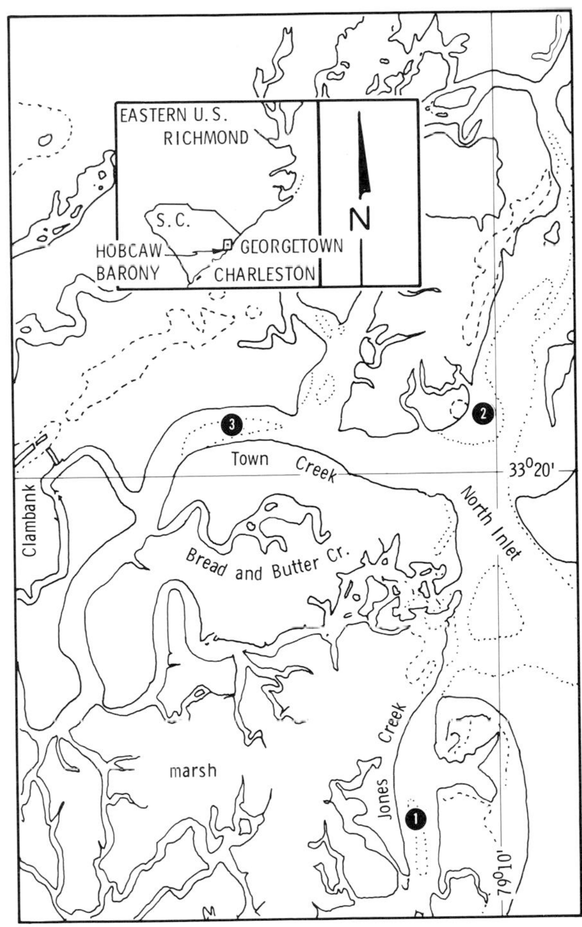

Fig. 1. Map of the North Inlet area showing relative geographic location and the exact location of the three sandbars sampled.

Salinity and Temperature

Tidal creek salinity (bottom and surface) and temperature were obtained at the time of sampling. Additional salinity and temperature data showing seasonal ranges and previous trends were available for 1972-1973 from an annual survey conducted by the Baruch Institute for Marine Biology and Coastal Research.

Sediment temperature profiles were taken at 50-m intervals along transverse transects to a depth of 25 cm using a Yellow-Springs telethermometer and thermistor probe. In addition, sediment temperature profiles taken over a tidal cycle were available from a previous study of one of the sandbars.

Elevation

Elevation above mean low water (MLW) was measured along all transects using a surveyor's level and level rod. National Ocean Survey bench marks were used as reference points.

Sediment Characteristics

Sediment samples were taken to a depth of 10 cm in an area located adjacent to each 0.25-m^2 sample, and processed using the procedures outlined by Buchannan and Kain (1971). For the purposes of this study, sediments were classified into the following major types: (1) sandy sediments composed of less than 3% silts and clays; and (2) muddy-sandy sediments composed of 3-15% silts and clays. Sediment traps as discussed by Young (1971) were placed 15 cm above the sediment surface along the established transects in each study area. The contents of the sediment traps following one tidal cycle were dried at 60°C, weighed, and processed in the same manner as other sediment samples. Each sample site was also examined for the presence of a surface film of benthic microalgae by visual examination of cores taken with a plexiglass core liner.

Analytical Methods

The Bray-Curtis similarity coefficient (Bray and Curtis 1957; Field 1971) was used as a measure of similarity among stations. The sums of squares agglomeration clustering technique using relative distances (Orloci 1967; Pielou 1969) and the trellis diagram technique (McFayden 1963) were used to group like stations. Once similar stations had been identified, discriminant analysis as discussed by Lachenbruch (1975) and Polgar (1975) was used to characterized and evaluate any observed differences between faunal assemblages.

Three diversity indices were used: (1) the Shannon-Wiener function, H' (Pielou 1969); (2) a species richness measure, H'_{max} (Pielou 1969); and (3) a species evenness measure, J (Pielou 1966). All logarithms were to the base e. The relative merits of each index are discussed by Pielou (1969). The joint utilization of diversity indices to describe community structure is reviewed by Boesch (1973).

Fager's rank analysis (Fager 1957) was used to rank the numerically dominant species. This procedure was also used to evaluate the sediment trap data. Kendall's tau (τ) value (Kendall 1962) was used to compare rankings.

RESULTS

Sandbar Morphology

The size and shape of the three sandbars varied. However, all could be divided into similar subregions which reflected both biological and physical characteristics. To facilitate reference to the subregions the following terminology was adopted. The lagoon area was that part of the sandbar farthest from the nearest tidal creek; the tidal creek fringe was that part nearest a tidal creek. The point region was that part of the sandbar nearest a major connection with the sea. Tidal channels were those parts transected by tidal currents during rising and falling tides. The central region was that part with the highest elevation above MLW. Central regions were 40-80 cm above MLW. All other subregions were 0-40 cm above MLW. Figure 2 visually presents the relative locations of the various subregions on the sandbars.

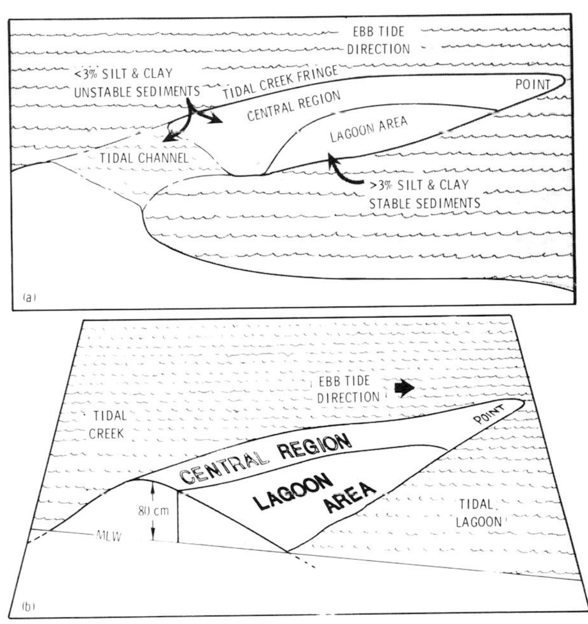

Fig. 2. Conceptual diagrams of the general characteristics of sandbars from the North Inlet area of South Carolina. a, aerial view; b, cross-sectional view.

Physical Characteristics

There were no signficiant differences in salinity among the three sandbars in June and July, 1972. In addition, salinity records for 1972 and 1973 indicate that all three were located in regions where mean annual salinity was >32 $^{o}/oo$ (Holland and Sansbury 1973). During extremely wet periods tidal creek salinities below 25 $^{o}/oo$ were reported in the general area of the sandbars. However, these lower salinity conditions were characteristically of short duration and confined to low phases of tidal cycles. Thus, salinity could be expected to have a minor effect upon intertidal organisms inhabiting these three sandbars.

No significant difference in surface sediment temperature at low tide was observed among or within sample areas. Sediment temperature varied with depth below the sediment-water interface. Sediments 10-20 cm below the interface were 2-3°C cooler during sampling than the sediments at the surface. Surface sediment temperature also varied with tidal phase. However, sediment temperature below 20 cm did not vary as a function of tidal condition.

Table 1 summarizes the physical characteristics of the sediments of the four subregions of the sandbars. Sediments in lagoon areas of the sandbars consisted of greater than 3% silts and clays. Sediments in tidal channels, point regions, tidal creek fringes, and central regions consisted of less than 3% silts and clays. All sediments were well sorted. Microalgal surface films were observed only in the lagoon areas of these sandbars.

Table 1. Summary of some of the physical characteristics of sandbars from the North Inlet area of South Carolina.

Sedimentary Characteristics	Tidal Creek Fringes (n = 30)	Tidal Channels and Point Regions (n = 30)	Central Regions (n = 30)	Lagoon Areas (n = 30)
Elevation above MLW (cm)	0-40	0-40	40-80	0-40
M.D. (ϕ)[1]	2.15±0.01[2]	2.25±0.01[2]	2.25±0.01[2]	2.30±0.02[2]
% silts and clays	2.0±0.1	1.5±0.1	2.0±0.1	8.5±4.6
% carbonate	2.0±0.4	3.6±0.7	4.0±1.0	2.5±1.0
% organic	0.1±0.1	0.1±0.1	0.2±0.1	0.6±0.2
Trask sorting value	1.16±0.1	1.19±0.1	1.16±0.1	1.11±0.1
Surface trap sediments				
% silts and clays	8.5±2.1	8.0±3.0	7.5±2.3	25.1±7.5
% organic	0.5±0.1	0.5±0.1	0.5±0.1	1.3±0.1
Sediment movement[3] and resuspension	high	high	very high	low
Surface film[4]	not observed	not observed	not observed	present

[1]M.D. (ϕ) is the standard abbreviation for median diameter of sediment samples in phi units (phi unit=ϕ=$\log_2$ median particle diameter in mm).

[2]$\bar{X}$ ± 1 S.D.

[3]Only a summary of sediment trap data is presented in this table. The difference between high and low values are significant at the 1% level as indicated by Kendall's tau (τ).

[4]Only the presence or absence of an obvious film of benthic microalgae was observed.

Sediment traps located in lagoon areas consistently collected less sediment than sediment traps in other regions of the same sandbar. These differences were significant at the 0.05 level (Kendall's tau). In addition, sediments trapped in lagoon areas were higher in organic content and composed of relatively higher percentages of silts and clays than those trapped in other subregions of the same sandbar. Sediment traps in sandy areas would become filled to capacity if left for more than one tidal cycle. These data indicate that the surface sediments of the sandy areas (e.g., tidal channels, point regions, central regions, and tidal creek fringes) were more mobile than were the surface sediments of the lagoon areas.

Quantitative Sampling Program

In the 32 samples, 64 species of benthic invertebrates were obtained. Fifty-one percent of the species occurred in only one or two samples and were considered rare. Many of these rare species are reported by the literature to be characteristic of subtidal habitats and probably represent organisms that have become accidentally stranded in the intertidal zone. Seven species accounted for over 95% of the number of individuals. A summary of the quantitative data is available from the senior author.

Grouping of Stations Composed of Similar Faunal Assemblages

Figure 3 is a trellis diagram of the 32 stations. On the basis of similarity within subregions, stations were divided into three groups characteristic of (1) lagoon areas; (2) central regions; and (3) low elevation regions (tidal channels, point regions, and tidal creek fringes). Although stations from tidal channels and point regions appear to be different from tidal creek fringe stations, these two groups could not be readily separated using this technique.

□ < 25% SIMILARITY ☒ 25-50% SIMILARITY ▒ > 50% SIMILARITY

	TIDAL CHANNEL & POINT REGION				TIDAL CREEK FRINGE													CENTRAL PORTION					LAGOON AREA								
TIDAL CHANNEL & POINT REGION	87	59	71	68	48	42	52	39	50	31	29	57	36	57	49	19	8	2	3	3	3	5	8	11	11	16	6	10	11	16	8
		50	64	64	53	40	51	42	47	35	33	56	34	55	56	19	9	2	2	3	3	4	9	14	14	20	8	13	13	19	11
			62	68	52	24	32	49	27	42	41	37	22	36	58	15	6	1	0	1	2	2	2	5	8	12	3	5	5	13	4
				80	36	36	45	39	46	36	35	55	37	57	35	18	4	2	2	2	2	3	2	4	6	12	4	5	7	18	4
					35	30	39	33	38	30	28	39	28	42	38	20	4	2	3	3	2	5	1	2	5	5	1	2	2	6	1
TIDAL CREEK FRINGE						29	29	68	34	43	40	37	19	33	70	12	11	1	1	1	2	2	14	19	19	30	13	21	21	42	17
							72	24	71	16	16	52	89	52	26	14	5	0	0	0	2	1	6	7	7	9	6	7	8	12	6
								30	75	19	20	65	70	70	32	16	5	1	0	0	1	1	5	4	4	4	3	3	3	5	3
									34	50	56	39	22	45	60	10	9	0	0	0	1	1	5	10	13	20	8	11	19	43	12
										26	25	61	68	61	25	15	6	2	2	8	3	12	4	5	6	11	4	6	8	21	5
											83	52	18	46	41	11	6	1	1	1	1	2	1	3	8	15	4	5	9	29	3
												43	18	45	41	10	7	0	0	1	1	1	2	6	7	14	6	11	12	29	7
													51	84	35	16	8	3	3	1	2	1	5	6	9	15	6	7	10	23	6
														52	21	20	14	6	5	5	6	8	2	1	2	3	1	1	3	7	1
															34	16	6	0	0	0	1	1	2	4	5	9	4	6	8	19	6
																13	13	1	1	1	3	2	26	26	23	25	13	27	18	26	22
																	40	73	59	64	72	86	2	0	2	2	2	1	1	2	0
																		30	23	25	31	39	10	9	11	11	6	10	10	11	10
CENTRAL PORTION																			84	89	99	72	1	0	0	0	0	0	0	0	0
																				94	84	66	1	0	0	0	0	0	0	0	0
																					89	69	1	0	0	0	0	0	0	0	0
																						72	2	2	2	2	1	2	2	2	2
																							2	0	1	1	1	1	0	1	1
LAGOON AREA																								51	76	62	63	55	74	27	74
																									50	48	32	71	51	35	60
																										69	57	52	75	35	71
																											56	52	79	57	67
																												39	56	32	51
																													55	35	72
																														44	72
																															31

Fig. 3. Trellis diagram of stations using quantitative data and the Bray-Curtis coefficient as a measure of similarity among stations.

A dendrogram of stations using relative distances and the sums of squares agglomeration (Orloci 1967) is presented in Figure 4. Stations clustered into 4 groups that corresponded to the various subregions of the sandbars. This technique treats each sample as an individual entity without *a priori* assumptions about how it should be grouped. Clusters of stations obtained by this method were similar to groupings obtained by the trellis diagram technique. In addition, this method established that stations from tidal channels and point regions were sufficiently different from those of tidal creek fringes to justify testing for the significance. This clustering technique has the disadvantages that divisions may be imposed when they have little ecological meaning and it is sometimes difficult to decide what constitutes a group. Further, differences among groups cannot be directly tested.

When discriminant analysis (Fig. 5) was applied to the groups obtained by trellis and clustering techniques, they differed significantly at the 0.05 level (Hotelling's T^2 test). In order to preserve the robustness of this analysis, the number of samples in each group was maintained symmetrically (i.e., only 5 stations were

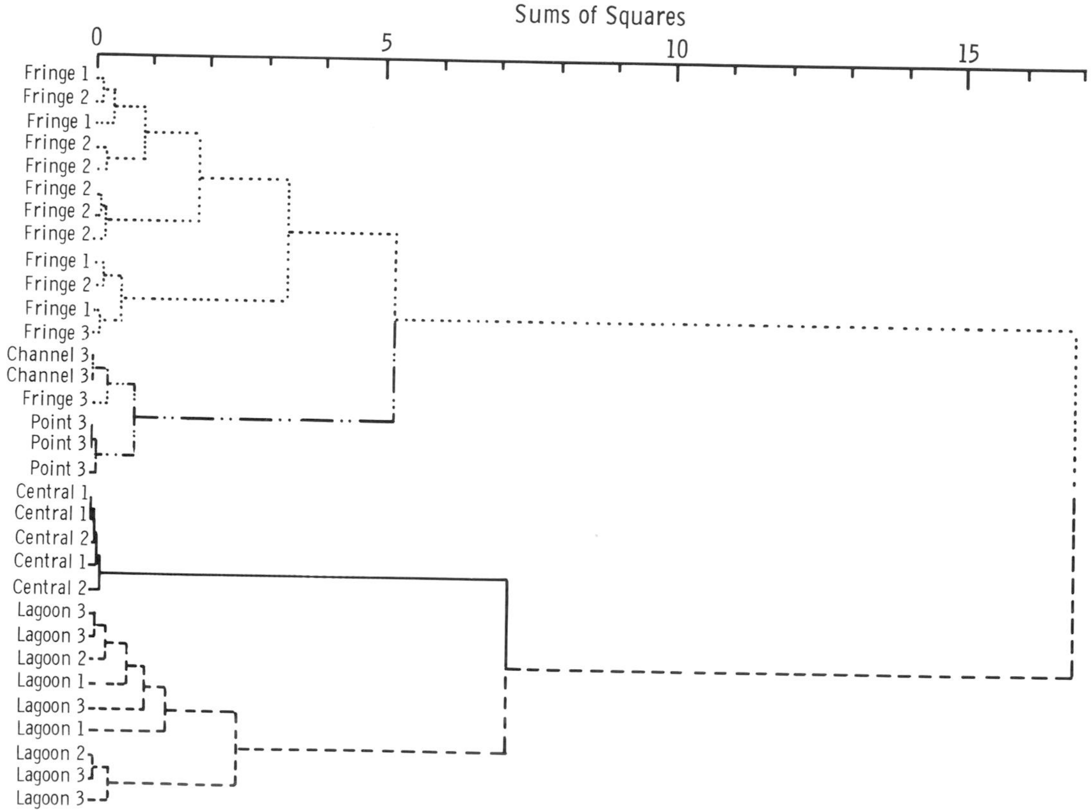

Fig. 4. A dentogram showing a single linkage clustering of samples by sums of squares agglomeration using relative distances (Orloci 1967).

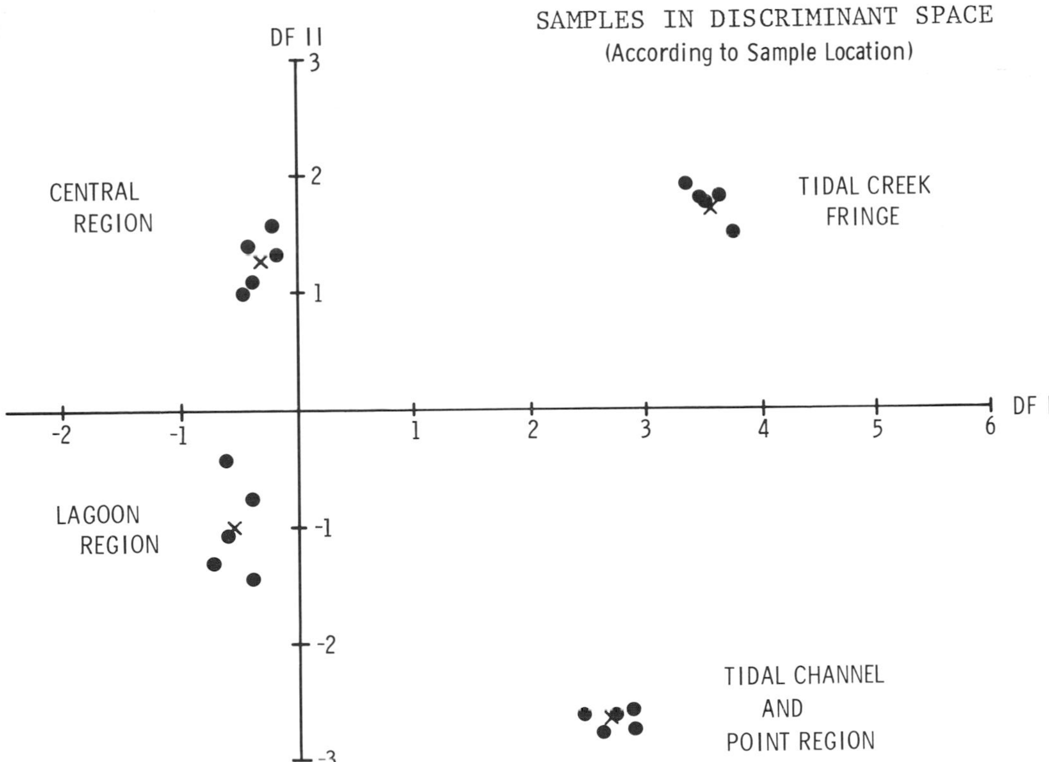

Fig. 5. Discriminant analysis of the samples using an initial grouping by subregions.

randomly chosen from each subregion). Two additional discriminant analyses were conducted using different sets of randomly selected data and the results of these analyses were essentially the same as those depicted by Figure 5. Discriminant function I accounted for 70% of the variability among stations and discriminant function II accounted for 30%.

Faunal Assemblages Characteristic of Each Subregion

Each subregion was characterized by a unique faunal assemblage, of which the dominant species are presented in Table 2.

Acanthohaustorius millsi and *Pseudohaustorius caroliniensis* were dominant species along tidal creek fringes. These two species of haustoriid amphipods were the most abundant and most common organisms in this subregion. Densities of two other numerically dominant species, *Heteromastus filiformis* and *Spiophanes bombyx*, were an order of magnitude lower than densities of the two amphipods. These less abundant species were ubiquitous and inhabited a wide range of habitats. They were not particularly characteristic of any specific subregion.

Acanthohaustorius millsi were also dominant in tidal channels and point regions, where *Protohaustorius* nr *deichmannae* (another haustoriid amphipod) was co-dominant instead of *Pseudohaustorius*

Table 2. Dominant species by subregion as determined by Fager's rank analysis (Fager 1957). Mean abundance per 0.25 m^2 ($\bar{x}$) and the relative frequency of occurrence (f) is indicated for each species.

Tidal Creek Fringes	$\bar{x}$	f	Tidal Channels and Point Regions	$\bar{x}$	f	Central Regions	$\bar{x}$	f	Lagoon Areas	$\bar{x}$	f
Acanthohaustorius millsi	224	100	*Acanthohaustorius millsi*	113	100	*Lepidactylus dysticus*	1455	100	*Heteromastus filiformis*	78	100
Pseudohaustorius caroliniensis	31	91	*Protohaustorius* nr *deichmannae*	50	100	*Haploscoloplos fragilis*	85	100	*Glycera dibranchiata*	9	78
Heteromastus filiformis	7	82	*Haploscoloplos fragilis*	20	100				*Pseudohaustorius caroliniensis*	6	78
Spiophanes bombyx	9	82	*Tellina texana*	15	100						
			Heteromastus filiformis	9	100						

caroliniensis. Other abundant, and common species (*Haploscoloplos fragilis*, *Tellina texana* and *Heteromastus filiformis*) inhabiting this subregion were ubiquitous but not particularly characteristic of any specific subregions.

Lepidactylus dysticus, a fourth haustoriid amphipod observed, was dominant in the central portion of the sandbars. The polychaete, *Haploscoloplos fragilis*, was the only other numerically important or frequently occurring organism inhabiting this subregion.

The ubiquitous polychaete, *Heteromastus filiformis*, was the dominant species in lagoon areas. Other abundant and common species in this subregion were *Glycera dibranchiata* and *Pseudohaustorius caroliniensis*. It is interesting to note that *P. caroliniensis* was the only haustoriid amphipod observed in the lagoon area with any regularity or in densities sufficient to indicate occurrence was not accidental.

Species Diversity

The total number of species, mean number of species per 0.25-m^2 sample, species diversity (H'), species richness (H'_{max}), and evenness of distribution of the individuals among the species (J) are presented in Table 3. All species diversity measures decreased with elevation above MLW. Samples from the central regions of the sandbars (40-80 cm above MLW) were characterized by assemblages composed of relatively few but numerically abundant species. Samples from the other subregions of the sandbars (0-40 cm above MLW) were composed of a larger number of different kinds of organisms. In addition, individuals were also more evenly distributed among the species.

Distribution of Feeding Types

Classification of species into feeding types is an arbitrary process where, in many cases, the categories are not mutually exclusive. However, in spite of these limitations the distribution of feeding types as a function of environmental setting often provides much insight into the community biology of a habitat (e.g., Rhoads and Young 1970). Three basic feeding types of organisms occurred in these samples: (1) deposit feeders obtaining nutritional

Table 3. Summary of species diversity information by subregion for sandbars in the North Inlet area of South Carolina.

Measure of Species Diversity	Tidal Creek Fringes	Tidal Channels and Point Regions	Central Regions	Lagoon Areas
Total number of species observed	44	27	15	37
Mean number of species per 0.25 m^2	12.5	12.4	5.2	10.6
Mean value Shannon-Wiener index (H')	1.10	1.44	0.23	1.13
Mean value species richness index (H'_{max})	2.42	2.50	1.59	2.00
Mean value species evenness index (J)	0.44	0.58	0.15	0.46

needs from the organic content of ingested sediments; (2) suspension feeders-obtaining nutritional needs through a filtering mechanism; and (3) omnivores-opportunistically feeding on available organic material. Suspension feeders dominated the sandy subregions and deposit feeders dominated the muddy-sandy lagoon areas (silt-clay content >3 $^{o}/oo$).

Fractionation of Sandbars by Haustoriidae

Differences in faunal assemblages among the four subregions were largely the result of the spatial distribution pattern of the four species of haustoriid amphipods that inhabited these sandbars. Each observed species of haustoriid amphipod had a different spatial distributional pattern that closely paralleled the physical characteristics of the four subregions.

Lepidactylus dysticus was spatially separated from all other haustoriid amphipods and was generally restricted to the central regions of the sandbars. The density of this species decreased rapidly toward other subregions. *Protohaustorius* nr *deichmannae* was co-dominant with *Acanthohaustorius millsi* in tidal channels and point regions. This was not unexpected as these two species have similar sediment preferences (Sameoto 1969). These two species are ecologically separated as they have different reproductive periods (Dexter 1967; Bousfield 1973), different body sizes and shapes (Bousfield 1973; Howard and Elders 1970), different vertical distributional patterns (Bousfield personal communication; Howard and Elders 1970), and different burrowing patterns (Howard and Elders 1970). *Acanthohaustorius millsi* and *Pseudohaustorius caroliniensis* were co-dominant along tidal creek fringes. This was unexpected as *P. caroliniensis* is reported to be a relatively rare species in any habitat (Croker 1967; Dexter 1967; Bousfield personal communication). These two species were ecologically separated as they have different reproductive periods (Dexter 1967), burrowing patterns (Howard and Elders, 1970), and vertical distributions (Bousfield personal communication). In addition to inhabiting tidal creek fringe areas, *P. caroliniensis* also inhabited the muddier lagoon areas.

DISCUSSION

The communities discussed in this paper were not unlike those of the North Carolina (Dexter 1969) and Georgia coasts (Croker 1967; Dörjes 1972), and again demonstrate the importance of haustoriid amphipods in eastern U.S. sandy intertidal habitats. Virtually nothing is known about the functional importance of these numerically dominant species and this subject would be a productive line of future research.

At least 4 macrofaunal communities inhabited the sandbars in the North Inlet area. Each community occurred in a well defined region of the sandbars and was identifiable on a statistically rigorous basis. The communities inhabiting low elevations (<40 cm above MLW) were struc minities inhabiting low elevations (<40 cm above MLW) were struc- turally more complex than the single community inhabiting higher elevations (>40 cm above MLW). Low elevation communities were not only composed of more species, but the individuals were more equitably distributed among the component species. These data agree with the findings of other investigations on the effect of an elevational gradient upon macrofaunal community structure (e.g., Johnson 1970). The three low intertidal communities were all similar in structural complexity when diversity indices were used to depict structural complexity. However, the other analytical techniques used demonstrate that each of these low intertidal communities were distinctly different. The observed differences in the low intertidal communities undoubtedly result from a combination of community responses to externally controlling physical gradients and to variations in resource partitioning. Although the reasons why the three low intertidal communities differed cannot be explained in a dynamic sense, the fact that these communities have been identified is the first step toward designing studies which will provide answers to this question.

Faunal assemblages changed rapidly along the elevation and sedimentary gradients sampled. Assemblages inhabiting extremes of "steep" environmental gradients (e.g., lagoon areas and central regions) were distinctly different. Boundaries between these communities were "sharp" and easily detected. Faunal assemblages occurring along gradually changing environmental gradients (e.g., tidal creek fringe to point region) were not as obviously different. These assemblages often shared species. However, the overlapping species occurred in different relative proportions. The boundaries between these were not "sharp" and were more difficult to define.

It is well established that sediment type affects subtidal

faunal assemblages (e.g., Sanders 1958; Rhoads and Young 1970; Young and Rhoads 1971; Boesch 1973). However, the present findings are among the first to show that faunal assemblages of sandy intertidal benthic communities occurring along the eastern U.S. are also strongly influenced by sediment type, and agree with the concepts presented by Newell (1970). The difference in community structure as it pertains to feeding type between sandy and muddy-sandy substrates is probably due to the fact that the suspension feeding mechanism of haustoriid amphipods, numerically dominant organisms in sandy sediments, is only efficient when interstitial water moves freely and the organic content of interstitial spaces is continually renewed with each tidal cycle (Bousfield, personal communication). Such a feeding mechanism would work well in the mobile sandy sediments characteristic of central regions, tidal creek fringes, tidal channels and point regions of sandbars. However, with the decreased sediment mobility that occurs in lagoon areas, interstitial spaces become filled with smaller sediment particles and other substances (e.g., detritus, organic matrix of benthic diatoms). In this subregion a suspension feeding mechanism, such as that of the haustoriid amphipods, would no longer be successful. This process probably explains why this family of amphipods does not frequently inhabit muddy-sandy and muddy sediments in higher densities. Deposit feeding polychaetes were the numerically dominant feeding type in sediments containing greater than 3.0% silts and clays.

The role of the benthic microalgal surface film in organism-sediment interactions cannot be assessed from observational data of this study, but should be further investigated. Experimental information has shown that these films can significantly stabilize sediments in the laboratory (Neumann et al. 1970; Holland et al. 1974), and the preliminary evidence in this study suggested this also applies to the field situation.

Although there was apparent overlap in distributional ranges of the co-occurring species of haustoriid amphipods, all species pairs were spatially (horizontally and vertically) and biologically separated. This family of amphipods has thus fractionated the rigorous sandbar environment into at least four subregions. The published data on physiological tolerances of haustoriid amphipods to environmental stress experienced along the environmental gradients common to these sandbars aids in explaining the distributional pattern of these organisms at high elevations (Croker 1967; Sameoto 1969). However, data on physiological tolerance cannot explain the distributional pattern of this family of amphipods at low elevations. Increased number of species, higher species diversity, and more structured faunal assemblages at lower elevations suggest that biological interactions may be important in controlling distributional patterns at lower elevations.

REFERENCES

Boesch, D. F. 1973. Classification and community structure of macrobenthos in Hampton Roads area, Virginia. Mar. Biol. 21: 226-244.

Bousfield, E. L. 1973. Shallow-water Gammaridean Amphipoda of New England. Cornell University Press.

Bray, J. R. and J. T. Curtis. 1957. An ordination of the upland forest communities of Southern Wisconsin. Ecol. Monogr. 27: 325-249.

Buchannan, J. B. and J. M. Kain. 1971. Measurement of the physical and chemical environment, pp. 30-58. In N. A. Holme and A. D. McIntyre [eds.], Methods for the study of the benthos. Blackwell Scientific Publications.

Connell, J. H. 1961. The influence of interspecific competition and other factors on the distribution of the barnacle, *Chthamalus stellatus*. Ecology 42: 710-723.

Croker, R. A. 1967. Niche diversity in five sympatric species of intertidal amphipods (Crustacea: Haustoriidae). Ecol. Monogr. 37: 173-200.

Dexter, D. M. 1967. Distribution and niche diversity of Haustoriidae amphipods in North Carolina. Chesapeake Sci. 8: 187-192.

_____. 1969. Structure of an intertidal sandy-beach community in North Carolina. Chesapeake Sci. 10: 93-98.

Dörjes, J. 1972. Georgia coastal region, Sapelo Island, USA: Sedimentology and biology. VII. Distribution and zonation of macrobenthic animals. Senckenbergiana Marti. 4: 183-216.

Fager, E. W. 1957. Determination and analysis of recurrent groups. Ecology 38: 586-595.

Field, J. G. 1971. A numerical analysis of changes in the soft bottom fauna along a transect across False Bay, South Africa. J. Exp. Mar. Biol. Ecol. 7: 215-253.

Green, R. H. 1968. Mortality and stability in a low diversity subtropical intertidal community. Ecology 49: 848-854.

_____, K. D. Hobson, and S. L. Santos. 1967. Analysis of invertebrate distribution in the intertidal zone of Barnstable Harbor. Biol. Bull. 133: 454-455.

Holland, A. F. and C. E. Sansbury. 1973. A study of the annual salinity and temperature regime of the North Inlet Estuary. Bull. S. C. Acad. Sci. 35: 129.

_____, R. G. Zingmark, and J. M. Dean. 1974. Quantitative evidence concerning the stabilization of sediments by marine benthic diatoms. Mar. Biol. 27: 191-196.

Howard, J. D. and C. A. Elders. 1970. Burrowing patterns of haustoriid amphipods from Sapelo Island, Georgia, pp. 243-262. In J. P. Crimes and J. C. Harper [eds.], Trace Fossils. Liverpool.

Hughes, R. N. and M. L. H. Thomas. 1971a. The classification and ordination of shallow water benthic samples from Prince Edward Island, Canada. J. Exp. Mar. Biol. Ecol. 7: 1-39.

_____. 1971b. Classification and ordination of benthic samples from Bedique Bay, an estuary in Prince Edward Island, Canada. Mar. Biol. 10: 227-235.

Johnson, R. G. 1970. Variations in diversity within benthic marine communities. Am. Nat. 104: 285-300.

Kendall, M. G. 1962. Rank correlation methods. Hafner Publishing Company.

Lachenbruch, P. A. 1975. Discriminant analysis. Hafner Publishing Company.

McFayden, A. 1963. Animal ecology. Wiley and Sons.

McNulty, J. K., R. C. Work, and H. B. Moore. 1962. Some relationships between the infauna of the level bottom and the sediment in South Florida. Bull. Mar. Sci. Gulf and Caribbean 12: 322-332.

Neumann, A. C., C. D. Gibelein, and T. P. Scoffin. 1970. Composition, structure, and erodability of subtidal mats, Abaco, Bahamas. J. Sediment. Petrol. 49: 249-273.

Newell, R. C. 1970. The biology of intertidal animals. American Elsevier.

Orloci, L. 1967. An agglomerative method for classification of plant communities. J. Ecol. 55: 193-206.

Paine, R. T. 1966. Food web complexity and species diversity. Am. Nat. 100: 65-75.

Pielou, E. C. 1966. The measurement of diversity in different types of biological collections. J. Theor. Biol. 13: 131-144.

_____. 1969. An introduction to mathematical ecology. Wiley-Interscience.

Polgar, T. T. 1975. Characterization of benthic community responses to environmental variations by multiple discriminant analysis. In S. B. Saila [ed.], Fisheries and energy production. Lexington Books.

Rhoads, D. C. and D. K. Young. 1970. The influence of deposit feeding organisms on sediment stability and community trophic structure. J. Mar. Res. 28: 150-178.

Sameoto, D. D. 1969. Physiological tolerances and behavior responses in five species of Haustoriidae (Amphipoda: Crustacea) to five environmental factors. J. Fish. Res. Bd. Can. 26: 2283-2298.

Sanders, H. L. 1958. Benthic studies in Buzzards Bay I. Animal-sediment relationships. Limnol. Oceanogr. 3: 245-258.

_____. 1960. Benthic studies in Buzzards Bay III. The structure of the soft-bottom community. Limnol. Oceanogr. 5: 138-153.

_____, R. R. Hessler, and G. R. Hampson. 1965. An introduction to the deep-sea faunal assemblages along the Gay Head-Bermuda transect. Deep-Sea Res. 12: 845-867.

_____, E. M. Goudsmit, E. L. Mills, and G. E. Hampson. 1962. A study of the intertidal fauna of Barnstable Harbor, Massachusetts. Limnol. Oceanogr. 1: 63-79.

Stephenson, W., W. T. Williams, and G. N. Lance. 1970. The macrobenthos of Moreton Bay. Ecol. Monogr. 40: 459-494.

Woodin, S. A. 1974. Polychaete abundance patterns in a marine soft-sediment environment: The importance of biological interactions. Ecol. Monogr. 44: 171-187.

Young, D. K. 1971. Effects of infauna on the sediment and seston of a subtidal environment. Extrait de Vie et Milieu Troisieme Symposium Supplement No. 22: 557-571.

_____, and D. C. Rhoads. 1971. Animal-sediment relations in Cape Cod Bay, Massachusetts. I. A transect study. Mar. Biol. 11: 242-254.

Macro-Infauna of Northern New England Marine Sand: Long-Term Intertidal Community Structure

Robert A. Croker
Department of Zoology
and Jackson Estuarine Laboratory
University of New Hampshire
Durham, NH 03824

ABSTRACT

Temporal variability of community structure was examined for 4 years at two New Hampshire and Maine intertidal sand habitats differing primarily in exposure to wave action, and species composition of peracarid crustaceans and polychaetes. Yearly species additions over baseline 1971 resulted in a minor increase in overall abundance, primarily among three polychaete species persisting at the semi-protected habitat. Community structure indices (species diversity, evenness, and species richness) were higher, and less variable at the semi-protected habitat. Seasonal trends in contributions to diversity of evenness and species richness differed over the study period. Low overall diversity, with H' falling in the range reported for similar temperate, boreal, and tropical habitats, suggested a diversity limit for intertidal sand macro-infauna, and no obvious latitudinal pattern. Five amphipod species were responsible for overall increase in abundance and biomass, particularly at the more wave-exposed habitat. The amphipod component fluctuated overall by a geometric mean factor of 4, and reflected mainly life histories, breeding periods, and behavior. The communities are considered to be quite resilient.

INTRODUCTION

Intertidal sand habitats in northern New England have received less attention from ecologists than have rocky shores. Communities of burrowing invertebrates range over the gradient from high energy, exposed shores to habitats well protected from wave action. Amphipod crustacean species (mostly Haustoriidae) are abundant, and form an ecological unit by sharing similar feeding, brooding, and life span characteristics (Bousfield 1970, 1973; Croker et al. 1975). Recent work has stressed the relationship between regional patterns of community structure and physical factors, and autecology of component species (Gnewuch and Croker 1973; Croker et al. 1975; Scott 1975).

Knowledge of spatial variability of these communities is available for assessing temporal variability at well-known habitats. This paper considers fluctuations in abundance and biomass, and species composition of intertidal macro-infauna at two contrasting habitats in Maine and New Hampshire over a 4-year period. Patterns of the changing relationships between species populations living in this "below ground" portion of the coastal ecosystem are stressed. No attempt is made to exhaustively review the literature; rather, only pertinent literature from the past decade bearing on the objectives is discussed.

I thank R. P. Hager and K. J. Scott, and numerous students and colleagues for their assistance and advice over the past 10 years. M. Pettibone graciously supplied information on polychaetes. Special thanks are due E. L. Bousfield for his continued counsel. Contribution No. 21, Jackson Estuarine Laboratory. Research supported by National Science Foundation (Oceanography Section) Grants GB-18590 and GA-33743.

METHODS

Collections were made during March and July 1971-1974 at Long Sands, Maine, and Foss Beach, N. H. Triplicate $0.04m^2$ samples, 10-cm deep, were collected at each of 5 to 6 levels on a transect from the highest levels where animals were retrievable to MLW (0.0), and were washed through a 0.5-mm mesh sieve. Coarse residues were returned to the laboratory for elutriation and microscopic examination. Approximately 53,000 animals were identified and counted. Coefficient of variation for raw abundance counts of the dominant amphipod component averaged 12%. Two additional replicates would have been required to reduce sampling error below 10%.

Raw abundance and biomass data were transformed by $\log_{10}(x+1)$, since log/log plots showed means and variances were not independent, and a few zeros were present. Mean abundance and biomass as reported are derived (geometric) means.

Species diversity indices i.e., Shannon's H' $\log_2$, Margalef's species richness, and Pielou's evenness (Pielou, 1969) were computed on summation of means of triplicate samples for each species per sampling date for both abundance and biomass.

Sand samples of the upper 5 cm were taken for sand grain analyses. Aliquots were separated with an Emery settling tube, and parameters estimated after Folk (1968). Other methods were as in Croker et al. (1975).

RESULTS

Habitats

Long Sands, Maine (LS) is a moderately exposed sandy shore facing ESE. Beach width is about 165 m to MLW; slopes average 1:48

to 1:68 depending on season and frequency of storm erosion. Sand is fine (Mz = 0.197 to 0.220), and well sorted (τ = 0.37 to 0.43), with generally <1% of coarse sand present. During winter, sand may freeze during low tide above half-tide level (1.3 m).

Foss Beach, N. H. (FB) faces E and is semi-protected from daily wave action by an adjacent boulder shore, and rock outcrops to the south. Beach width is about 60 m; slopes average 1:28 to 1:37 depending on severity of storm erosion. A seawall precludes presence of sand above MHW (2.65 m). Sand is very fine (Mz = 0.113 to 0.120), and very well sorted (τ = 0.31 to 0.32), with no coarse sand component. Periodic removal of sand from the upper shore by early spring and summer storms has been observed, revealing an underlying gravel and cobble pavement.

Organic carbon and total nitrogen concentrations of sand were uniformly low on a weight basis at both habitats. Percent carbon and nitrogen ranged from 0.062 to 0.203, and 0.003 to 0.011, respectively. Neither element varied significantly with tidal level ($p > 0.05$, F test on variance ratios). Occasional between-habitat, and seasonal within-habitat differences were apparent, but showed no consistent pattern. Carbon/nitrogen ratios averaged 16 to 28, indicating large amounts of plant detritus.

<u>Species Composition</u>

Croker et al. (1975) listed 31 species of macro-infauna for northern New England intertidal sands, including 10 at LS, and 9 at FB during 1971. In subsequent years the cumulative occurrence list increased at both LS and FB (Table 1), but only three species not reported earlier. were added. Year-by-year numbers of species at both habitats are shown in Figure 1 (bottom).

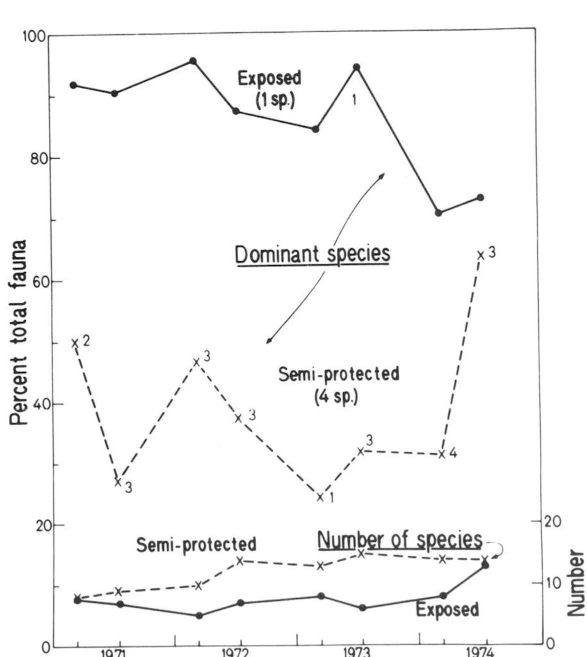

Fig. 1. Contribution of the most abundant species to total faunal abundance, and total numbers of species collected (bottom). Numbered dominant species are: 1. *Amphiporeia virginiana* (suspension feeder), 2. *Mancocuma stellifera* (epistrate feeder), 3. *Scolelepis squamata* (deposit feeder), 4. *Acanthohaustorius millsi* (suspension feeder).

Few species were added at both habitats since 1971. At LS additions were mostly < 5 individuals/species; all occurred sporadically. Species included the polychaete, *Paraonis fulgens*; the oedicerotid amphipod, *Synchelidium americanum* (new to list); the cumacean, *Mancocuma stellifera*; and the tanaids, *Leptochelia savignyi* and *Leptognatha caeca* (both new to list). At FB, seven sporadically occurring species with < 3 individuals/species were supplemented by three more abundant polychaete species persisting during 1972-74. These were *P. fulgens*, *Capitella capitata*, and *Spiophanes bombyx*.

Table 1. Cumulative number of macro-infaunal species at two contrasting intertidal sand habitats 1971-74.

Fauna	LS No.	LS %	FB No.	FB %
Crustacea	(11)	73.3	(9)	47.4
Amphipoda	6		6	
Cumacea	1		1	
Isopoda	2		1	
Tanaidacea	2		1	
Nemertea	1	6.7	1	5.2
Polychaeta	3	20.0	9	47.4
Total	15		19	
Grand Total		21		

Almost all northern New England intertidal species are now known to occur subtidally. Species common to most intertidal habitats and subtidal sands to 7-m depths are listed in Table 2 (Gnewuch 1971; Normandeau Assoc. 1973; Croker et al. 1975). Excluding *Bathyporeia quoddyensis*, these species and the strictly intertidal *Haustorius canadensis* are important at LS and FB, and will be considered in detail.

Table 1 shows the predominance of peracarid crustaceans (particularly at LS) and polychaetes, and the absence of mollusks at both habitats. Both habitats fall in the middle of the gradient from quite protected habitats where up to 43 species are found (Scott 1975), to high energy, more coarse sand (Mz = 0.260 to 0.329) habitats where only four species are represented, i.e., the four shallowest living species in Table 2 (Hager unpublished).

Table 2. Macro-infaunal species common to intertidal and subtidal sands to 7 m depths, excluding very exposed intertidal habitats.

	Species	Depth (m)	Feeding* type
Amphipoda	*Acanthohaustorius millsi*	55	SF
	Amphiporeia virginiana	3	SF
	Bathyporeia quoddyensis	18	EP
	Psammonyx nobilis	33	O
Cumacea	*Mancocuma stellifera*	7	EP
Polychaeta	*Nephtys bucera*	179	O
	Paraonis fulgens	68	DF
	Scolelepis squamata	25	DF,SF

*SF=suspension feeder, EP=epistrate feeder, O=omnivore, DF=deposit feeder.

Species Diversity

The percent contribution of the most abundant species to the total fauna over the 4-year period at both habitats is shown in Figure 1. One species, the suspension feeding *Amphiporeia virginiana*, consistently dominated at LS, while three crustaceans and the polychaete *Scolelepis squamata* alternately dominated the fauna at FB with only the latter species surpassing 50% dominance.

Variation of H' calculated on abundance data was essentially the converse of dominance shown in Figure 1, i.e. highest H' value (1.5) in March 1974 at LS (4-year mean .73 ± .37), and highest H' value (2.93) in March 1973 at FB (4-year mean 2.46 ± .36).

Species richness increased at both habitats during 1971-74 and peaked in 1974. Four-year means were .91 ± .34 at LS, and 2.06 ± .43 at FB.

Evenness was highest at FB (4-year mean .71 ± .09), decreasing most in July 1974 with strong dominance by *S. squamata*. Decreasing dominance by *A. virginiana* at LS was reflected in increasing evenness values during the study period (4-year mean .24 ± .10), with a peak in 1974.

Seasonal changes in community structure, as indicated by diversity indices calculated on abundance data, differed for the initial, and latter 2-year periods. Both H' and evenness increased at both habitats from March to July of 1971 and 1972, and decreased during the same monthly periods of 1973 and 1974, thus following species dominance relationships (Fig. 1). The species richness component decreased every year between March and July at FB, but alternately decreased and increased for this period over the entire 4 years at LS.

Diversity indices calculated on biomass data indicated a decrease in the difference between LS and FB, particularly evenness (4-year means .50 ± .07, and .60 ± .11, respectively). Seasonal changes at LS were similar to those described for abundance indices, reflecting over-dominance by *A. virginiana*; seasonal changes at FB were more random, but reflected the contributions of the large *Psammonyx nobilis*.

Abundance and Biomass

The contribution of the amphipod component to total abundance and biomass is shown in Figure 2 (top four curves). At LS, both statistics generally remained above 95%; the biomass decrease in

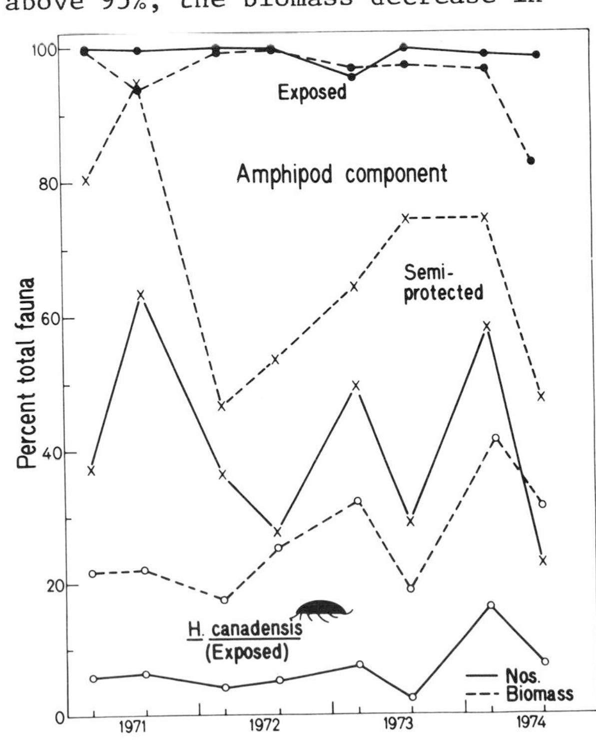

Fig. 2. Contribution of the amphipod component (top four curves), and *Haustorius canadensis* alone at LS (bottom), to total faunal abundance and biomass.

July 1974 was due to a few large *Nephtys bucera*. At FB, mean percent contributions of amphipods to abundance and biomass were 41 and 67, respectively. Maximum peaks for biomass were primarily due to *P. nobilis*.

The contribution of the strictly intertidal, sub-dominant *H. canadensis* to abundance and biomass at LS increased during 1973-74 in association with decreasing dominance by *A. virginiana* (Fig. 1 and Fig. 2 bottom). Overall, *H. canadensis* contributed 7% of numbers, and one-quarter of biomass at LS. *Amphiporeia virginiana* contributed almost two-thirds of biomass at LS, while *Acanthohaustorius millsi* contributed 6% of numbers and biomass.

At FB, the polychaetes *S. squamata* and *P. fulgens* made up 40% of numbers during 1971-74. *Acanthohaustorius millsi* contributed almost 20%. Biomass at FB was dominated by *P. nobilis* (46%), except during 1972 when *S. squamata* was predominant.

Estimates of abundance and biomass for the amphipod component are shown in Figures 3 and 4. Abundance estimates at LS indicate decreasing combined population levels from 1972 onward, with most of the variability due to *A. virginiana*. Winter estimates were 30% higher than summer, primarily because of high fall recruitment in *A. virginiana* (Hager unpublished), and a tendency for this species to range higher in the intertidal zone during colder months. *Haustorius canadensis* showed low amplitude fluctuations over the 4-year period.

At FB, where *A. virginiana* contributed only 10% to numbers, abundance estimates were less variable and almost two-thirds higher during summer, primarily because of summer recruitment in *A. millsi* and *P. nobilis*.

Mean annual abundance of the total fauna based on transformed data, and extrapolated to 1 m^2 at LS and FB, was estimated as 3100 and 500 animals, respectively.

Biomass estimates indicate increased seasonal differences at LS compared to abundance data, largely because 30 to 50% of populations of amphipods were juveniles during summer; winter biomass averaged 45% higher than summer. The pattern of variation for *H. canadensis* alone was similar, with winter estimates 25% higher than summer. Biomass estimates for amphipods at FB showed little seasonal differences.

Mean annual dry weight biomass of the total fauna at LS and FB was estimated as 2.6 and 0.4 gm m^{-2}, respectively. Annual geometric mean abundance and biomass estimates fluctuated by a factor of 4 during 1971-74.

DISCUSSION

At least two-thirds of intertidally occurring species in northern New England are northern species limited southward, with distributions continuing south of Cape Cod. Only four species are

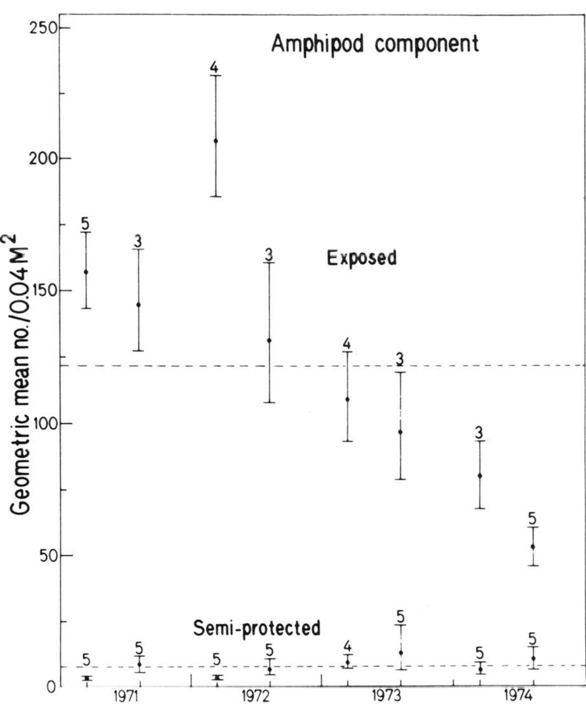

Fig. 3. Abundance estimates of the amphipod component showing geometric means and 95% confidence intervals. Numbers above intervals are numbers of amphipod species. Dotted, horizontal lines are 4-year means.

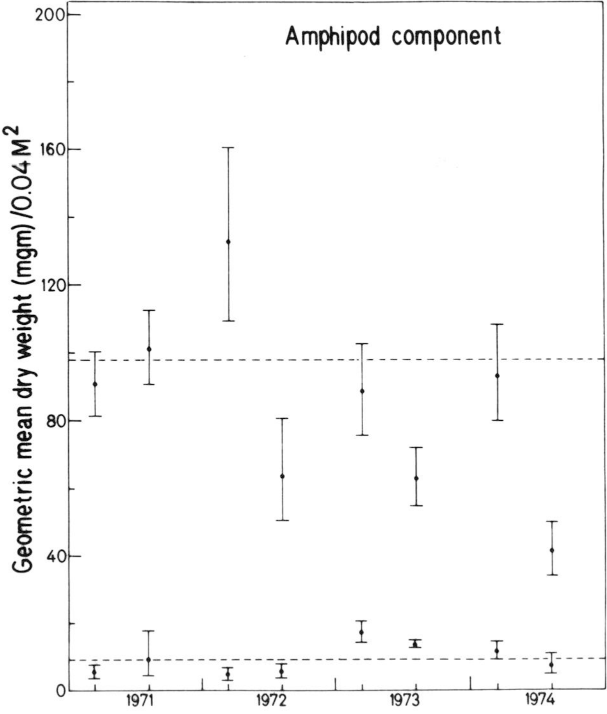

Fig. 4. Dry weight biomass estimates of the amphipod component as in Figure 3.

boreal: *Nephtys longosetosa*, *M. stellifera*, *L. caeca*, and *P. nobilis*. One-half of amphipod species are southern species limited northward: *A. millsi*, *H. canadensis*, and *Protohaustorius deichmannae* (Bousfield 1973).

Couplings between intertidal and subtidal sand species assemblages are recognized (McIntyre and Eleftheriou 1968; Fincham 1971; Croker et al. 1975); intertidal sand represents space and food resources for those species able to tolerate the relatively sharp gradient of physical factors at the edge of the sea. The choice of MLW level for the lower collection limit of this study was one of convenience and economy only. Similarity analyses of intertidal and subtidal assemblages in northern New England do, however, show the uniqueness of each (Scott 1975).

Bathymetric analyses of constituent species show that about one-third of intertidally occurring species are distributed to < 10-m depths. Fifty-eight percent are distributed > 30 m sometime during the year, these being mainly polychaetes and mollusks.

Increasing numbers of polychaete species, and then mollusk species are evident as exposure decreases in boreal regions (McIntyre 1970; Croker et al. 1975). This pattern has also been observed in the Saco Bay, Maine sand crescent, where changes in species composition of the intertidal fauna, and the population ecology of *A. virginiana* are correlated with the wave energy refraction gradient and sediment parameters (Farrell 1972; Hager unpublished). Protected Prouts Neck at the northern end of the crescent lacks *A. virginiana* but has four bivalve species not found further south (Croker et al. 1975).

The diversity index H' was relatively low for the habitats reported here. Indices based on abundance data (mean 2.45) were also generated for several other northern New England intertidal sand habitats (Scott 1975). Compared to similar habitats elsewhere, our data generally fall within the range reported for 25 intertidal sand communities in North Carolina, Washington, Scotland, and tropical Panama, Costa Rica, Colombia, and India (Dexter 1972, 1974; Gray 1974). Comparisons are made only with communities sampled with 0.5-mm sieves. They yielded from 3 to 43 species, and generated H' values ranging from 0.17 to 2.77 (mean 1.55). The available data suggest a diversity limit for intertidal sand macro-infauna, with no obvious latitudinal pattern.

Species richness and evenness variously affect H' on a seasonal basis, with the pattern differing from year to year. Overall however, our data from four contrasting intertidal sand communities including LS and FB (Scott 1975), indicate as Boesch (1973) suggests, that between-habitat species diversity differences are primarily a function of species richness, while evenness is more important for within-habitat seasonal differences.

Numerical dominance of intertidal macro-infauna by haustoriid amphipods has been reported for the eastern and western Atlantic Ocean (Colman and Segrove 1955; Croker 1967; Dexter 1969; Sameoto 1969a). Important contributions of polychaete and mollusk species were also noted depending on latitude on the American coast. Dexter's (1969) comprehensive study of community structure in the western Atlantic observed six haustoriid species made up 91% of the fauna at a coastal inlet, with 83% due to *Neohaustorius schmitzi*.

Increased protection from wave action (e.g. FB), is correlated with increasing numerical domination of communities by three polychaete species in northern New England: *S. squamata*, *Pygospio elegans*, and *P. fulgens* (Croker et al. 1975; Scott 1975), species that also occur in boreal European habitats (McIntyre and Eleftheriou 1968). The possession of pelagic larvae by *S. squamata*, a cosmopolitan distribution, and the ability to switch from deposit to suspension feeding (Day 1973; Wolff 1973), confers on this species marked flexibility for intertidal existence.

No other studies of similar duration are available for comparison with fluctuations observed in this study. Fluctuations of *A. virginiana* on a very exposed Maine shore were more pronounced than those reported here, particularly after severe storms, but return to pre-storm population levels was observed within 30-days (Hager unpublished). I earlier observed (Croker 1968) little change in zonation, and minimal changes in population abundance of five species of southeastern U. S. haustoriids within 2 days after each of two hurricanes.

Three shorter term studies have noted marked increases in population abundances of intertidal crustacean species during warmer months (Sameoto 1969a; Dexter 1971; McIntyre and Eleftheriou 1968).

Biomass estimates for some other boreal, or near-boreal habitats showed that total faunal biomass did not differ seasonally where amphipod contribution was < 10% (McIntyre and Eleftheriou 1968), or that total amphipod estimates were the same order of magnitude as those reported here, where amphipods were dominant (Sameoto 1969a). Our biomass estimates probably fall in the middle of the arithmetic range of biomass reported for Scottish intertidal habitats (McIntyre 1970).

Peracaridan crustacean species, particularly amphipods, obviously dominate intertidal sand communities in the middle of the exposure gradient. Species characteristics of four dominant amphipods (Table 3) are important influences on seasonal community structure and dynamics. Species range from 2 to 18 mm in length, live from 6 to 24 months, and excepting *P. nobilis*, have relatively low fecundity (Scott 1975; Hager unpublished). Broods are restricted to one per

Table 3. Characteristics of four dominant amphipod species from intertidal sand communities.

Species	Distrib.	Breeding	Fecundity Range	Fecundity Mean	Life span (mos)	Notes
A. virginiana	Boreal to S.C.	Jan-Sept	4-21	9	6-12	Abundance peak MTL-MLW all year, ranges higher in winter
H. canadensis	Virginian to central Maine Gulf of St.Law.	May-Sept	4-17 (5-25)*	8 (11)	12	Only intertidal, highest penetration landward, lower during winter
A. millsi	Carolinian to Saco Bay,Maine	May-Sept	3-9 (4-23)*	5 (8)	12-17	Lower shore, moves seaward at exposed habitats in winter
P. nobilis	Boreal to N.J.	Jan-May	8-52	22	24	Lower shore, absent at exposed habitats in summer

*Data for Cape Cod (Sameoto 1969a, b).

female per breeding period. Annual dominance in abundance and biomass of *A. virginiana* is assisted by bivoltine reproduction at this latitude, i.e. young hatched in spring may mature and breed by fall, producing an overwintering generation. Winter biomass at preferred semi-protected habitats is assisted by winter breeding of the northern *P. nobilis*. Staggered breeding periods of dominant amphipod species result from summer breeding of the southern *H. canadensis* and *A. millsi*. The evacuation of higher shore levels by these latter two species during winter is also correlated with habitation of higher levels by *A. virginiana* as already described.

Little information is available concerning limiting factors for population growth of these amphipod species, and is restricted to *A. virginiana* and *P. nobilis*. Water content of intertidal sands appears limiting for landward penetration of the former species; increased mortality above MTL has been observed for all life stages (Hager unpublished). *Psammonyx nobilis* serves as the intermediate host for the fish cestode, *Bothrimonus sturionis*. Infection rates with a fall peak as high as 30% of females has been observed at FB. Parasitized females have undeveloped gonads, thus reducing potential fecundity of the species (Scott and Bullock 1974). Predation by near-shore fish on *P. nobilis* is also important, since the species makes up a large part of the diet of flounder, cod, pollock, and hake (Normandeau Assoc. 1974).

These intertidal sand communities are resilient (Holling 1973) and reflect predictable species composition, with higher probability of continuity of additive species at the semi-protected habitat. Species diversity, evenness, and species richness were higher, and less variable at this same habitat, reflecting lack of high dominance, while the opposite held for the more wave-exposed habitat. Fluctuations in abundance and biomass of the amphipod component were moderate in amplitude, and variability in the abundance estimates at the more wave-exposed habitat was primarily due to increased reproductive capacity of *A. virginiana*. Work now in progress will continue to monitor community structure, and the amplitude and frequency of fluctuations.

REFERENCES

Boesch, D. F. 1973. Classification and community structure of macrobenthos in the Hampton Roads area, Virginia. Mar. Biol. 21: 226-244.

Bousfield, E. L. 1970. Adaptive radiation in sand-burrowing amphipod crustaceans. Chesapeake Sci. 11: 143-154.

_____. 1973. Shallow-water gammaridean Amphipoda of New England. Comstock Publ. Assoc., Cornell Univ.

Colman, J. S., and F. Segrove. 1955. The fauna living in Stoup Beck Sands, Robin Hood's Bay (Yorkshire, North Riding). J. Anim. Ecol. 24: 426-444.

Croker, R. A. 1967. Niche diversity in five sympatric species of intertidal amphipods (Crustacea: Haustoriidae). Ecol. Monogr. 37: 173-200.

______. 1968. Distribution and abundance of some intertidal sand beach amphipods accompanying the passage of two hurricanes. Chesapeake Sci. 9: 157-162.

______, R. P. Hager, and K. J. Scott. 1975. Macroinfauna of northern New England marine sand. II. Amphipod-dominated intertidal communities. Can. J. Zool. 53: 42-51.

Day, J. H. 1973. New Polychaeta from Beaufort, with a key to all species recorded from North Carolina. NOAA Tech. Rept., NMFS Circ. 375, 140 p.

Dexter, D. M. 1969. Structure of an intertidal sandy-beach community in North Carolina. Chesapeake Sci. 10: 93-98.

______. 1971. Life history of the sandy-beach amphipod *Neohaustorius schmitzi* (Crustacea: Huastoriidae). Mar. Biol. 8: 232-237.

______. 1972. Comparison of the community structures in a Pacific and an Atlantic Panamanian sandy beach. Bull. Mar. Sci. 22: 449-462.

______. 1974. Sandy-beach fauna of the Pacific and Atlantic coasts of Costa Rica and Colombia. Rev. Biol. Trop. 22: 51-66.

Farrell, S. C. 1972. Present coastal processes, recorded changes, and the post-Pleistocene geologic record of Saco Bay, Maine. Ph. D. thesis, Univ. Mass., Amherst. 292 p.

Fincham, A. A. 1971. Ecology and population studies of some intertidal and sublittoral sand-dwelling amphipods. J. Mar. Biol. Assoc. U. K. 51: 471-488.

Folk, R. L. 1968. Petrology of sedimentary rocks. Hemphill's Univ. Texas. 170 pp.

Gnewuch, W. T. 1971. Studies on the biology of *Mancocuma stellifera* Zimmer, 1943 (Crustacea: Cumacea). Ph.D. thesis, Univ. N. H., Durham. 160 p.

______, and R. A. Croker. 1973. Macroinfauna of northern New England marine sand. I. The biology of *Mancocuma stellifera* Zimmer, 1943 (Crustacea: Cumacea). Can. J. Zool. 51: 1011-1020.

Gray, J. S. 1974. Animal-sediment relationships. Oceanogr. Mar. Biol. Ann. Rev. 12: 223-261.

Holling, C. S. 1973. Resilience and stability of ecological systems. Annu. Rev. Ecol. & Syst. 4: 1-23.

McIntyre, A. D. 1970. The range of biomass in intertidal sand, with special reference to the bivalve, *Tellina tenuis*. J. Mar. Biol. Assoc. U. K. 50: 561-575.

______, and A. Eleftheriou. 1968. The bottom fauna of a flatfish nursery ground. J. Mar. Biol. Assoc. U. K. 48: 113-142.

Normandeau Associates, Inc. 1973. The benthos of the area offshore Hampton and Seabrook Beaches, New Hampshire. Seabrook Ecological Study-1972, Tech. Rept. IV-5, Normandeau Assoc., Inc. Manchester, N. H., 76 p.

______. 1974. Finfish ecology investigations at the Hampton-Seabrook Estuary, New Hampshire and adjoining coastal waters. Tech. Rept. V-3, Normandeau Assoc., Inc., Manchester, N. H., 184 p.

Pielou, E. C. 1969. An introduction to mathematical ecology. Wiley-Interscience.

Sameoto, D. D. 1969a. Comparative ecology, life histories, and behaviour of intertidal sand-burrowing amphipods (Crustacea: Haustoriidae) at Cape Cod. J. Fish. Res. Bd. Can. 26: 361-388.

_____. 1969b. Some aspects of the ecology and life cycle of three species of subtidal sand-burrowing amphipods (Crustacea: Haustoriidae). J. Fish. Res. Bd. Can. 26: 1321-1345.

Scott, K. J. 1975. Studies on the ecology of *Psammonyx nobilis* (Stimpson), 1853 (Crustacea: Amphipoda). Ph.D. thesis, Univ. N. H., Durham, 150 p.

_____, and W. L. Bullock. 1974. *Psammonyx nobilis* (Amphipoda: Lysianassidae), a new host for *Bothrimonus sturionis* (Cestoda: Pseudophyllidae). Proc. Helminthol. Soc. Wash. 41: 256-257.

Wolff, W. J. 1973. The estuary as a habitat, and analysis of data on soft-bottom macrofauna of the estuarine area of the rivers Rhine, Meuse, and Scheldt. Zool. Verhand (Leiden). 126: 1-242.

INDEX

SYSTEMATIC INDEX

Page numbers shown in italics represent listings in tables only.

SUBJECT INDEX

QH541.5 S3 E24
Sci +Ecology of marine benthos / edite
0 00 02 0281682 3
MIDDLEBURY COLLEGE